PHYSIOLOGICAL PHARMACOLOGY

A Comprehensive Treatise

Volume IV

The Nervous System — Part D

Autonomic Nervous System Drugs

PHYSIOLOGICAL PHARMACOLOGY

A Comprehensive Treatise

Volume I:	The Nervous System — Part A, Central Nervous System Drugs
Volume II:	The Nervous System — Part B, Central Nervous System Drugs
Volume III:	The Nervous System — Part C, Autonomic Nervous System Drugs
Volume IV:	The Nervous System — Part D, Autonomic Nervous System Drugs

IN PREPARATION

Volume V:	Blood and the Cardiovascular System — Part A
Volume VI:	Blood and the Cardiovascular System — Part B
Volume VII:	Respiration
Volume VIII:	The Kidney
Volume IX:	The Gastrointestinal System
Volume X:	The Endocrine Glands
Volume XI:	Special Topics

PHYSIOLOGICAL PHARMACOLOGY

A Comprehensive Treatise

Edited by

Walter S. Root and Frederick G. Hofmann

College of Physicians and Surgeons
Columbia University, New York

Volume IV

The Nervous System — Part D

Autonomic Nervous System Drugs

1967

ACADEMIC PRESS New York and London

ACADEMIC PRESS INC.
111 Fifth Avenue, New York, New York 10003

United Kingdom Edition published by
ACADEMIC PRESS INC. (LONDON) LTD.
Berkeley Square House, London W.1

LIBRARY OF CONGRESS CATALOG CARD NUMBER 62-13123

PRINTED IN THE UNITED STATES OF AMERICA

Contributors to Volume IV

Numbers in parentheses indicate the pages on which the authors' contributions begin.

JOSEPH M. BENFORADO, *Department of Pharmacology, School of Medicine, State University of New York at Buffalo, Buffalo, New York* (*331*)

CHANDLER MCCUSKEY BROOKS, *Department of Physiology, State University of New York, Downstate Medical Center, Brooklyn, New York* (*1*)

SYDNEY ELLIS,* *Department of Pharmacology, Woman's Medical College of Pennsylvania, Philadelphia, Pennsylvania* (*179*)

ALFRED P. FISHMAN, *Department of Medicine, Columbia University College of Physicians and Surgeons, and the Cardiorespiratory Laboratory of the Presbyterian Hospital, New York, New York* (*97*)

NORMAN K. HOLLENBERG,† *Department of Pharmacology and Therapeutics, University of Manitoba, Faculty of Medicine, Winnipeg, Manitoba, Canada* (*243*)

P. A. NASMYTH, *Department of Pharmacology, St. Mary's Hospital Medical School, Paddington, London, England* (*129*)

MARK NICKERSON, *Department of Pharmacology and Therapeutics, University of Manitoba, Faculty of Medicine, Winnipeg, Manitoba, Canada* (*243*)

HSUEH-HWA WANG, *Department of Pharmacology, College of Physicians and Surgeons, Columbia University, New York, New York* (*307*)

R. F. WHELAN, *Department of Human Physiology and Pharmacology, University of Adelaide, South Australia* (*29*)

BERNARD C. WHALER, *Department of Physiology, Queen Elizabeth College* (*University of London*), *London, England* (*339*)

JOHN A. WOOD, *Department of Medicine, Columbia University College of Physicians and Surgeons, and the Cardiorespiratory Laboratory of the Presbyterian Hospital, New York, New York* (*97*)

* Present address: Department of Pharmacology and Toxicology, the University of Texas Medical Branch, Galveston, Texas.

† Present address: Cardiorenal Unit, Peter Bent Brigham Hospital, Boston, Massachusetts.

Foreword

PHYSIOLOGICAL PHARMACOLOGY is designed to be an authoritative account of the effects of drugs on physiological systems. To achieve this purpose, it is anticipated that this treatise will eventually consist of approximately eleven volumes, of which this is the fourth. The selection of topics for inclusion and the nominations of contributors are made by the Editors in consultation with the distinguished scientists making up the Editorial Advisory Board.

In the past decade there has been an impressive growth in our knowledge of how drugs may alter physiological systems, and many of these newer findings have been ably summarized in reviews. It is not the purpose of this treatise to summarize merely recent data, but, rather, to record and interpret all of the significant findings, regardless of age, and thereby to portray the framework of experimental evidence upon which pharmacodynamics is built.

It is intended that each contribution to this treatise represent an authoritative, systematic presentation of current concepts of the effects of drugs upon physiological systems as well as what is known of their mechanisms of action. Emphasis has been placed upon those experimental findings that have led to our current concepts. Findings have not been excluded because of age nor have they been included solely because of newness. Observations made in human beings have been neither featured nor omitted. The coverage of the literature is international in scope. Moreover, contributors have been encouraged to present not only factual evidence, but also theoretical interpretations presently receiving serious consideration.

It is the hope of the Editors that the scope and the depth of this treatise will make it of value to those who must teach, those who must learn, and those who conduct investigations in the complex area of pharmacodynamics.

WALTER S. ROOT
FREDERICK G. HOFMANN

Contents

Contributors to Volume IV v
Foreword vii
Contents of Previous Volumes xiii

III. Adrenergic Drugs

A. The Effects of Adrenergic Drugs on the Heart

Chandler McCuskey Brooks

I. Introduction 1
II. Possible Drug Actions on the Heart 4
III. Actions of the Adrenergic Drugs 8
IV. Summary and Conclusions 21
References 22

B. The Effects of Adrenergic Drugs on the Systemic Circulation

R. F. Whelan

I. Introduction 29
II. Epinephrine and Arterenol 30
III. Other Sympathomimetic Drugs 62
References 81

C. The Effects of the Adrenergic Compounds on the Pulmonary Circulation

John A. Wood and Alfred P. Fishman

I. Introduction and Physiologic Considerations 97
II. The Adrenergic Compounds: General Considerations 100
References 123

D. The Effects of Adrenergic Agents on Smooth Muscles Other Than Those of the Vascular System

P. A. Nasmyth

I. Introduction 129
II. The Intestine 130

III. Uterine Muscle 147
IV. The Nictitating Membrane 160
References 173

E. The Effects of Sympathomimetic Amines and Adrenergic Blocking Agents on Metabolism

SYDNEY ELLIS

I. Introduction 179
II. Effects on Carbohydrate Metabolism 180
III. Effects on Fat Metabolism 191
IV. Effects on Oxygen Consumption 200
V. Effects on Cations 208
References 213

IV. Adrenergic Blocking Drugs

A. Blockade of α-Adrenergic Receptors

MARK NICKERSON AND NORMAN K. HOLLENBERG

I. Introduction 243
II. Major Groups of α-Adrenergic Blocking Agents 245
III. Responses of Various Effector Systems to α-Adrenergic Blockade 257
IV. Therapeutic Use of α-Adrenergic Blockade 283
References 291

B. Blockade of β-Adrenergic Receptors

HSUEH-HWA WANG

I. Introduction 307
II. Direct Effects of β-Receptor Blocking Compounds 310
III. Specificity of β-Receptor Blockade 311
IV. Effects of Catecholamines on Physiological Systems After β-Receptor Blockade 312
V. The Antiarrhythmic Action of β-Receptor Blocking Compounds 319
VI. Application of β-Receptor Blocking Compounds 322
References 324

V. The Veratrum Alkaloids

JOSEPH M. BENFORADO

I. Introduction 331
II. The Chemistry of Veratrum Alkaloids 333
III. Pharmacological Actions 339

VI. Neurotoxins

BERNARD C. WHALER

Contents of Previous Volumes

Volume I

The Nervous System—Part A

Central Nervous System Drugs

I. Depressant Drugs

A. General Anesthetics

1. Absorption, Distribution, and Elimination
JOHN ADRIANI

2. Effects upon Physiological Systems
S. H. NGAI

B. The Alcohols
JORGE MARDONES

C. Sedatives and Hypnotics

1. Absorption, Fate, and Excretion
MILTON T. BUSH

2. Effects upon Physiological Systems

a. The Electrophysiological Effects of Barbiturates on the Brain
MARY A. B. BRAZIER

b. Nonbarbiturates
SOLOMON MARGOLIN

D. Analgesic and Antipyretic Drugs

1. Strong Analgesics
WILLIAM R. MARTIN

2. Non-Narcotic Analgesics
LOWELL O. RANDALL

E. Tranquilizers

1. Phenothiazine Derivatives
P. B. BRADLEY

2. *Rauwolfia* Derivatives
J. J. LEWIS

3. Diphenylmethane Derivatives
THEODORE R. SHERROD

F. Physiological Aspects of Tolerance and Physical Dependence
MAURICE H. SEEVERS AND GERALD A. DENEAU

AUTHOR INDEX–SUBJECT INDEX

Volume II

The Nervous System—Part B

Central Nervous System Drugs

I. Depressant Drugs (Continued)

G. Relaxants of Skeletal Muscle
Cedric M. Smith

H. Anticonvulsant Drugs
J. Gordon Millichap

I. Antitussive Drugs
K. Bucher

II. Psychic Energizers and Antidepressant Drugs
P. Holtz and E. Westermann

III. Emetic and Antiemetic Drugs
S. C. Wang

IV. Effects of Drugs Upon the Eye
Albert M. Potts

V. Synaptic Transmission in the Central Nervous System
H. McLennan

Author Index–Subject Index

Volume III

The Nervous System—Part C

Autonomic Nervous System Drugs

I. Cholinergic Drugs

A. Cardiovascular Effects of Choline Esters
M. J. Rand and Anne Stafford

B. Effects of Choline Esters on Smooth Muscle and Secretions
H. W. Kosterlitz

C. Pharmacologic, Toxicologic, and Therapeutic Properties of Anticholinesterase Agents
A. G. KARCZMAR

II. Cholinergic Blocking Drugs

A. Muscarinic Blocking Drugs
HARRY CULLUMBINE

B. Ganglion-Blocking Drugs
D. F. J. MASON

C. Neuromuscular Blocking Drugs
DAVID GROB

AUTHOR INDEX–SUBJECT INDEX

III. ADRENERGIC DRUGS

A. The Effects of Adrenergic Drugs on the Heart*

Chandler McCuskey Brooks

Department of Physiology, State University of New York, Downstate Medical Center, Brooklyn, New York

I. Introduction 1
II. Possible Drug Actions on the Heart 4
A. Membrane 4
B. Pacemaker Action 5
C. Conduction 6
D. Contraction 6
E. Additional Actions 7
III. Actions of the Adrenergic Drugs 8
A. Classification and Modes of Action 8
B. Epinephrine, Norepinephrine, and Their Precursors and Derivatives: Directly Acting Compounds 12
C. Isoproterenol (Isopropylarterenol, Isuprel®) and Other Directly Acting Compounds 17
D. Tyramine and Indirectly Acting Compounds 18
E. Ephedrine and Its Derivatives: Direct and Indirect Actions . . 20
F. Additional Drugs with Adrenergic Actions 20
IV. Summary and Conclusions 21
References 22

I. INTRODUCTION

The adrenergic drugs are so classified because their actions or structural properties resemble those of epinephrine (Adrenalin®). Epinephrine, norepinephrine, and numerous other adrenergic compounds are produced by body tissues, but principally by postganglionic sympathetic fibers and the adrenal medulla. Numerous synthetic adrenergic drugs have been produced in recent years in an attempt to obtain compounds

* The original investigative work done in this field by the author was supported largely by grants from the Life Insurance Medical Research Fund, Inc., and the New York Heart Association.

having the desired effects but none of the undesirable actions of naturally occurring catecholamines. It would be desirable to have a cardiac-stimulating drug which cannot promote fibrillation or tachycardias that reduce cardiac output.

Pharmacologists are also interested in the relationship of structure to function, and thus they become concerned with related compounds. Such knowledge has also assisted in the study of the basic processes of adrenergic drug action. In any study such as this it becomes important to know whether a similar mechanism of action on a single basic process is involved in control of particular functions.

The effects of epinephrine, norepinephrine, and other catecholamines on the heart have been extensively studied. Although the mechanism of action of these naturally occurring compounds is not fully understood, the observational analysis of their influences is rather complete. Description of the ways in which cardiac functions are modified by these definitive adrenergic agents is one of the basic aims of this review.

A more difficult task is that of discussing the basic mechanism of action of adrenergic drugs. The first difficulty is one of classification. As stated previously, in the past a drug was considered adrenergic if its action resembled that of "adrenaline." It also seemed justifiable to classify a drug as an adrenergic agent if it had a structural resemblance to the catecholamines produced by the adrenal gland and other body tissues. Chemically, most of the adrenergic agents are related to β-phenylethylamine. Several hundred compounds with such a relationship and possessing adrenergic activity have been found or developed and studied. About 25 of these are used in medical practice as cardiac excitants, in certain cardiac arrhythmias, as pressor agents, and to treat asthma or anaphylactic reactions.

Once classification has been made, the problem becomes that of subdividing the group as their individual mechanisms of action become better understood. This progress in knowledge has revealed, in many instances, that the basis for original classification was a little too simple. Some drugs do act on receptor tissues in much the same fashion as does epinephrine; other compounds exert their adrenergic action merely by liberating stored catecholamines; still other adrenergic drugs appear to have both a direct and an indirect action on the heart. Some compounds with apparent adrenergic action have been found to liberate acetylcholine, which in turn causes a discharge of catecholamines from storage. Finally, many additional drugs have actions which eventuate in a discharge of catecholamines from storage. It may be that in a few more years this matter of definition will be clarified, but for the present the situation is somewhat muddled and the effects produced by classical "adrenergic drugs" must be studied individually, regardless of the fact that this classification implies a similarity of action.

The early history of the discovery, isolation, identification, and synthesis of epinephrine has been well reviewed by Hartung (40). The possibility of classifying drugs as "adrenergic" arose only after Oliver and Schäfer in 1894 had demonstrated the action of extracts of the adrenal medulla and after Abel, in 1899, Takamine, in 1901, and Aldrich, in 1901 had isolated and analyzed the active compounds in such extracts. In 1905, adrenaline or epinephrine was synthesized by Stolz and Dakin independently. Flächer separated its isomers in 1908. Stolz had synthesized norepinephrine in 1904. It was not until recent times, however, that knowledge of the precursors, the formulation, and the metabolism of epinephrine and norepinephrine was obtained (93). Enough was known, nonetheless, by the early 1900's to enable pharmacologists to study the action of these and similar compounds effectively (7).

Barger and Dale in 1910 examined a large series of synthetic amines, defining the basic structural requirements for pharmacological activity as an adrenergic agent. They introduced the term "sympathomimetic" to describe this group of compounds. Many new compounds have since been produced and classified in somewhat the same manner as autonomic agents belonging to either the parasympathomimetic or sympathomimetic family of drugs. Since it is now known through the work of Dale and others (see 7) that some postganglionic fibers of the sympathetic division of the autonomic outflow are cholinergic whereas others are adrenergic, the term sympathomimetic is devoid of a precise chemical or pharmacological meaning. It certainly is not now considered to be synonymous with adrenergic.

One of the early difficulties was the fact that compounds exciting the heart inhibited some other tissues. For this and other reasons the concept of a receptor substance was advanced at a relatively early date (Langley, 1907). In a later section of this volume there will be a discussion of α- and β-receptors and the adrenergic blocking agents. Classification of drugs with respect to the receptors on which they act is now common.

A list of the drugs mentioned as adrenergic agents in a half dozen textbooks of pharmacology is rather long and contains compounds which bring about an adrenergic effect indirectly. The purpose of this review, however, is to discuss the known actions of the adrenergic drugs on the heart, not to discuss the pro's and con's of their classification as such. Therefore, the drugs to be considered are those adrenergic compounds listed in recent pharmacology texts (23) and pharmacopias as being the principal or typical agents acting much as does epinephrine. Compounds of major interest, therefore, are epinephrine, norepinephrine, and other catecholamines; isoproterenol; ephedrine and its derivatives; amphetamine and its analogs; tyramine; and various other naturally occurring and synthetic compounds of more or less related structures such as metaraminol (Aramine®), methoxamine (Vasoxyl®), and mephentermine (Wyamine®). The effects of these compounds on cardiac function will be considered after discussion of possible modes and sites of action in the heart.

II. POSSIBLE DRUG ACTIONS ON THE HEART

In brief summary it can be said that drugs acting on the heart may modify those processes involved in maintaining the cell membrane in its normal resting state, or they may act on excitatory and depolarizing phenomena, on conduction, on excitation-contraction coupling, or on the contractile and relaxing processes. These are the possibilities which must be considered in the analysis of any drug action; therefore, one must know something of what is involved in maintenance of steady states and in cellular reactions before a complete analysis can be made.

A. Membrane

Much of our knowledge of the cell membrane, its properties and its function, is derived from the work of Hodgkin and Huxley (44, 45) on the squid giant axon. Cardiac cells do not perform in quite the same way as the squid nerve, skeletal muscle cells, and other tissues which have been extensively studied, but there are striking resemblances. Excellent reviews of our knowledge of cardiac cell membranes and cell function have been written by Weidmann (96, 97), Woodbury (103), and Hoffman and Cranefield (46). Processes involved in the excitation of the heart have also been extensively studied (96, 97).

A thin membrane, the plasma membrane, surrounds heart cells, separating their cytoplasm from interstitial fluid. Its ultrastructure has been studied (27). The membrane, though only a thin multimolecular structure of some 10 nanometers (100 Å) in thickness, presents resistance to electrical current flow and to ion movements. The aqueous solutions on the two sides of the membrane are osmotically similar, but differ in ionic composition. The extracellular fluid shows a high concentration of Na^+ and Cl^- but is low in K^+. Concentrations in the intracellular fluid are the reverse; phosphate ions and organic acid radicals constitute the chief intracellular anion components. The membrane shows a charge or resting potential of some —70–90 mV (inside negative to outside) and possesses a selective permeability. K^+ and Cl^- move more freely through the membrane than does Na^+, but the resting state of the membrane and the ionic gradients are maintained by the metabolic activity of the membrane. Sodium ions constantly leaking into the cell are moved by a transport mechanism from inside the cell to the outside, and a K^+ ion influx balances the Na^+ ejection. The adrenergic drugs have very little if any effect upon the membrane's resting potential or its selective permeability. They do, however, modify stability and membrane reactions. These matters will be amplified later.

Excitation of cardiac cells by an applied electrical, mechanical, or chemical stimulus involves depolarization of the membrane to a critical potential, the threshold potential (96). When this is reached, a regenerative depolarization occurs and propagation of an action potential begins. If resting potential is normally about —90 mV, threshold potential is attained when the membrane is depolarized to approximately —70 mV. Drugs can affect excitability by modifying either resting potential or threshold potential or the relationship between the two.

In excitation, according to the Hodgkin-Huxley concept, there is a loss of membrane impermeability to sodium ion when threshold potential is reached and a Na^+ influx begins. Subsequently, there is a K^+ efflux which eventually results in an equilibrium and restoration of the normal membrane potential. The terms used in describing the beginning and and ending of this sodium influx are *activation* and *inactivation*. Adrenergic drugs affect these fluxes and modify the electrical response to stimulation (8).

The action potentials of heart cells differ from those of neurons. The existence of prepotentials, a rising phase and overshoot, a plateau phase, and, in some cells, an overshoot of the repolarization process provide opportunity for observation of selective actions of drugs. In addition to the standard absolute and relative refractory periods following excitation, there exist periods of vulnerability to fibrillation, a "dip" or phase of abnormal excitability during the relative refractory period and a later period of supernormality (8, 79). Changes in these properties are effected by adrenergic drugs.

B. Pacemaker Action

One of the unique properties of the heart is its spontaneous rhythm. The sinoatrial and atrioventricular nodes and the ventricular conducting system contain cells which depolarize spontaneously. Normally, the heart is driven by the sinoatrial nodal pacemaker, which is the dominant pacemaker, and subsidiary pacemaker activities are suppressed (60).

These pacemaker tissues are characterized by a spontaneous depolarization (22) thought to be due to a progressive loss of potassium permeability (46). The coincident rise in impedance is diagnostic of this reduced permeability and diminished ion flux. Pacemakers, in addition to showing this spontaneous depolarization to threshold potential, have a slower rise time of their spike potentials, an inconspicuous plateau, and a slow repolarization which overshoots into a hyperpolarization. Subsidiary pacemakers have a slower depolarization than do cells of the sinoatrial node, and thus they normally are driven by this faster pacemaker.

Adrenergic drugs greatly accelerate the rate of depolarization in pacemaker cells of all types; they shorten the action potentials and diastolic intervals (51, 52). They also foster recovery of pacemakers from suppression by overdrive (60) or vagus overaction (94). The tendency of some adrenergic drugs to produce arrhythmias is thought to be due to their ability to arouse pacemaker action in subsidiary pacemakers and to their abilities to accelerate conduction and affect excitability. It should be pointed out, however, that these drugs, or many of them, have a biphasic action which results in an initial lowering of excitability and fibrillatory thresholds followed by a rise above normal as a late "depressor" action occurs (8). This late depressor action is not so apparent in pacemaker tissues.

C. Conduction

Conduction in the heart is a matter of propagation of depolarization or of the excitatory process. The voltage of the action potential can be considered to indicate the strength of the propagating force. Spike height is, of course, related to membrane potentials of the heart cells. At any rate, this force is greater than that needed to propagate activity, and thus there is a "safety factor" for propagation. This factor of safety has been variously measured and is thought to be of the order of three to six times the diastolic threshold requirement (76, 91). Propagation through the special conducting system is very rapid, but at junctions and through the atrioventricular node it is very difficult and slow, and block occurs quite readily (71). The factor of safety is about 1 at these nodal and Purkinje-myocardial junctions. The adrenergic drugs are known to accelerate conduction and to aid transmission. They tend to abolish heart block.

D. Contraction

Cardiac pacemaker and conduction system cells contain only a few scattered myofibrils, though they do possess some ability to contract (74). The contractile processes within the contractile myocardium are normally triggered by the propagated action potential or the depolarization of the cell membrane. In some cells relaxation does not begin until repolarization occurs (54). Chemical processes and ion shifts are involved in these couplings, and they can be modified by adrenergic drug actions. It is well known that the catecholamines have an inotropic effect. They accelerate the rate of contraction and relaxation and augment tension development, thus increasing the effectiveness of the contractile process (78). This family of drugs can, therefore, modify the basic processes of actin-myosin combination. They also modify treppe and postextrasystolic potentiation, phenomena dependent upon excitation-contraction rate adjustments.

In discussing the action of adrenergic drugs on the heart, all these phenomena of function should be considered. The observed fact that a drug has an effect merely raises additional questions. Whether the drugs have a direct action can be determined to some degree by blocking possible secondary actions, for example, by depleting tissue stores of catecholamines or blocking the action or release of acetylcholine. A more difficult question is how each specific drug which acts directly brings about its effects on function.

The adrenergic drugs are supposed to work through tissue receptors. If excitation occurs when adrenergic drugs are administered, they are thought to have worked through an excitatory receptor. Tissues which are inhibited by adrenergic drugs are considered to possess different receptors. Just what the mechanism of coupling between drug and receptor consists of and how resulting reactions are mediated is not exactly known (1, 59). Since adrenergic drugs excite rather than inhibit cardiac reactions, only one receptor seems to be involved. Nomenclature and relationships of receptors will be described elsewhere in this volume. It suffices to state here that the function of β-receptors in the heart was associated by Ahlquist (1) with cardioacceleration and augmentation of myocardial contraction.

E. Additional Actions

There is still another aspect to the action of adrenergic drugs which must be considered as individual drugs are discussed. Adrenergic drugs have some usefulness in cases of abnormal heart function. They also can produce dangerous effects under certain abnormal circumstances. The catecholamines facilitate pacemaker action and can thus foster arrhythmias, but, on the other hand, they tend to abolish asystole. Since they tend to promote or accelerate conduction, they are useful in overcoming heart block and conduction abnormalities. A great deal of work has been done in this field of the production and amelioration of abnormal function by adrenergic drugs. The therapeutic usefulness of the adrenergic drugs will be discussed as they are considered individually.

Finally, it can be said that adrenergic drugs probably affect other aspects of cardiac cell response. Minimal gradient requirements for excitation by applied stimuli have not been studied much, but they are known to be modified by adrenergic drugs (92). Similarly, the ability to accommodate to continuous or long-lasting current flow is possessed by cardiac as well as nerve tissue (6). Such current flow certainly occurs about localized injuries, and the action of drugs upon the excitatory effects of a current of injury should be very important. Some of the effects of adrenergic drugs on injured hearts might be due to some action on the phenomenon of accommodation. This is an example of the many aspects of adrenergic drug action which have not been fully explored.

III. ACTIONS OF THE ADRENERGIC DRUGS

A. Classification and Modes of Action

All the adrenergic (sympathomimetic) drugs have a number of actions in common (29, 88). They differ chiefly in the quantitative aspects of their actions. All have a stimulating effect due to combination with β-receptors; they block action of other drugs on β-receptors; they release norepinephrine from stores; they are taken up in and block storage sites, thus preventing uptake of norepinephrine and enhancing the effect of exogenous norepinephrine; they block monamine oxidase. The influence of structure on their physiological activities has been well studied (23, 40).

The adrenergic drugs are divided into three categories, chiefly on the basis of pharmacological evidence: those that act directly, those that act indirectly, and those that act both indirectly and directly. The indirectly acting agents do so by releasing stored catecholamine, principally norepinephrine, from the cardiac tissues. When this release is blocked or the stores are depleted, these indirectly acting compounds cease to have an effect, whereas in the case of drugs with a direct and indirectly produced effect there is merely a diminution of response. The ability of compounds such as reserpine (5, 70), guanethidine (82), tyramine (98), and metaraminol (90) to cause depletion of norepinephrine from the heart in various mammalian species is well known. Tyramine and metaraminol are generally considered to be indirectly acting adrenergic drugs, but reserpine and guanethidine are normally not so classified even though, as a result of the catecholamine release, the heart accelerates, beats more strongly, and generally responds as if an injection of norepinephrine had been made. Guanethidine, though releasing norepinephrine, partially blocks the action of reserpine (42). A compound considered to be a normal derivative of dopamine, 6-hydroxydopamine, has an action resembling that of guanethidine (72).

The conclusion that reserpine depletes catecholamine storage in heart muscle has been based on histological evidence and on bioassay of muscle treated with the drug. One of the studies of reserpine action has suggested a relationship between catecholamine storage and a perimysial plexus (18). Silver-stained preparations of heart tissue reveal a meshwork of fine tortuous structural elements enveloping cardiac cells. Reserpinization significantly reduces this silver-stainable network. Vagotomy, which does not reduce catecholamine storage, reduces this network (17). It is not known whether this network is neural, nor is it understood what relationship it has to norepinephrine storage. Schümann has shown that, in the storage granules of cells, norepinephrine is bound to adenosine triphosphate stoichiometrically. Many pharmacologists consider that most of the storage and synthesis is in nerve terminals.

This matter of normal and abnormal release of norepinephrine from storage is complicated (57). It is thought by some (10, 11) that autonomic fibers act through the acetylcholine release of norepinephrine. Certainly acetylcholine and nicotine, like guanethidine and bretylium, release norepinephrine. They will also ultimately block sympathetic nerve action. Figure 1 and Tables I, II, and III give some concept of the

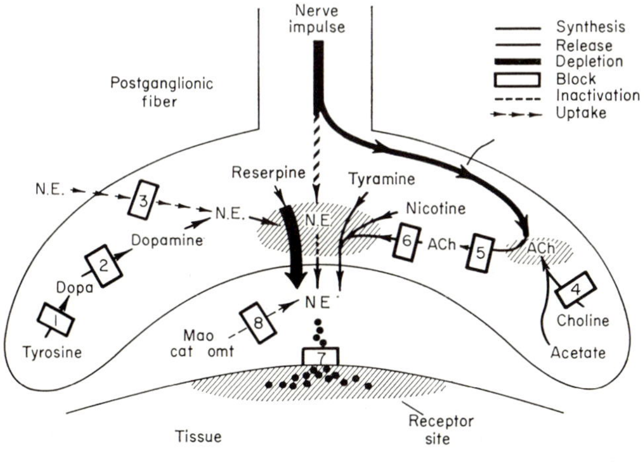

FIG. 1. Schema showing transmission of nerve impulse through humoral agents from a sympathetic postganglionic fiber to target cell. Receptor sites, sites of action of blocking agents indicated. ACh = acetylcholine; N.E. = norepinephrine; Mao = monoamineoxidase; cat omt = catechol *o*-methyl transferase. From (16).

release problem (16). Acetylcholine and nicotine are not normally considered adrenergic drugs, although, if release of norepinephrine from tissues were the sole criterion, they would qualify.

Whatever the storage site and ability may be, and however these sites may be depleted, they can be refilled not only by new synthesis, which in the heart proceeds at the rate of 0.05–0.10 μg/gm/hour (73), but also by perfusion of the tissue with adrenergic agents. Perfusion of depleted tissue with norepinephrine restores tissue stores and tissue re-

TABLE I

SOME DRUGS ACTING ON SYMPATHETIC GANGLIA

Augment sympathetic activity	Depress sympathetic activity
By stimulation of ganglion cell	*By blocking of ganglion cell*
Acetylcholine	Acetylcholine (high conc.)
Nicotine	Anticholinesterases (high conc.)
	Azamethonium (Pendiomid®)
By anticholinesterase activity	Chlorisondamine (Ecolid®)
DFP (diisopropylfluorophosphate)	Decamethonium (C-10; Syncurine®) (high conc.)
Eserine (physostigmine)	*d*-tubocurarine (high conc.)
Neostigmine (Prostigmine®)	Hexamethonium (Bistrium®) (C-6)
OMPA (octamethyl pyrophosphoramide)	Mecamylamine (Inversine®)
Parathion	Methantheline (Banthine®)
TEPP (tetraethyl pyrophosphate)	Nicotine (high conc.)
	Pentamethonium (C-5)
	Pentolinium (Ansolysen®)
	Propantheline (Probanthine®)
	Succinylcholine (Anectine®) (high conc.)
	Tetraethylammonium (Etamon®) (TEA)
	Trimethaphan (Arfonad®)

activity. Epinephrine is less effective in such restorative action, but dopamine is almost as good a replenisher as norepinephrine, possibly because norepinephrine is formed from it. More remarkable is the fact that adrenergic drugs, such as tyramine and metaraminol (Aramine), can occupy these receptor sites, although they are taken up less readily. Like the normal norepinephrine, they can be released by reserpine. Nerve stimulation likewise discharges the foreign adrenergic agents from storage (57). Block of their release by nerves can be effected without block of release by reserpine (20). This observation of the possible replacement of norepinephrine stores by other adrenergic drugs suggests that in case of overaction of sympathetic nerves some amelioration of

TABLE II

SOME SUBSTANCES ACTING ON TERMINAL PORTIONS OF SYMPATHETIC POSTGANGLIONIC FIBERS

Augment sympathetic activity	Depress sympathetic activity
By release of norepinephrine Acetylcholine, nicotine (after atropine) Reserpine, syrosingopine, guanethidine (immediate action) Tyramine, ephedrine, amphetamine, methamphetamine, mephenteramine *By block of enzymes* MAO inhibitors or catechol *o*-methyl transferase inhibitors	*By prevention of acetylcholine synthesis* Hemicholiniums *By prevention of acetylcholine release* *Botulinus* toxin *By prevention of norepinephrine synthesis* α-methyl dopa *By prevention of norepinephrine release by acetylcholine* Bretylium Guanethidine Xylocholine (TM 10) *By depletion of norepinephrine* Guanethidine Reserpine, syrosingopine

TABLE III

SOME DRUGS ACTING ON ALPHA RECEPTORS INNERVATED BY POSTGANGLIONIC SYMPATHETIC FIBERS

Augment sympathetic activity	Depress sympathetic activity[a]
Cyclopentamine (Clopane®) Epinephrine (Adrenalin) Metaraminol (Aramine) Methoxyphenamine (Orthoxine®) Naphazoline (Privine®) Norepinephrine (Levarterenol; Levophed®) Phenylephrine (Neosynephrine®) Propylhexedrine (Benzedrex®) Tuaminoheptane (Tuamine®)	Azapetine (Ilidar®) Chlorpromazine (Thorazine®) Dibenzyl B chloroethylamine (Dibenamine®) Ergot, ergotamine, dihydroergot compounds Phenoxybenzamine (Dibenzylone®) Phentolamine (Regitine®) Piperoxan (Benodaine®; 933 F) Tolazoline (Priscoline®) Yohimbine

[a] These are often called adrenergic blocking agents, peripheral sympathetic blocking agents, adrenolytic agents, sympatholytic agents, and α-receptor blockers.

their effects could be produced by substituting a less effective amine, such as metaraminol, in their storage sites (20).

Another conclusion pertinent to storage and release of sympathomimetic agents is that these processes are not simple. It appears that stored catecholamines or materials supplanting them are held in an "available" and "less readily available" form. There is a shift with time after restoration from an available to a less available state (87).

The various classes of adrenergic agents and the individual drugs, in addition to possessing common properties, have peculiarities. The most prominent agents should be considered individually, and it is best to begin with an analysis of the action of epinephrine. Norepinephrine can be considered simultaneously, since it differs from epinephrine only in not having the amino nitrogen methylated and its actions are similar (93).

B. Epinephrine, Norepinephrine, and Their Precursors and Derivatives: Directly Acting Compounds

1. *Metabolic Actions*

Epinephrine and related amines have metabolic effects of a generalized nature which affect the heart as well as other organs. They also effect the secretion and utilization of various hormones. This subject has been reviewed by Ellis (25), and these basic actions must be considered in discussions of the effects of adrenergic drugs on the heart.

Epinephrine causes hepatic glycogenolysis, which raises blood glucose levels, and muscle glycogenolysis, which tends to raise blood lactic acid levels. Cori and Cori (19) have stated that, after epinephrine, in spite of a diminished blood sugar utilization, there is an increase in carbohydrate oxidation. Thus, it seems that the metabolic activities of tissues are directly or indirectly heightened.

The hyperglycemia-producing, metabolism-raising potencies of sympathomimetic amines are influenced by their structure. There are species differences, too, which must be considered. Isoproterenol is a potent hepatic glycogenolytic agent in the rabbit, but not in the rat. Ephedrine has a weaker hyperglycemic action than epinephrine in most species. These differences have been summarized by Ellis (25). With respect to the heart, there has been some controversy, but the consensus is that, both *in vivo* and *in vitro*, heart tissue assimilates more glucose under epinephrine stimulation. There is an associated augmentation of phosphorylase activation.

The calorigenic effect of epinephrine has been ascribed by some to hyperlacticacidemia, but others believe it is a result of a multiplicity of changes, such as increased activity of the heart, plethora of blood glucose and lactic acid, and an increased cellular metabolism (34). Norepinephrine has about one-tenth the effect of epinephrine on oxygen metabolism; ephedrine has a small effect; isoproterenol also has a slight action; other adrenergic drugs also differ in their calorigenic effects (25).

Under certain conditions epinephrine augments protein catabolism. This action is indicated by an increased urinary nitrogen excretion. Epinephrine also increases catabolism of fat and fat transport.

One of the most important aspects of epinephrine's metabolic action with respect to heart action is its effect on "inorganic metabolism" or the ion exchanges. The effects of adrenergic drugs on potassium exchange have been reviewed by Fenn (26) and Fleckenstein (28). In brief summary, it can be said that epinephrine in relatively large doses decreases intracellular potassium and increases muscle sodium. Norepinephrine also modifies potassium equilibrium, and it has been suggested that such disequilibrium may be a factor in production of changes in excitability of the heart (83) and in production of cardiac arrhythmias by epinephrine and norepinephrine (63). More will be said later of the action of these compounds on the heart cell.

Actions of epinephrine on endocrine glands and the functions of their hormones have only indirect bearing on the heart's activity, but the matter is not devoid of importance. Epinephrine elevates ACTH discharge and consequently activates the adrenal cortex. Norepinephrine has much less potency. Probably the most important from the standpoint of the cardiac physiologist is the adrenal-thyroid relationship. Excess thyroid activity or hormone augments the actions of epinephrine and some other adrenergic drugs. The heart's response to epinephrine is greatly increased. The association of tachycardia and arrhythmias with hyperthyroidism is thus explained. Epinephrine is thought to increase the rate of peripheral thyroxine utilization. Extirpation of the thyroid glands reduces epinephrine effects.

Effects on phosphorylase activity and mechanical responses of the heart have been compared. There are considerable data suggesting that the transformation of phosphorylase b to the a form may be involved in the process whereby the sympathomimetic amines enhance the force of cardiac contraction (39, 68). The general conclusion is that these changes are not quantitatively related and thus phosphorylase change does not cause contraction tension change.

One of the metabolic effects studied most thoroughly is the change in high-energy phosphate produced by these drugs. Furchgott and Lee (30), however, showed that epinephrine and norepinephrine can produce a 200–300% increase in contractile strength of cardiac tissue without a change in the high-energy phosphate content of heart tissue. There remains much uncertainty as to the energy transformations related to heart muscle contraction and the mechanism of action of epinephrine thereon.

2. *Action on Cell Membranes*

It has been reported (24) that application of epinephrine consistently increases the membrane potential of dog atrial fibers. This effect, if significant, does not relate well with other reported actions of the drug. Epinephrine lowers threshold potential (46) and creates an instability of the membrane and other effects suggestive of a facilitation of the sodium carrier system so that the g Na is above normal (51, 52, 103). There is no effect on potassium permeability or flux, although epinephrine actions oppose those of the vagus and acetylcholine on pacemaker tissue. Perfusion of the sinoatrial node by solutions containing high concentrations of sympathomimetic amines produces maximum acceleration and refractoriness of the node to vagal and ACh effects (53). It is known that acetylcholine promotes K^+ permeability ($g\ K^+$), which hyperpolarizes the membrane, slows impulse generation, and increases membrane conductance. Epinephrine, which acts primarily on pacemakers, markedly increases the rate of depolarization during phase 4 (prepotential). The rate of rise of the action potential is increased and the overshoot is augmented. This effect on pacemakers, nodal and ideoventricular, explains some of the arrhythmia-producing actions of the adrenergic drugs (33, 62, 69). If epinephrine is given just before vagus stimulation, the automaticity of ventricular pacemakers is so augmented that vagus escape or development of abnormal rhythms is fostered. Other adrenergic agents are more or less effective by this test (2). The action on pacemakers is of a different order from that on cell excitability and it can be blocked, though not easily (64). The effects of norepinephrine and several other sympathomimetic amines appear to be the same as those of epinephrine (46). The action is basically on Na^+ flux and threshold potential.

3. *Action on the Contractile Process*

Adrenergic drugs or the catecholamines particularly have an inotropic effect on both isolated and *in situ* heart tissues (58, 85, 100, 101). This consists of a quicker shortening, a greater force of contraction, and a faster relaxation of the muscle (78).

The generally accepted concept (35, 41, 102) is that, upon depolarization of the membrane, an influx of calcium ion into the muscle fiber begins and these ions initiate or at least catalyze the contractile process.

Tracer studies have shown that alterations in contractile tension brought about by the staircase phenomena correlate well with changes in "calcium influx per beat" (102). If the perfusion medium has a high enough concentration of calcium, treppe cannot be demonstrated (55).

It has been suggested that the inotropic action of epinephrine on the heart arises from an increase in Ca^{++} transport. In support of this, there is an observed reciprocal relationship between the amount of extracellular calcium concentration and the inotropic effect from epinephrine (12). Extracellular calcium concentration can be raised to a point where contraction cannot be further augmented by epinephrine. It has been found (35) that epinephrine and norepinephrine do cause a threefold to fourfold increase in calcium turnover as they increase contraction of the heart. Strophanthine-K has a similar action. Some compounds which oppose action of epinephrine on the heart, such as acetylcholine and adenosine, and which have a negative inotropic action, reduce calcium ion influx.

Some drugs, such as ryanodine, have a negative inotropic action which does not modify calcium ion flux. There are also factors modifying calcium ion flux independent of catecholamine action. The outward driving force on the potassium ion, in a potassium-free medium, may increase the contractile activity (36). A greater outward flux of K^{+} is associated with a greater calcium uptake (86).

There are still other statements which can be made concerning effects of epinephrine and norepinephrine on contraction (56). The early relaxation induced by epinephrine occurs well in advance of membrane repolarization, but this is antagonized by increasing calcium concentrations. The length-tension relationships are undiminished in a calcium-rich medium, and epinephrine in a dose which markedly *augments* twitch tensions (1–2 μg/ml) profoundly *decreases* tensions developed during potassium chloride–induced contractures, at least in frog ventricle strips and cat papillary muscle.

Difficulty in interpreting the inotropic effect of epinephrine solely in terms of Ca^{++} influx arises from the fact that the faster relaxation should be antagonized by Ca^{++}. In order to get around this difficulty, it has been considered that the Ca carrier is a K exchange mechanism and that both Na and K ions can compete with calcium for it. This permits a new statement pertinent to excitation-contraction coupling and the effects of epinephrine on contraction (56), namely, that depolarization initiates an efflux of K^{+} which is augmented by epinephrine and/or norepinephrine. This efflux moves carrier which can transport Ca ion from extracellular reservoirs. This Ca ion triggers contraction. Strength of response is thus related to K efflux and Ca ion influx. This process tends to be self-limiting since, as the strong efflux of K^+ continues, it creates an extracellular K^+ concentration which with Na^+ competes with Ca^{++} for carrier, eventually blocking it to Ca^{++} so that relaxation can begin. Thus, epinephrine will not have an inotropic effect on contracture produced by KCl depolarization of a cell membrane. Thus, not only the quickness and amplitude but also the shortened duration of contraction produced by adrenergic agents such as epinephrine are due to an augmented potassium flux.

4. *Uses*

Epinephrine through its chronotropic and inotropic effects on the heart and its effects on the peripheral circuit increases cardiac output until the rate goes too high to permit effective filling. The bases for effects on coronary flow are not fully determined. Flow increases, but this may be an indirect effect rather than due to a dilator action of epinephrine. It is stated that neither epinephrine nor isopropylarterenol should be used as coronary dilators. Norepinephrine is considered to be better, but the increase in flow does not satisfy the increased energy need of the muscle.

Epinephrine is occasionally used in Stokes-Adams syncope to stimulate a high ventricular pacemaker, but it occasionally causes an undesirable ventricular tachycardia. It has been used in cardiac arrest but may cause or "fix" fibrillation (2). Epinephrine can improve contractility in a hypodynamic state. This cannot be a very specific action, since adenosine triphosphate, steroids, and a number of other compounds have a similar action. Hajdu has discussed the materials promoting this strengthening of contraction and their mechanism of action. He advanced evidence for the presence in the blood of cardioglobulins, which can improve performance of the mammalian heart (37).

5. *Destruction of Epinephrine and Related Compounds*

The intensity and duration of action of epinephrine and other adrenergic drugs depends on their rate of inactivation. Epinephrine is inactivated by oxidative deamination. Amine oxidase oxidizes many primary, secondary, and tertiary amines such as tyramine and phenylethylamine, their phenolic derivatives, and cyclohexylethylamine. The end products, an aldehyde and ammonia, are converted by other enzymes to a carboxyl compound and urea. Iproniazid (1-isonicotinyl-2-isopropylhydrazine) inhibits amine oxidase.

Epinephrine is also destroyed by oxidation through the phenolic hydroxyl groups and by conjugation of the phenolic portion with sulfuric or glucuronic acid. Thus there exist several enzyme systems capable of inactivating the dihydroxyphenyl adrenergic amines (57). It is not known at present which is principally responsible for *in vivo* inactivation. The liver is of principal importance in inactivation, and rate of inactivation is increased by hyperthermia and decreased by hypothermia, ephedrine, or cocaine (2).

C. Isoproterenol (Isopropylarterenol, Isuprel®) and Other Directly Acting Compounds

Isoproterenol (3,4-dihydroxyphenylethanolisopropylamine) is an isopropyl analog of epinephrine and norepinephrine. It is the most potent β-adrenergic agent now in use. Although it is produced in small quantity by the adrenal gland (61), it is not considered to be a normal transmitter. It does, however, have a direct action independent of cardiac catecholamine storage. It appears to be ten times as effective as epinephrine in enhancing the escape of supraventricular (SA node) and lower pacemakers (low AV node, bundle of His, Purkinje fiber) when vagus block is preventing transmission. Escape rhythms arise above and below the node during vagus block when isoproterenol is given (94). It is also used in heart block which occurs clinically and in Stokes-Adams attacks. It enhances ideoventricular rhythmicity and atrioventricular conduction (67, 105), but the papers just mentioned state that in this action it is less effective than are some other catecholamines (75).

Isoproterenol can arouse pacemaker action in quiescent hearts (32) and accelerate such activity in normally beating isolated and *in situ* hearts (3, 80). Since it stimulates normally dominant pacemakers and favors conduction, this drug has been used to treat cardiac arrhythmias (80). Isoproterenol also has a strong inotropic action on the ventricle (81). It is less likely than epinephrine to produce paroxysmal tachycardia. Its use as an antifibrillatory agent in ventricular fibrillation in association with electrical defibrillation has been suggested (50). Differences between isoproterenol and epinephrine are of degree rather than kind, but these differences do make it the drug of choice in some circumstances.

Dopamine (3,4-dihydroxyphenylethylamine) is a naturally occurring biochemical precursor of norepinephrine and epinephrine. It definitely causes an increase in cardiac output. Both rate and force of contraction are increased, and effects last much longer than those of norepinephrine. It does not cause late depression as does norepinephrine (47). This material is not the final transmitter which normally acts between nerve and muscle. It is of interest, however, that it has actions so similar to the end products of the transmitter synthesis.

Other precursors and metabolites of epinephrine or norepinephrine which similarly modify heart action have been tested in the hope of finding useful products, but no strikingly different or more useful actions have been revealed.

D. Tyramine and Indirectly Acting Compounds

Tyramine (4-hydroxyphenylethylamine), the product of the decarboxylation of tyrosine, occurs naturally as a result of protein autolysis and is normally extractable from ergot and mistletoe. Recent publications from respectable sources (49) report that certain cheeses, chianti wine, and certain other wines and beers contain sufficient tyramine to cause undesirable stimulation of the heart, especially in subjects receiving monamine oxidase inhibitors.

Though tyramine possesses only about one-fiftieth the potency of norepinephrine, its action is similar, though longer lasting and with no rebound fall in cardiac output. It was one of the first adrenergic agents to be used clinically, for uterine stimulation, but it is not used now. Andrus in 1924 showed that tyramine increased the rate and amplitude of atrial contractions. Other workers demonstrated its inotropic action on the ventricle.

In 1958, Burn and Rand (9) suggested that tyramine has no direct sympathomimetic action but that its entire effect is due to liberation of norepinephrine from endogenous stores. Their conclusion was based on the observation that the drug had no effect on tissues pretreated with reserpine. Reinfusion of norepinephrine restored tyramine action promptly.

There is abundant evidence that tyramine does cause a release of norepinephrine from organs reacting to the drug (15, 21, 65, 84), but the amounts liberated are too small to have of themselves caused the observed effects (38). It was observed that minute amounts of norepinephrine, when given with tyramine, restored the action of tyramine on reserpinized tissue (65, 84). Finally, it is well known that an injection of tyramine has a much more protracted action than does norepinephrine on strength and rapidity of heart action (48). These evidences that tyramine has an independent action have been countered by a "strategic liberation" hypothesis suggesting that it is the locus of liberation or the local concentration of norepinephrine which is responsible for effects. If norepinephrine were liberated near the sinoatrial node, its concentration and its effect would be greater than could be brought about by a large amount of norepinephrine injected into the systemic circulation. Tyramine, however, has a simultaneous inotropic effect which is not readily explained by a "strategic liberation" near the sinoatrial node.

In order to avoid the implication of a direct action of tyramine and retain the concept that it acts through norepinephrine liberation, a new hypothesis has been advanced. This suggests that tyramine competes with norepinephrine for storage space, thus liberating norepinephrine. It does not compete for "receptor site space." Thus, liberated norepinephrine would be more effective than injected norepinephrine because of the availability of receptor site space only after the giving of tyramine. This occupation of storage site space would also prolong the action of liberated norepinephrine beyond that of injected norepinephrine. This does not explain the reversal of effect from norepinephrine which does not occur after tyramine.

Tyramine does not impede the inactivation of norepinephrine by catechol-*o*-methyl transferase. Thus, those who accept the conclusion that tyramine does not have a direct adrenergic action on cardiac tissues can explain results on the basis of a potentiation concept which visualizes tyramine as prolonging and increasing the effectiveness of small amounts of norepinephrine. This potentiation conceivably could come from a strategic focus action, a block of storage site action, or a combined action of the two amines (4, 87).

There is some difference of opinion concerning the completeness of abolition of tyramine action by pretreatment with reserpine. Carlsson *et al.* (14) state that action on the pacemaker is abolished. Holmes and Fowler (47, 48) and Nasmyth (66) agree that tyramine acts in part through norepinephrine release, but they believe there is a residual direct effect of tyramine on heart rate and contraction force even after reserpine. Trendelenburg (88) has advanced a slightly different idea. He suggests that the very small replacement or small amount of norepinephrine required to reestablish tyramine action after reserpinization suggests that the norepinephrine has the effect of enabling tyramine to act directly on the cell.

Cocaine is generally thought of as an epinephrine or norepinephrine potentiator. It has a biphasic action, tending to cause liberation of stored norepinephrine from the heart in low concentration and blocking release in high concentration. Cocaine antagonizes the release of norepinephrine by tyramine and minimizes the cardiac effects of tyramine (13, 29). Cocaine is not an adrenergic drug, but in low concentrations it can liberate enough norepinephrine and potentiate it enough to affect heart action.

From the literature one does not get the impression that a pure secondary effect, through release of stored norepinephrine, has been fully demonstrated. Certainly, however, direct actions are small in the case of tyramine and a few other compounds.

E. Ephedrine and Its Derivatives: Direct and Indirect Actions

Ephedrine occurs in plants of the genus *Ephedra.* This ancient Chinese remedy was isolated, identified, and synthesized by a number of Japanese pharmacologists in the late years of the last century (23). It was reintroduced into clinical practice about 1925. Chemically it is phenylisopropanolmethylamine. The oral effectiveness and long action of this drug are apparently due to the presence of a methyl group on the α carbon atom. This configuration renders the molecule refractory to deamination by amine oxidases of the liver. It may inhibit the action of this enzyme on epinephrine, and one theory is that ephedrine has no other means of action (31). It is stated by others (23), however, that ephedrine acts on the adrenergic receptors in a manner similar but not necessarily identical to that of epinephrine. Ephedrine also sensitizes tissues (receptors) to epinephrine. Finally, ephedrine is classified as an indirectly acting adrenergic drug which exerts its effect by liberating norepinephrine from storage (16). Like epinephrine, it stimulates phosphorylase activity in the heart (39).

Whatever its mechanism of action, it increases the force of ventricular contraction (95). Ephedrine also acts on pacemaker tissues to excite their action during vagus block (2). Ephedrine and phenylephrine are much less effective in this respect than isoproterenol and epinephrine. It has a longer action than epinephrine, but in subsequent doses a biphasic effect may occur and the heart is depressed. Ephedrine has been used with some success in heart block. Thus, it possesses all the properties of action shown by epinephrine. Pretreatment with reserpine reduces but does not abolish its action. *meta*-Tyramine, phenylpropanolamine, ephedrine and its derivatives on such basis are considered to act directly and indirectly. Ephedrine can facilitate and also block epinephrine action to some degree, since it competes for β-receptors.

F. Additional Drugs with Adrenergic Action

Numerous other compounds are known to have adrenergic actions on the heart. A brief listing of them and their effects will be given without elaborate description of their relationships:

1. The methylxanthines, theophylline, aminophylline, and related compounds *increase* the metabolism of cardiac muscle and catalyze transformation of phosphorylase b to phosphorylase a as does epinephrine (43). These compounds are used as mild general stimulants and

not thought of as cardiac drugs, though they do have an adrenergic action.

2. Amphetamine, methamphetamine, and mephentermine (Wyamine), like tyramine, have an action which is similar to that of norepinephrine and which is much reduced by pretreatment with reserpine. Once reduced, it is restored by norepinephrine (89). Another newer compound has a similar action. It is *cis*-2-amino-4-methyl-5-phenyl-2-oxazoline (McN-822). Its action is blocked by dichloroisoproterenol hydrochloride (DCI) (104). Unquestionably, mephentermine and related drugs increase cardiac oxygen consumption and myocardial efficiency (99). Finally, hydroxyamphetamine is quite effective in heart block. These drugs also are not considered to be cardiac drugs primarily. Amphetamine is generally thought of as a central nervous system excitant. This compound and methamphetamine also resemble ephedrine, but their action is more central than that of ephedrine.

3. Metaraminol (Aramine) and methoxamine (Vasoxyl), which are frequently discussed with mephentermine (Wyamine), are considered to act primarily on the peripheral circuit. They do act on the heart, liberating norepinephrine, but their actions differ somewhat. Metaraminol has less tendency to create vulnerability to fibrillation (33, 77). These agents have been used primarily because of their peripheral actions, but they have effects on the heart as well (77).

4. Aranthol (6-methyl-6-hydroxy-2-methylaminoheptane) is an aliphatic amine related to Oenethyl®. It has shown some promise as a stimulant in case of congestive failure, but the search for drugs giving a digitalis-like action has led in other directions.

IV. SUMMARY AND CONCLUSIONS

The drugs mentioned here are those adrenergic compounds affecting the heart which have been most studied. There are many other related compounds mentioned in textbooks of pharmacology. It should be pointed out that practically all drugs may have some effect on the heart directly or through the endocrine glands or autonomic nervous system. In this review there has been no discussion of structural relationships and dosages. These facts can be obtained from the references given.

The primary aim was to discuss what is known of the mechanism of action of these adrenergic drugs, which affect heart function to a significant degree. They do release stored carbohydrate, activating phosphorylase, and they increase the basal metabolic rates of tissues, but the bases of this action are not fully known. It is clear that the catecholamines favor sodium influx, and this explains many actions on the membrane, on excitation-contraction coupling, and on the contraction-relaxation process. They stimulate pacemaker tissues, possibly again by favoring sodium permeability. There are degrees of directness and indirectness of action demonstrated by the autonomic drugs. The processes involved in integrated heart function are not equally affected by epinephrine. Thus, a degree of disorganization, or arrhythmia, is to be expected from use of strong dosages. The relative time scales of action and degrees of the early excitation and late suppressor effect by some adrenergic compounds may explain disorganizations of heart actions, or the arrhythmias.

References

1. Ahlquist, R. P., A study of the adrenotropic receptors. *Am. J. Physiol.* **153,** 586 (1948).
2. Ahlquist, R. P., Adrenergic drugs. *In* "Drill's Pharmacology in Medicine," 2nd Ed., Chapt. 27, p. 380. McGraw-Hill, New York, 1958.
3. Barcroft, H., and Konzett, H., On the actions of noradrenalin, Adrenalin and isopropyl noradrenalin on the arterial blood pressure, heart rate and muscle blood flow in man. *J. Physiol.* (*London*) **110,** 194 (1949).
4. Battersby, E. J., and Newman, E. V., Chronotropic effects of norepinephrine and tyramine: a system response analysis. *Circulation Res.* **15,** 112 (1964).
5. Bertler, Å., Carlsson, A., and Rosengren, E., Release by reserpine of catecholamines from rabbit's heart. *Naturwissenschaften* **43,** 521 (1956).
6. Brooks, C. McC., Gilbert, J. L., Kavaler, F., Suckling, E. E., Ang, M. K., and Lange, G., The phenomenon of accommodation in the ventricular myocardium. *Arch. Kreislaufforsch.* **33,** 102 (1960).
7. Brooks, C. McC., Gilbert, J. L., Levey, H. A., and Curtis, D. R., "Humors, Hormones and Neurosecretions." State Univ. of New York, Albany, New York, 1962.
8. Brooks, C. McC., Hoffman, B. F., Suckling, E. E., and Orias, O., "Excitability of the Heart." Grune & Stratton, New York, 1955.
9. Burn, J. H., and Rand, M. J., Action of sympathomimetic amines in animals treated with reserpine. *J. Physiol.* (*London*) **144,** 314 (1958).
10. Burn, J. H., A new view of adrenergic nerve fibers, explaining the action of reserpine, bretylium and guanethidine. *Brit. Med. J.* No. 5240, p. 1623 (1961).
11. Burn, J. H., The liberation of norepinephrine. *Physiol. Physicians* **1,** No. 10 (1963).
12. Burridge, W., Some new properties of cardiac muscle. *Arch. Intern. Pharmacodyn.* **62,** 399 (1939).
13. Campos, H. A., Stitzel, R. E., and Shideman, F. E., Actions of tyramine and cocaine on catecholamine levels in subcellular fractions of isolated cat hearts. *J. Pharmacol. Exptl. Therap.* **141,** 290 (1963).
14. Carlsson, A., Rosengren, E., Bertler, Å., and Nilsson, J., *In* "Psychotropic Drugs." Elsevier, Amsterdam, 1957.
15. Chidsey, C. A., Harrison, D. C., and Braunwald, E., Release of norepinephrine from the heart by vasoactive amines. *Proc. Soc. Exptl. Biol. Med.* **104,** 488 (1962).

16. Comroe, J. H., The mechanism of action of some drugs on the sympathetic nervous system. *Physiol. Physicians* **1**, No. 10 (1963).
17. Cooper, T., "Nervous Control of the Heart." Williams & Wilkins, Baltimore, Maryland, 1964.
18. Cooper, T., Jellinek, M., and Firsch, E. F., Reserpine: Its effect on silver-stained structures of the heart. *Science* **141**, 526 (1963).
19. Cori, C. F., and Cori, G. T., The mechanism of epinephrine action. *J. Biol. Chem.* **79**, 321 (1928).
20. Crout, J. R., Alpers, H. S., Tatum, E. L., and Shore, P. A., Release of metaraminol (Aramine) from the heart by sympathetic nerve stimulation. *Science* **145**, 828 (1964).
21. Davey, M. J., and Farmer, J. B., The mode of action of tyramine. *J. Pharm. Pharmacol.* **15**, 178 (1963).
22. Draper, M. H., and Weidmann, S., Cardiac resting and action potentials recorded with an intracellular electrode. *J. Physiol.* (*London*) **115**, 74 (1951).
23. Drill, V. A., "Pharmacology in Medicine," 2nd Ed., McGraw-Hill, New York, 1958.
24. Dudel, J., and Trautwein, W., Die Wirkung von Adrenalin auf das Ruhepotential von Myokardfasern des Vorhofs. *Experientia* **12**, 396 (1955).
25. Ellis, S., The metabolic effects of epinephrine and related compounds. *Pharmacol. Rev.* **8**, 485 (1956).
26. Fenn, W. D., The role of potassium in physiological processes. *Physiol. Rev.* **20**, 377 (1940).
27. Fernándes-Morán, H., Cell membrane ultrastructure. *In* "Symposium on the Plasma Membrane." New York Heart Assoc., New York, 1962.
28. Fleckenstein, A., "Der Kalium-Natrium-austausch." Springer, Berlin, 1955.
29. Furchgott, R. F., Kerpekar, S., Rieker, M., and Schwab, A., Actions and interactions of norepinephrine, tyramine, and cocaine on aortic strips of rabbit and left atria of guinea pig and cat. *J. Pharmacol. Exptl. Therap.* **142**, 39 (1963).
30. Furchgott, R. F., and Lee, K. S., High energy phosphates and the force of contraction of cardiac muscle. *In* "The Myocardium—Its Biochemistry and Biophysics." New York Heart Assoc., New York, 1960.
31. Gaddum, J. H., and Kwiatkowski, H., The action of ephedrine. *J. Physiol.* (*London*) **94**, 87 (1938).
32. Garb, S., Penna, M., and Ganz, A., Effects of epinephrine, norepinephrine, and isopropyl arterenol on the isolated auricles of four mammalian species. *Am. J. Physiol.* **185**, 337 (1956).
33. Gilbert, J. L., Lange, G., and Brooks, C. McC., Influence of sympathomimetic pressor drugs on arrhythmias caused by multiple stimuli. *Circulation Res.* **7**, 417 (1959).
34. Griffith, F. R., Fact and theory regarding the calorigenic action of adrenaline. *Physiol. Rev.* **31**, 151 (1951).
35. Grossman, A., and Furchgott, R. F., The effects of various drugs on calcium exchange in the isolated guinea pig left auricle. *J. Pharmacol. Exptl. Therap.* **145**, 162 (1964).
36. Hajdu, S., Mechanism of staircase and contracture in ventricular muscle. *Am. J. Physiol.* **174**, 371 (1953).
37. Hajdu, S., and Leonard, E., Cardiac active principles in blood plasma. *Circulation* **24**, 530 (1961).

38. Hall, W. J., The action of tyramine on the dog isolated atrium. *Brit. J. Pharmacol.* **20,** 245 (1963).
39. Hanem, I. El. S. Ali, Antonio, A., and Haugaard, N., The action of sympathomimetic amines and adrenergic blocking agents on tissue phosphorylase activity. *J. Pharmacol. Exptl. Therap.* **145,** 142 (1964).
40. Hartung, W. H., Epinephrine and related compounds: influence of structure on physiological activity. *Chem. Rev.* **9,** 389 (1931).
41. Heilbrunn, L. U., and Wiercinski, F. J., The action of various catrons on muscle protoplasm. *J. Cellular Comp. Physiol.* **29,** 15 (1947).
42. Hertting, G., Axelrod, J., and Patrick, R. W., Actions of bretylium and guanethidine on the uptake and release of [^{3}H]-noradrenaline. *Brit. J. Pharmacol.* **18,** 161 (1962).
43. Hess, M. E., Hottenstein, D., Shanfeld, J., and Haugaard, N., Metabolic effects of theophylline in cardiac and skeletal muscle. *J. Pharmacol. Exptl. Therap.* **141,** 274 (1963).
44. Hodgkin, A. L., The Croonian Lecture: Ionic movements and electrical activity in giant nerve fibers. *Proc. Roy. Soc.* (*London*) **B148,** 1 (1958).
45. Hodgkin, A. L., and Huxley, A. F., A quantitative description of membrane current and its application to conduction and excitation in nerve. *J. Physiol.* (*London*) **117,** 500 (1952).
46. Hoffman, B. F., and Cranefield, P. F., "Electrophysiology of the Heart." McGraw-Hill, New York, 1960.
47. Holmes, J. C., and Fowler, N. D., Direct cardiac effects of dopamine. *Circulation Res.* **10,** 68 (1962).
48. Holmes, J. C., and Fowler, N. D., Cardiac effects of tyramine. *Circulation Res.* **11,** 364 (1962).
49. Horwitz, D., Lovenberg, W., Engelman, K., and Sjoerdsma, A., Certain tyramine-rich foodstuffs can cause blood-pressure rise in MAO-inhibited patients. *Heart-Res. News* Sept., p. 10 (1964).
50. Hossli, G., Immediate relief of cardiac arrest. *Triangle. Sandoz J. Med. Sci.* **6,** 26 (1963).
51. Hutter, D. F., Mode of action of autonomic transmitters on the heart. *Brit. Med. Bull.* **13,** 176 (1957).
52. Hutter, D. F., and Trautwein, W., Vagal and sympathetic effects on the pacemaker fibers in the sinus venosus of the heart. *J. Gen. Physiol.* **39,** 715 (1956).
53. James, T. N., and Nadeau, R. A., Effects of sympathomimetic amines studied by direct perfusion of the sinus node. *Am. J. Physiol.* **204,** 591 (1963).
54. Kavaler, F., Membrane depolarization as a cause of tension development in mammalian ventricular muscle. *Am. J. Physiol.* **197,** 968 (1959).
55. Kavaler, F., Uniformity of the contractile response of ventricular muscle in high-calcium Tyrode's solution. *Nature* **196,** 1104 (1962).
56. Kavaler, F., and Morad, M., Paradoxical effects of epinephrine on excitation-contraction coupling in cardiac muscle. *Circulation Research* **18,** 492 (1966).
57. Kopin, I. J., Storage and metabolism of catecholamines: the role of monamine oxidase. *Pharmacol. Rev.* **16,** 179 (1964).
58. Kruta, U., and Zadina, R., Recherches sur la pharmacodynamie du muscle cardiaque; influence de l'adrinaline et de la tyramine sur la contraction du myocarde. *Arch. Intern. Physiol. Biochim.* **59,** 198 (1938).

59. Lands, A. M., Sympathetic receptor action. *Am. J. Physiol.* **169,** 11 (1952).
60. Lange, G., Lu, H. H., and Brooks, C. McC., Suppression of sinoatrial node pacemaker action by overdrive. *Federation Proc.* **23,** No. 2 (1964).
61. Lockett, M. F., Bronchial sympathin in the cat. *J. Physiol.* (*London*) **133,** 73P (1956).
62. Matsuda, K., Hoshi, T., and Kameyama, S., Action of acetylcholine and Adrenalin upon the membrane potential of the atrioventricular node. *Tohoku J. Exptl. Med.* **68,** 16 (1958).
63. Melville, K. I., Mazurkiewicz, I., and Korol, B., Potassium disequilibrium as a factor in production of cardiac irregularities following epinephrine and norepinephrine. *Federation Proc.* **14,** 369 (1955).
64. Moran, N. C., Moore, J. I., Holcomb, A. K., and Mushet, G., Antagonism of adrenergically-induced cardiac arrhythmias by dichloroisoproterenol. *J. Pharmacol. Exptl. Therap.* **136,** 327 (1962).
65. Nasmyth, P. A., Some observations on the effects of tyramine. *In* "Adrenergic Mechanisms." Little, Brown, Boston, Massachusetts, 1960.
66. Nasmyth, P. A., An investigation of the action of tyramine and its interrelationship with the effects of other sympathomimetic amines. *Brit. J. Pharmacol.* **18,** 65 (1962).
67. Nathanson, M. H., and Miller, H., The action of norepinephrine, epinephrine and isopropylnorepinephrine on the rhythmic function of the heart. *Circulation* **6,** 238 (1952).
68. Nayler, W. G., and Wright, J. E., Effect of epinephrine on the mechanical and phosphorylase activity of normal and hypothermic hearts. *Circulation Res.* **13,** 199 (1963).
69. Otsuka, M., Die Wirkung von Adrenolin auf Purkinje-Fasern von Säugetierherzen. *Arch. Ges. Physiol. Pfluegers* **266,** 512 (1957–1958).
70. Paasonen, M. K., and Krayer, D., The release of norepinephrine from the mammalian heart by reserpine. *J. Pharmacol. Exptl. Therap.* **123,** 153 (1958).
71. Paes de Carvalho, A., Cellular electrophysiology of the atrial specialized tissues. *In* "The Specialized Tissues of the Heart" (A. Paes de Carvalho, W. C. DeMello, and B. F. Hoffman, eds.), p. 115. Elsevier, Amsterdam, 1961.
72. Porter, C. C., Totaro, J. A., and Stone, C. A., Effect of 6-hydroxydopamine and some other compounds on the concentration of norepinephrine in the hearts of mice. *J. Pharmacol. Exptl. Therap.* **140,** 308 (1963).
73. Potter, L. F., and Axelrod, J., Studies on the storage of norepinephrine and the effect of drugs. *J. Pharmacol. Exptl. Therap.* **140,** 199 (1963).
74. Rhodin, J. A. G., del Missier, P., and Reid, L. C., The structure of the specialized impulse-conducting system of the steer heart. *In* "The Myocardium—Its Biochemistry and Biophysics," pp. 349–367. New York Heart Assoc., New York, 1960.
75. Riker, W. F., Depierre, F., Roberts, J., Roy, B. B., and Reilly, J., The epinephrine and hydrocarbon-epinephrine disturbance in the cat. *J. Pharmacol. Exptl. Therap.* **114,** 1 (1955).
76. Rothschuh, K. E., "Elektrophysiologie des Herzens." Steinkopff, Darmstadt, 1952.
77. Sarnoff, S. J., Case, R. B., Berglund, E., and Sarnoff, L. C., Ventricular function. V. The circulatory effects of Aramine; mechanism of action of vasopressor drugs in cardiogenic shock. *Circulation* **10,** 84 (1954).

78. Sarnoff, S. J., and Mitchell, J. H., The control of the function of the heart. "Handbook of Physiology, Circulation," Vol. 1, Sect. 2, p. 489. Am. Physiol. Soc., Washington, D.C., 1962.
79. Scher, A. M., Excitation of the heart. "Handbook of Physiology, Circulation," Vol. 1, Sect. 2, p. 287. Am. Physiol. Soc., Washington, D.C., 1962.
80. Schumacker, E. E., and Schmock, C. L., The control of certain cardiac arrhythmias with isopropyl norepinephrine. *Am. Heart J.* **48,** 933 (1954).
81. Schwartz, S. P., and Schwartz, L. S., The Adams-Stokes syndrome during normal sinus rhythm and transient heart block. *Am. Heart J.* **57,** 849 (1959).
82. Sheppard, H., and Zimmerman, J., Effect of guanethidine on tissue catecholamines. *Pharmacologist* **1,** 69 (1959).
83. Siebens, A. A., Hoffman, B. F., Ensen, Y., Farrell, J. E., and Brooks, C. McC., Effects of *l*-epinephrine and *l*-norepinephrine on cardiac excitability. *Am. J. Physiol.* **175,** 1 (1953).
84. Smith, E. R., The effect of norepinephrine infusions upon some responses of reserpine treated spinal cats to tyramine. *J. Pharmacol. Exptl. Therap.* **139,** 321 (1963).
85. Sonnenblick, E., Force-velocity relations in mammalian heart muscle. *Am. J. Physiol.* **202,** 931 (1962).
86. Thomas, L. J., Jr., Increase of labeled calcium uptake in heart muscle during potassium lack contracture. *J. Gen. Physiol.* **43,** 1193 (1960).
87. Trendelenburg, U., Modification of the effect of tyramine by various agents and procedures. *J. Pharmacol. Exptl. Therap.* **134,** 8 (1961).
88. Trendelenburg, U., and Crout, J. R., The norepinephrine stores of isolated atria of guinea pigs pretreated with reserpine. *J. Pharmacol. Exptl. Therap.* **145,** 151 (1964).
89. Trendelenburg, U., Gomez Alonso de la Sierra, B., and Muskus, A., Modification by reserpine of the response of the atrial pacemaker to sympathomimetic amines. *J. Pharmacol. Exptl. Therap.* **141,** 301 (1963).
90. Udenfriend, S., and Zoltzman-Nirenberg, P., On the mechanism of norepinephrine release produced by α-methylmeta-tyrosine. *J. Pharmacol. Exptl. Therap.* **138,** 194 (1962).
91. Ushiyama, J., and Brooks, C. McC., Intracellular stimulation and recording from single cardiac cells. *Am. J. Cardiol.* **10,** 688 (1962).
92. Ushiyama, J., and Brooks, C. McC., Electronic and chemical effects on minimal gradient requirements for cardiac muscle. *Am. J. Physiol.* **202,** 487 (1962).
93. von Euler, U. S., "Noradrenaline." Thomas, Springfield, Illinois, 1956.
94. Wallace, G., and Daggett, W. M., Pacemaker activity during vagal escape rhythms. *Circulation Res.* **15,** 93 (1964).
95. Walton, R. P., and Brodie, O. J., Cardiovascular effect of two aliphatic amines and ephedrine. *J. Pharmacol. Exptl. Therap.* **96,** 341 (1949).
96. Weidmann, S., Membrane excitation in cardiac muscle. "The Myocardium—Its Biochemistry and Biophysics" (A. P. Fishman, ed.). New York Heart Assoc., New York, 1960.
97. Weidmann, S., "Elektrophysiologie der Herzmuskelfaser." Huber, Bern, 1956.
98. Weiner, N., Draskóczy, P. R., and Burack, W. R., The ability of tyramine to liberate catecholamines *in vivo*. *J. Pharmacol. Exptl. Therap.* **137,** 47 (1962).
99. Welch, G. H., Braunwald, E., Case, R. B., and Sarnoff, S. J., The effect of mephentermine sulfate on myocardial oxygen consumption, myocardial efficiency and peripheral vascular resistance. *Am. J. Med.* **24,** 871 (1958).

100. Wiggers, C. J., Studies on the cardiodynamic actions of drugs. II. The mechanism of cardiac stimulation by epinephrine. *J. Pharmacol. Exptl. Therap.* **30,** 233 (1927).

101. Wiggers, C. J., and Katz, L. N., The specific influence of the accelerator nerves on the duration of ventricular systole. *Am. J. Physiol.* **53,** 49 (1920).

102. Winegrad, S., and Shanes, A. M., Calcium flux and contractility of guinea pig atria. *J. Gen. Physiol.* **45,** 371 (1962).

103. Woodbury, J. W., Cellular electrophysiology of the heart. "Handbook of Physiology, Circulation," Vol. 1, Sect. 2, p. 237. Am. Physiol. Soc., Washington, D.C., 1962.

104. Yelnosky, J., and Katz, R., Sympathomimetic actions of *cis*-2-amino-4-methyl-5-phenyl-2-oxazoline. *J. Pharmacol. Exptl. Therap.* **141,** 180 (1963).

105. Zoll, P. M., Linenthal, A. J., Gibson, W., Paul, M. H., and Norman, L. R., Intravenous drug therapy of Stokes-Adams disease. Effects of sympathomimetic amines on ventricular rhythmicity and atrioventricular conduction. *Circulation* **17,** 325 (1958).

B. The Effects of Adrenergic Drugs on the Systemic Circulation

R. F. Whelan

Department of Human Physiology and Pharmacology, University of Adelaide, South Australia

I. Introduction 29
II. Epinephrine and Arterenol 30
A. Epinephrine 32
B. Arterenol 47
C. Isoproterenol 56
D. Mixtures 60
III. Other Sympathomimetic Drugs 62
A. Tyramine 68
B. Ephedrine 70
C. Amphetamine 73
D. Phenylephrine 76
E. Dopamine 78
References 81

I. INTRODUCTION

Adrenergic drugs may be defined as drugs which stimulate structures innervated by adrenergic nerves and are therefore sympathomimetic. The adrenergic drugs selected for consideration in this section are those which occur naturally in the body and also a number of others which, although not naturally occurring, are of importance because their use and study has played a part in advancing physiological knowledge.

The following drugs are discussed: epinephrine, arterenol, isoproterenol, mixtures of these, tyramine, ephedrine, amphetamine, phenylephrine, and dopamine. In each case the effect of the drug on the systemic circulation has been considered under the following headings: (1) structure, formation, and breakdown; (2) general circulatory effects, including cardiac output, arterial blood pressure, and peripheral resistance; and (3) specific vascular beds, including skin circulation, muscle circulation, intestinal circulation, kidney circulation, spleen circulation, and cerebral circulation. The coronary and pulmonary circulations have not been considered, since these will be dealt with in other sections of this work.

II. EPINEPHRINE AND ARTERENOL

One of the earliest clues to the functions of the adrenal medulla and to the actions of the adrenal amines on the circulation was provided by the experiment of Brown-Sequard in 1856 which showed that stimulation of the adrenal gland produced constriction of the cerebral vessels (42). Oliver in 1894 administered an extract of the adrenal gland to one of his children and noted a decrease in the size of the radial artery and a rise in blood pressure (75, 243). Oliver was a medical practitioner in Harrogate who was interested in hypertension and after his experiments discussed them with Schäfer, who was professor of physiology at University College, London. Oliver and Schäfer (228) together continued these studies and showed that the active principle of the adrenal gland was in the medulla and not in the cortex.

The possibility of chemical mediation of sympathetic nerve impulses was suggested by the work of Lewandowsky (194), Langley (189), and Elliott (90), who noted the similarity between the effects of epinephrine and those of sympathetic activity. Subsequent workers (Cannon, Bacq, Rosenblueth, Feldberg, and Gaddum, among others) during the 1930's produced further evidence for the liberation of a chemical transmitter at sympathetic nerve ends in dogs and cats and showed that the actions of this substance, "sympathin" (56), and the effects of sympathetic nerve stimulation were very similar to the effects of epinephrine. It became generally accepted that epinephrine was the transmitter substance released at sympathetic nerve endings, and this idea persisted until the 1940's.

Although there was a close similarity between the sympathetic transmitter and epinephrine in both chemical tests and biological action, there were certain differences, and it is of some interest that these differences were commented on as early as 1910 by Barger and Dale, who pointed out that epinephrine exaggerated inhibitor as compared to motor effects to a greater degree than did the sympathetic transmitter and went on to say that "the action of some of the other bases, particularly of the amino–and ethylamino–bases of the catechol group, corresponds more closely with that of sympathetic nerves than does that of adrenaline" (22).

The differences mentioned were noted by others (198), and it was to explain the anomalies between epinephrine and the actual transmitter substance that Cannon and Rosenblueth postulated the formation of two different substances, "sympathin I" and "sympathin E," formed at different end organs by the combination of released epinephrine with different substances in the cells (59).

Bacq in 1934 (13) suggested that the effects of sympathetic nerve stimulation were due to the liberation of a substance which behaved like arterenol—really restating the suggestion of Barger and Dale 24 years earlier—and this was supported by the observations of Stehle and Ellsworth (261) and of Melville (213). Since then a voluminous literature has grown up on the effects of epinephrine and arterenol on various preparations and systems in different species.

Gaddum and Goodwin (110) observed the blood pressure, pupil reactions, and uterine contractions in cats in response to intravenous epinephrine and to hepatic nerve stimulation and concluded that the substance liberated by the hepatic nerves was not epinephrine but was probably, though not certainly, arterenol.

von Euler further clarified the situation (92). He extracted from the hearts of cattle, horses, and cats a substance which behaved like arterenol to both chemical and biological tests, and he also showed that the same substance regularly occurred in the splenic nerves of cattle. von Euler concluded that the transmitter substance liberated by the sympathetic nerves was arterenol.

Tullar in 1948 (269) separated arterenol, which until then had only been obtained in the synthetic *dl* form, into its optical isomers *d*- and *l*-, and von Euler (93) then demonstrated that the sympathomimetic substance of the sympathetic nerves (splenic nerves of cattle) corresponded qualitatively and quantitatively with *l*-arterenol and later showed its presence in the sympathetic chain in man.

It was then established that the suprarenal glands of cattle, dogs, cats, and pigs contained arterenol as well as epinephrine (96, 123, 247). Holton (156) found arterenol and epinephrine in extracts of three human pheochromocytomas (chromaffin tumors of the adrenal medulla). Holtz and Schümann (159) reported that arterenol was present with epinephrine in the normal human suprarenal medulla as well as in that of the dog, cat, and pig, but not in that of the rabbit. In 1951 West and Hunter demonstrated the presence of arterenol in normal human (postmortem) adrenal medullas to the extent of about 14% of the total amines, while in children under 1 year it constituted about 90% (273). In 1949 Bulbring and Burn demonstrated that arterenol as well as epinephrine was released from the normal adrenal gland of the cat (43).

Thus by the 1950's it was clear that both epinephrine and arterenol were to be found in animal and human adrenal glands. The effects of sympathetic nerve stimulation, however, were more closely matched by arterenol than by epinephrine, so that it seemed that the sympathetic substance in most sites was arterenol.

From the point of view of the circulation it seems probable that the liberation of arterenol in small amounts from the sympathetic nerve endings is responsible for the maintenance of vasomotor tone and the regulation of the peripheral resistance. Little, if any, leaks away, and it can be considered as a hormone with a local action.

Epinephrine, on the other hand, can be considered as a generally acting hormone having widespread effects and liberated from the adrenal medulla by sympathetic activity in time of stress. Recent evidence (94) suggests that the proportions of epinephrine and arterenol liberated by the gland may vary in different circumstances. The gland responds to circulatory stress which tends to lower the blood pressure by secreting mainly arterenol, thus raising the peripheral resistance. Metabolic stress, on the other hand, such as a fall in blood sugar, will provoke an output of epinephrine. Such a concept implies that there must be separate brain centers controlling the output of the two hormones, and separate cells in the adrenal medulla for producing epinephrine and arterenol respectively. Stimulation of different areas in the hypothalamus has been shown to produce different amounts of the two amines, supporting the suggestion of preferential controlling centers (104). There is also histological evidence that some of the cells secrete epinephrine and some arterenol (148), and tumors of the gland may produce solely epinephrine, solely arterenol, or a mixture of the two.

There remains a good deal to be learned about the relative roles of epinephrine and arterenol in cardiovascular and other responses, particularly in the human subject, and, although indirect evidence is suggestive, it is by no means proved that arterenol is the sympathetic transmitter substance in man.

A. Epinephrine

1. *Structure, Formation, and Breakdown*

The amine epinephrine (methylaminoethanol catechol; adrenaline B.P.) may be represented as shown. Although both dextro- and levo-

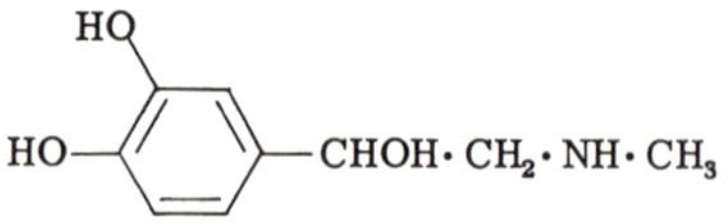

rotatory forms exist, only the latter is present in biological materials, and when epinephrine is subsequently referred to the *l*-form is implied.

Blaschko (35) proposed that the chemical reactions shown below are involved in the formation of epinephrine.

The major route of metabolism of epinephrine is by methylation to metanephrine, two-thirds of which is excreted in the urine in conjugated forms. The remaining third is converted by monoamine oxidase to 3-methoxy-4-hydroxymandelic acid (VMA). A small amount of epinephrine is inactivated by direct oxidative deamination followed by methylation to VMA and a small amount is excreted in the urine conjugated with glucuronic acid.

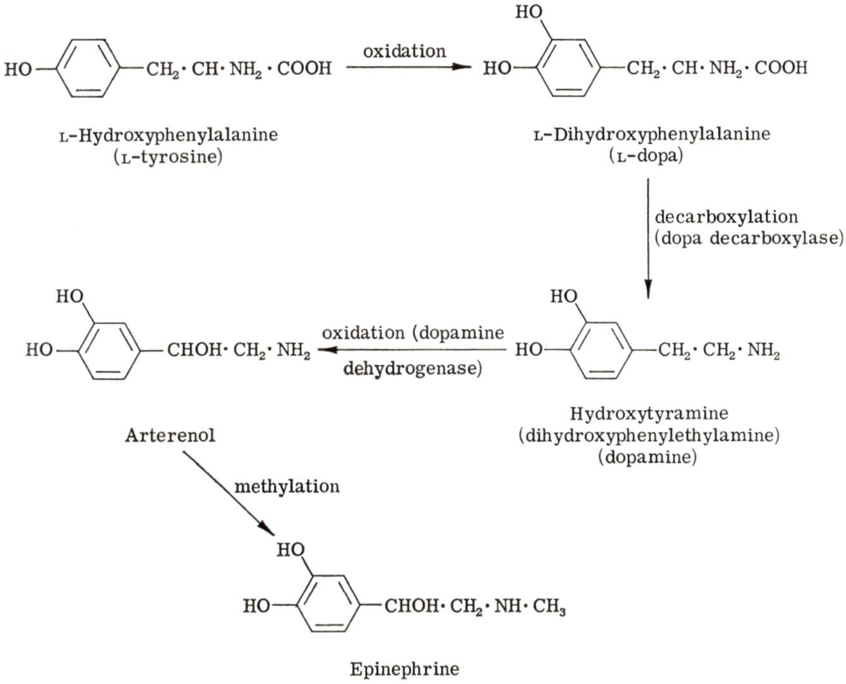

2. *General Circulatory Effects*

a. Cardiac Output. Epinephrine perfused through the coronary vessels of an isolated heart causes an increase in the rate and force of ventricular contraction, and in the heart-lung preparation these changes result in an increase in cardiac output, which is sustained by an associated increase in venous return.

Hamilton and Remington (142, 237) found that in the anesthetized dog the usual response to epinephrine was to reduce the stroke volume and external work. They attributed this to intense peripheral vasoconstriction causing an acute rise in blood pressure and increased aortic resistance to ejection which outweighed the cardiac stimulation. The doses used were 5–25 μg/kg as a single intravenous injection, which represent large doses even for the dog.

Epinephrine in more physiological doses such as can be given with safety to conscious human subjects has invariably resulted in an increase in cardiac output. Starr *et al.* (259), using the ballistocardiogram, found that subcutaneous administration of therapeutic amounts of epinephrine (0.45–1.0 mg) increased the cardiac output by about 50% with only small elevation of arterial systolic pressure and a fall in diastolic. Similar observations were made by Ranges and Bradley (236), also with the ballistocardiogram, and McMichael and Sharpey-Schäfer (223) employed the direct Fick method and found increases in cardiac output after epinephrine in doses which were insufficient to alter the blood pressure or heart rate (3 μg/minute for 2 minutes intravenously).

Goldenberg *et al.* (124) measured cardiac output using the technique of right heart catheterization and the direct Fick principle in eight normotensive and three hypertensive patients during intravenous infusions of epinephrine and recorded increases in cardiac output in both groups with doses sufficient to cause significant hypertension (10–25 μg/minute for 10–35 minutes). Barcroft and Starr (19) infused epinephrine intravenously in a dose of 10 μg/minute for 5 minutes in normotensive subjects and demonstrated similar increases in output using the ballistocardiogram.

Difference in dose level is not the only factor responsible for the difference in responses found in animals and man, however, and species differences in responsiveness and sensitivity are also probably involved. In the rabbit, for example, intravenous injections of 5–10 μg/kg of epinephrine have little or no effect on cardiac output, while 50 μg/kg causes a significant decrease (212).

b. Arterial Blood Pressure. The effect of epinephrine (2 μg/kg) on systemic arterial pressure in the anesthetized dog is described by Ahlquist (5) as follows: "There is an acute rise in systolic, diastolic and mean pressures. Usually the diastolic pressure at first rises more rapidly than the systolic, thereby reducing pulse pressure. This decrease is often obscured by the early appearance of vagal slowing and an attendant increase in pulse pressure. The pressure at which slowing first occurs depends on the sensitivity of the vagal reflex. Most evidence indicates that the beginning of the epinephrine pressor response is due entirely to peripheral vasoconstriction. After a few beats, the cardiac effect of epinephrine appears; the pulse pressure increases, independent of the heart rate, and tachycardia may occur if the vagal reflex is weak or blocked."

This sort of observation led to the generally accepted concept that epinephrine is a pressor agent depending for its effect chiefly on an intensive vasoconstriction, the direct cardiac action being only accessory. Similar results were obtained on other animals such as the cat and rabbit. Although a hypotensive action of epinephrine when given in small doses in the dog had been reported as early as 1900 (217) and the same effect had been extensively studied in the cat (1/μg intravenously in 1–5 seconds) by Cannon and Lyman (57), this depressor action of epinephrine was generally regarded as being of minor physiological importance. The latter workers found that in the rabbit even the smallest doses failed to have a depressor effect, although this was contrary to the observations of Ogawa (227).

It was not until studies were made in man using moderate dose levels, a conscious subject, and manometric apparatus which recorded diastolic as well as systolic pressures that a more refined analysis of epinephrine's action on the blood pressure became possible. Swan (264) has compared the symptoms recorded by 60 subjects after epinephrine infusion with those experienced during times of stress and calculated that during stress epinephrine enters the blood stream at rates not greater than 10 μg/minute (0.15 μg/kg/minute). While larger doses in man will in some instances increase diastolic as well as systolic pressures, doses which come more within the physiological range cause a fall in diastolic pressure. Hassencamp (145), for example, infused 50 μg/minute for 5 minutes intravenously and observed a rise in both systolic and diastolic pressures. Sandiford (242) injected 500 μg subcutaneously and noted a rise in systolic and a fall in diastolic, while Freeman and Carmichael (107) injected 50 μg intravenously as a single dose and a fall occurred in diastolic pressure in some subjects and a rise in others.

Gordon and Levitt (128) and Pickering and Kissin (234) observed that the first change to occur after the commencement of an injection of epinephrine intravenously in man (1–15 μg in 30 seconds) was a transient fall in both systolic and diastolic blood pressures, and this effect was confirmed by Allen *et al.* (8) using doses of 10–20 μg/minute for 3 minutes. Subsequent to the initial transient effect the systolic pressure rose and the diastolic either showed no change or fell slightly, the pulse pressure being thus increased and the mean arterial pressure little altered. Barnett *et al.* (23) also observed this transient fall in pressure 45 seconds after commencement of an infusion of 30 μg/minute, the diastolic pressure thereafter remaining at about the same level as before the infusion began.

Prolonged infusions of pressor doses of epinephrine have shown that the hypertension is only transient (14, 91, 108) and a sustained elevation of blood pressure cannot be maintained. Blacket *et al.* (33) gave intravenous epinephrine continuously in the rabbit for 4 days in a dose of 1–1.9 μg/minute. The greatest rise occurred on the first day, and thereafter the pressure was very little above the base line. Stopping the infusion was accompanied by a profound fall in arterial pressure lasting for 3 days. The transient nature of epinephrine hypertension and the hypotension which follows had been observed by others in animals (108) and in man (136) and has usually been attributed to the release of a vasodilator substance (33) or peripheral tissue anoxia (108). More recently it has been suggested, however, that the receptors on the smooth muscle of the vessels may become saturated, making them unresponsive to the drug (53).

It seems clear that the effect of epinephrine on the blood pressure in animals and man is dose dependent, large doses causing a rise in both systolic and diastolic pressures while moderate or low doses result in a fall in diastolic with a resultant increase in pulse pressure, and thus often little or no change in mean blood pressure.

c. Peripheral Resistance. While large doses of epinephrine in anesthetized animals may increase the total peripheral resistance and hence have a pressor effect, smaller doses in most animals and moderate to small doses in man have a depressor action, which indicates a drop in over-all peripheral resistance. Cannon and Lyman (57) inferred that the fall in blood pressure which they observed in the cat probably resulted from lessened peripheral resistance due to vasodilatation, and this was supported by their finding of a simultaneous increase in volume of the hind leg. Allen *et al.* (8) suggested that the fall in diastolic pressure on intravenous infusion might be due to vasodilatation in the peripheral vascular system, while Barnett *et al.* (23) noted that the initial transient drop in pressure on infusion of 30 μg/minute corresponded in time with an enormous increase in forearm blood flow. Hence, although epinephrine is well known to constrict blood vessels in sites such as the skin and mucous membranes, the evidence from studies of the blood pressure and cardiac output indicates a vasodilatation in other vascular beds sufficient for the over-all effect to result in a drop in peripheral resistance.

Taylor and Page (267) have postulated that chemoreceptors responsive to epinephrine are present within the brain, since its introduction into the perfusion circuit of the isolated perfused brain of the dog, connected to the body only by the nervous system, resulted in a fall in blood pressure. The authors consider that this cerebral buffer system is probably of importance in determining the response to humoral vasoactive substances.

3. *Specific Vascular Beds*

a. Skin Circulation. Epinephrine given intravenously, intra-arterially, topically, or by iontophoresis causes a reduction in skin blood flow in all species of animal studied (137), and this effect appears to be due to constriction of arterioles and not of capillaries (82). The vessels of the skin of the hand and forearm in man are also constricted (20, 255). An after-dilatation of hand vessels follows the cessation of intravenous infusions and appears to be nervously mediated, since the response is absent in sympathectomized limbs and on intra-arterial infusion. This effect coincides with marked flushing of the face (263).

Robertson *et al.* (240) found that intravenous injection of 5-hydroxytryptamine in patients with carcinoid tumor did not produce the flushing characteristic of the disease, but that injection of epinephrine did do so. Epinephrine has been shown to release a kinin peptide from perfused salivary gland (149), and Oates *et al.* (226) observed that in patients with carcinoid tumors bradykinin (100 μg intravenously) had effects similar to those of epinephrine (1 μg). They demonstrated the presence of a kinin-forming enzyme in the tumor tissue and a raised level in the hepatic venous blood which increased further after injection of epinephrine. An increase was seen in subjects without carcinoid tumor, although it was much smaller, and the authors suggest that catecholamines act not only on carcinoid tissue but also on the cells of the normal intestine, pancreas, and lung to activate the release of a kinin peptide. Thus the possibility that epinephrine causes the release of a vasodilator hormone is postulated and deserves further study.

During prolonged infusions of epinephrine intravenously (10 μg/minute for 60 minutes), the initial constrictor effect on the vessels of the hand diminishes and by the end of the infusion period the flow is sometimes much higher than the previous resting level (276). Intra-arterial infusions (0.25–1.0 μg/minute for 30 minutes), however, produce a constriction which is maintained throughout the infusion period, and no after-dilatation occurs (119). The dilatation with the intravenous infusion is difficult to explain on the basis of desensitization of α (constrictor) receptors, which might be expected to occur to an equal degree with intra-arterial infusion. A central, nervously mediated effect of epinephrine when given intravenously or the release of a vasodilator hormone could be involved.

b. Skeletal Muscle Circulation. Hoskins *et al.* (167) demonstrated that intravenous doses of epinephrine (4 μg) in the dog caused an increase in the volume in the skinned limb while that of the unskinned limb diminished. This effect was attributed to dilatation of muscle vessels and constriction of skin vessels and was subsequently confirmed by many other workers. Hartman *et al.* (144) observed the muscle vessels of the cat's leg microscopically and noted dilatation with small doses (2–20 μg), but with larger doses (100 μg or more) the capillaries alone dilated while the other vessels constricted. These findings were confirmed by Folkow *et al.* (105), who concluded that epinephrine in low concentration dilates, and in high concentration constricts, the muscular vessels in the cat.

The vasodilator action of epinephrine on the muscular segment of the limbs has been extensively studied in man, and a number of possible mechanisms for this effect have been explored.

Grant and Pearson (130) and Holling (154) measured forearm blood flow by venous occlusion plethysmography and found that small intravenous doses of epinephrine (1 μg) produced an increase while the hand blood flow was reduced, and subcutaneous or intramuscular administration had the same effect (179). Allen *et al.* (8) confirmed these findings using intravenous infusions of 1, 10, and 20 μg/minute for 10 minutes and also concluded that the effect was a peripheral one since the response was unaltered in the sympathectomized forearm, and on intra-arterial infusion (2 and 3 μg/minute). A marked transient increase in forearm flow to 5 or 6 times the resting level occurs in the first 2–3 minutes of the infusion and is followed by a fall to about double the resting value which is sustained throughout the remainder of the infusion period, even when this is continued for an hour (276). Duff and Swan (85), however, further investigated these responses of the forearm vessels to epinephrine and reported that the second sustained phase of vasodilatation did not occur in the sympathectomized limb and was also absent in normal limbs when epinephrine was given by intra-arterial infusion, and they concluded that the effect was nervously mediated. Whelan (275) confirmed these observations using intravenous (10 μg/minute) and intra-arterial (0.001–0.1 μg/minute) infusions, but found that the sustained vasodilatation was present immediately after blocking of the nerves to the limb with local anesthetic and also in the early days following cervical sympathectomy, after which it gradually diminished, being very slight or absent 3 months later. It was suggested that this phenomenon was related to the rapid return of "intrinsic tone" or the development of increased sensitivity of the vessels to the constrictor action of epinephrine. An after-dilatation was also seen following intra-arterial infusions, and after intravenous infusion in the sympathectomized limb. It was concluded that the adrenaline dilatation was not nervously mediated, and the possibility of the secondary release of a vasodilator substance during intravenous infusions was discussed.

Bock *et al.* (36), however, used a calorimeter probe to follow changes in forearm muscle blood flow and reported a sustained increase not only on intravenous infusion but also with small doses given intra-arterially. Infusion of 0.01 μg/minute into the brachial artery caused an initial transient dilatation, after which the flow returned to the resting level. When now the dose was reduced to 0.001 μg/minute the flow immediately rose, to remain higher for the remainder of the infusion period. This suggested that whether a constrictor or dilator effect occurred depended upon the dose given, and the release of a vasodilator substance need not be postulated.

Support for this view came with the use of epinephrine antagonists in the analysis of the vascular response to intra-arterial infusion in the forearm. Chlorpromazine and phenoxybenzamine introduced intra-arterially into the limb caused a reversal of the constrictor effect of even large doses of epinephrine (1 μg/minute), and a marked dilatation occurred (9, 182). Pronethalol and dichloroisoproterenol given intra-arterially have the effect of abolishing all dilator manifestations of epinephrine in the forearm, and a marked constriction alone is seen (84, 115, 200). Clearly the action of epinephrine on the blood flow through the forearm represents a balance between a constrictor effect and a less potent and often masked vasodilator effect. The dilator effect is more manifest during intravenous than during intra-arterial infusions.

That the vasodilatation in the muscle vascular bed may be masked by constriction in the overlying skin is apparent from the observations of Golenhofen (125), who followed the blood flow in forearm and calf muscles with a heated thermocouple and demonstrated an increase in flow with intra-arterial as well as intravenous infusions of 0.04–8 μg/minute, and Skinner and Whelan (255), who showed the relative effects of epinephrine on the skin and muscle circulation. The total forearm flow was measured by venous occlusion plethysmography, and changes in muscle and skin blood flow were followed by determination of the oxygen saturation of venous blood samples from deep and superficial veins respectively. The oxygen saturation of skin blood fell during infusions of epinephrine into the brachial artery in doses ranging from 0.05–0.2 μg/minute, indicating a reduction in blood flow, and with larger doses (0.5–1.0 μg/minute) samples were unobtainable, demonstrating that the skin circulation was shut down. With doses of 0.05–0.2 μg/minute the muscle blood saturation showed an initial transient rise and then fell to a less marked but still elevated level which was sustained during the remainder of the infusion at a time when total forearm blood flow had either returned to, or was reduced below, the resting level. With doses of 0.5 μg/minute and 1 μg/minute both the muscle oxygen saturation and the forearm flow fell below their respective resting levels after the initial transient rise. After the infusions ceased, the after-dilatation in forearm flow was accompanied by a similar increase in muscle oxygen saturation.

A local dilator action of epinephrine on muscle blood vessels has thus been established. The mechanism whereby this effect is brought about has been the subject of considerable study.

Burn and Dale (49) postulated that the dilator action of epinephrine might be due to liberation of histamine, but this suggestion was later rejected, though not as a result of measurements of blood histamine, by Dale and Richards (77), who concluded that the vasodilator effect of small doses of epinephrine was due to the arrival of the substance itself in the arterial stream. Staub (260) found an increase in plasma histamine level in human subjects during intravenous infusions of epinephrine and credited histamine with the indirect dilator action. Mongar and Whelan (216) were unable to confirm the finding of an increased histamine level either in the antecubital venous blood or in the arterial blood arriving at the forearm in the brachial artery. Furthermore, antihistamines were found to have no effect on the epinephrine response (277).

Lundholm (204) proposed that the muscle dilatation could be accounted for by release of lactic acid from the muscles, and an increase in venous blood lactate concentration during intravenous epinephrine infusion has been demonstrated in animals and in man (16, 139, 204).

Hildes, Purser, and Sherlock (147) had been unable to demonstrate an increase in femoral venous lactate level or a reduction in the glycogen content of gastrocnemius muscle on infusions into the femoral artery, which indicated that in man, contrary to animal studies, epinephrine had no direct metabolic action on the skeletal muscles. However, de la Lande *et al.* (180) studied the forearm, where the site of epinephrine infusion into the brachial artery is closer to the limb segment under examination than in the case of the leg, with a catheter inserted into a vein draining the forearm muscles. Evans blue dye infused into the artery was recovered through the venous catheter, providing evidence that the blood being sampled was draining the area which was being perfused. Epinephrine given intra-arterially in a dose of 0.05 μg/minute, which had no general actions and the effect of which was confined to the infused arm, was found to cause an increase in glycogenolytic activity in the forearm muscles as manifested by an increase in lactic and pyruvic acids and a fall in potassium and phosphate levels in the effluent venous blood.

While it was thus possible that one of the products of the metabolic activity in muscle might account for or contribute to the vasodilatation during epinephrine infusions, it appears that the change in the lactic acid is not responsible. Contrary to the findings of Lundholm (204) in the cat, de la Lande and Whelan (183) failed to obtain any increase in forearm blood flow during infusions of sodium lactate in doses ranging from 1.3–20 mg/minute for 4–10 minutes or of lactic acid solutions buffered to pH values down to 3.3. Lactic acid given simultaneously with epinephrine also had no dilator effect. These doses were sufficient to elevate the lactic acid level of the venous effluent blood to values many times higher than that seen during epinephrine infusions. Glover and Shanks (117) also concluded that the vasodilator actions of epinephrine were not due to its ability to raise the lactic content of the muscle venous blood, since the dilator effects were abolished by dichloroisoproterenol, which, however, did not prevent the rise in venous blood lactate.

It thus seems unlikely that in man epinephrine vasodilatation can be attributed to the lactic acid output of the muscles. Whether any of the other products of metabolic action participate in the vascular responses remains to be decided. Potassium uptake by the muscles is increased by epinephrine (180), and potassium has been shown to dilate forearm vessels (116, 202), but its role in epinephrine dilatation has not been elucidated. Barcroft and McArdle (personal communication) found a normal response of the forearm vessels to intravenous epinephrine in a patient whose muscles contained no phosphorylase, and concluded that its dilator effect could not be due to its action on carbohydrate metabolism in muscle.

The possibility that the vasodilator action of epinephrine is due to release of isoproterenol from the liver was suggested by Eakins and Lockett (88) from blood assays during intravenous infusions of epinephrine in the cat, and by Dorner (83), who observed leg muscle dilatation with infusions into the aorta above the celiac axis and superior mesenteric arteries, but not with infusion below this point. Dichloroisoproterenol was shown by Glover, Greenfield and Shanks (115) to abolish the dilator action of both epinephrine and isoproterenol on the forearm, which finding was consistent with the latter being responsible for the action of epinephrine. Attempts to show a rise in the blood level of this substance during epinephrine infusions in man, however, have so far been unsuccessful (Barcroft and Ginsburg, personal communication).

The action of epinephrine on the limb vessels has been explained with reference to the concept of separate constrictor and dilator adrenotropic receptors in the vessel wall as proposed by Ahlquist (4) and elaborated by Youmans, Green, and Denison (282), Green and Kepchar (137), and Ginsburg and Cobbold (114). The transient increase in flow is attributed to initial stimulation of β (dilator) receptors. Stimulation of α (constrictor) receptors then opposes this dilatation, and the flow consequently falls to a level that depends upon the balance between the two opposing effects. On this basis the "after-dilatation" seen on cessation of intra-arterial infusions can be attributed to a rapid wearing off of the α-response while the β-effect persists. Since vasoconstriction is seen with large doses, while small doses result in dilatation, it can be presumed that the β-receptors have a lower threshold to epinephrine, as suggested by Green and Kepchar (137).

This is one of the most attractive theories to account for the complex action of epinephrine on the limb vessels, and it removes the necessity to search for secondary dilator products. It is supported by the finding that after treatment of the arm with chlorpromazine or phenoxybenzamine (α-blockers) the constrictor effect of intra-arterial adrenaline is reversed, and a marked vasodilatation (β-effect) ensues (9, 182). β-Adrenergic blockade with pronethalol abolishes all components of the dilator response and the constrictor effect is enhanced (200). Glover and Shanks (117) suggest that the failure of intravenous epinephrine to produce a vasodilatation in the sympathectomized limb is due to the development of increased sensitivity of the vessels to the α but not to the β component of its effect, since a dilatation was observed after administration of phenoxybenzamine.

Lowe and Robinson (201) explain the modest dilator effect of intra-arterial infusions compared to those given intravenously as being due to the difference between the dilutions of the infused solutions in the two cases. With intravenous infusions the concentration of the drug arriving at the forearm tissue will be unaffected by any changes in forearm blood flow, while with intra-arterial infusion the concentration will fall when the blood flow increases and rise if it becomes reduced. They conclude that there is no need to postulate that intravenous infusion releases a secondary dilator substance, thus reiterating the conclusion reached by Dale and Richards in 1927 and supporting a similar suggestion made by Burton (55).

Glover and Shanks (118), however, gave prolonged infusions and observed that when epinephrine (0.25–0.5 μg/minute) was infused into the brachial artery the marked fall in forearm blood flow during the second to fifth minute gradually became less as the infusion continued and frequently gave way to a vasodilatation by the end of the 30-minute infusion. This dilatation was thought to occur in the muscles of the limb. It was considered unlikely that it was due to a lessening of the constrictor action of the drug, since no such effect was seen with arterenol, which is believed to act on the same adrenergic constrictor receptors. The release of a dilator metabolite was considered a likely explanation.

c. Liver Circulation. An increase in hepatic flow during epinephrine infusion was described by Bradley (40), who used hepatic vein catheterization and the bromsulphalein clearance method. Intramuscular injection caused up to a threefold increase in flow. This action of epinephrine was confirmed by Bearn *et al.* (25), who gave 0.1 μg/kg/minute intravenously for 30 minutes in normal human subjects and observed an increase to approximately double the resting flow. Farrand *et al.* (99) also found an increase in liver flow in dogs during 10-minute infusions of epinephrine (0.1 μg/kg/minute) which caused no change in mean arterial pressure. Earlier studies using large single doses of epinephrine (25–50 μg intravenously) in animals had shown a reduction in hepatic blood flow (68, 222). Bearn *et al.* (25) considered the possibility that epinephrine causes initial splanchnic vasoconstriction which is then followed by vasodilation. Such a vasoconstriction, if it occurred, must have been very transient, since their results 5 minutes after the commencement of the infusion already showed increases in hepatic flow. It seems most probable that the discrepancy, as is often the case with epinephrine, is due to the differences in the doses given. The large doses given in earlier studies (68, 222) are probably outside the physiological range, while those employed by Bearn *et al.* more closely approximate the levels of epinephrine circulating in ordinary bodily activity and are less than those believed to be liberated in moments of stress (58, 263). While it may be assumed from present evidence that the vasodilator action of epinephrine on hepatic vessels is a direct one and resembles the β-receptor stimulant action in skeletal muscle, the possibility of α-receptor stimulation has not been excluded nor has the possibility of the response being nervously mediated or due to release of a secondary hormone. Grayson and Johnson (131) used a calorimetric method to follow changes in liver blood flow in the rabbit and rat and concluded that the direct action of epinephrine on the liver vessels was to cause vasoconstriction. Intravenous infusions (5 μg/minute for 5 minutes) caused an initial rise in flow which was not sustained, but returned toward the resting level during the infusion. This dilator response did not occur if the arterial pressure was not permitted to rise, and was also abolished by section of the depressor nerves and clamping of the carotid arteries. These authors concluded that the dilatation of liver vessels was a reflex baroreceptor response to the rise in pressure and not a passive increase in flow.

d. Intestinal Circulation. Oliver and Schäfer (229) made no direct determinations of the action of suprarenal extracts on the intestinal circulation but observed that vasoconstriction in the gut wall followed their administration. Elliott (90), who painted epinephrine on the wall of the intestines of a fowl, also gave an intravenous injection and noted an intense vasoconstriction. Brodie and Dixon (41) added epinephrine to the perfusate and recorded a decrease in flow through the vessels of the isolated intestines. A similar observation was made by Ahlquist (4), who gave arterial injections of epinephrine (1 μg) into the mesenteric artery in the dog and noted a marked rise in vascular resistance. On the other hand Hoskins and Gunning (164) measured gut volume and venous outflow in the dog with intravenous administration of epinephrine (11–36 μg/minute) and found that the most prominent feature was an augmentation of gut volume, often preceded by contraction; sometimes contraction alone occurred. Increase in the venous outflow was always encountered, sometimes preceded by a decrease during the first part of the reaction. The changes were not related to alterations in blood pressure. "After-dilatation" often occurred at a time when the blood pressure had returned to normal. Grayson and Swan (132) recorded temperature change as an index of flow in the exposed mucous membrane of the colon in patients with colostomies or ileostomies. A fall in temperature was produced by intravenous infusions of 10 μg/minute for 2–5 minutes, indicating a vasoconstriction. In some experiments an "after-dilatation" was observed, and corresponded in time with that reported in the hand.

e. Kidney Circulation. Constriction of the vessels of the kidney in dogs, cats, and rabbits as a result of injection of extracts of the suprarenal capsules was inferred by Oliver and Schäfer (229) from the reduction of the kidney volume which occurred. Ranges and Bradley (236) determined renal plasma flow in normal human subjects given 0.5–1.5 μg of epinephrine subcutaneously and intramuscularly and found that it was decreased. An initial rise in filtration fraction indicated that the efferent glomerular arterioles were constricted, confirming the observations of Chasis *et al.* (61). Barclay, Cooke, and Kenney (15) gave intravenous infusions at rates of 0.5 to 10 μg/minute for 25–40 minutes and noted reduction in plasma flow averaging 40% in eight subjects. Ahlquist (5) pointed out that the renal vascular bed possesses no receptor mechanism for adrenergic vasodilatation (6, 258), although Ogawa (227) reported dilatation in the rabbit kidney when small doses were used and Hoskins and Gunning (165) described an experiment where the kidney volume increased after a preliminary reduction, and the increase persisted at a time when the blood pressure had returned to normal. Bardier and Frenkel (21) described a secondary dilatation of the kidney as a characteristic feature of the response to epinephrine infusions in the cat. The reason for the dilator effects of epinephrine described by these earlier workers has not been determined, nor is it clear why their observations differ from those in more recent times.

f. Spleen Circulation. The usual effect of suprarenal extract on the dog's spleen was observed by Oliver and Schäfer (229) to be a marked contraction, and a slight preliminary expansion of the organ was attributed to a passive response to the accompanying increase in heart action. Hoskins and Gunning (166) made a more detailed study also in the dog, and found that epinephrine intravenously in all effective doses, whether injected (10–20 μg) or infused (28 μg in 65 seconds), caused a brief increase in the splenic volume which preceded a more marked reduction, the latter persisting during the infusion period (up to 10 minutes). These changes in volume were accompanied by a brief increase and then a decrease in outflow from the splenic veins. Occasionally a secondary rise occurred after the epinephrine was discontinued. The increase in volume was obtained with doses of epinephrine which were depressor as well as with pressor doses, and the dilator effects were considered not to be passive.

These changes in the spleen volume can be attributed to the responses of the smooth muscle fibers in the capsule and may not reflect effects on the blood vessels. In human subjects, in whom the splenic capsule contains no smooth muscle, contraction of the spleen has not been demonstrated. Subcutaneous injection (0.8 mg) in man usually increases the red cell count, the hematocrit (from 44.7 to 46.1%), the hemoglobin concentration (from 14.5 to 15.2 gm/100 ml), and the plasma protein concentration (from 6.6 to 7.0 gm/100 ml). These changes are attributed to mobilization of blood from depots, especially the spleen, but changes of the same magnitude occur in splenectomized patients and may be due to hemoconcentration due to movement of fluid out of the blood (172).

g. Cerebral Circulation. Studies of the effect of epinephrine on the cerebral blood flow in animals have yielded conflicting results. Most workers have found that topical application to the brain surface results in modest constriction of pial vessels in cats and monkeys (103, 106, 281), although Florey (102) reported that it had no effect on the vessel caliber but increased the speed of the blood stream. Intracarotid injections also usually constrict the pial vessels (28) and reduce the blood flow (37, 86, 173). However, a dilatation of pial vessels with intracarotid injections is described by Forbes *et al.* (106), and an increase in cerebral blood flow was reported by Schmidt and Hendrix in the cat (244) and by Norcross (225). The reason for the difference in results obtained is not clear but may be related to differences in the doses used, the species of animal studied, and the condition of the preparation. It seems clear that any constrictor effect is a mild one, and Forbes *et al.* (106), who compared the effects of the drug on cerebral and skin vessels, concluded that a given dose was about 25% less effective on the pial vessels.

Intravenous administration has usually been accompanied by an increase in cerebral blood flow, but again a variety of responses has been described. Sokoloff (257) points out that on intravenous administration the pial vessels have been reported by some to dilate (103, 106) and by others to constrict (103), while the cerebral or spinal cord blood flow has been raised (225, 246), lowered (100), or increased and then decreased (86), and he accounts for this variability by differences in dosage and means of administration and their effect on blood pressure, concluding that when blood pressure is unchanged the action of epinephrine is to constrict pial vessels and decrease cerebral blood flow. Increases in blood pressure have usually been associated with increased flow, and often, when the blood pressure returned toward normal, there was constriction of the vessels. Finesinger and Putman (101) and Fog (103) controlled the blood pressure experimentally and found that injections of epinephrine in cats and monkeys invariably constricted pial arteries when blood pressure was artificially maintained constant and dilated them when it was allowed to rise. It would appear that the weak direct constrictor action of epinephrine on the cerebral vessels is easily overcome either by passive dilatation by the rise in blood pressure or as a result of some reflex or other indirect response to elevated pressure.

A possible explanation for the discrepancies in the results of various workers is that the method of measurement may not distinguish between the effects on intra- and extracerebral vessels, between which there are numerous connections. Green and Denison (134) dissociated the intercranial and the extracranial circulations and noted that intra-arterial injection of epinephrine in doses which had marked effects on all other vascular beds (0.3–10 μg) were without effect on the intercranial vascular bed supplied by the internal carotid artery. Marked constriction occurred in the vascular beds supplied by the internal maxillary and external carotid arteries. It was concluded that there are no significant adrenergic constrictor receptors in the intercranial arterioles supplied by the internal carotid artery in the dog.

Studies in unanesthetized man have failed to demonstrate any constrictor action of epinephrine on cerebral vessels. Gibbs *et al.* (113) employed the heated thermocouple technique to follow changes in cerebral flow and reported an increase following intravenous injection of epinephrine (100–200 μg), probably secondary to the increase in blood pressure (systolic but not diastolic pressure was recorded). However, smaller doses (5–10 μg) which did not raise arterial pressure or which produced a fall also caused definite though lesser increases in blood flow indicating cerebral vasodilatation. King *et al.* (177) made more quantitative measurements of flow by the nitrous oxide technique and gave intravenous infusions of 19–73 μg/minute in seven subjects and obtained an increase in cerebral flow which paralleled a rise in mean blood pressure so that there was no significant change in resistance. The increased vascular tone necessary to maintain resistance constant in the face of the raised perfusion pressure is probably a myogenic reflex such as is seen in vessels elsewhere in the body.

There is thus little evidence of any marked direct action of epinephrine on the cerebral vessels in man, and the dilator effect of subpressor doses is small. It seems unlikely that the amount of epinephrine which may be expected to circulate in physiological circumstances and which does not elevate the mean blood pressure has any significant effect on the cerebral circulation in the human.

B. Arterenol

1. *Structure, Formation, and Breakdown*

Arterenol (amino-ethanol catechol; norepinephrine; noradrenaline, B.P.) differs from epinephrine only in the absence of a methyl group and may be represented as shown. Both dextro- and levo-rotatory forms

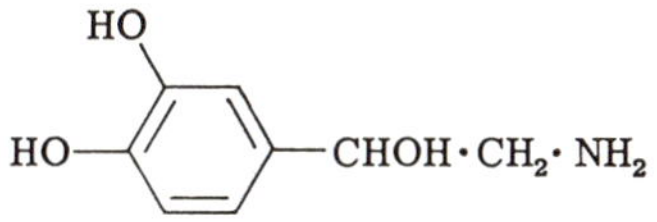

exist, but only the latter is present in biological materials. When arterenol is subsequently referred to the levo-form is implied.

It seems probable that arterenol is formed in the adrenal medulla by cells which are distinct from those that produce epinephrine (94, 148). The process of formation is likely to be the same as for epinephrine with the exception of the final methylation. Breakdown almost certainly follows the same pathways as for epinephrine.

2. *General Circulatory Effects*

a. Cardiac Output. The direct effect of arterenol is to excite the heart, increasing its rate and the stroke volume (4, 272). In what was probably the first study of the cardiovascular responses to arterenol in man, Goldenberg *et al.* (124) observed that the cardiac output, measured by the direct Fick method, was either unchanged or showed a moderate decrease. The arterenol was given by intravenous infusion in a dose of 0.11–0.40 μg/kg/minute for a period of 14–22 minutes. There was an associated decrease in heart rate which appeared to be of vagal origin since it was abolished by atropine. Barcroft and Starr (19) followed changes in cardiac output by means of the ballistocardiogram with intravenous arterenol (10 μg/minute for 5 minutes) and observed a reduction in output ranging from 17–41%. These findings have since been confirmed by many investigators, and it seems clear that this reduced output is a result of the reflex bradycardia which is in turn a compensatory response to the rise in blood pressure (170). When vagal reflex activity is reduced or abolished by the administration of atropine the cardiac output is probably increased, since the bradycardia is not seen and may be replaced by a tachycardia, which corresponds to the direct action of arterenol on the mammalian heart (4, 203). Swan (262) gave 5 μg/minute of arterenol intravenously in man after atropine (2 mg intravenously) and observed an increase in heart rate of about 10 beats per minute, preceded by a transient fall. Barnett *et al.* (23) confirmed this observation, giving arterenol intravenously in a dose of 10 μg/minute. After atropine (1.8 mg intravenously) the onset of the effects of arterenol was associated with a transient and slight slowing of the heart, after which a marked acceleration occurred. These investigators deduced that the acceleration was due to the direct action of arterenol becoming more evident with partial paralysis of the vagus, and in addition suggested that since they observed an increased venous pressure in one subject a rise in right auricular pressure might occur and lead to cardiac acceleration.

a. Arterial Blood Pressure. Diastolic and systolic pressures both rise during intravenous infusions of arterenol over a wide range of doses in normal human subjects, the systolic increase being greater than the diastolic (124). This observation has been confirmed by others (18, 23). Swan (262) demonstrated the potentiation of the pressor response following the administration of atropine which can be attributed to a rise in cardiac output. Before atropine was given arterenol (5 μg/minute) raised the systolic arterial pressure from 120 to 150 and the diastolic from 80 to 100 mm Hg. After 2 mg atropine intravenously the same dose of arterenol caused the systolic pressure to rise to 210 and the diastolic to 150 mm Hg. Similar observations were made by Barnett *et al.* (23). The baroreceptor compensatory reflexes inducing bradycardia thus exert a marked effect in limiting the magnitude of the pressor response to arterenol. Condon and Sheehan (71) gave small doses (0.01–0.17 μg/kg) of arterenol intravenously to dogs and noted that the initial pressor effect was followed by a depressor phase similar to that produced by carotid compression. It was suggested that the depression could be due to overcompensation by baroreceptor reflexes.

Prolonged infusions of arterenol were given in the rabbit by Blacket *et al.* (33) for periods up to 8 days. An initial rise in pressure was not maintained despite an increasing dosage, and on cessation of the infusion a profound fall in arterial pressure quickly followed which lasted in a lesser degree for several days. As in the case of epinephrine this phenomenon was attributed to release of vasodilator substance or substances. Lever *et al.* (193) gave intravenous infusions of arterenol (10–30 μg/minute) for 1–2 hours in normal adult human subjects and noted the occurrence of hypotension after the infusion ceased and a progressive increase in muscle blood flow which commenced during the infusion. The production of a circulating vasodilator substance was considered the most likely explanation of the findings. Burn and Rand (53) studied the response to prolonged infusion of arterenol on the cat's blood pressure (65 μg/minute for 30 minutes) and attributed the failure to maintain the pressure to the saturation of the receptors on the smooth muscle of the blood vessels with a consequent attenuation of the constrictor effect. The postinfusion hypotension was attributed to reduced sensitivity of the vessels to the normally circulating amines.

Glover and Shanks (119), however, did not observe any diminution of the constrictor action of arterenol on the forearm or hand blood vessels during infusions into the brachial artery lasting 30–40 minutes, nor did a dilatation occur after the infusion was stopped. The mechanism of the postinfusion hypotension is thus still uncertain, and a combination of factors may be responsible. Langford (188) had demonstrated a fall in cardiac output in dogs after arterenol infusion (7–60 μg/kg/minute for 30–60 minutes) and suggested that a reduction in blood volume may be involved. However, an increase in the volume of blood in the heart and lungs was observed by Shadle *et al.* (251) during intravenous arterenol in the dog (0.5–2.5 μg/kg/minute). Studies of the responsiveness of the peripheral vessels to arterenol before and after prolonged arterenol infusions have not been made in man. The only relevant observations are those of Hodge and Scroop (152), who studied two patients suffering from pheochromocytoma who had high levels of amines circulating in the blood for many months. They observed that the responsiveness of the hand blood vessels to intra-arterial infusions of arterenol was approximately one-quarter of normal before removal of the tumor and had returned to normal values 3 and 5 weeks after the operation. These findings suggest a reduced sensitivity of the peripheral vessels to arterenol, but the influence of the associated high blood pressure and resting level of flow before operation is difficult to evaluate.

c. Peripheral Resistance. The marked rise in mean arterial pressure during intravenous infusions of arterenol despite no change or a fall in cardiac output implies that the pressor effect is produced by an over-all rise in peripheral resistance. Not all peripheral vascular beds are constricted, but nevertheless, in contrast to epinephrine, no matter how small the dose given, and whatever the species studied, a fall in over-all peripheral resistance has not been reported.

The local direct action of arterenol as seen on local tissue injection or intra-arterial administration is usually to cause vascular constriction. An increase in flow produced by intravenous administration is usually accounted for by the increased perfusion pressure or by reflex responses overcoming the direct constrictor effect.

3. *Specific Vascular Beds*

a. Skin Circulation. The skin vessels in man are constricted by arterenol whether it is injected intradermally or administered by iontophoresis, intra-arterially, or intravenously (72). As in the case of epinephrine, arterenol has been reported not to have a direct effect on capillaries in human skin, the blanching being due to constriction of larger vessels (82), and the same is true for all other species and for all skin areas studied (137). The intensity of the vasoconstriction is usually reported to be less marked than with epinephrine (89, 190, 262). Despite the less marked constrictor action of arterenol, gangrene has been observed adjacent to the vein in patients who have received prolonged infusions of the drug, presumably as a result of leakage around the needle or through the vein wall (168). No such effect has been reported with epinephrine, which, however, is unlikely to be given therapeutically in this way over long periods. Hour-long infusions of 10–20 μg/minute in normal subjects did not have any injurious effect on the infused vein or overlying skin (unpublished data). Flushing of the skin, particularly of the face, accompanied by a feeling of warmth may occur on stopping an intravenous infusion of arterenol (23), and this response is similar to that observed after epinephrine. An "after-dilatation" in the hands such as that described following epinephrine has not been reported after arterenol. Lever *et al.* (193), however, report a transient increase in finger blood flow after prolonged infusions which coincided with a flushing of the skin.

b. Skeletal Muscle Circulation. The effect of arterenol on the circulation through the muscle vascular bed is complex and depends upon the dose given and the route of administration. Folkow *et al.* (105) observed constriction of the muscle vessels of the cat when arterenol was given by intra-arterial injection into the skinned limb (0.1, 1.0, and 2.0 μg), and this response was abolished but not reversed by Dibenamine®. In a minority of experiments with doses of 10 μg or more a very slight vasodilator action on the muscular vessels was revealed under the influence of Dibenamine. Cobbold and Vass (70) describe a fall in flow in the skinned limb of the cat with intra-arterial administration, while intravenous injections (1–5 μg/kg) or infusions (1–5 μg/kg/minute) produced an initial increase in flow attributed to the accompanying abrupt rise in blood pressure. Thereafter the flow decreased. McDowall (220), on the other hand, reported that arterenol dilated muscle vessels and that this response was associated with a fall in arterial and a rise in venous pressure. Imig *et al.* (169) found that, given intravenously in the dog, arterenol caused an increased blood flow through both normal and denervated limbs when infused in doses which did not significantly alter the blood pressure.

In man, intra-arterial infusion of arterenol has invariably been reported to cause a fall in forearm and calf blood flow, and a constriction in muscle vessels has been deduced. Barcroft and Konzett (18) gave 3 μg/minute for 3 minutes into the femoral artery and observed a fall in calf blood flow to about one-third of the resting level and attributed the response mainly to vasoconstriction in the skeletal muscles, and also to a small extent to cutaneous constriction. Similar observations have been made in the forearm (114). Cooper *et al.* (72) confirmed the observation that the reduction in flow in the forearm is due to constriction of both skin and muscle vessels by following the changes in the two tissues independently by measurement of venous blood oxygen saturation.

There have been conflicting reports of the effects on muscular limb segments of intravenous infusions of arterenol. Barcroft and Konzett (18) noted an increase in forearm blood flow with infusions of 20 μg/minute for 3 minutes which they concluded was due to a passive dilatation by the increased blood pressure. Duncanson *et al.* (87) found a slight decrease in forearm blood flow with 5–10 μg/minute, less marked than that in the hand. Barnett *et al.* (23) gave 15–30 μg/minute in 10 subjects and noted a decrease in forearm flow on each occasion, though it was only slight in two subjects. Constriction of muscle vessels was inferred. Lever *et al.* (193) observed an increase in forearm muscle blood flow in man during and after prolonged intravenous infusions of arterenol (10–30 μg/minute) and also in the dog leg muscle after denervation. The response was attributed to release of a vasodilator substance.

Barcroft *et al.* (17) confirmed previous observations that intra-arterial arterenol (0.025–0.1 μg/minute) caused a fall in forearm blood flow, but found that intravenous infusions (10–20 μg/minute) caused an initial increase in flow followed either by a return to the resting level or by an increase in flow sustained throughout the infusion period. A fall in flow was seen, however, if the limb had been sympathectomized or the nerves were blocked by local anesthetic. It was concluded that the dilator effect was in muscle and was mediated by the sympathetic nerves.

Bock *et al.* (36) suggested an alternative explanation of the above findings, namely, that in the nerve-blocked or sympathectomized limb the skin flow would be high and the constrictor action of arterenol would consequently be more marked and hence could mask the muscle dilatation. Confirmation of this view is to be found in the recent observations of Cooper *et al.* (72), who demonstrated that the level of skin blood flow plays an important part in the response of the forearm flow to arterenol. The skin and muscle flows were followed independently and simultaneously with measurements of total forearm flow. The skin vessels were constricted by both intra-arterial and intravenous infusions of arterenol. However, the magnitude of the skin constriction to any given dose and therefore its contribution to the total forearm flow response was greater when the resting level of skin flow was high. The direct action of arterenol on the muscle vessels was constrictor, but in the case of intravenous infusions a vasodilator component opposed the direct constrictor action and the resultant effect on the muscle vessels was a balance of these two forces. With intra-arterial infusion the constrictor effects on skin and muscle vessels were additive and a fall in forearm flow was seen with all dose levels. With intravenous infusion the change in total forearm flow was found to be variable and to depend upon the resultant of the direct constrictor actions on the skin and muscle vessels and the opposing dilator action on muscle vessels. An "after-dilatation" was usually seen following intravenous infusions and was confined to muscle.

Following sympathectomy and nerve block the blood flow in the forearm is higher than on the control side, the increase being due to vasodilatation in both skin and muscle (241). The apparent absence of a dilator response to arterenol in the forearm under these conditions is accounted for by a marked constriction of skin vessels and a reduction in skin flow masking a more modest increase in flow in muscle. The total forearm flow would thus fall despite a muscle dilatation. This has been shown to occur during intra-arterial infusion of epinephrine (255) and of arterenol (72) when the skin flow is high.

The question whether in man the dilator action of arterenol on muscle vessels is a sympathectically mediated reflex or a passive response to a rise in blood pressure is still to be settled. von Euler (94) points out that in animals a reflex dilatation of vessels as a result of administration of arterenol, and usually in conjunction with bradycardia, has been described by a large number of authors. Meier *et al.* (212) observed that changes in flow caused by arterenol in various regions are independent to a marked degree of the height and duration of the blood pressure increase. von Euler (94) attributes the peripheral vasodilatation to a reflex elicited by the raised blood pressure acting on the pressor receptor areas in the aorta and carotid sinus, or possibly to a direct contraction of the wall of the carotid artery. Dorner (83) has discussed whether the general vasodilatation after intravenous injection of arterenol is due to release of constrictor tone, and whether activation of vasodilator fibers occurs. Gruhzit *et al.* (140) have described a reflex dilatation in the femoral vessels induced by arterenol in the dog, which was not prevented by thoracic sympathectomy, alone or combined with vagotomy and carotid denervation, but was abolished by section of the thoracic dorsal roots.

Further work is required before the mechanism of the dilator response of the muscle vascular bed to arterenol can be elucidated.

c. Liver Circulation. Bearn *et al.* (25), using the bromsulphalein method, found that intravenous administration of arterenol in man in a dose of 0.1 μg/kg/minute for 30 minutes resulted in slight decrease in hepatic flow in 21 of 22 normal subjects. In one there was no change. The fall in flow coincided with a rise in mean arterial blood pressure, and the calculated splanchnic vascular resistance increased, indicating vasoconstriction. With the exception of four observations, the values for hepatic flow returned to normal before the end of the infusion of arterenol. In some instances there was a slight vasodilatation after the infusion ceased. Similar observations have been made on the anesthetized dog (99, 256). Grayson and Johnson (131) used a calorimetric method employing heated thermocouples to follow changes in the liver circulation in rats and rabbits. The local action of arterenol was to cause constriction. Intravenous infusions (10 μg/minute) caused a small fall in flow accompanying the rise in pressure. When a compensating device was used to maintain the pressure constant, the same dose produced a very much greater fall in liver flow. It was suggested that, when the rise in blood pressure occurred, this reflexly induced dilatation of the liver vessels which opposed the direct constrictor action of the drug. The resultant level of blood flow thus represented a balance between these two effects.

d. Intestinal Circulation. Burn and Hutcheon (50) gave 4 μg arterenol intravenously in cats and dogs and found a dilatation of intestinal vessels which also occurred when the blood pressure was kept artificially constant. Other observers, however, noted a reduction in weight of a loop of gut in dogs following injection of 20 μg arterenol and deduced a fall in vascular volume due to vasoconstriction (221). Green and his co-workers (80, 133) gave 1, 3, and 10 μg arterenol into the mesenteric artery of the dog and, using an electromagnetic flow meter, found that constriction of the vessels always occurred. A mild secondary vasodilatation followed the constriction. These doses did not have any effect on the systemic arterial pressure. Folkow *et al.* (105) found that arterenol constricted the splanchnic vessels of the cat when given intra-arterially and intravenously. In man a number of observers have noted a vasoconstriction of the mucosa of the bowel. Barnett *et al.* (23) reported that the mucous membrane of the ileum seen in an ileostomy paled during the intravenous infusion of 25 μg/minute, and the rectal mucosa seen through a proctoscope also paled slightly. Injection into the mucous membrane of the ileum also produced local pallor. Temperature measurements as an index of blood flow confirmed the constrictor effect of arterenol on the human colonic mucosa (132).

e. Kidney Circulation. Gaddum *et al.* (112) found that arterenol caused constriction of the perfused renal vessels of the rabbit, and Burn and Hutcheon (50) gave intravenous injections (8–16 μg) in the anesthetized cat and observed a fall in renal vein outflow. Intravenous infusion of arterenol (20–30 μg/minute) in normal conscious man has been shown to cause a considerable fall in diodone clearance, while inulin clearance showed little change. Filtration fraction was thus increased (23). An increase in total renal resistance leads to a decrease in renal plasma flow (12, 215, 271). Reduction of renal blood flow by arterenol has also been observed in anesthetized subjects (67) and in dogs (118, 235). Some authors report an associated rise in glomerular filtration rate in the dog (235); others have found a fall (218). While large doses of arterenol may severely reduce the renal blood flow in animals (208) and in man (176), moderate doses do not have any significant effect on glomerular filtration rate or urinary secretion in normal subjects (191). Pickford and Watt (235) concluded from their studies on the dog using moderate doses that neither arterenol nor epinephrine has a direct action on kidney activity but that they affect it by altering the condition of the systemic circulation.

f. Spleen Circulation. Arterenol given intravenously in most animals causes constriction of the spleen, the effect being approximately one-half that of epinephrine (6, 50). Ottis *et al.* (230) gave injections of arterenol (0.1 and 1.0 μg) into the splenic artery of the dog and observed that splenic artery inflow was markedly reduced and splenic vein outflow initially increased. The latter then fell below the control level. After partial adrenergic blockade with phenyoxybenzamine, arterenol increased arterial inflow and venous outflow.

Arterenol appears to have a constrictor effect on the splenic arterioles which is about equal to that of epinephrine. It has a less marked action on the smooth muscle of the capsule or sinusoids, so that the emptying effect is less than that of epinephrine. Holtz *et al.* (158) concluded that, while epinephrine acts mainly on the capsule and trebeculae, arterenol exerts its action mostly on the vessels, notably on the veins. This view is supported by the rapid replenishment of the spleen emptied by arterenol, while the filling after epinephrine occurs more slowly. In normal human subjects, neither contraction of the spleen by arterenol nor the blood storage function of this organ have been demonstrated.

g. Cerebral Circulation. In contrast to epinephrine, which has little direct effect on the cerebral vessels and brings about changes in cerebral blood flow mainly by its effect on blood pressure, arterenol has been reported to constrict the vessels of the brain in man and reduce blood flow, even when the blood pressure is simultaneously elevated (177, 250). Green and Kepchar (137) report studies in the dog, however, indicating that there are prominent communications between extracranial structures and the transverse sinus and postulate that communications may exit between extracranial structures and the jugular bulb in man and the monkey. If so, the nitrous oxide technique usually employed to measure cerebral flow might measure some fraction of extracranial as well as intracranial flow.

The reported constrictor responses of the cerebral vessels to arterenol in man could thus have been due to an effect on an extracranial component of the total flow. When steps were taken to obtain intracranial blood uncontaminated by extracranial blood, arterial injections of arterenol had no effect on outflow from the brain substance (134).

These authors (137) suggest that previously reported evidence of adrenergic receptors in the cerebral vessels may be in error and believe that the intracranial vessels lack receptors which are capable of responding by either vasoconstriction or vasodilatation to any reasonably physiological dose of either arterenol or epinephrine. They consider that there is no crucial evidence at present for the existence of sympathetic adrenergic constrictor fibers in the cerebral vascular bed. The pial vessels may, however, constrict weakly in response to adrenergic substances and to sympathetic nerve stimulation. This view is in complete contrast to that of Kety (174), who concluded that recent investigations did not substantiate the earlier belief that cerebral blood flow passively followed changes in arterial blood pressure. He points out that intracranial nerves are known to parallel the cerebral vessels throughout the brain, and both constrictor and dilator properties of these nerves have been demonstrated in animals although their role in man remains to be established.

C. Isoproterenol

Konzett (178) investigated the effects of *N*-propyl, -isopropyl, -butyl, and iso-butyl homologs of epinephrine on the bronchial muscles of guinea pigs. They were found to be markedly dilator, and the isopropyl homolog was shown to be particularly potent. It had widespread inhibitory properties, dilating the coronary vessels and relaxing the intestinal muscle.

Lands *et al.* (185, 186) examined the effect of isoproterenol in the frog and rabbit and demonstrated a direct stimulant action on the heart, a fall in blood pressure, dilatation of bronchioles, and relaxation of the uterus, small intestine, and colon. Trace quantities of a substance which resembled isoproterenol in its pharmacological actions were obtained from saline extracts of adrenal glands of cats, monkeys, and man (196) and from the blood perfusing cat heart-lung preparations on stimulation of the bronchial nerves (196). It was considered likely that this third amine was identical with isoproterenol and was the transmitter of bronchial sympathetic nerves. Subsequently the blood level of this amine was shown to be increased during intravenous infusions of epinephrine in the cat and it was postulated that the third amine might be a metabolite of epinephrine, which, however, could have a physiological function (197). It has been shown that the liver is the major site of formation of the metabolite (88). Since it is probable that this amine is not identical with isoproterenol but a breakdown product of epinephrine, there is no certainty that isoproterenol is formed in the body. It is of considerable physiological and pharmacological interest, however, because it appears to have a pure β-stimulant action on vascular smooth muscle, in contrast to the α-effect of arterenol and the mixed α and β effects of epinephrine. It is thus of value as an investigative tool in elucidating receptor mechanisms and the action of antagonists. Its most important clinical value lies in its property of bronchiolar dilatation (254).

1. *Structure, Formation, and Breakdown*

Isoproterenol (isopropylaminoethanol; isoprenaline, B.P.) differs from epinephrine in the presence of an isopropyl instead of a methyl group in the side-chain, and can be represented as shown. The isoproterenol-

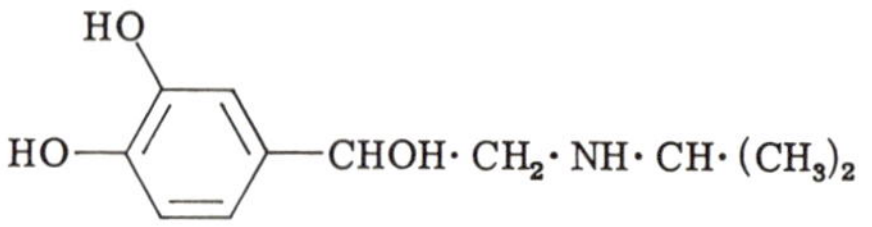

like substance described by Lockett (195) is considered to be formed by the action of *o*-methyltransferase, mainly in the liver, and to be broken down by monoamine oxidase. It is likely that isoproterenol is handled in the same way.

2. *General Circulatory Effects*

a. Cardiac Output. Isoproterenol causes a marked increase in the heart rate and cardiac output of the anesthetized dog when given intravenously in doses of 2.5 μg/kg (142, 178). Kaufman *et al.* (171) were probably the first to demonstrate the effect of isoproterenol on the cardiac output in man. Ballistocardiographic measurement showed that sublingual or subcutaneous administration caused a rise in cardiac output associated with decreased peripheral resistance. A quantitative comparison of isoproterenol and epinephrine on the perfused frog heart and tortoise sinoauricular preparation made by Lands and Howard (184) showed that the increases in rate and amplitude of contraction were much greater with the former drug. Very small doses caused an increase in heart rate, stroke volume, and work per beat. Gorten *et al.* (129) observed an average of 6% increase in cardiac output in man using the dye dilution technique and an intravenous dose of 1 μg/minute. The stroke volume increased from 83 ml to 105 ml and the heart rate rose by only 9 beats per minute.

b. Arterial Blood Pressure. The depressor effect of isoproterenol has been demonstrated on a number of species of animals (184, 185, 207). Intravenous or intramuscular injections into anesthetized dogs (0.1–1.0 μg/kg) caused a marked fall in pressure (184, 185). Administration of 0.1–0.5 μg/kg by mouth to unanesthetized dogs caused a marked tachycardia which developed rapidly and was associated with a rise in systolic blood pressure. As the cardiac effect of the drug diminished, blood pressure rapidly returned to normal and, in most experiments, continued to decline to levels below those of a control period. Barcroft and Konzett (18) gave intravenous infusions of *dl*-isoproterenol in doses of 2, 2.5, 5, 10, and 20 μg/minute in normal human subjects and observed an increase in systolic pressure and a marked fall in diastolic pressure as measured by auscultation. Cobbold, Ginsburg, and Paton (69) gave *dl*-isoproterenol in a dose of 0.1 μg/kg/minute intravenously for 30 minutes and noted that coincident with the increase in heart rate there was a transient fall in both systolic and diastolic pressure within 2 minutes of the start of the infusion and lasting about 10 seconds. The pressure then rose from the resting average of 100/70 mm Hg to a mean of 120/40 mm Hg at 2 minutes and 135/40 mm Hg at 15 minutes after the beginning of the infusion. The pulse pressure was thus doubled. This effect persisted throughout the remainder of the infusion period, after which the pressure returned to the resting value over 15–20 minutes.

Contrary to the findings in man and other animals studied, Ahlquist (4) reports that in the rabbit isoproterenol produces a slight pressor response which is attributed in part to vasoconstriction. The author, however, does not state which vascular beds showed constrictor responses. An occasional depressor effect was seen after Dibenamine.

c. Peripheral Resistance. Lands *et al.* (185) noted that after oral administration of isoproterenol to dogs there was a rise in systolic pressure, but observed that this was accompanied by evidence of peripheral vasodilatation, inasmuch as unpigmented skin areas became pink. The drop in diastolic pressure which accompanies intravenous infusion and the increase in cardiac output together imply a drop in over-all peripheral resistance. The degree of the fall is greater than that seen with epinephrine and suggests that there must be widespread peripheral vasodilatation (142).

3. *Specific Vascular Beds*

a. Skin Circulation. Flushing of the skin after injection of isoproterenol has been observed in dogs and rabbits (185, 207), and Barcroft and Konzett (18) and Cobbold *et al.* (69) observed that a flush of the face was sometimes seen after intravenous infusions in man. The blood flow through the hand and foot showed a slight transient increase within a minute or two of commencing intravenous infusions, but thereafter returned to the resting level. During intra-arterial infusions of 10 minutes' duration a slight increase in blood flow occurred, but whether this represented a vasodilatation of skin vessels similar to that noted by Walters *et al.* (270) in the leg of the dog, or whether it was due to dilatation in the muscles of the hand and foot, could not be determined.

b. Skeletal Muscle Circulation. Konzett (178) observed an increase in blood flow in the limbs of dogs and cats when isoproterenol was given, and others have reported that the muscle flow is increased (138, 270). Barcroft and Konzett (18) injected isoproterenol into the femoral artery in man in a dose of 0.75 μg/minute for 3 minutes and noted an increase in blood flow of the calf from a resting value of 1.5 ml/100 ml/minute to 8 ml/100 ml/minute. The effect was transient, and the flow had returned to the resting value within 2 minutes of the infusion, but the period of infusion was too short for the sustained effect of the drug to be determined. A similar though less marked increase in flow was seen in the forearm during intravenous infusions of 2–20 μg/minute for 3 minutes.

These changes in forearm and calf blood flow were attributed to dilatation of muscle vessels, and this view was supported by observations made on the muscle circulation in dogs (138, 270). In the human, Cobbold *et al.* (69) gave infusions intravenously (0.1 μg/kg/minute) for 30 minutes and intra-arterially into the brachial artery (0.05–0.2 μg/minute) for 10 minutes and noted in both cases that after the initial vasodilatation the blood flow through the forearm reached a value of 2–3 times the resting level and remained so throughout the remainder of the infusion period. The flow gradually returned to the resting level 5–10 minutes after the infusion had stopped. Increases in calf flow occurred during intravenous infusions but were of lesser degree. Since the calf and forearm blood flow were considered to represent mainly muscle flow and since the foot and hand flow (which is mainly through skin) was little altered, it was concluded that the increases in calf and forearm flow reflected dilatation of muscle vessels.

The dilator action of isoproterenol on muscle vessels is considered to be due to stimulation of β-receptors with an absence of any action on α-receptors (137, 282). Its effect is not altered by the administration of α-blocking agents such as phenoxybenzamine (9), but it is abolished by dichloroisoproterenol and by pronethalol and no constrictor effect is thereby revealed as is the case with epinephrine (114, 200). The very slight effect which this drug exerts on the skin vessels of the hand indicates that β-receptors are sparse or absent in these vessels. Whether the facial flush produced by isoproterenol is due to β-receptor stimulation has not been determined, nor has it been demonstrated whether the vessels of the forearm and calf skin participate in the dilator response of these limb segments.

c. Liver Circulation. Isoproterenol injected into the hepatic artery or into the portal vein of the dog in a dose of 10 μg had no effect on vessels of the liver (135). No studies in man have been reported.

d. Intestinal Circulation. Green *et al.* (133) recorded the flow in the mesenteric artery of the dog using an electromagnetic flow meter and found that intra-arterial injections (1, 3, and 10 μg) resulted in vasodilatation. The dilator response was reduced, but not abolished, by the adrenergic blocking agent Ilidar®. It was concluded from a comparison of these effects with responses to epinephrine and arterenol that the mesenteric vascular bed is qualitatively different from the cutaneous and renal vascular beds, but similar to though less reactive than that of skeletal muscle.

e. Kidney Circulation. Corcoran and Page found that injections of isoproterenol (10 μg intravenously) in conscious dogs produced a small decrease in renal vascular resistance (73). However, a direct vasodilator action on the renal vessels has not been demonstrated with injections of 30 μg into the renal artery, which produced slight vasoconstriction (260). In anesthetized dogs, on the other hand, Aviado *et al.* (12) observed that this drug had a local renal dilator action when injected into the renal artery in a dose of 1 μg. With intravenous injections (1–3 μg/kg) renal blood flow was decreased as a result of the arterial depressor action.

The effect of the drug on the kidney in man is not known.

f. Spleen Circulation. Injections of 0.1–1.0 μg of isoproterenol into the splenic artery of the dog caused a slightly greater increase in splenic artery inflow than in splenic vein outflow, with no change in splenic vein pressure (230). The changes indicate dilatation of the afferent arterioles.

g. Cerebral Circulation. A recent comprehensive review of the action of drugs on the cerebral circulation makes no mention of isoproterenol (257).

D. Mixtures

1. *Epinephrine and Arterenol*

Both of these amines are present in the adrenal glands of most animals and of humans, and both are released into the circulation. Bulbring and Burn (43) showed that, in spinal eviscerated cats, stimulation of one splanchnic nerve produced effects which could be matched by a mixture of epinephrine and arterenol but not by either substance alone. The proportion of epinephrine varied considerably from cat to cat and fell with repeated stimulation. Percentages from 98% to 0% were found, most being between 80% and 20%.

Goldenberg *et al.* (123) concluded that as long as the arterenol content was not greater than about 18% the effects of the secretion would be predominantly those of epinephrine. These investigators infused mixtures of equal parts of the two amines intravenously in man, the mixture following immediately upon an infusion of arterenol alone. The addition of the epinephrine blocked the constrictor action of the arterenol.

de Largy *et al.* (190) gave intravenous infusions of mixtures of the amines in ratios of epinephrine to arterenol of 1 : 1.1, 1 : 3, 1 : 8, 0.8 : 1, 2.1 : 1 and 5.7 : 1 and observed the following effects:

a. Heart Rate: Epinephrine containing 12–18% arterenol caused an increase in heart rate, with a peak increase of about 25 beats/minute 1–5 minutes after the infusion started, followed by a sustained increase of about 15 beats per minute. Arterenol caused a sustained fall of about 15 beats per minute. The epinephrine effect predominated when a mixture of equal parts was given, and the effects balanced at epinephrine-arterenol ratios between 1 : 3 and 1 : 8.

b. Arterial Blood Pressure: Epinephrine raised the systolic pressure and lowered the diastolic, while arterenol raised both the systolic and the diastolic pressures. Mixtures of equal parts raised the systolic pressure, but the diastolic was usually unchanged.

c. Calf Blood Flow: Epinephrine caused a large transient increase in blood flow through the calf, followed by a smaller secondary increase. Arterenol decreased the flow. The epinephrine effect predominated when the mixture contained equal parts and with an epinephrine-arterenol ratio of 1 : 3, but the arterenol effect predominated with a ratio of 1 : 8.

The general conclusion was reached that there was an even gradation of response with the different mixtures, that a small quantity of either substance fails to block the effects of the other, and that with mixtures of equal parts the effects of epinephrine will predominate.

2. *Isoproterenol and Arterenol*

In 1955 Walters *et al.* (270) concluded, from their studies of the vascular responses of muscle and skin vessels in the dog, that epinephrine behaved as if it were a composite of both arterenol and isoproterenol. Green *et al.* (138) measured the responses of the leg muscles of the dog to intra-arterial injection of epinephrine and arterenol made before and during infusions of isoproterenol and with varying degrees of adrenergic blockade. They concluded that isoproterenol saturated the dilator receptors and thus unmasked the constrictor action of epinephrine, which then became manifest. Similar observations were made by Ginsburg and Cobbold (114) in the human forearm. These findings supported the concept of α (constrictor) and β (dilator) receptors on the forearm vessels, both of which are stimulated by epinephrine, while arterenol is purely α-stimulant and isoproterenol purely β-stimulant.

In an analysis of the effects of epinephrine on the human forearm Glover *et al.* (120, 121) and Lowe and Robinson (201) gave mixtures of arterenol and isoproterenol intra-arterially and intravenously and were able to obtain patterns of response simulating the effects of epinephrine, supporting the view that the effect of the latter drug is due to simultaneous stimulation of α and β receptors. A consideration of the time course and concentration curves of epinephrine infusions by Lowe and Robinson also showed that the difference in route of administration and hence of concentrations of the drugs arriving in the limb accounted for the differences which had been observed between intravenous and intra-arterial infusions.

In a further extension of this study Lowe (199) used the dose response curves for the separate α- and β-adrenergic effects to construct models of the curves which should be obtained if the α- and β-receptors were stimulated simultaneously and were situated on resistances in series or in parallel. The conclusion was reached that the response of muscle vessels to epinephrine could only be explained on the assumption that the α- and β-receptors are situated neither in series nor in parallel, but on the same resistance.

III. OTHER SYMPATHOMIMETIC DRUGS

In addition to their therapeutic uses the sympathomimetic agents have contributed greatly to our understanding of the physiology of the autonomic nervous system. Elucidation of the mechanism of action of drugs such as ephedrine and tyramine and their use as instruments in the study of sympathetic nerve activity has led to the recent development of new concepts about the nature of sympathetic nerve transmission. The evidence of Burn (48) and his colleagues relating to the role of acetylcholine as the primary transmitter substance at all autonomic nerve endings, which, in the case of sympathetic nerves is responsible for the further release of arterenol from peripheral stores, is of pharmacological importance and has possible therapeutic implications.

The work of Barger and Dale (22) suggested that the sympathomimetic drugs had a similar action to that of epinephrine, but Tainter and Chang (266) found that the pressor action of tyramine was abolished by cocaine while that of adrenaline was not (109). Various subsequent studies substantiated the differences between the actions of epinephrine and tyramine, particularly the fact that denervation of a tissue abolished its response to tyramine and ephedrine while that of epinephrine was enhanced (45, 54). Despite these differences in action the sympathomimetics were generally considered to act as did epinephrine and on the same receptive mechanism. Gaddum and Kwiatkowski (111), however, carried out studies which suggested that ephedrine acted by inhibiting the destruction of the adrenergic transmitter by amine oxidase. This theory of the action of ephedrine and other amines of similar structure was widely accepted until as recently as 1958, although by this time there were some who held reservations. Ahlquist (5) summarized the evidence at that time and observed "That ephedrine acts by preventing the oxidation of epinephrine should be regarded as only a possibility, not as a proved fact."

The demonstration by Bertler *et al.* (30) that reserpine caused depletion of arterenol from the treated tissues resulted in its use as a powerful tool in the investigation of autonomic mechanisms. Tyramine was found to have no pressor action in the cat previously treated with reserpine

(Carlsson *et al.*, 1957; quoted by Burn, 47). Since its action was alsc abolished by denervation, which procedure had been demonstrated to result in the disappearance of arterenol from the tissue (98, 126), the possibility that the action of tyramine might depend on the release of arterenol was raised (47). Nasmyth (224) found no reduction in the arterenol content of guinea pig heart after prolonged perfusion with tyramine and suggested that its action was a direct one and that arterenol merely plays a facilitating role. Chidsey *et al.* (65), on the other hand, found that arterenol was released from the dog's heart with intravenous infusions of tyramine, phenylethylamine, tryptamine, amphetamine, ephedrine, and mephenteramine.

In human subjects Mahon and Mashford (205) found that pretreatment with reserpine (0.06 mg/kg intravenously) produced a significant reduction in the pressor response to tyramine (0.2 mg/kg). Burn (45) had observed that in the perfused hind leg of the dog which had ceased to respond to tyramine, the response could be restored by a slow infusion of epinephrine. Burn (46) at that time suggested the presence of a peripheral store of sympathetic transmitter amine, and he and his colleagues subsequently showed that the pressor response to tyramine, which was abolished in the reserpine-treated cat, could be restored by an infusion of arterenol and that this amine was more effective in this regard than epinephrine (47). The actions of other amines, β-phenylethylamine, ephedrine, and amphetamine, were also abolished by reserpine treatment and could be restored by arterenol in the same way as was that of tyramine. The pressor actions of arterenol and of epinephrine in the cat were unchanged by pretreatment with reserpine (27), as were the effects of phenylephrine and dopamine, and an infusion of arterenol reduced their pressor effect.

It became apparent that ephedrine and tyramine brought about their effects on the vessels by release of arterenol from a peripheral store, while arterenol itself, epinephrine, and amines such as phenylephrine exerted a direct effect on the smooth muscle. Infusions of arterenol do not restore the action of tyramine if the preparation has been denervated, suggesting that the store is in, or dependent upon, the sympathetic nerves (47).

Burn and Rand (53) classified the sympathomimetic amines into those that have a direct effect on vessels, those that have an indirect effect by releasing arterenol, and those that have both direct and indirect effects. They consider that arterenol and phenylephrine fall into the first group, ephedrine and the amphetamines into the second, and methoxamine and metaraminol into the third. In the case of the members of the last group, their effect on the blood pressure was diminished but not completely lost in animals which had been treated with reserpine. Trendelenberg (268), however, has concluded that, although sympathomimetic amines have direct or indirect effects, or both, they do not fall into three distinct groups but are distributed between the two extremes of "pure direct" and "pure indirect" action. He suggested that these extremes exist only in theory and that every sympathomimetic amine has both direct and indirect actions. The results of a study by Parks *et al.* (231) of the action of these amines on the peripheral vessels in normal human subjects, in patients who had undergone surgical cervical sympathectomy some months previously, and in three patients suffering from idiopathic autonomic degeneration, do not coincide with either of the above views. Hand and forearm blood flow was measured plethysmographically, and the amines were administered as a constant infusion into the brachial artery of one side, while the other side was used as a control. In this way it was possible to determine the actions of infused drugs on the vessels without the infused drug entering the general circulation in amounts sufficient to affect the blood pressure, heart, or nervous system. As in the case of animal studies, arterenol and phenylephrine were as effective in constricting the limb vessels in the sympathectomized and autonomically degenerated patients as in normal subjects, indicating a direct action on the vessels. The constrictor effects of ephedrine and methylamphetamine were absent in the patients after sympathectomy and in those with autonomic degeneration, confirming the view that these amines depend for their action on the integrity of the sympathetic nerves, probably releasing arterenol from a store within the endings.

The responses to methoxamine and metaraminol were not reduced in the sympathectomized or degenerated limbs; if anything they appeared to be somewhat enhanced.

If, as Burn and Rand (53) suggested, the action of methoxamine and metaraminol on the vessels is due to release of arterenol, these findings suggest that the store must be independent of the sympathetic nerves. No definite increase in the sensitivity to arterenol was detected in the hand blood vessels of the sympathectomized subjects nor in the patients suffering from autonomic degeneration, although in one of the sympathectomized hands the duration of the response was increased. When a drug is administered by the intra-arterial route, it is impossible to be certain that the whole hand is receiving a uniform concentration, despite the use of a vasodilator drug as a check that the solution infused in the brachial artery is reaching the hand. Thus, though the presence or absence of the response to a drug will be quite clear, deductions cannot be made regarding sensitivity compared to other subjects or the same subject at different times, unless the differences in responses are large and consistent.

Barnett *et al.* (24) concluded that their patients with autonomic degeneration showed increased vascular sensitivity to arterenol because they exhibited abnormally great increases in blood pressure to small doses of arterenol given intravenously. In such cases, however, the compensatory reflex adjustments of peripheral resistance will be impaired or absent, and the response could well be a consequence of the absence of those vascular reflexes which normally tend to restrain the rise in blood pressure. Thus, in such cases conclusions cannot be drawn about vascular smooth-muscle sensitivity by observing changes in blood pressure alone. The same considerations apply to animal studies in which autonomic blocking or depleting agents such as reserpine, guanethidine, or bretylium are used and changes in blood pressure measured as an index of the response of peripheral vessels to drugs. Apparent sensitization of blood pressure responses by blocking drugs can occur as long as any cardiovascular baroreceptor reflexes remain intact, and to abolish these completely animals must be pithed and vagotomized. Mantegazza *et al.* (206) reported enhanced pressor responses to intravenous arterenol after hexamethonium, but Hodge and Whelan (153) were unable to demonstrate any change in sensitivity of the limb vessels in man when the drugs were given intra-arterially.

The concept of a peripheral store of arterenol led to a search for its site. Arterenol occurs in the adrenal medulla in cells whose granules give a chromaffin reaction, and cells giving this reaction have been demonstrated elsewhere in the body tissues. Adams-Ray and Nordenstam (3) found them in human skin and their presence was confirmed by Burch and Phillips (44). It was postulated that these cells might constitute a peripheral store of constrictor substance which exerts a controlling influence over the blood vessels (233). Burn *et al.* (51) found similar cells in the arrectores pili of the skin of the cat's tail and in the nictitating membrane and demonstrated that they were depleted by sympathectomy. Studies with the electron microscope indicated that the chromaffin cells were distinct from mast cells (146, 238). Burn (47) was at pains to point out that he and Rand did not necessarily believe at that time that the peripheral store upon which tyramine acted lay in chromaffin tissue. They had discussed this as a possibility, but he believed it likely that the store lay within the sympathetic nerve endings. Mercantini (214) was unable to demonstrate chromaffin cells in human skin, and Richardson (239) could not identify the cells in the arrectores pili of the cat's tail as chromaffin in nature and believed them to be mast cells. Matz and Skinner (210) examined biopsy specimens from the finger and forearm and, while recognizing the cells described by Burch and Phillips (44), did not consider their staining characteristics to be chromaffin in nature. Treatment of the limb by reserpine did not cause any alteration in the appearance of these cells, which they also believed to be mast cells. The changes in appearance of the cells seen in animals after reserpine treatment may have been due to the general cellular damage which is caused by large doses of the drug (283). The cells were present and had a normal appearance in the skin of patients with idiopathic autonomic degeneration who had complete postganglionic degeneration of the sympathetic fibers in the area (231).

Parks *et al.* (232) studied the action of reserpine on the peripheral limb vessels in man by administering the drug intra-arterially and observed a prolonged dilator action which could probably be accounted for by depletion of arterenol from a store which was exerting a degree of vascular tone. The response of the vessels to ephedrine and methylamphetamine was, however, unaltered after treatment of the limb with reserpine, and sympathetic vasomotor reflexes were intact (181). It was concluded that there must be two components to the peripheral store of arterenol, one of which was readily released by reserpine and the other of which was more resistant to depletion; the latter would be responsible for nervous transmission. It was from the latter that ephedrine and amphetamine released the constrictor substance which was responsible for their effect, and this accounted for the abolition of their action after sympathetic degeneration (278).

Following cervical sympathectomy the constrictor effect of ephedrine on the hand vessels gradually declines as the nerves degenerate, until, between 3 and 6 weeks after the operation, its effect is completely abolished. The dilator response to reserpine, which is absent immediately after the operation and then gradually returns over the succeeding 3 to 6 weeks, parallels the return of tone to the vessels. This latter effect cannot be attributed to regeneration of nerve fibers, since the response to large doses of ephedrine remains absent at this time.

The possibility is suggested that a component of the peripheral store of sympathetic amine becomes replenished after sympathectomy, perhaps from the circulating amines, and this process may be in part, at least, responsible for the return of vascular tone which is so commonly seen (278). Since this store is independent of the integrity of the nerve fibers, it is likely that it is present in the walls of the vessels. It is not improbable that the nature of the amine might differ between nerve and the vessel store, and one might be arterenol and the other epinephrine. von Euler (95) cut the postganglionic sympathetic nerves and observed that when the fibers degenerated the concentration of arterenol in the denervated tissues declined whereas that of epinephrine did not. There is so far no conclusive evidence concerning the nature of the sympathetic transmitter substance in man.

The mechanism of action of the sympathomimetic amines at the sympathetic nerve endings is of importance in relation to the effect which some of the drugs exert in antagonizing the action of adrenergic blocking agents. Boura and Green (39) found that cocaine antagonized the blocking effect of bretylium on rabbit gut and cat nictitating membrane, and Day (78) demonstrated that dopamine, dexamphetamine, mephenteramine, hydroxyamphetamine, and ephedrine were all effective in preventing or reversing adrenergic neurone blockade by bretylium and guanethidine in the isolated rabbit ileum and cat nictitating membrane. It was suggested that the antagonism was competitive in nature (79). Subsequent work added arterenol, histamine, 5-hydroxytryptamine, and carbacol to the list of antagonists of bretylium and guanethidine in the guinea pig hypogastric–vas deferens preparation (28, 29).

A small number of clinical reports of antagonism of adrenergic blocking drugs have appeared. Four hypertensive patients taking amphetamine compounds for weight reduction failed to respond to bretylium until the amphetamine was withdrawn (279). Methylamphetamine prevented the fall in pressure in two patients suffering from postural hypotension as a result of treatment with guanethidine (192). These findings do not necessarily prove that sympathetic transmission had been restored by the amphetamines, since release of adrenal and possibly peripheral stores of catecholamines could account for the response, and since complete blockade is rarely achieved in clinical therapy and the amphetamine could act through intact or partly blocked neurones. Hodge (151) endeavored to obtain direct evidence for reversal of adrenergic neurone blockade in man by introducing blocking agents in both arms by bilateral brachial artery infusion. When the reflex constrictor responses of the hand vessels had disappeared, methylamphetamine was infused into one side. Some restoration of the reflex responses of the vessels of this side was seen in all cases, but the effect was slight and inconsistent. Intravenous administration of the adrenergic blocking agent bethanidine in one subject resulted in sympathetic reflex blockade of the hand vessels and postural hypotension on tilting 45° feet down. Methylamphetamine (2 mg intravenously) restored the blood pressure to above the pretilt level, but the reflex responses of the hand vessels were still absent at this time.

The incompleteness of the reversal of adrenergic blockade by amphetamine in man may be related to the relatively low concentrations of the drug which can be given. In animal studies high concentration for long periods were necessary to demonstrate the effect.

A. Tyramine

1. *Structure, Formation, and Breakdown*

Tyramine is parahydroxyphenol ethylamine and may be represented as shown. It is formed from the amino acid tyrosine by decarboxylation.

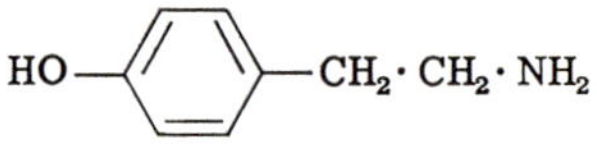

It occurs in preparations of ergot and was first identified in putrefying flesh. It is present in the alimentary tract.

Tyramine is in part converted to parahydroxyphenylacetic acid in the liver.

2. *General Circulatory Effects*

a. Cardiac Output. Dale and Dixon (76) reported an increase in cardiac output in the cat after intravenous tyramine (1 μg), and this was confirmed in cats and dogs by Chen and Meek (62) using cardiometric and teleroentgenographic methods.

Tainter (265) recorded an increase in systolic output from the heart and diminution in heart volume in the cat and dog after intravenous injections, and these changes preceded any peripheral effects. This direct stimulant action on the heart was confirmed in the isolated heart of the cat, but there was little effect on the heart of the frog.

Mashford *et al.* (209), however, measured cardiac output in normal human subjects using the dye dilution technique and found that single injections of 0.2–0.4 μg/kg caused changes in cardiac output which were variable in size and direction, the mean for 11 subjects being a decrease of 0.05 liters/minute.

Harakal *et al.* (143) gave intravenous injections of 450 μg/minute in anesthetized open chest dogs and found an increased cardiac output associated with an increased heart rate, but no significant change in stroke volume. In the case of conscious intact dogs, however, the cardiac output response was more variable, three dogs showing a decrease or no change, while six others showed an increase. The average change in cardiac output in 12 dogs was an increase, but this was significant only in the latter part of the pressor response.

b. Blood Pressure. The pressor effect of tyramine has been demonstrated in a number of species, including the rabbit, cat, and dog (62, 76, 265). The doses used ranged from 0.2–4.0 μg as a single injection. Large doses, however (20–80 μg/kg), given intravenously in the dog, lowered the blood pressure. In man, 100 μg by mouth had no pressor effect (62).

Destruction of the brain and medulla of rabbits did not abolish the rise in pressure caused by tyramine (22, 265), which indicated that the site of the pressor action was peripheral. That it is partly cardiac and partly vascular in animals is indicated by the observation that the initial rise in pressure is associated with evidence of increased heart output and only later do peripheral vascular changes occur (265). In man, intravenous administration of tyramine (0.05–0.4 μg/kg) produces an elevation of both systolic and diastolic pressures (209). The finding that cardiac output changes are small and variable indicates that the pressor response is mainly due to a rise in peripheral resistance.

c. Peripheral Resistance. The rise in diastolic pressure which occurs with moderate doses of tyramine is indicative of an over-all increase in peripheral resistance. That the peripheral vasoconstrictor response is not uniform was demonstrated by the finding that in some peripheral organs there was a passive dilatation produced apparently by the rise in blood pressure (143, 265).

3. *Specific Vascular Beds*

a. Skin Circulation. Dale and Dixon (76) observed a shrinkage in volume of the dog's ear after intravenous injection of 1 mg tyramine, which could be attributed to constriction of skin vessels. A similar response was obtained by Tainter (265) when tyramine was injected into the perfusion fluid of the isolated rabbit's ear.

b. Skeletal Muscle Circulation. Arteriolar constriction in the perfused isolated hind limb of the cat was observed by Dale and Dixon (76), probably occurring in the muscle vascular bed. Tainter (265), however, gave intravenous injections and obtained variable changes in the hind limb of the anesthetized cat. In two experiments the leg volume was reduced, in one there was no change, in one the volume was increased throughout, and in one experiment it increased during the cardiac rise in blood pressure and then fell during a further increase in blood pressure.

Infusions of 20 μg/kg/minute into the femoral artery of the dog caused a reduction in flow as measured by a rotameter, while intravenous infusions (200 μg/kg/minute) caused an increase in flow, and the change in calculated vascular resistance was variable (143).

Abboud and Eckstein (1) gave tyramine sulfate intravenously in 14 normal human subjects (0.1 mg/kg in 3 minutes) and found that the forearm blood flow was unchanged and, since the blood pressure was elevated by a mean value of 21.4 mm Hg, a rise in forearm vascular resistance was deduced. After treatment with oral reserpine the blood pressure response to tyramine was abolished, and, since forearm blood flow again showed no change, calculated forearm vascular resistance was unaltered.

c. *Intestinal Circulation.* Dale and Dixon (76) observed that tyramine injected into the perfusion fluid caused constriction of the vessels of the small intestine of the dog. More recently Harakal *et al.* (143) measured the blood flow in the superior mesenteric artery of the anesthetized dog using a rotameter. Intra-arterial injection of 20 μg/kg/minute caused a decrease in flow, indicating an increased vascular resistance. A dose of 200 μg/kg/minute intravenously, however, increased the blood pressure to such a degree that the local direct action of the drug on the vessels was offset either by the passive effect of the increased perfusion pressure or by reflex baroreceptor reactions, and the blood flow rose, the resistance showing variable changes.

d. *Kidney Circulation.* The only observations appear to be those of Harakal *et al.* (143), who found that the direct action of tyramine when given into the renal artery (10 μg/kg/minute) was to increase vascular resistance and reduce the blood flow. Intravenous infusion (100 μg/kg/minute) increased renal blood flow and resistance was variously increased, decreased, or unchanged. The dilator effect seen on intravenous administration was attributed to a passive effect of the blood pressure rise and/or a baroreceptor reflex.

e. *Other Vascular Beds.* No reports have been found of the action of tyramine on other vascular beds such as those of the liver, spleen, or brain.

B. Ephedrine

1. *Structure, Formation, and Breakdown*

Ephedrine is phenyl-isopropanol-methylamine and can be represented as shown. It is an alkaloid contained in *Ephedra equisetina* (Ma

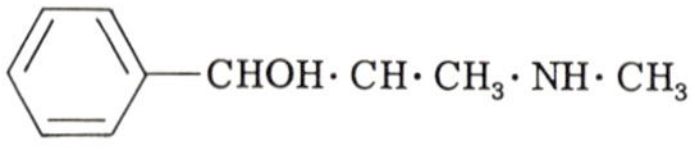

Huang), and it is also produced synthetically. It is resistant to amine oxidase, and, although in some animals deamination and conjugation

may occur to some extent in the liver (5), in man almost 100% of the administered dose is excreted unchanged in the urine within 48 hours (26).

2. *General Circulatory Effects*

a. Cardiac Output. A stimulant effect of ephedrine on the heart's action was demonstrated in the dog by Chen and Schmidt (64) using a myocardiograph and intravenous injection of 0.25–20 mg of the drug. Wilson *et al.* (280) also studied dogs, giving 0.5–1 mg/kg intravenously and 1–2 mg/kg subcutaneously and measuring cardiac output by the Fick method. Immediately following intravenous injection there was a decrease in output (averaging 11%) in three experiments, while in three others there was an increase (averaging 26.9%). After 30 minutes the output had returned to normal. Subcutaneous administration caused an increase in output in five dogs (32.6%), a decrease in one (23.5%), and no change in three.

Starr *et al.* (259) gave 50 mg of ephedrine subcutaneously in 12 normal human subjects and found an increase in cardiac output in every case using the ballistocardiographic method. Similar observations were made by Ranges and Bradley (236).

b. Arterial Blood Pressure. Amatsu and Kobota (11) were probably the first to demonstrate a rise in blood pressure in rabbits after intravenous injections of ephedrine. A prolonged rise in pressure after injection of 0.25–20 mg intravenously was observed by Chen and Schmidt (64) in the dog, cat, and rabbit, although larger doses (20–65 mg/kg) lowered the pressure, sometimes permanently (62). Chen and Schmidt (64) gave 40–60 mg intramuscularly and orally in normal human subjects and noted a rise of 20–30 mm Hg in systolic pressure while the pulse rate decreased.

Starr *et al.* (259) and Ranges and Bradley (236) found that 50–75 mg subcutaneously in normal subjects resulted in a rise in systolic pressure without much change in diastolic. Allen (7) gave 60 and 90 mg ephedrine hydrochloride intramuscularly and found that the systolic pressure was invariably raised considerably; the diastolic was generally raised but was occasionally unchanged and, rarely, was slightly depressed for a short time. When ephedrine was given after atropine (2 mg intramuscularly) a greater rise in blood pressure occurred, and the heart rate, which before atropine was slowed by ephedrine, showed a marked rise. It would appear that the slowing of the heart and the modest effects on cardiac output are a consequence of vagal reflex activity resulting from the rise in arterial pressure.

c. Peripheral Resistance. The changes in peripheral resistance induced by ephedrine are inconstant. Ranges and Bradley (236) reported that after 50–75 mg intramuscularly in normal subjects there were no marked alterations in peripheral resistance, which remained unchanged in three instances, fell in one, and rose somewhat in another. Starr *et al.* (259) found a decrease in total peripheral resistance after 50 mg subcutaneously associated with a rise in systolic pressure and increased cardiac output. The diminution of peripheral resistance was taken to indicate that vessels had dilated somewhere and that the increased blood pressure could be entirely explained by increased heart output.

3. *Specific Vascular Beds*

a. Skin Circulation. Chen and Schmidt (64) report a modest degree of constriction of skin vessels in the dog with intravenous injections (0.25–20 mg). A dilatation of skin vessels was sometimes seen, presumably a consequence of increased blood pressure.

Intramuscular injections of 90 mg ephedrine in normal subjects resulted in a marked and sustained fall in hand blood flow, which can be attributed to constriction of the skin blood vessels (7); intravenous administration (37 mg) reduced finger volume (252). A similar constriction of hand vessels is seen on infusion into the brachial artery (50–100 mg/minute), the effect of the larger doses being very prolonged (231).

b. Skeletal Muscle Circulation. A vasoconstriction in the limb of the dog (attributed to muscle vessels) was observed by Chen and Schmidt (64), but this was a weak effect, since vasodilatation occurred if there was a marked rise in blood pressure. Chen and Meek (63) found a dilatation in the dog's leg in the majority of cases when the drug was given intravenously, but a prolonged vasoconstriction was uniformly observed when the leg was perfused with ephedrine dissolved in Ringer's solution.

Forearm blood flow in man was recorded by Allen (7) after intramuscular injection of 90 mg of ephedrine. The flow varied irregularly but was always increased. Intra-arterial infusions (50–100 μg/minute) into the brachial artery result in a fall in forearm blood flow, but whether this is a consequence of constriction of skin or muscle vessels or both has not been determined (231).

c. Liver Circulation. No record of the effect of ephedrine on liver blood flow in animals or in man has been noted.

d. Intestinal Circulation. Intravenous injections (0.25–20 mg) in the dog usually result in constriction of intestinal vessels (64). However, the rise in blood pressure often results in a subsequent increase in intestinal volume. Chen and Meek (63) reported an increase in intestinal volume after intravenous injection of 10 mg in the dog.

e. Kidney Circulation. Ephedrine hydrochloride in doses of 0.25–20 mg intravenously in the dog was found by Chen and Schmidt (64) to cause a fall in volume of the kidney concurrently with a rise in arterial blood pressure, and this fall in volume was attributed to constriction of the kidney vessels. Sometimes the first injection was followed by dilatation of kidney vessels.

Introduction of ephedrine into the perfusate produced vasoconstriction in the isolated perfused dog's kidney. Aviado *et al.* (12) found that 1 mg of ephedrine injected into the renal artery of the anesthetized dog caused a reduction in kidney blood flow. Renal constriction was not always seen on intravenous injections (1 mg/kg), indicating that the local constrictor action was overcome by the accompanying increase in arterial pressure.

In man ephedrine given intramuscularly in doses of 50–75 mg caused a reduction in renal plasma flow without significant change in glomerular filtration rate, and the filtration fraction increased, indicating efferent arteriolar vasoconstriction (236).

f. Spleen Circulation. Perfusion of the dog's spleen with ephedrine solution resulted in prolonged vasoconstriction and reduction in splenic volume. A vasoconstriction also occurred on intravenous injection of 10 mg (63).

g. Cerebral Circulation. An increase in cerebral blood flow as measured by a thermocouple technique was observed in cats given intravenous and intracarotid injections of ephedrine, the response being similar to that to epinephrine, but less marked and more prolonged (225). Schmidt and Hendrix (244) also gave intracarotid injections of ephedrine in cats and found an increased cerebral flow; the extracranial blood flow was simultaneously reduced.

Sokoloff (257) pointed out that these responses do not necessarily imply a cerebral vasodilator action but may reflect a passive response of the cerebral circulation to a rise in systemic blood pressure. This would be compatible with the findings of Bouckaert and Jourdan (38), who injected 1 mg ephedrine into the perfused cerebral circulation and observed a reduction in cerebral volume, indicative of vasoconstriction.

C. Amphetamine

1. *Structure, Formation, and Breakdown*

Amphetamine is α-methylphenethylamine and can be represented as shown. It is a synthetic preparation. About 50% is excreted in the urine and the remainder is slowly inactivated in the body.

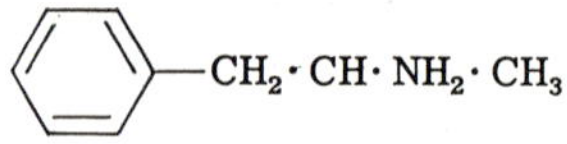

The *l*-isomer has a more marked pressor action than the *d*-isomer, the latter being a powerful analeptic.

2. *General Circulatory Effects*

a. Cardiac Output. Churchill-Davidson and Swan (66) gave intravenous infusions of methylamphetamine (2 mg/minute for 5 minutes) in seven normal subjects. From an analysis of the changes in blood pressure, pulse rate, and peripheral vascular resistance, they deduced that an increase in cardiac output must have occurred, but no direct measurements were made.

b. Blood Pressure. Allen (7) gave 20 mg of methylamphetamine intramuscularly in man and recorded an increase in systolic pressure. The diastolic pressure either did not change or showed a slight increase. The heart rate change was variable, the rate usually increasing slightly but sometimes slowing. After administration of atropine the same dose resulted in a marked tachycardia and an enhanced blood pressure response.

Churchill-Davidson and Swan (66) infused 10 mg of methylamphetamine intravenously over 5 minutes in seven normal human subjects and found an elevation of systolic pressure averaging 21 mm Hg while the diastolic rise was about the same (average 22 mm Hg). Compared with an equipressor dose of arterenol, the maximum effect of methylamphetamine on systolic pressure took longer to develop (8½ minutes as compared with 4½ minutes for arterenol). The diastolic pressure rose later than with arterenol and to a slightly lower level. The duration of effect of methylamphetamine was much greater than that of arterenol, the pressure still being elevated 20 minutes after the end of the infusion, although the diastolic pressure fell much earlier. The heart rate also returned to normal at a time when the systolic pressure was still elevated, and cardiac output was assumed to be increased at the time.

c. Peripheral Resistance. The fact that the diastolic pressure increased to the same degree as the systolic indicates a rise in total peripheral resistance.

3. *Specific Vascular Beds*

a. Skin Circulation. A fall in hand blood flow was observed by Allen (7) after intramuscular injection of 20 mg of methylamphetamine in man, and Parks *et al.* (231) demonstrated a constriction of hand vessels with doses of 50–100 μg infused into the brachial artery over 1 minute. The effect was abolished by sympathectomy.

Churchill-Davidson and Swan (66) found very little fall in hand blood flow after intravenous methylamphetamine (10 mg in 5 minutes), and a sharp rise in flow occurred 5 minutes after the infusion.

b. Skeletal Muscle Circulation. The forearm blood flow increased after intramuscular methylamphetamine (7), and this effect was enhanced after atropine, when a greater rise in blood pressure occurred. Intravenous infusions of 10 mg of methylamphetamine resulted in a fall in calf blood flow during and after the infusion, and there was a rise in calculated calf resistance. The effect was assumed to be in muscle, but there was no direct evidence of this. The flow and resistance returned to normal at a time when the arterial pressure was still elevated, and a slight increase in flow with a drop in resistance was seen at this time (66).

Injections of methylamphetamine into the brachial artery (50–1000 μg/minute for 1 minute) reduced forearm blood flow, and the larger doses had an effect which was prolonged for over an hour (231). Whether the constrictor action affects skin or muscle vessels or both had not been determined. The constrictor action diminished after cervical sympathectomy, and even large doses had no effect 3 months after the operation.

c. Kidney Circulation. The effect of amphetamine on the renal vessels in the dog has been shown to be very slight when the drug is injected into the renal artery (12). Intravenous injection (1 mg/kg) caused an increase in renal blood flow attributable to the change in arterial blood pressure.

In five out of six anesthetized patients an increase in renal blood flow (averaging 20%) occurred after intravenous administration of 25–120 mg methylamphetamine. The sixth patient showed a fall in flow. These changes were associated with marked rises in systolic and diastolic pressures (67).

d. Cerebral Circulation. Amphetamine is without notable effect on the cerebral circulation. Dumke and Schmidt (86) gave intracarotid injections in the monkey and found a reduction in cerebral blood flow at a time when the arterial blood pressure was unchanged, indicating some degree of cerebral vasoconstriction. Intravenous injections of as much as 5 mg were without effect on cerebral blood flow (245). In man no consistent effects on cerebral circulation have been observed following intravenous administration of 20 mg amphetamine sulfate (2). Six of nine subjects showed a fall in flow and three showed a rise.

e. Liver, Intestine, and Spleen Circulation. No information on the effects of amphetamine on hepatic, intestinal, or splenic vessels is available.

D. Phenylephrine

1. *Structure, Formation, and Breakdown*

Phenylephrine is hydroxyphenylmethylaminoethanol and may be represented as shown. It is a synthetic compound. Its mechanism of breakdown does not appear to have been studied.

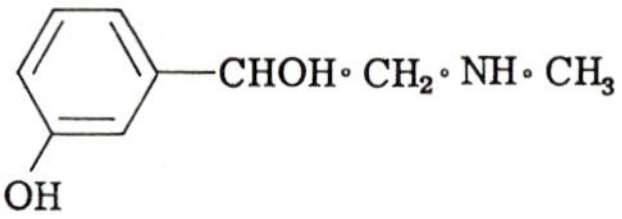

2. *General Circulatory Effects*

a. Cardiac Output. Phenylephrine exhibits hardly any cardiac stimulant activity. Reflex slowing of the heart occurs in response to the elevated blood pressure, but there is no such effect on the denervated heart. Although bradycardia has been reported when the drug was given in animals in which the vagi were cut, it has been pointed out that this could have been due to inhibition of the intact sympathetic nervous tone (26).

Studies in man (175) using the acetylene method have shown that phenylephrine (3.5–10 mg subcutaneously) causes a large increase (30%) in the stroke output but the minute volume is decreased. Slight reduction in cardiac output has been observed in anesthetized dogs using the Fick method and in conscious male subjects using ballistocardiography (161).

b. Arterial Blood Pressure. Keys and Violante (175) gave subcutaneous injections of 3–10 mg of phenylephrine in normal human subjects and noted that a rise in both systolic and diastolic pressures always occurred. The response was enhanced after the administration of atropine, and a tachycardia resulted after an initial transient fall in heart rate. Similar results were obtained in normal unanesthetized dogs and rabbits. Horvath and Knapp (161) gave intravenous injections of 0.1–1.5 mg of phenylephrine in anesthetized dogs and normal human subjects and observed increases in systolic and diastolic blood pressures in every case.

c. Peripheral Resistance. The rise in both systolic and diastolic blood pressure despite a fall in cardiac output implies that the hypertensive effect of phenylephrine is attributable to an increase in peripheral vascular resistance. Any direct stimulant effect on the heart is offset by the reflex vagal bradycardia.

3. *Specific Vascular Beds*

a. Skin Circulation. Shaw *et al.* (252) recorded blood pressure, pulse rate, digital pulsations, and finger volume in normal human subjects, and gave phenylephrine (1.5–2.0 mg) intravenously. Associated with increased systolic and diastolic pressures and reduced heart rate there was a marked reduction in finger volume and in the amplitude of digital pulsations. These effects were attributed to constriction of the finger vessels, which in this situation are mainly cutaneous. Pretreatment of the subject with Dibenamine (4–5 mg/kg intravenously) reduced the responses of the finger vessels to phenylephrine, which indicates that this drug acts on the same receptors as does arterenol.

b. Kidney Circulation. Crosley *et al.* (74) found that intravenous and intramuscular administration of phenylephrine (3–5 mg) in five normotensive subjects caused an increase in mean blood pressure and a decrease in pulse rate accompanied by an increase in renal peripheral resistance sufficient to cause a decreased renal blood flow. The filtration fraction was increased, indicating that the increased resistance was primarily in the efferent arterioles. Similar observations were made in anesthetized dogs by Mills *et al.* (215).

Injection of 1 μg into the renal artery in dogs was shown by Aviado *et al.* (12) to cause a reduction in renal blood flow with no change in aortic blood pressure, indicating constriction of renal resistance vessels.

c. Cerebral Circulation. Intravenous injection of phenylephrine (100 μg/ml) in anesthetized dogs caused an increase in cerebral blood flow (150), but, as Sokoloff (257) points out, this increase may reflect a passive response of the cerebral circulation to the rise in systemic pressure and/or the effects of an increased cerebral metabolic rate. The response does not necessarily indicate a cerebral vasodilator action of the drug.

d. Circulation in Muscle, Spleen, Liver, Intestine. Since the over-all action of phenylephrine is to raise the peripheral vascular resistance it can be assumed that its effect on the vessels of the spleen, liver, intestine, and muscle would be constrictor. However, no direct evidence is available of the action of this drug on these vascular beds nor of the effect of the raised perfusion pressure in opposing a reduction in blood flow due to vasoconstriction.

E. Dopamine

Blaschko (34) suggested that dopamine was formed by decarboxylation of dihydroxyphenylalanine (dopa) in the adrenal medulla in the synthesis of arterenol and epinephrine. The amine was extracted from sympathetic nerves and ganglia by Schümann (248), and Carlsson *et al.* (60) demonstrated its presence in the brain, where it appears to be concentrated in sites other than those containing arterenol (31, 32). In some organs, such as the lung, liver, jejunum, and colon, the catecholamine content consists almost entirely of dopamine, and in these sites it has been shown to be stored in the granules of non-nervous cells (97, 249). While the role of dopamine as a precursor of arterenol and epinephrine appears to be established, the question whether it has any other physiological role in the body remains to be answered.

1. *Structure, Formation, and Breakdown*

Dopamine (hydroxytyramine) is 3 : 4 dihydroxyphenylethylamine and may be represented as shown.

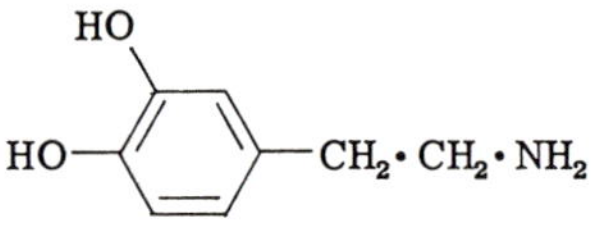

Labeled dopa has been shown to be converted to dopamine and arterenol on incubation with homogenates of adrenal medulla (81) by the action of *l*-dopadecarboxylase (187, 274). Small amounts of dopamine itself have been shown to be present in the glands of sheep, ox, and cow, though not of pig, dog, cat, rabbit, or man (126, 253). The formation of dopamine has also been shown to occur in sympathetic nerves and ganglia (127).

The enzyme dopamine β-oxidase has been demonstrated in the cytoplasmic granules in which dopamine is stored (81) and converts it to arterenol. Whether dopamine is released from the adrenal medulla or from sympathetic nerve endings is unknown. What its fate and manner of excretion would be in this event is a matter for speculation.

2. *General Circulatory Effects*

a. Cardiac Output. Gurd (141) observed an increase in output and in heart rate in the cat heart-lung preparation when dopamine was introduced, and a similar effect was reported by Holmes and Fowler (155) in the dog preparation. An elevation of output in the anesthetized dog was recorded by Maxwell *et al.* (211) following intravenous administration of 50 μg/kg/minute for 30 minutes, but the heart rate was unchanged.

In hypertensive patients Horwitz *et al.* (163) deduced from the elevation in systolic pressure and fall in diastolic that an increase in cardiac output occurred with intravenous infusions of 230–325 μg/minute for 15 minutes. Since the heart rate was unchanged an increase in stroke volume was inferred. In a subsequent study in normal volunteers Horwitz *et al.* (162) measured cardiac output by the dye dilution technique and found that intravenous infusions of 5.3–10.5 μg/kg/minute caused an increase in all of six subjects in both cardiac index and stroke volume, with little or no change in heart rate.

b. Blood Pressure. A pressor action of dopamine in the anesthetized cat which was similar to that of epinephrine but less marked in degree was described by Barger and Dale (22). Holtz *et al.* (157) also demonstrated the pressor action of dopamine in the cat but found a depressor effect in the guinea pig and rabbit, and this has been confirmed by others (160).

The depressor effect of dopamine in the guinea pig and rabbit was attributed by Burn and Rand (52) to competition with arterenol for receptor sites. Dopamine would replace arterenol for some of these sites, but since it is a much feebler constrictor agent its occupation of these sites would result in a fall in vascular tone. Treatment of these animals with reserpine to cause depletion of arterenol from the nerve endings and artery walls resulted in the depressor action of dopamine being reversed to a pressor effect. This was interpreted to imply that after reserpine the dopamine would find fewer receptor sites occupied by arterenol and would produce a rise in blood pressure by occupying those which were free.

Goldberg and Sjoerdsma (122) observed that intravenous injection of dopamine in the anesthetized dog (20 μg/kg) caused a rise in arterial pressure followed by a marked fall. McDonald and Goldberg (219) administered dopamine intravenously to anesthetized dogs in doses ranging from 4–64 μg/kg. The smaller doses caused a fall in arterial pressure, middle doses caused a pressor-depressor effect, and the largest doses increased blood pressure without an obvious depressor component. The depressor action was not blocked by dichloroisoproterenol nor by diphenhydrazine. After phenoxybenzamine the effect of larger doses of dopamine was changed from pressor to depressor. These findings suggested that the pressor action of dopamine is similar to that of other catecholamines but the depressor action appears to be produced by a different mechanism. The first study of the effect of dopamine on the blood pressure in man was made by Horwitz *et al.* (163), who gave intravenous infusions of 230–325 μg/minute for 15 minutes in seven patients with hypertension. These caused an elevation of about 25 mm Hg in systolic pressure, while the diastolic pressure and the heart rate were not significantly altered. Similar results have been obtained from a subsequent study of normotensive subjects (10, 162).

c. Peripheral Resistance. The rise in systolic pressure unaccompanied by change in diastolic pressure during dopamine infusions (163) and the associated increase in cardiac output (162) indicate that dopamine causes little change in peripheral resistance in man. Horwitz *et al.* (162) calculated total peripheral resistance from blood pressure and cardiac output changes during intravenous infusions and found a decrease in five subjects and no change in the sixth. These findings are in agreement with those of Maxwell *et al.* (211) on the anesthetized dog, in which changes in peripheral resistance were insignificant though marked rises in systemic blood pressure occurred.

3. *Specific Vascular Beds*

a. Skin Circulation. Infusions of dopamine (50 μg/minute) into the brachial artery in man caused about 50% fall in hand blood flow in both the normal and the sympathectomized limb (10). Intravenous administration (1 mg/minute) had a variable effect on hand blood flow, and skin pallor was not observed to occur. Observations on the circulation in the skin of other regions and in other species appear to be lacking.

b. Skeletal Muscle Circulation. As in the case of the skin circulation, the only observations relate to the muscle of the upper limb in man. Allwood and Ginsburg (10) observed an increase in forearm blood flow as determined plethysmographically during intravenous infusions of 1 mg/minute, and measurement of changes in deep muscle venous oxygen saturation showed this to be due to dilatation of muscle vessels (Allwood, Greenwood, and Whelan, unpublished). Intra-arterial infusions of 50 μg/minute either had no effect or caused a slight fall in forearm flow, but after treatment of the arm with phenoxybenzamine, a sustained vasodilatation occurred (10). These observations indicated that dopamine resembles epinephrine in its action on the forearm vessels and that it stimulates both α- and β-receptors. Its effects were considered to be unlikely to be due to its transformation into arterenol in the blood or tissues.

As in the case of epinephrine, the differences in the responses to intravenous and intra-arterial infusions can be accounted for by the differences in the concentrations of the drug arriving at the vessels with the two routes of administration. The effect of β-receptor blocking drugs on the response of muscle vessels to dopamine has not been studied.

Allwood and Ginsburg (10) found that dopamine differs from other catecholamines in that it produces piloerection in the forearm skin during intrabrachial infusions. This effect is not seen with infusions of arterenol or epinephrine, and it is suggested that dopamine may be involved in emotional responses and its physiological role may not be solely as a precursor of arterenol. This view is also supported by the different distributions of dopamine and of arterenol in the brain (32).

c. Other Vascular Beds. No information is available on the actions of dopamine on the vascular beds of liver, intestine, kidney, spleen, or brain.

References

1. Abboud, F. M., and Eckstein, J. W., Effects of small oral doses of reserpine on vascular responses to tyramine and norepinephrine in man. *Circulation* **29,** 219 (1964).
2. Abreu, B. E., Liddle, G. W., Burks, A. L., Sutherland, V., Elliott, H. W., Simon, A., and Mangolis, L., Influence of amphetamine sulfate on cerebral metabolism and blood flow in man. *J. Am. Pharm. Assoc. Sci. Ed.* **38,** 186 (1949).
3. Adams-Ray, J., and Nordenstam, H., Un system des cellules chromaffines dans peau humaine. *Lyon Chir.* **52,** 125 (1956).
4. Ahlquist, R. P., A study of the adrenotropic receptors. *Am. J. Physiol.* **153,** 586 (1948).
5. Ahlquist, R. P., Adrenergic drugs. *Pharmacol. Med. Ed.* **2,** 378 (1958).
6. Ahlquist, R. P., Taylor, J. P., Rawson, C. W., and Sydow, V. L., Comparative effects of epinephrine and levarterenol in the intact anaesthetized dog. *J. Pharmacol. Exptl. Therap.* **110,** 352 (1954).
7. Allen, W. J., The action of adrenaline, ephedrine and methedrine on the circulation in man. *Clin. Sci.* **6,** 269 (1948).
8. Allen, W. J., Barcroft, H., and Edholm, O. G., On the action of adrenaline on the blood vessels in human skeletal muscle. *J. Physiol.* (*London*) **105,** 255 (1946).
9. Allwood, M. J., and Ginsburg, J., The effect of phenoxybenzamine (dibenyline) on the vascular response to sympathomimetic amines in the forearm. *J. Physiol.* (*London*) **158,** 219 (1961).
10. Allwood, M. J., and Ginsburg, J., Peripheral vascular effects of dopamine in man. *Proc. 22nd Intern. Congr., Intern. Union Physiol. Sci., Leiden, 1962.* Vol. II, Abstr. 185. Exerpta Medica Foundation.
11. Amatsu, H., and Kobota, S., Quoted by Chen and Meek, ref. 62. *Kyoto Igaka Zasshi* **14,** 5 (1917).
12. Aviado, D. M., Wnuck, A. L., and deBeer, E. J., The effects of sympathomimetic drugs on renal vessels. *J. Pharmacol. Exptl. Therap.* **124,** 238 (1958).
13. Bacq, Z. M., La pharmacologie du systeme nerveuse autonome, et particulierement du sympatheque d'apres la theorie neurohumorale. *Ann. Physiol. Physicochim. Biol.* **10,** 467 (1934).
14. Bainbridge, F. A., and Trevan, J. W., Surgical shock and some allied conditions. *Brit. Med. J. M.R.C. Mem.* **I,** 381 (1917).

15. Barclay, J. A., Cooke, W. T., and Kenney, R. A., Observations on the effects of Adrenalin on renal function and circulation in man. *Am. J. Physiol.* **151,** 621 (1947).
16. Barcroft, H., and Cobbold, A. F., The action of adrenaline on muscle blood flow and blood lactate in man. *J. Physiol.* (*London*) **132,** 372 (1956).
17. Barcroft, H., Gaskell, P., Shepherd, J. T., and Whelan, R. F., The effect of noradrenaline infusions on the blood flow through the human forearm. *J. Physiol.* (*London*) **123,** 443 (1954).
18. Barcroft, H., and Konzett, H., On the action of noradrenaline, adrenaline and isopropyl noradrenaline on the arterial blood pressure, heart rate and muscle blood flow in man. *J. Physiol.* (*London*) **110,** 194 (1949).
19. Barcroft, H., and Starr, I., Comparison of the actions of adrenaline and noradrenaline on the cardiac output in man. *Clin. Sci.* **10,** 295 (1951).
20. Barcroft, H., and Swan, H. J. C., "Sympathetic Control of Human Blood Vessels." Arnold, London, 1953.
21. Bardier, E., and Frenkel, H., La diurese et la circulation renale. *J. Physiol. Pathol. Gen.* **I,** 950 (1899).
22. Barger, G., and Dale, H. H., Chemical structure and sympathomimetic action of amines. *J. Physiol.* (*London*) **41,** 19 (1910).
23. Barnett, A. J., Blacket, R. B., Depoorter, A. E., Sanderson, P. H., and Wilson, G. M., The action of noradrenaline in man and its relation to phaeochromocytoma and hypertension. *Clin. Sci.* **9,** 151 (1950).
24. Barnett, A. J., Hamilton, M. D., and Kay, H. B., Severe orthostatic hypotension. *Australasian Ann. Med.* **4,** 183 (1955).
25. Bearn, A. G., Billing, B., and Sherlock, S., The effect of adrenaline and noradrenaline on hepatic blood flow and splanchnic carbohydrate metabolism in man. *J. Physiol.* (*London*) **115,** 430 (1951).
26. Beckman, H., Pharmacology. The nature, action and use of drugs. 2nd Ed., p. 434. (1961). Saunders, Philadelphia, Pennsylvania.
27. Bein, H. J., Gross, F., Tripod, J., and Meier, R., Experimentelle Untersuchungen über "Serpasil" (Reserpin), ein neues, sehr wirksames Rauwolfia alkaloid mit neuartiger zentraler Wirkung. *Schweiz. Med. Wochschr.* **83,** 1007 (1953).
28. Bentley, G. A., Studies on sympathetic mechanisms in isolated intestinal and vas deferens preparations. *Brit. J. Pharmacol.* **19,** 85 (1962).
29. Bentley, G. A., and Sabine, J. R., The effects of ganglion-blocking and postganglionic sympatholytic drugs on preparations of the guinea-pig vas deferens. *Brit. J. Pharmacol.* 21, 190 (1963).
30. Bèrtler, A., Carlsson, A., and Rosengren, E., Release by reserpine of catechol amines from rabbit's hearts. *Naturwissenschaften* **43,** 521 (1956).
31. Bertler, A., and Rosengren, E., Occurrence and distribution of dopamine in brain and other tissues. *Experientia* **15,** 10 (1959).
32. Bertler, A., and Rosengren, E., On the distribution in brain of monoamines and of enzymes responsible for their formation. *Experientia* **15,** 382 (1959).
33. Blacket, R. B., Pickering, G. W., and Wilson, G. M., The effects of prolonged infusions of noradrenaline and adrenaline on the arterial pressure of the rabbit. *Clin. Sci.* **9,** 247 (1950).
34. Blaschko, H., The specific action of L-dopa decarboxylase. *J. Physiol.* (*London*) **96,** 50 (1939).
35. Blaschko, H., Formation of catechol amines in the animal body. *Brit. Med. Bull.* **13,** 162 (1957).

36. Bock, K. D., Hensel, H., and Ruef, J., Die wirkung von adrenalin und noradrenalin auf die muskel und hautdurchblutung des menchen. *Arch. Ges. Physiol.* **261,** 322 (1955).

37. Bouckaert, J. J., and Jourdan, F., Recherches sur la physiologie et la pharmacodynamie des vaisseaux cerebraux. IV Influence de l'adrenaline. *Arch. Intern. Pharmacodyn.* **54,** 109 (1936).

38. Bouckaert, J. J., and Jourdan, F., Recherches sur la physiologie et la pharmacodynamie des vaisseause cerebraux. *Arch. Intern. Pharmacodyn.* **54,** 168 (1936).

39. Boura, A. L. A., and Green, A. F., The actions of bretylium: adrenergic neurone blocking and other effects. *Brit. J. Pharmacol.* **14,** 536 (1959).

40. Bradley, S. E., Studies of hepatic blood flow in man. *J. Clin. Invest.* **25,** 918 (1946).

41. Brodie, T. G., and Dixon, W. E., Contributions to the physiology of the lungs. II. On the innervation of the pulmonary blood vessels; and some observations on the action of suprarenal extract. *J. Physiol.* (*London*) **30,** 476 (1904).

42. Brown-Sequard, M. E., Recherches experimentales sur la physiologie et la pathologie des capsules surrenales. *Compt. Rend.* **43,** 422 (1856).

43. Bulbring, E., and Burn, J. H., Liberation of noradrenaline from the suprarenal gland. *Brit. J. Pharmacol.* **4,** 202 (1949).

44. Burch, G. E., and Phillips, J. H., Chromaffin reacting cells in human digital skin. *Circulation Res.* **6,** 416 (1958).

45. Burn, J. H., The action of tyramine and ephedrine. *J. Pharmacol. Exptl. Therap.* **46,** 75 (1932).

46. Burn, J. H., On vasodilator fibres in the sympathetic and on the effect of circulating adrenaline in augmenting the vascular response to sympathetic stimulation. *J. Physiol.* (*London*) **75,** 144 (1932).

47. Burn, J. H., Tyramine and other amines as noradrenaline-releasing substances. *Ciba Found. Symp. Adrenergic Mechanisms* 326 (1960).

48. Burn, J. H., "The Autonomic Nervous System." Blackwell, Oxford, 1963.

49. Burn, J. H., and Dale, H. H., The vaso-dilator action of histamine, and its physiological significance. *J. Physiol.* (*London*) **61,** 185 (1926).

50. Burn, J. H., and Hutcheon, D. E., Action of noradrenaline. *Brit. J. Pharmacol.* **4,** 373 (1949).

51. Burn, J. H., Leach, E. H., Rand, M. J., and Thompson, J. W., Peripheral effects of nicotine and acetylcholine resembling those of sympathetic stimulation. *J. Physiol.* (*London*) **148,** 332 (1959).

52. Burn, J. H., and Rand, M. J., The depressor action of dopamine and adrenaline. *Brit. J. Pharmacol.* **13,** 471 (1958).

53. Burn, J. H., and Rand, M. J., Fall of blood pressure after a noradrenaline infusion and its treatment by pressor agents. *Brit. Med. J.* **I,** 394 (1959).

54. Burn, J. H., and Tainter, M. L., An analysis of the effect of cocaine on the actions of adrenaline and tyramine. *J. Physiol.* (*London*) **150,** 169 (1931).

55. Burton, A. C., A critical survey of methods available for the measurement of human peripheral blood flow. *Ciba Found. Symp. Peripheral Circulation* 91 (1954).

56. Cannon, B. W., and Bacq, Z. M., Studies on the conditions of activity in endocrine organs. XXVI, A hormone produced by sympathetic action on smooth muscle. *Am. J. Physiol.* **96,** 392 (1931).

57. Cannon, W. B., and Lyman, H., The depressor effect of adrenaline on arterial pressure. *Am. J. Physiol.* **31,** 376 (1913).
58. Cannon, W. B., and Rapport, D., Studies on the conditions of activity in endocrine glands. VI Further observations on the denervated heart in relation to adrenal secretion. *Am. J. Physiol.* **58,** 308 (1921).
59. Cannon, W. B., and Rosenblueth, A., Studies on conditions of activity in endocrine organs. XXIX. Sympathin E and sympathin I. *Am. J. Physiol.* **104,** 557 (1933).
60. Carlsson, A., Lindquist, M., Magnussen, T., and Waldeck, B., On the presence of 3-hydroxytyramine in brain. *Science* **127,** 471 (1958).
61. Chasis, H., Ranges, W., Goldring, W., and Smith, H. W., The control of renal blood flow and glomerular filtration in normal man. *J. Clin. Invest.* **17,** 683 (1938).
62. Chen, K. K., and Meek, W. J., A comparative study of ephedrine, tyramine and epinephrine with special reference to the circulation. *J. Pharmacol. Exptl. Therap.* **28,** 59 (1926).
63. Chen, K. K., and Meek, W. J., Further studies of the effect of ephedrine on the circulation. *J. Pharmacol. Exptl. Therap.* **28,** 31 (1926).
64. Chen, K. K., and Schmidt, C. F., The action of ephedrine, the active principle of the Chinese drug, ma huang. *J. Pharmacol. Exptl. Therap.* **24,** 339 (1924).
65. Chidsey, C. A., Harrison, D. C., and Braunwald, E., Release of norepinephrine from the heart by vasoactive amines. *Proc. Soc. Exptl. Biol. Med.* **109,** 488 (1962).
66. Churchill-Davidson, H. C., and Swan, H. J. C., Noradrenaline and methedrine—a comparison of their circulatory actions. *Anaesthesia* **7,** 4 (1952).
67. Churchill-Davidson, H. C., Wylie, W. D., Miles, B. E., and de Wardener, H. E., The effects of adrenaline, noradrenaline, and methedrine on the renal circulation during anaesthesia. *Lancet* **II,** 803 (1951).
68. Clarke, G. A., A comparison of the effects of adrenaline and pituitrin on the portal circulation. *J. Physiol.* (*London*) **66,** 274 (1928).
69. Cobbold, A. F., Ginsburg, J., and Paton, A., Circulatory, respiratory and metabolic responses to isopropylnoradrenaline in man. *J. Physiol.* (*London*) **151,** 539 (1960).
70. Cobbold, A. F., and Vass, C. C. N., Responses of muscle blood vessels to intra-arterially and intravenously administered noradrenaline. *J. Physiol.* (*London*) **120,** 105 (1953).
71. Condon, E., and Sheehan, J. D., Effect of intravenous noradrenaline in low dosage on the arterial blood pressure of the dog. *Arch. Intern. Pharmacodyn.* **144,** 370 (1963).
72. Cooper, C. J., Fewings, J. D., Hodge, R. L., Scroop, G. C., and Whelan, R. F.. The role of skin and muscle vessels on the response of forearm blood flow tc noradrenaline. *J. Physiol.* (*London*) **173,** 65 (1964).
73. Corcoran, A. C., and Page, I. H., Renal hemodynamic effects of adrenaline and "Isuprel." Potentiation of effects of both drugs by tetraethylammonium. *Proc. Soc. Exptl. Biol. Med.* **66,** 148 (1947).
74. Crosley, A. P., Clark, J. K., and Barker, H. G., The renal hemodynamic effects of phenylephrine (Neo Synephrine) hydrochloride in man. *J. Pharmacol. Exptl. Therap.* **101,** 153 (1951).
75. Dale, H., Natural chemical stimulators. *Edinburgh Med. J.* **45,** 461 (1938).

76. Dale, H. H., and Dixon, W. E., The action of pressor amines produced by putrefaction. *J. Physiol. (London)* **39,** 25 (1909).
77. Dale, H. H., and Richards, A. N., The depressor (vaso-dilator) action of noradrenaline. *J. Physiol. (London)* **63,** 201 (1927).
78. Day, M. D., Effect of sympathomimetic amines on the blocking action of guanethidine, bretylium and xylocaine. *Brit. J. Pharmacol.* **18,** 421 (1962).
79. Day, M. D., and Rand, M. J., Evidence for a competitive antagonism of guanethidine by dexamphetamine. *Brit. J. Pharmacol.* **20,** 17 (1963).
80. Deal, C. P., and Green, H. D., Comparison of changes in mesenteric resistance following splanchnic nerve stimulation with responses to epinephrine and norepinephrine. *Circulation Res.* **4,** 38 (1956).
81. Demis, D. J., Blaschko, H., and Welch, A. D., The conversion of dihydroxyphenylalanine-2-C^{14} (dopa) to norepinephrine by bovine adrenal medullary homogenates. *J. Pharmacol. Exptl. Therap.* **117,** 208 (1956).
82. Demis, D. J., Zimmer, J. G., Verhonick, P. J., and Catalano, P. M., The pharmacology of human skin I. Epinephrine and norepinephrine; catecholamine–serotonin combinations. *J. Invest. Dermatol.* **39,** 419 (1962).
83. Dorner, J., Zur Ursache der primaren Mehrdurchblutung der Skeletmuskulatur nach Injektion von Adrenalin und Arterenol. *Arch. Ges. Physiol.* **257,** 464 (1953).
84. Dornhorst, A. C., and Robinson, B. F., Clinical pharmacology of a beta-adrenergic-blocking agent (nethalide) *Lancet* **2,** 314 (1962).
85. Duff, R. S., and Swan, H. J. C., Further observations on the effect of adrenaline on the blood flow through human skeletal muscle. *J. Physiol. (London)* **114,** 41 (1951).
86. Dumke, P. R., and Schmidt, C. F., Quantitative measurements of cerebral blood flow in the macacque monkey. *Am. J. Physiol.* **138,** 421 (1943).
87. Duncanson, D., Stewart, T., and Edholm, O. G., Effect of *l*-arterenol on the peripheral circulation in man. *Federation Proc.* **8,** 37 (1949).
88. Eakins, K. E., and Lockett, M. F., The formation of an isoprenaline-like substance from adrenaline. *Brit. J. Pharmacol.* **16,** 108 (1961).
89. Ekmanner, S., and Persson, H., The control of the circulation of the blood. "The Effects of Noradrenaline on Circulation," p. 86. Dawson, London, 1951. Quoted by von Euler, ref. 94.
90. Elliott, T. R., The action of adrenaline. *J. Physiol. (London)* **32,** 401 (1905).
91. Erlanger, J., and Gasser, H. S., Studies in secondary traumatic shock. III Circulatory failure due to adrenalin. *Am. J. Physiol.* **49,** 345 (1919).
92. von Euler, U. S., The presence of a sympathomimetic substance in extracts of mammalian heart. *J. Physiol. (London)* **105,** 38 (1946).
93. von Euler, U. S., Identification of the sympathomimetic ergone in adrenergic nerves of cattle (Sympathin-N) with laevo-noradrenaline. *Acta Physiol. Scand.* **16,** 63 (1948).
94. von Euler, U. S., "Noradrenaline. Chemistry, physiology, pharmacology, and clinical aspects." Thomas, Springfield, Illinois, 1956.
95. von Euler, U. S., Contribution to discussion. *Ciba Found. Symp. Adrenergic Mechanisms* 509 (1960).
96. von Euler, U. S., and Hamberg, U., *l*-nor-adrenaline in the suprarenal medulla. *Nature* **163,** 642 (1949).
97. von Euler, U. S., and Lishajko, F., Dopamine in mammalian lung and spleen. *Acta Physiol. Pharmacol. Neerl.* **6,** 295 (1957).

98. von Euler, U. S., and Purkhold, A., Effect of sympathetic denervation on the noradrenaline and adrenaline content of the spleen, kidney, and salivary glands in the sheep. *Acta Physiol. Scand.* **24,** 212 (1951).

99. Farrand, E. A., Larsen, R., and Horvath, S. M., Effects of *l*-epinephrine and *l*-norepinephrine on the splanchnic bed of intact dogs. *Am. J. Physiol.* **189,** 576 (1957).

100. Field, E. J., Grayson, J., and Rogers, A. F., Observations on the blood flow in the spinal cord of the rabbit. *J. Physiol.* (*London*) **114,** 56 (1951).

101. Finesinger, J., and Putnam, T. J., Cerebral circulation. XXIII. Induced variations in volume flow through the brain perfused at constant pressure. *A.M.A. Arch. Neurol. Psychiat.* **30,** 775 (1933).

102. Florey, H., Microscopical observations on the circulation of the blood in the cerebral cortex. *Brain* **48,** 43 (1925).

103. Fog, M., Cerebral Circulation. I. Reaction of pial arteries to epinephrine by direct application and by intravenous injection. *A.M.A. Arch. Neurol. Psychiat.* **41,** 109 (1939).

104. Folkow, B., and von Euler, U. S., Selective activation of noradrenaline and adrenaline producing cells in the cat's adrenal gland by hypothalamic stimulation. *Circulation Res.* **2,** 191 (1954).

105. Folkow, B., Frost, J., and Uvnäs, B., Action of adrenaline, noradrenaline and some other sympathomimetic drugs on the muscular, cutaneous and splanchnic vessels of the cat. *Acta Physiol. Scand.* **15,** 412 (1948).

106. Forbes, A. S., Finley, K. H., and Mason, G. I., Cerebral circulation. *A.M.A. Arch. Neurol. Psychiat.* **30,** 957 (1933).

107. Freeman, H., and Carmichael, H. T., A pharmacodynamic study of the autonomic nervous system in normal man. The effects of intravenous injections of epinephrine, atropin, ergotamine and physostigmine upon the blood pressure and pulse rate. *J. Pharmacol. Exptl. Therap.* **58,** 409 (1936).

108. Freeman, N. E., Freedman, H., and Miller, C. C., The production of shock by prolonged continuous injection of Adrenalin in unanesthetized dogs. *Am. J. Physiol.* **131,** 545 (1941).

109. Fröhlich, A., and Loewi, O., Über eine steigerung der adrenalinem-pfindlichkeit durch cocain. *Arch. Exptl. Pathol. Pharmakol.* **62,** 159 (1910).

110. Gaddum, J. H., and Goodwin, L. G., Experiments on liver sympathin. *J. Physiol.* (*London*) **105,** 357 (1947).

111. Gaddum, J. H., and Kwiatkowski, H., The action of ephedrine. *J. Physiol.* (*London*) **94,** 87 (1938).

112. Gaddum, J. H., Peart, W. S., and Vogt, M., The estimation of adrenaline and allied substances in blood. *J. Physiol.* (*London*) **108,** 467 (1949).

113. Gibbs, F. A., Gibbs, E. L., and Lennox, W. G., The cerebral blood flow in man as influenced by adrenaline, caffein, amyl nitrite and histamine. *Am. Heart J.* **10,** 916 (1935).

114. Ginsburg, J., and Cobbold, A. F., The effects of adrenaline, noradrenaline and isopropylnoradrenaline in man. *Ciba Found. Symp. Adrenergic Mechanisms* 173 (1960).

115. Glover, W. E., Greenfield, A. D. M., and Shanks, R. G., Effect of dichloroisoprenaline on the peripheral vascular responses to adrenaline in man. *Brit. J. Pharmacol.* **19,** 235 (1962).

116. Glover, W. E., Roddie, I. C., and Shanks, R. G., The effect of intra-arterial potassium chloride infusions on vascular reactivity in the human forearm. *J. Physiol.* (*London*) **163,** 22 (1962).

117. Glover, W. E., and Shanks, R. G., Observations on the relation between the vasodilator and metabolic actions of adrenaline in the human forearm. *J. Physiol.* (*London*) **167,** 280 (1963).

118. Glover, W. E., and Shanks, R. G., The mechanism of the response of the chronically sympathectomized forearm to intravenous adrenaline. *J. Physiol.* (*London*) **167,** 263 (1963).

119. Glover, W. E., and Shanks, R. G., Forearm blood flow during prolonged intra-arterial infusions of adrenaline, and the effects of intra-arterial adrenaline on post-exercise hyperaemia. *J. Physiol.* (*London*) **167,** 268 (1963).

120. Glover, W. E., Shanks, R. G., and Stanford, C. F., Peripheral vascular effects of mixtures of isopropylnoradrenaline and noradrenaline in man. *Nature* **196,** 999 (1962).

121. Glover, W. E., Shanks, R. G., and Stanford, C. F., Peripheral vascular effects of mixtures of isoprenaline and noradrenaline in man. *Brit. J. Pharmacol.* **22,** 166 (1964).

122. Goldberg, L. I., and Sjoerdsma, A., Effects of several monoamine oxidase inhibitors on the cardiovascular actions of naturally occurring amines in the dog. *J. Pharmacol. Exptl. Therap.* **127,** 212 (1959).

123. Goldenberg, M., Faber, M., Alston, E. J., and Chargaff, E. C., Evidence for the occurrence of nor-epinephrine in the adrenal medulla. *Science* **109,** 534 (1949).

124. Goldenberg, M., Pines, K. L., Baldwin, E. de F., Greene, D. G., and Roh, C. E., The haemodynamic response of man to nor-epinephrine and its relation to the problem of hypertension. *Am. J. Med.* **5,** 792 (1948).

125. Golenhofen, K., Sustained dilatation in human muscle blood vessels under the influence of adrenaline. *J. Physiol.* (*London*) **160,** 189 (1962).

126. Goodall, McC., Studies of adrenaline and noradrenaline in mammalian hearts and suprarenals. *Acta Physiol. Scand.* **24,** Suppl. 85 (1951).

127. Goodall, McC., and Kirshner, N., Biosynthesis of epinephrine and nor-epinephrine by sympathetic nerves and ganglia. *Circulation* **17,** 366 (1958).

128. Gordon, W., and Levitt, G., Blood pressure changes in normals and in hypertensives after intravenous epinephrine and histamine. *J. Clin. Invest.* **14,** 367 (1935).

129. Gorten, R., Gunnells, J. C., Weissler, A. M., and Stead, E. A., Effects of atropine and isoproterenol on cardiac output, central venous pressure, and mean transit time of indicators placed at three different sites in the venous system. *Circulation Res.* **9,** 979 (1961).

130. Grant, R. T., and Pearson, R. S. B., The blood circulation in the human limb; Observations on the differences between the proximal and distal parts and remarks on the regulation of body temperature. *Clin. Sci.* 3, 119 (1938).

131. Grayson, J., and Johnson, D. H., The effect of adrenaline and noradrenaline on the liver blood flow. *J. Physiol.* (*London*) **120,** 73 (1953).

132. Grayson, J., and Swan, H. J. C., Action of adrenaline, nor-adrenaline, and dihydroergocornine on the colonic circulation. *Lancet* **I,** 488 (1950).

133. Green, H. D., Deal, C. P., Bardhanabaedya, S., and Denison, A. B., On the effects of adrenergic substances and ischaemia on the blood flow and

peripheral resistance of the canine mesenteric vascular bed before and during adrenergic blockade. *J. Pharmacol. Exptl. Therap.* **113,** 115 (1955).

134. Green, H. D., and Denison, A. B., Absence of vasomotor responses to epinephrine and arterenol in an isolated intra cranial circulation. *Circulation Res.* **4,** 565 (1956).

135. Green, H. D., Hall, L. S., Sexton, J., and Deal, C. P., Autonomic vasomotor responses in the canine hepatic arterial and venous beds. *Am. J. Physiol.* **196,** 196 (1959).

136. Green, D. M., Johnson, A. D., Lobb, A., and Cusick, G., The effects of Adrenalin in normal and hypertensive patients in relation to the mechanism of sustained pressure elevations. *J. Lab. Clin. Med.* **33,** 332 (1948).

137. Green, H. D., and Kepchar, J. H., Control of peripheral resistance in major systemic vascular beds. *Physiol. Rev.* **39,** 617 (1959).

138. Green, H. D., Shearin, W. T., Jackson, T. W., Keach, L. M., and Denison, A. B., Isopropylnorepinephrine blockade of epinephrine reversal. *Am. J. Physiol.* **179,** 287 (1954).

139. Griffith, F. R., Fact and theory regarding the calorigenic action of adrenaline. *Physiol. Rev.* **31,** 151 (1951).

140. Gruhzit, C. C., Freyberger, W. A., and Moe, G. K., The nature of the reflex vasodilatation induced by epinephrine. *J. Pharmacol. Exptl. Therap.* **112,** 138 (1954).

141. Gurd, M. R., Physiological action of dihydroxyphenylethylamine and sympatol. *Quart. J. Pharm. Pharmacol.* **10,** 188 (1937).

142. Hamilton, W. F., and Remington, J. W., Some factors in the regulation of the stroke volume. *Am. J. Physiol.* **153,** 287 (1948).

143. Harakal, C., Sevy, R. W., and Rusy, B. F., Hemodynamic effects of tyramine. *J. Pharmacol. Exptl. Therap.* **144,** 89 (1964).

144. Hartman, F. A., Evans, J. I., and Walker, H. G., The action of epinephrine upon the capillaries and fibres of skeletal muscle. *Am. J. Physiol.* **85,** 91 (1928).

145. Hassencamp, E., Zur Frage der adrenaliniverkung bein menschen. *Deut. Med. Wochschr.* **50,** 1044 (1924).

146. Hibbs, R. G., Burch, G. E., and Phillips, J. H., Electron microscopic observations on human mast cells. *Am. Heart J.* **60,** 121 (1960).

147. Hildes, J. A., Purser, S. H., and Sherlock, S., The effects of intra-arterial adrenaline on carbohydrate metabolism in man. *J. Physiol.* (*London*) **109,** 232 (1949).

148. Hillarp, N. Å., and Hökfelt, B., Evidence of adrenaline and noradrenaline in separate adrenal medullary cells. *Acta Physiol. Scand.* **30,** 55 (1953).

149. Hilton, S. M., and Lewis, G. P., The relationship between glandular activity, bradykinin formation and functional vasodilatation in the submandibular salivary gland. *J. Physiol.* (*London*) **134,** 471 (1956).

150. Himwich, H. E., Daly, C., and Fazekas, J. F., Effect of neosynephrine on gaseous exchange of the brain. *Proc. Soc. Exptl. Biol. Med.* **53,** 78 (1943).

151. Hodge, R. L., Studies on some cardiovascular drugs in man. M.D. Thesis, Univ. of Adelaide, South Australia, 1964.

152. Hodge, R. L., and Scroop, G. C., Vascular sensitivity studies and the use of angiotensin as a pressor agent in two cases of phaeochromocytoma. (To be published.)

153. Hodge, R. L., and Whelan, R. F., Effect of hexamethonium on the vascular response to noradrenaline in man. *Brit. J. Pharmacol.* **18,** 331 (1962).

154. Holling, H. E., Observations on the oxygen content of venous blood from the arm vein and on the oxygen consumption of resting human muscle. *Clin. Sci.* **4,** 103 (1939).
155. Holmes, J. C., and Fowler, N. O., Direct cardiac effects of dopamine. *Circulation Res.* **10,** 68 (1962).
156. Holton, P., Noradrenaline in adrenal medullary tumors. *Nature* **163,** 217 (1949).
157. Holtz, P., Credner, K., and Koepp, W., Die enzymatische entstehung von oxytryramin in organismus und die physioligische bedeutung der dopa-decarboxylase. *Arch. Exptl. Pathol. Pharmakol.* **200,** 356 (1942).
158. Holtz, P., Backmann, F., Engelhardt, A., and Greeff, K., Die milzwirkung des adrenalins und arterenols. *Arch. Ges. Physiol.* **255,** 232 (1952).
159. Holtz, P., and Schümann, E. J., Arterenol content of the mammalian and human adrenal medulla. *Nature* **165,** 683 (1950).
160. Hornykiewiez, O., The action of dopamine on the arterial blood pressure of the guinea-pig. *Brit. J. Pharmacol.* **13,** 91 (1958).
161. Horvath, S. M., and Knapp, D. W., Hemodynamic effects of neosynephrine. *Am. J. Physiol.* **178,** 387 (1954).
162. Horwitz, D., Fox, S. M., and Goldberg, L. I., Effects of dopamine in man. *Circulation Res.* **10,** 235 (1962).
163. Horwitz, D., Goldberg, G. I., and Sjoerdsma, A., Increased blood pressure responses to dopamine and norepinephrine produced by monoamine oxidase inhibitors in man. *J. Lab. Clin. Med.* **56,** 747 (1960).
164. Hoskins, R. G., and Gunning, R. E. L., Effect of Adrenalin on the distribution of the blood. V. Volume changes and venous discharge in the intestine. *Am. J. Physiol.* **43,** 399 (1917).
165. Hoskins, R. G., and Gunning, R. E. L., The effects of Adrenalin on the distribution of the blood. III. Volume changes and venous discharge in the kidney. *Am. J. Physiol.* **43,** 304 (1917).
166. Hoskins, R. G., and Gunning, R. E. L., The effects of Adrenalin on the distribution of the blood. II. Volume changes and venous discharge in the spleen. *Am. J. Physiol.* **43,** 298 (1917).
167. Hoskins, R. G., Gunning, R. E. L., and Berry, E. L., The effects of adrenin on the distribution of the blood. I. Volume changes and venous discharge in the limb. *Am. J. Physiol.* **41,** 513 (1916).
168. Humphreys, J., Johnston, J. H., and Richardson, J. C., Skin necrosis following intravenous noradrenaline. *Brit. Med. J.* **II,** 1250 (1955).
169. Imig, C. J., Randall, B. F., and Hines, H. M., Effects of epinephrine and nor-epinephrine on blood flow through normal and denervated limbs of dogs. *Am. J. Physiol.* **109,** 22 (1952).
170. Kapper, A., Sutton, G. C., Reale, A., Skoglund, K.-H., and Nylin, G., The clinical response of human beings to *l*-nor-adrenaline and its clinical applicability. *Acta Cardiol.* **5,** 121 (1950).
171. Kaufman, J., Iglauer, A., and Herwitz, G. K., Effect of Isuprel (isopropyl-epinephrine) on circulation of normal man. *Am. J. Med.* **11,** 442 (1951).
172. Keele, C. A., and Neil, E., "Samson Wright's Applied Physiology," 10th Ed., p. 364. Oxford Univ. Press, London and New York, 1962.
173. Keller, C. J., Die regelung der Blutversorgung des Gehirnes. *Z. Ges. Neurol. Psychiat.* **167,** 281 (1939).
174. Kety, S. S., The control of the circulation of the blood. *In* "The Cerebral Circulation" (McDowell, ed.), p. 176. Dawson, London, 1956.

175. Keys, A., and Violante, A., The cardiocirculatory effects in man of Neo-Synephrine (*l*-α-hydroxy-β-methylamino-3-hydroxy-ethyl-benzene hydrochloride). *J. Clin. Invest.* **21**, 1 (1942).
176. King, S. E., and Baldwin, D. S., Production of renal ischaemia and proteinuria in man by adrenal medullary hormones. *Am. J. Med.* **20**, 217 (1956).
177. King, B. D., Sokoloff, L., and Wechsler, R. L., The effects of *l*-epinephrine and *l*-nor-epinephrine upon cerebral circulation and metabolism in man. *J. Clin. Invest.* **31**, 275 (1952).
178. Konzett, H., Zur pharmakologie neuer adrenalinverwandter Körper. *Arch. Exptl. Pathol. Pharmakol.* **197**, 41 (1940).
179. Kunkle, P., Stead, E. A., and Weiss, S., Blood flow and vasomotor reactions in the hand, forearm, foot and calf in response to physical and chemical stimuli. *J. Clin. Invest.* **18**, 225 (1939).
180. de la Lande, I. S., Manson, J., Parks, V. J., Sandison, A. G., Skinner, S. L., and Whelan, R. F., The local metabolic action of adrenaline on skeletal muscle in man. *J. Physiol.* (*London*) **157**, 177 (1961).
181. de la Lande, I. S., Parks, V. J., Sandison, A. G., Skinner, S. L., and Whelan, R. F., The peripheral dilator action of reserpine in man. *Australian J. Exptl. Biol. Med. Sci.* **38**, 313 (1960).
182. de la Lande, I. S., and Whelan, R. F., The effect of antagonists on the response of the forearm vessels to adrenaline. *J. Physiol.* (*London*) **148**, 548 (1959).
183. de la Lande, I. S., and Whelan, R. F., The role of lactic acid on the vasodilator action of adrenaline in the human limb. *J. Physiol.* (*London*) **162**, 151 (1962).
184. Lands, A. M., and Howard, J. W., A comparative study of the effects of *l*-arterenol, epinephrine and isopropylarterenol on the heart. *J. Pharmacol. Exptl. Therap.* **106**, 65 (1952).
185. Lands, A. M., Nash, V. L., McCarthy, H. M., Granger, H. R., and Dertunger, B. L., The pharmacology of *N*-alkyl analogues of epinephrine. *J. Pharmacol. Exptl. Therap.* **90**, 110 (1947).
186. Lands, A. M., Luduena, F. P., and Tullar, B. F., The pharmacologic activity of the optical isomers of isopropylarterenol (Isuprel) compared with that of the optically inactive analog (1-3,4-dihydroxyphenyl)-2-isopropylamino ethane HCl. *J. Pharmacol. Exptl. Therap.* **111**, 469 (1954).
187. Langemann, H., Enzymes and their substrates in the adrenal gland of the ox. *Brit. J. Pharmacol.* **6**, 318 (1951).
188. Langford, H. G., Hypotension after noradrenaline. *Brit. Med. J.* **I**, 861 (1959).
189. Langley, J. N., Observations on the physiological action of extracts of the supra-renal bodies. *J. Physiol.* (*London*) **27**, 237 (1901).
190. de Largy, C., Greenfield, A. D. M., McCorry, R. L., and Whelan, R. F., The effects of intravenous infusion of mixtures of *l*-adrenaline and *l*-noradrenaline on the human subject. *Clin. Sci.* **9**, 71 (1950).
191. Latham, W., Marks, P. A., Roof, B. S., and Bradley, S. E., The effect of *l*-norepinephrine on urine composition and acid-base equilibrium in man. *J. Lab. Clin. Med.* **50**, 588 (1957).
192. Laurence, D. R., and Rosenheim, M. L., Clinical effect of drugs which prevent the release of adrenergic transmitter. *Ciba Found. Symp. Adrenergic Mechanisms*, 201 (1960).

193. Lever, A. F., Mobray, J. F., and Peart, W. S., Blood flow and blood pressure after noradrenaline infusions. *Clin. Sci.* **21,** 69 (1961).
194. Lewandowsky, M., Ueber die Wirkung des Nebennierenextracts auf die glatten Muskeln, im Besonderen des Auges. *Arch. Anat. Physiol.* P3. (Physiol. Abt.) 360 (1899).
195. Lockett, M. F., Identification of an isoprenaline-like substance in extracts of adrenal glands. *Brit. J. Pharmacol.* **9,** 498 (1954).
196. Lockett, M. F., The transmitter released by stimulation of the bronchial sympathetic nerves of cats. *Brit. J. Pharmacol.* **12,** 86 (1957).
197. Lockett, M. F., Changes induced in blood concentrations of adrenaline, noradrenaline and third amine by the intravenous injection of adrenaline in cats. *J. Physiol. (London)* **146,** 15 (1959).
198. Loewi, O., and Navratil, E., Über humorale Übertragbarkeit der Herznervenwirkung. *Arch. Ges. Physiol.* **206,** 123 (1924).
199. Lowe, R. D., Functional location of adrenergic receptors on blood vessels in muscle. *Nature* **202,** 400 (1964).
200. Lowe, R. D., and Robinson, B. F., Effect of differential adrenergic blockade on response of forearm blood flow to infused catecholamines. *Clin. Sci.* **26,** 81 (1964).
201. Lowe, R. D., and Robinson, B. F., The influence of route of administration upon the response of the forearm blood flow to adrenaline infusions. *Clin. Sci.* **26,** 89 (1964).
202. Lowe, R. D., and Thompson, J. W., The effect of intra-arterial potassium chloride infusion upon forearm blood flow in man. *J. Physiol. (London)* **162,** 69 (1962).
203. Luduena, F. P., Anamenka, E., Siegmund, O. H., and Miller, L. C., Comparative pharmacology of the optical isomers of arterenol. *J. Pharmacol. Exptl. Therap.* **95,** 155 (1949).
204. Lundholm, L., The mechanism of the vasodilator effect of adrenaline. 1. The effect on skeletal muscle vessels. *Acta Physiol. Scand.* **39,** Suppl. 133, 3 (1956).
205. Mahon, W. A., and Mashford, M. L., The pressor effect of tyramine in man and its modification by reserpine pretreatment. *J. Clin. Invest.* **42,** 338 (1963).
206. Mantegazza, P., Tyler, C., and Zaimis, E., The peripheral action of hexamethonium and of pentolinium. *Brit. J. Pharmacol.* **13,** 480 (1958).
207. Marsh, D. F., Pelletier, M. H., and Ross, C. A., The comparative pharmacology of the *n*-alkylarterenols. *J. Pharmacol. Exptl. Therap.* **92,** 108 (1947).
208. Marson, F. G. W., Effect of noradrenaline on urine and renal blood flow. *Brit. J. Pharmacol.* **11,** 431 (1956).
209. Mashford, M. L., Philipson, J. B., Wolochow, D. A., and Mahon, W. A., Pharmacological action of tyramine on the cardiovascular system in man. *Proc. Soc. Exptl. Biol. Med.* **8,** 308 (1962).
210. Matz, L. R., and Skinner, S. L., Evidence against presence of chromaffin cells in human skin. *Circulation Res.* **11,** 418 (1962).
211. Maxwell, G. M., Rowe, G. G., Castillo, C. A., Crumpton, C. W., and Clifford, J. E., Effects of 3-OH tyramine upon the systemic, pulmonary and coronary hemodynamics and metabolism of the intact dog. *Pharmacologist* **1,** 69 (1959).
212. von Meier, R., Tripod, J., and Wirz, E., Fortlaufende Bestimmung des Schalagvolumens mit Hilfe des Fickschen Prinzipes. Beeinflussung der

Herzleistung am Kaninchen durch Coramin und Adrenalin. *Helv. Physiol. Pharmacol. Acta* **7**, 210 (1949).
213. Melville, K. I., The antisympathomimetic action of dioxane compounds (F883 & F933) with special reference to the vascular responses to dihydroxyphenyl ethanolamine (arterenol) and nerve stimulation. *J. Pharmacol. Exptl. Therap.* **59**, 317 (1937).
214. Mercantini, E. S., Failure to show the presence of a chromaffin system of cells in the human skin. *J. Invest. Dermatol.* **34**, 317 (1960).
215. Mills, L. C., Moyer, J. H., and Handley, C. A., Effects of various sympathomimetic drugs on renal hemodynamics in normotensive and hypotensive dogs. *Am. J. Physiol.* **198**, 1279 (1960).
216. Mongar, J. L., and Whelan, R. F., Histamine release by adrenaline and *d*-tubocurarine in the human subject. *J. Physiol.* (*London*) **120**, 146 (1953).
217. Moore, B., and Purinton, C. O., Ueber den Einfluess minimaler Mengen Nebennierenextracts auf den arteriellen Blutruch. *Arch. Ges. Physiol.* **81**, 483 (1900).
218. Moyer, J. H., and Handley, C. A., Norepinephrine and epinephrine effect on renal hemodynamics. *Circulation* **5**, 91 (1952).
219. McDonald, R. H., and Goldberg, L. I., Analysis of the cardiovascular effects of dopamine in the dog. *Federation Proc.* **21**, 127 (1962).
220. McDowall, R. J. S., Reactive hyperemia. *Ciba Found. Symp. Visceral Circulation* 93 (1952).
221. MacLean, L. D., Brackney, E. L., and Visscher, M. B., Effects of epinephrine, norepinephrine and histamine on canine intestine and liver weight continuously recorded *in vivo*. *J. Appl. Physiol.* **9**, 237 (1956).
222. McMichael, J., The portal circulation. I. The action of adrenaline and pituitary extract. *J. Physiol.* (*London*) **75**, 241 (1932).
223. McMichael, J., and Sharpey-Schäfer, E. P., Cardiac output in man by a direct Fick method. Effects of posture, venous pressure change, atropine and adrenaline. *Brit. Heart J.* **6**, 33 (1944).
224. Nasmyth, P. A., Some observations on the effects of tyramine. *Ciba Found. Symp. Adrenergic Mechanisms* 337 (1960).
225. Norcross, N. C., Intracerebral blood flow; an experimental study. *A.M.A. Arch. Neurol. Psychiat.* **40**, 291 (1938).
226. Oates, J. A., Melmon, K., Sjoerdsma, A., Gillespie, L., and Mason, D. T., Release of a kinin peptide in the carcinoid syndrome. *Lancet* **I**, 514 (1964).
227. Ogawa, S., Beiträge zur Gefäbwirkung des Adrenalins. *Arch. Exptl. Pathol. Pharmakol.* **67**, 89 (1912).
228. Oliver, G., and Schäfer, E. A., On the physiological action of extract of the suprarenal capsules. *J. Physiol.* (*London*) **17**, 9P (1895).
229. Oliver, G., and Schäfer, E. A., The physiological effects of extracts of the suprarenal capsules. *J. Physiol.* (*London*) **18**, 230 (1895).
230. Ottis, K., Davis, J. E., and Green, H. D., Effects of adrenergic and cholinergic drugs on splenic inflow and outflow before and during adrenergic blockade. *Am. J. Physiol.* **189**, 599 (1957).
231. Parks, V. J., Sandison, A. G., Skinner, S. L., and Whelan, R. F., Sympathomimetic drugs in orthostatic hypotension. *Lancet* **I**, 1133 (1961).
232. Parks, V. J., Sandison, A. G., Skinner, S. L., and Whelan, R. F., The mechanism of the vasodilator action of reserpine in man. *Clin. Sci.* **20**, 289 (1961).

233. Phillips, J. H., Burch, G. E., and Hibbs, R. G., Significance of tissue chromaffin cells and mast cells in man. *Circulation Res.* **8,** 692 (1960).
234. Pickering, G. W., and Kissin, M., The effects of adrenaline and of cold on the blood pressure in human hypertension. *Clin. Sci.* **2,** 201 (1936).
235. Pickford, M., and Watts, J. A., Comparison of some of the actions of adrenaline and noradrenaline on the kidney. *Quart. J. Exptl. Physiol.* **36,** 205 (1951).
236. Ranges, H. A., and Bradley, S. E., Systemic and renal circulatory changes following the administration of adrenalin, ephedrine and paredrinol to normal man. *J. Clin. Invest.* **22,** 687 (1943).
237. Remington, J. W., Hamilton, W. F., and Ahlquist, R. P., Interrelation between the length of systole, stroke volume and left ventricular work in the dog. *Am. J. Physiol.* **154,** 6 (1948).
238. Rhodin, J., Adams-Ray, J., and Nordenstam, H., Electron microscopy of human skin cells containing chromaffin granules. *Zellforsch. Mikroskop. Anat.* **49,** 275 (1959).
239. Richardson, K. C., Cited by Burn, J. H., and Rand, M. J., *Advan. Pharmacol.* **1,** 26 (1962).
240. Robertson, J. I. S., Peart, W. S., and Andrews, T. M., The mechanism of facial flushes in the carcinoid syndrome. *Quart. J. Med.* **31,** 103 (1962).
241. Roddie, I. C., Shepherd, J. T., and Whelan, R. F., The vasomotor nerve supply to the skin and muscle of the human forearm. *Clin. Sci.* **16,** 67 (1957).
242. Sandiford, I., The effect of the subcutaneous injection of Adrenalin chlorid on the heat production, blood pressure and pulse rate in man. *Am. J. Physiol.* **51,** 407 (1920).
243. Schäfer, E. A., On the present condition of our knowledge regarding the functions of the suprarenal capsules. *Brit. Med. J.* **I,** 1277 (1908).
244. Schmidt, C. F., and Hendrix, J. P., The action of chemical substances on cerebral blood vessels. *Res. Publ. Assoc. Res. Nervous Mental Disease* **18,** 229 (1957).
245. Schmidt, C. F., Kety, S. S., and Pennes, H. H., Gaseous metabolism of the brain of the monkey. *Am. J. Physiol.* **143,** 33 (1945).
246. Schmidt, C. F., and Pierson, J. C., The intrinsic regulation of the blood vessels of the medulla oblongata. *Am. J. Physiol.* **108,** 241 (1934).
247. Schümann, H. J., Arterenol in nebennierenmark, *Klin. Wochschr.* **26,** 604 (1948).
248. Schümann, H. J., Nachweis von oxytryramin (Dopamin) in sympathischen nerven und ganglien. *Arch. Exptl. Pathol. Pharmakol.* **227,** 566 (1956).
249. Schümann, H. J., Uber den hydroxytyramingehalt der organe. *Arch. Exptl. Pathol. Pharmakol.* **236,** 474 (1959).
250. Sensenbach, W., Madison, L., and Ochs, L., Effect of *l*-nor-epinephrine on the cerebral circulation in normotensive males. *Am. J. Med.* **11,** 250 (1951).
251. Shadle, O. W., Moore, J. C., and Billig, D. M., Effect of *l*-arterenol infusion on "central blood volume" in the dog. *Circulation Res.* **3,** 385 (1955).
252. Shaw, W. M., Papper, E. M., and Rovenstine, E. A., The influence of dibenamine upon circulatory reactions to ephedrine and Neo-Synephrine in normal man. *J. Lab. Clin. Med.* **34,** 669 (1949).
253. Shepherd, D. M., and West, G. B., Hydroxytyramine and the adrenal medulla. *J. Physiol.* (*London*) **120,** 15 (1953).

254. Siegmund, O. H., Granger, H. R., and Lands, A. M., The broncodilator action of compounds structurally related to epinephrine. *J. Pharmacol. Exptl. Therap.* **90,** 254 (1947).
255. Skinner, S. L., and Whelan, R. F., The circulation in forearm skin and muscle during adrenaline infusions. *Australian J. Exptl. Biol. Med. Sci.* **40,** 163 (1962).
256. Smythe, C. McC., Gilmore, J. P., and Hanaford, S. W., The effect of levarterenol (*l*-norepinephrine) on hepatic blood flow in the normal anaesthetized dog. *J. Pharmacol. Exptl. Therap.* **110,** 398 (1954).
257. Sokoloff, L., Action of drugs on the cerebral circulation. *Pharmacol. Rev.* **11,** 1 (1959).
258. Spencer, M. P., The renal vascular responses to vasodepressor sympathomimetics. *J. Pharmacol. Exptl. Therap.* **116,** 237 (1956).
259. Starr, I., Gamble, C. J., Margolies, A., Donal, J. S., Joseph, N., and Eagle, E., A clinical study of the action of 10 commonly used drugs on cardiac output, work and size; on respiration, on metabolic rate and on the electrocardiogram. *J. Clin. Invest.* **16,** 799 (1937).
260. Staub, H., Zum Wirkungsmechanismus des adrenalins. *Schweiz. Med. Wochschr.* **76,** 818 (1946).
261. Stehle, R. L., and Ellsworth, H. C., Dihydroxyphenyl ethanolamine (arterenol) as a possible sympathetic hormone. *J. Pharmacol. Exptl. Therap.* **59,** 114 (1937).
262. Swan, H. J. C., Effect of noradrenaline on the human circulation. *Lancet* **II,** 508 (1949).
263. Swan, H. J. C., Observations on a central dilator action of adrenaline in man. *J. Physiol. (London)* **112,** 426 (1951).
264. Swan, H. J. C., Noradrenaline, adrenaline, and the human circulation. *Brit. Med. J.* **I,** 1003 (1952).
265. Tainter, M. L., The actions of tyramine on the circulation and smooth muscle. *J. Pharmacol. Exptl. Therap.* **30,** 163 (1927).
266. Tainter, M. L., and Chang, D. K., The antagonism of the pressor action of tyramine by cocaine. *J. Pharmacol. Exptl. Therap.* **30,** 193 (1927).
267. Taylor, R. D., and Page, I. H., Peripheral vasomotor effects of adrenaline and nor-adrenaline acting upon the isolated perfused central nervous system. *Circulation* **4,** 563 (1951).
268. Trendelenberg, U., Supersensitivity and subsensitivity to sympathomimetic amines. *Pharmacol. Rev.* **15,** 225 (1963).
269. Tullar, B. F., The resolution of *dl*-arterenol. *J. Am. Chem. Soc.* **70,** 2067 (1948).
270. Walters, P. A., Cooper, T. W., Denison, A. B., and Green, H. D., Dilator responses to isoproterenol in cutaneous and skeletal muscle vascular beds; effects of adrenergic blocking drugs. *J. Pharmacol. Exptl. Therap.* **115,** 323 (1955).
271. Werko, L., Bucht, H., Josephson, B., and Ek, J., The effect of nor-adrenaline and adrenaline on renal hemodynamics and renal function in man. *Scand. J. Clin. Lab. Invest.* **3,** 255 (1951).
272. West, G. B., Quantitative studies of adrenaline and nor-adrenaline. *J. Physiol. (London)* **106,** 418 (1947).
273. West, G. B., and Hunter, R. B., Noradrenaline and the suprarenal medulla. *Lancet* **I,** 471 (1951).

274. Westermann, E., Uber die dopadecarboxylase des nebennierenmarks verschiedener tierarten. *Biochem. Z.* **328**, 405 (1957).
275. Whelan, R. F., Vasodilatation in human skeletal muscle during adrenaline infusions. *J. Physiol.* (*London*) **118**, 575 (1952).
276. Whelan, R. F., Observations on the effects of certain amines on the circulation and respiration in man. Ph.D. Thesis, Queen's Univ., Belfast, 75 (1955).
277. Whelan, R. F., Histamine and vasodilatation. *Ciba Found. Symp. Histamine* 220 (1956).
278. Whelan, R. F., and Skinner, S. L., Autonomic transmitter mechanisms. *Brit. Med. Bull.* **19**, 120 (1963).
279. Wilson, R., and Long, C., Action of bretylium antagonized by amphetamine. *Lancet* **2**, 262 (1960).
280. Wilson, C. P., Pilcher, C., and Harrison, T. R., The effects of drugs on cardiac output. vi. The effect of ephedrine on the minute cardiac output of normal dogs. *A.M.A. Arch. Internal Med.* **41**, 622 (1928).
281. Wolff, H. G., The cerebral circulation. *Physiol. Rev.* **16**, 545 (1936).
282. Youmans, P. L., Green, H. D., and Denison, A. B., Nature of the vasodilator and vasoconstrictor receptors in skeletal muscle of the dog. *Circulation Res.* **3**, 171 (1955).
283. Zaimis, E., Reserpine-induced circulatory failure. *Nature* **192**, 521 (1961).

C. The Effects of the Adrenergic Compounds on the Pulmonary Circulation*

John A. Wood and Alfred P. Fishman

From the Department of Medicine, Columbia University College of Physicians and Surgeons, and the Cardiorespiratory Laboratory of the Presbyterian Hospital, New York, New York

I. INTRODUCTION AND PHYSIOLOGIC CONSIDERATIONS

In some respects the pulmonary circulation is a pharmacologist's dream: the technique of right heart catheterization has brought mixed venous blood and pulmonary arterial pressure within reach; pulmonary blood flow can be reliably measured; even blood leaving the lung can be sampled since it undergoes no change in the composition of most of its ingredients between the lung and the peripheral arterial sampling site. On these accounts, the pulmonary circulation is an attractive one for study in the intact animal since there is virtually no other organ in which the afferent and efferent blood is so readily available without major surgery and where gas exchange can so readily be determined.

However, this dream can readily become a pharmacologist's nightmare. Because the pulmonary circulation is contained within the lungs, it is subjected to mechanical compression and stretching with each breath. Moreover, the vascular elements are exposed to varieties of pressures ranging from atmospheric in the alveoli to below atmospheric as pre- and postcapillary vessels traverse the thorax. Also, not only is it passively distorted by each breath, but the blood volume that it contains depends on the synchronous performance of the two ventricles between which

* The personal research referred to in this chapter was supported in part by Research Grants H-2299 and HE-05741 from The National Institutes of Health, Public Health Service, with additional support from the American Heart Association and the New York Heart Association.

it is housed. Acted upon by these strong mechanical forces, the pulmonary circulation is certainly in a poor position to display its capacity for independent action (22, 37, 42).

The recognition of pulmonary vasomotor activity is rendered even more difficult by the functional anatomy of the pulmonary circulation, which operates to maintain it as a low-pressure system over a wide range of blood flow. In such a system, where intense stimuli can elicit only slight changes in blood pressure, the identification of pulmonary vasomotor activity is destined to be difficult, particularly if the stimulus should simultaneously affect the breathing and the performance of the heart.

A more subtle source of confusion exists in the circulation of the lung in the form of the bronchial arteries which mysteriously inosculate with the pulmonary circulation in its terminal branches. Since these anastomoses potentially connect the high-pressure systemic circulation to the low-pressure pulmonary circulation, agents affecting blood pressure in the systemic vessels and the resistance of the anastomosis to blood flow may conceivably modify the behavior of the pulmonary circulation in an exceedingly elusive way (10, 22, 38).

It is because of these inherent limitations which complicate the study of the pulmonary circulation in the intact animal and man that pharmacologists and physiologists have resorted to models which would allow greater control of the complicated respiratory and circulatory influences that are not easily measured. The models have ranged from artificial circulations to isolated lungs and heart-lung preparations. But each step from natural conditions has introduced new artifacts and new complexities in interpretation. Some of the complications are readily apparent. As the lung is removed from the chest it begins to deteriorate and to become edematous (23, 27, 28). Rates of perfusion tend to decrease with time and resistance to flow to increase. Perfusates, which are often abnormal at the start of the experiment, become less physiological as noxious substances which are ordinarily removed by other organs accumulate (15, 19). The performance of the heart changes, systemic blood pressure is rarely steady, and the distribution of blood varies in curious ways. Obviously, even if the main interest of the investigator is in the isolated lung, this lung is changing with time so that briefer experiments are more apt to be of value than are ones of longer duration (87).

It is against this background of powerful mechanical influences that recognition of pulmonary vasomotor activity is often attempted. This assessment is generally based on the concept that a change in the ratio of the mean pressure difference between the pulmonary artery and the left atrium to the mean pulmonary blood flow ($\Delta P/Q$) implies a change in caliber and, if there are no discernible passive factors in operation, the change in pulmonary vascular caliber must have been brought about by heightened tone of vascular smooth muscle, i.e., by pulmonary vasoconstriction. Unfortunately, even this simple approach is complicated by the fact that the relationship between ΔP and Q is nonlinear so that it is not precisely predictable at different levels of pressure and flow. Therefore, for a change in this relationship to be interpretable in terms of vasomotor activity, either the passive $\Delta P/Q$ curve must be known or $\Delta P/Q$ relationships must be compared, under comparable conditions, at either identical blood pressures or blood flows (12, 39, 62).

It is clear that the stringent restrictions which are necessary for the interpretation of a change in $\Delta P/Q$ in terms of vasomotor activity are most easily satisfied under experimental conditions which allow blood pressures and/or flow to be carefully controlled. However, the penalty for resorting to these artificial preparations is that only the potential behavior, rather than the natural behavior, can be observed.

One other troublesome aspect of studying the behavior of the pulmonary circulation is the variation in anatomy from species to species. Thus, in comparison with the markedly muscular pulmonary arterioles of the rabbit, the precapillary vessels of the dog seem puny (84). Not only the precapillaries, but the veins and venules vary from species to species. Indeed, even within a single species such as man, pulmonary vascular hypertrophy from disease (29) or chronic residence at high altitude (39) may produce striking modifications in pulmonary vascular behavior. Moreover, behavior of the adult pulmonary circulation may be strikingly different from that of the fetus and newborn.

To this anatomical and physiological setting the pharmacologist brings his drugs and their own multifaceted problems of dosage and sites of action. For example, agents such as levarterenol may act not only locally but also via reflexes and from afar. Moreover, not all species are equally responsive to a given agent. Anesthesia may blunt the responsiveness of the preparation in certain ways and correspondingly enhance the appearance of features of the circulation which are ordinarily buried within the interplay of its complicated regulatory mechanisms (54, 67, 68, 69).

This introduction is not intended to discourage the pharmacologic study of the pulmonary circulation. Instead, it aims to point out the need for a clear understanding of the model and of the species before the drug is applied, and for the distinction between the behavior of an agent applied to a model under artificial conditions and to living organisms under natural or near-natural conditions.

II. THE ADRENERGIC COMPOUNDS: GENERAL CONSIDERATIONS

Levarterenol and epinephrine have excited interest on several different accounts: as natural constituents in animals, as adrenal medullary hormones, as adrenergic neurohumoral transmitters, and as therapeutic agents (32). Prior to von Euler's investigation of levarterenol, pharmacologists and physiologists were hampered by the lack of reliable chemical methods for estimating the concentration of that substance in blood or body tissues. Although a rise in pulmonary arterial pressure or a decrease in pulmonary blood flow might occur following injections of catecholamine, the investigator could never be certain that the elicited response would occur under natural conditions because there was no reliable way of relating the dosage used to the concentration present under natural or near-natural conditions. With the development of appropriate chemical methods, von Euler found that levarterenol was normally present in the blood of different species in concentrations of approximately 1 μg/liter (32). Other investigators, for example Goldring *et al.*, have demonstrated that resting levels of epinephrine and levarterenol in unanesthetized human subjects averaged 0.2 μg/liter and 0.3 μg/liter, respectively (53). Splanchnic nerve stimulation in the dog (32) increased the concentration of levarterenol in adrenal venous blood from less than 0.05 μg/liter to 210 μg/liter, while blood concentrations of levarterenol rose to levels as high as 10 times the normal during acute hypertensive episodes in patients with pheochromocytoma (32). In unanesthetized human subjects an infusion rate of 0.05 μg/kg per minute of levarterenol barely sufficed to raise the systemic arterial pressure, whereas an infusion rate of 0.25 μg/kg per minute elicited a brisk response averaging 38/22 mm Hg in systemic arterial blood pressure (52). von Euler (32) estimated that the infusion of levarterenol at the rate of 10 μg per minute provided a concentration in the systemic arterial blood of 4 μg/liter. Although all of the values above are approximate, they do indicate an order of magnitude which can serve to relate the quantities of levarterenol administered experimentally to the levels encountered under natural circumstances.

The molecular basis for the vasomotor effects of the adrenergic compounds has recently come under scrutiny. Aviado and Schmidt (4) have demonstrated that the actions of levarterenol and epinephrine probably depend upon the presence of hydroxyl substitutions on the β carbon atom, and in the number 3 and 4 positions of the benzene ring. In the isolated lung, the removal of one or more of these substitutions from the sites indicated decreased the potency of these compounds in producing pulmonary vasoconstriction.

Of prime importance with respect to considerations of the adrenergic compounds and their role as neurohumoral mediators is the innervation of the lungs. It is well known that the lungs receive both vasoconstrictor and vasodilator fibers. The postganglionic constrictor fibers are adrenergic; the vasodilator fibers have been designated as cholinergic (37). The pulmonary innervation has been most extensively studied in the dog and found to be quite complicated (20). The vasoconstrictor fibers are contained in the upper thoracic sympathetic outflow whereas the vasodilator fibers are carried both in the thoracic sympathetic outflow and in the vagus nerves. Unfortunately, the vasoconstrictor and vasodilator fibers are so inextricably mixed that it is difficult to separate not only vagal from sympathetic fibers but also vascular from either bronchial or cardiac fibers (21).

The greatest confusion exists with respect to the innervation of the small pulmonary vessels, primarily because of the technical difficulties involved in tracing fine fibers to their destinations and in deciding whether the fibers are coming or going. Nonetheless, anatomists have succeeded in showing that (*a*) the bronchial arteries are more amply innervated than any other pulmonary vessels, (*b*) the larger pulmonary arteries and veins are more richly innervated than the small ones, (*c*) the arterial portion of the pulmonary vascular tree is more amply innervated than the venous, and (*d*) the small intrapulmonary veins appear to be meagerly supplied with nerves relative to the small precapillary vessels (37, 59, 60, 61, 65).

One particularly ingenious pharmacological device for distinguishing between the innervation of the large and small pulmonary vessels is the measurement of the concentration of levarterenol in the walls of the large and small pulmonary vessels, using the concentration as a measure of the density of nerve endings. By this approach, von Euler and Lishajko (33) demonstrated in the cow that the large pulmonary vessels are more richly supplied with vasomotor fibers than the smaller ones.

A. Levarterenol

In keeping with the considerations outlined above, the experiments dealing with the effects of levarterenol on the pulmonary circulation may be assigned to two broad categories: (1) those which disclose the *potential* effects of levarterenol and (2) those which demonstrate its effects under natural or near-natural conditions.

1. *Potential Effects of Levarterenol*

There is a wide variety of experiments to indicate that levarterenol *can* cause pulmonary vasoconstriction. A dramatic example is the anatomical distortion of the pulmonary vascular tree which follows the injection of levarterenol (6–2500 μg/minute) into the pulmonary artery of the rabbit. At autopsy (Fig. 1) the small pulmonary vessels (<400 mμ) have a "gnarly" appearance (74), suggesting that intense pulmonary vasoconstriction has occurred.

Less dramatic, but entirely consistent with this anatomical demonstration, are the experiments on isolated perfused lungs (Table I) (4, 31, 49, 50, 58, 71, 85). For example, in the isolated lung of the dog, perfused at a constant rate (400 ml/minute) with its own blood, the injection of 5–30 μg of levarterenol produced an increase in pulmonary arterial pressure and a decrease in pulmonary blood volume (58). Ergotoxin promptly reversed these changes, thereby eliminating pulmonary edema as the basis for the changes. Other investigations on similar preparations (Table I) have supported the view that the direct effect of levarterenol on the blood vessels of the isolated lung is one of vasoconstriction.

Other experiments in which back-pressure from the left heart is avoided by special experimental arrangement (Table II) (6, 7, 24, 34, 36, 63, 67, 68, 79, 80, 83) are also consistent with the idea that levarterenol acts directly on the pulmonary blood vessels to produce vasoconstriction. For example, Rose *et al.* (79, 80) tested the effects of levarterenol on the pulmonary circulation of an open-chest preparation in which a mechanical pump was substituted for the left ventricle, thereby assuring that there would be no shift of blood from the systemic to the pulmonary circulation. Their experimental arrangement and results appear in Fig. 2. It may be seen that the injection of 3–10 μg of levarterenol during left ventricular bypass effected a prompt increase in pulmonary arterial pressure and a decrease in pulmonary venous outflow. The occurrence of a pressor response which could not be accounted for by an increased right ventricular output, back-pressure from the left heart, or the bronchial collateral circulation was strongly in favor of a pulmonary vasoconstricting effect of levarterenol. Additional support for this interpretation is to be found in the other reports listed in Table II.

2. *Effects of Levarterenol under Natural Conditions*

That levarterenol does exert a pulmonary vasoconstricting effect is much more difficult to demonstrate in an intact animal or man than under the experimental conditions indicated above. While all investi-

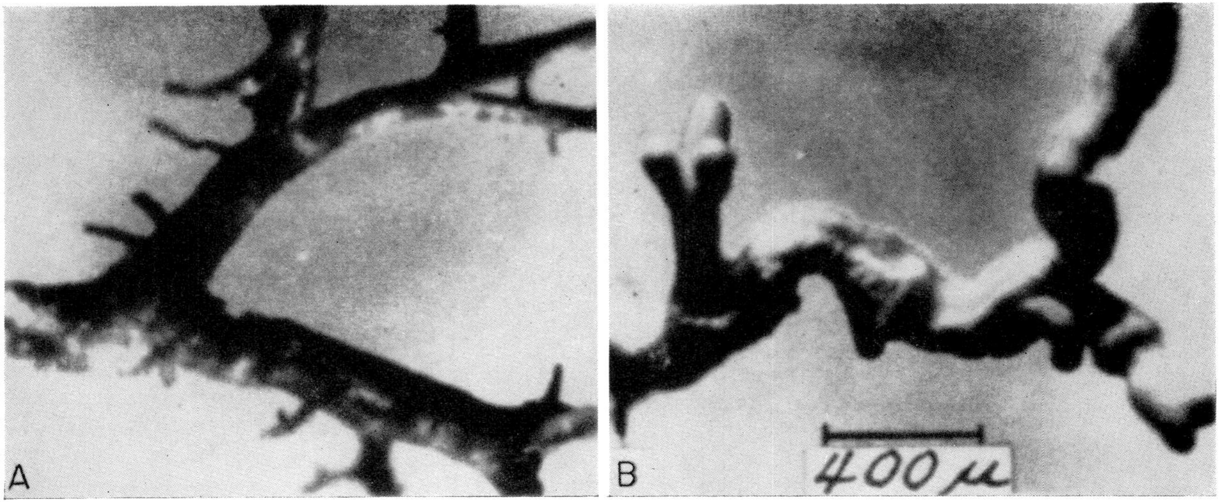

FIG. 1. Casts of small pulmonary arteries of rabbits to illustrate gnarliness. A, control; B, gnarly constriction following injection of levarterenol. From Patel and Burton (74); by permission of the American Heart Association, Inc.

TABLE I

EFFECT OF LEVARTERENOL ON PULMONARY CIRCULATION IN ISOLATED LUNGS

Author and year	Species	Type of preparation, ventilation, injection	Anesthesia	Bronchial circulation intact?	Dose of levarterenol
Konzett and Hebb (1949)	Dog (8–16 kg.)	Isolated lung; negative-pressure ventilation; single injection	None	No	5–30 μg
Nisell (1950)	Cat	Isolated lung; positive-pressure ventilation; single injection	Ether and chloralose, 50 mg/kg	No	5–50 μg racemic arterenol
Ginzell and Kottegoda (1953)	Cat	Isolated lung; no ventilation; single injection	Ether	Yes	50–100 μg
Tryer (1953)	Sheep (28 kg)	Isolated lung; positive-pressure ventilation; single injection	Sodium barbital i.v.	Yes	500 μg racemic arterenol
Aviado and Schmidt (1957)	Dog	3 types of isolated lungs; positive-pressure ventilation; single injection	Morphine, 2 mg/kg; chloralose, 70 mg/kg	No	1–3 μg/kg
Gilbert *et al.* (1958)	Dog	Isolated lung; constant-pressure ventilation; single injection	Pentobarbital, 30 mg/kg	No	2–50 μg
Eliakim and Aviado (1961)	Dog (15–24 kg)	Isolated lung; positive-pressure ventilation; single injection	Morphine, 2 mg/kg; chloralose, 70 mg/kg	Yes	1–10 μg/kg

gators appear to agree that an infusion of levarterenol (rates of infusion from 0.1–0.4 μg/kg/minute) produces an increase in pulmonary arterial pressure without appreciable increase in pulmonary blood flow (41, 52, 53, 75, 78), there is some disagreement about the role of back-pressure from the left heart in effecting this pressor response: Some have found that the pulmonary arterial "wedge" pressure increases and

TABLE I (*continued*)

Route of administration	Criteria for response	Interpretation	Remarks
Pulmonary artery tubing	Increase in pulmonary artery pressure and in blood volume in venous reservoir at constant volume inflow	Pulmonary vasoconstriction	Blood volume by venous reservoir; constant inflow 400 ml/min; drug effect reversible with ergotoxine
Pulmonary artery	Increase in pulmonary artery pressure at constant flow	Pulmonary vasoconstriction	Constant pressure perfusion at 20–30 cm H_2O
Pulmonary artery cannula	Decreased flow rate from reservoir to pulmonary artery = vasoconstriction	Pulmonary vasoconstriction	Cats bled out with alternate injections of epinephrine and Locke's solution. Reversible with ergotoxine; potentiated by tyramine; unaffected by lysergic acid diethylamide
Drug added to right atrial reservoir	Increase in mean pressure in pulmonary artery at constant flow	Pulmonary vasoconstriction	Pulmonary artery mean pressure rose 10 seconds before rise in systemic mean pressure. See Table IV
Femoral vein or pulmonary artery of perfused lobe	Increase in pulmonary arterial—left atrial gradient, decrease in lobar and venous outflow	Pulmonary vasoconstriction	Increased pulmonary lobar resistance and decreased pulmonary blood flow
Pulmonary artery	(1) Increase (at constant flow) in pulmonary artery–pulmonary "wedge" gradient and pulmonary "wedge"–pulmonary vein gradient; (2) increase in pulmonary blood volume	Pulmonary vasoconstriction	Elevation of pulmonary venous pressure at constant flow and increase in lung weight = pulmonary venous constriction in doses > 4 μg
Pulmonary artery	Increase in pulmonary arterial–left atrial pressure gradient at constant flow	Pulmonary vasoconstriction	Constant flow; left upper lobe and left middle lobe, with lung denervation in 4 dogs. Constriction of extrapulmonary portion of pulmonary vein

that the blood pressure gradient across the lungs does not widen as expected of pulmonary vasoconstriction (41, 53), whereas others find that the "wedge" pressure does increase and that the pressure drop widens (78). Large doses of levarterenol (20 μg/kg/minute) and assumptions of pulmonary venous pressures (75) have not helped to define the role of back-pressure. Intravenous injection of levarterenol in

TABLE II

LEVARTERENOL EFFECT ON PULMONARY CIRCULATION IN OPEN-CHEST AND INTACT ANIMALS

Author and year	Species	Type of preparation, ventilation, injection	Anesthesia	Bronchial circulation intact?	Dose of levarterenol
Ewing *et al.* (1954)	Dog	Open chest; artificial ventilation; single injection	Barbituate	Yes	Not specified
Luisada *et al.* (1955)	Dog	Open chest; apneic, lungs distended by a jet of O_2, air, or N_2; single injection	Not specified	Yes	500 μg
Nahas (1958); Nahas and MacDonald (1956)	Dog	Open chest; 100% O_2; positive-pressure ventilation with periods of apnea; single injection	Pentobarbital 25 mg/kg, i.v., and *d*-tubocurarine 0.1 mg/kg, i.v. (1956) or succinylcholine (1958)	Yes	1 μg/kg
Borst *et al.* (1956, 1957)	Dog (14–29 kg)	Open chest; positive-pressure ventilation of each lung separately, end expiratory pressure: + 5 cm H_2O; right ventricle replaced by pump; single injection	Morphine 1.6 mg/kg; Chloralose 67 mg/kg and Urethane 670 mg/kg or Pentobarbital 34 mg/kg	Yes	0.17–6.3 μg/kg (av. 2.2)
Daly and Luck (1959)	Dog (12.4–21.9 kg)	Open chest; positive-pressure ventilation; peak inspiratory pressure: 10–15 cm H_2O, or constant tidal volume; single injection	Morphine 1–2 mg/kg; chloralose 100 mg/kg i.v. or chloralose 50 mg/kg and urethane 500 mg/kg i.v. or 0.25 ml/kg of 1 : 1 mixture of [diallyl barbituric acid 0.1 gm and urethane 0.4 gm per ml] and pentobarbital, i.v.; in a few experiments pentobarbital 40 mg/kg i.v. without premedication	Yes	0.07–2.0 μg/kg

TABLE II *(continued)*

Route of administration	Criteria for response	Interpretation	Remarks
Intravenous	Increase in pulmonary artery pressure after increase in systemic pressure	Passive factors predominate	Increase in pulmonary artery pressure followed rise in systemic pressure in vagotomized preparations. Measured pulmonary artery, pulmonary venous and systemic pressure and pulmonary venous outflow from one lobe. See Table III for opposite effect in isolated lung
Jugular vein	Increase in pulmonary artery pressure and decrease in left atrial pressure; decrease in lung blood volume	Pulmonary vasoconstriction	Decrease in pulmonary blood volume measured by photoelectric cell
Right atrium	Increase in pulmonary artery–pulmonary venous pressure gradient = pulmonary vasoconstriction	1955: no effect 1958: pulmonary vasoconstriction after spinal section	1955: vagus intact 1958: vagotomy plus spinal section at C_1
Pulmonary artery tubing	Redistribution of blood flow toward control lung after injection into contralateral lung	Pulmonary vasoconstriction in test lung	Redistribution in 22 of 24 experiments; increase in systemic mean blood pressure of about 44%
Pulmonary artery	Pulmonary vascular resistance calculated as ratio of mean pressure difference between pulmonary artery and left atrium to mean pulmonary blood flow	Small doses (<3 μg) decreased pulmonary vascular resistance (increased pulmonary blood flow); doses large enough to produce bradycardia either caused no change or increased pulmonary vascular resistance (decreased pulmonary blood flow)	Vagotomy abolished or diminished bradycardia and transient reduction in pulmonary artery pressure and pulmonary blood flow but augmented subsequent increase in pressure and flow. Atropine (1-4 mg i.v.) decreased response to levarterenol. Exclusion of carotid sinuses diminished bradycardia and initial fall in pulmonary artery pressure and pulmonary blood flow, but subsequent rise in these parameters was either unchanged or augmented. Denervation of aortic arch and exclusion of carotid sinuses did not abolish the bradycardia following injection of levarterenol

TABLE II (*continued*)

Author and year	Species	Type of preparation, ventilation, injection	Anesthesia	Bronchial circulation intact?	Dose of levarterenol
Rose *et al.* (1955, 1962)	Dog (15–25 kg)	Open chest; positive-pressure ventilation with 100% O_2; intact dogs or pump in place of left ventricle; single injection	Pentobarbital 25 mg/kg	Yes	3–10 μg/kg
Smith *et al.* (1963)	Full-term fetal lamb	Intact animal before onset of respiration; constant rate i.v. infusion	Not specified	Yes	1 μg/min/kg
Feeley *et al.* (1963)	Dog (9.5–16.6 kg)	*Open chest;* controlled ventilation and end-expiratory pressure; left lateral decubitus, 100% O_2; *Closed chest;* spontaneous ventilation; supine, 100% O_2; constant-rate i.v. infusion	Morphine 1 mg/kg and thiopental 20 mg/kg, i.v.	Yes	2 μg/min/kg

human subjects on a teeter board displaces blood from the periphery to the thorax (46). Finally, the intravenous injection of 25 μg levarterenol in man increased the wedge pressure but did not modify the pressure drop across the lungs, suggesting that a combination of back pressure and pulmonary vasoconstriction had occurred (7).

One critical measurement in the intact animal or man has been the use of pulmonary arterial "wedge" pressure as a measure of pulmonary venous and left atrial pressure. As may be seen in Fig. 3, the pulmonary arterial wedge pressure closely resembles the left atrial pressure (cannula in left atrium) before and after the injection of levarterenol into the pulmonary artery (66). In this illustration, the pulmonary arterial–left atrial pressure drop narrows as the left atrial pressure rises, suggesting that the effects of this dosage (40 μg) on the pulmonary circulation is predominantly that of back-pressure.

It seems clear that, in the intact animal, a combination of opposite effects is elicited by levarterenol; the direct vasoconstricting effect on the pulmonary vessels that is so readily manifested when the pulmonary

TABLE II (*continued*)

Route of administration	Criteria for response	Interpretation	Remarks
Femoral vein and pulmonary artery	Increase in pulmonary artery pressure; decrease in pulmonary venous outflow without change in left atrial pressure or shift in blood volume from systemic to pulmonary circuit = pulmonary vasoconstriction	Pulmonary vasoconstriction	Vasoconstriction augmented when drug was allowed to flow through bronchial circulation
Pulmonary artery	Increase in flow through patent ductus	Pulmonary vasoconstriction	A very special case
Inferior vena cava	Effect of increase in pulmonary blood volume noted on calculated "resistances" of consecutive vascular segments	Pulmonary vasodilation	Increased stiffness of the pulmonary vessels (resulting from the direct action of levarterenol on the vessel walls) was opposed by increased transmural pressure (resulting from effect of levarterenol on heart and systemic vessels) with net effect of increase in pulmonary blood volume and decrease in pulmonary vascular "resistance"

circulation is separated from the left heart is opposed by the dilating effect of back-pressure from the left heart. The net effect of this combination is a virtually unchanged blood flow and pressure drop across the pulmonary circulation (36). That this stability represents considerable hemodynamic readjustment in the pulmonary circulation following injection of levarterenol may be adduced from examination of the instantaneous pulmonary capillary flow pulses. As may be seen in Fig. 4, the pulmonary capillary flow pulse increases in amplitude as the pressure drop across the pulmonary vascular tree increases, suggesting that the predominant mechanism involved in the pulmonary arterial pressor response to levarterenol is to be found distal to the pulmonary capillaries and probably (Fig. 3) within the left heart (66).

Attempts to gain additional insights into the effects of levarterenol on the pulmonary circulation by studying patients with cardiac and pulmonary disease have not been particularly rewarding (8, 70, 78), nor have studies of levarterenol in shock provided clear insights into the behavior of the pulmonary circulation (11, 13, 43, 51, 64, 81).

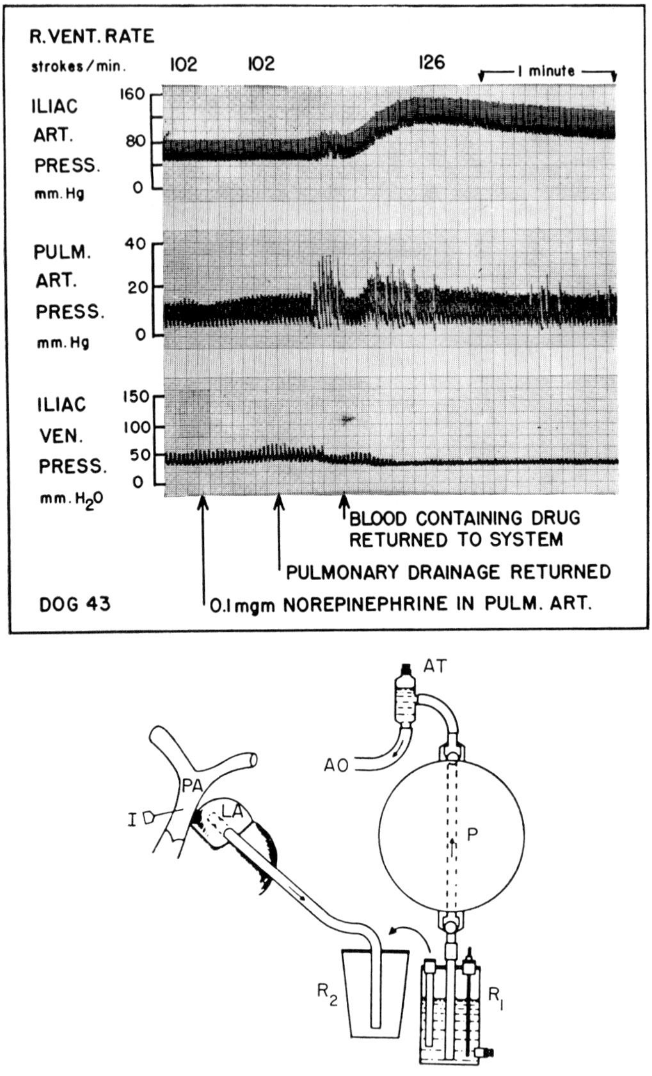

FIG. 2. Effect of injection of 0.1 mg levarterenol into the pulmonary artery of an anesthetized, open-chest dog in which a mechanical pump had been substituted in the left ventricle. Blood from the left atrium was diverted into R_2 for 45 seconds following injection, thereby preventing the injected levarterenol from entering the systemic circuit. There was a slight but immediate rise in pulmonary arterial pressure without any alteration in systemic arterial pressure. Pulmonary venous drainage (measured in R_2) decreased simultaneously with the increase in pulmonary artery pressure. R_1, R_2: reservoirs; P: mechanical pump; PA: pulmonary artery; AT: air trap; AO: aorta; ID: injection site. From Rose *et al.* (79), by permission of the American Journal of Physiology.

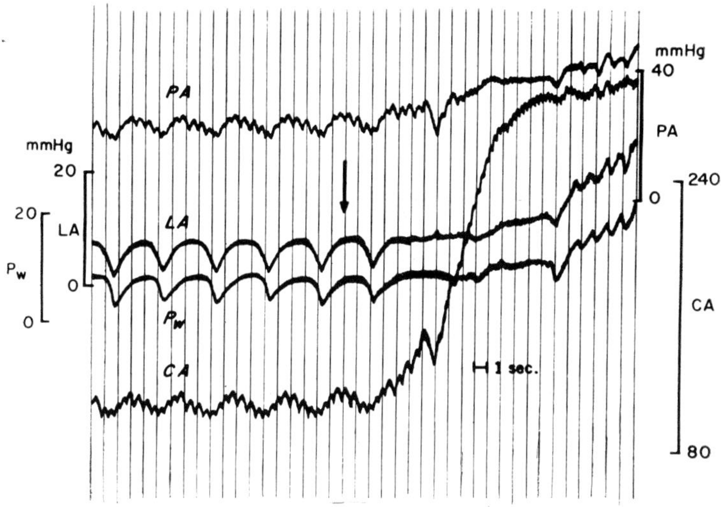

FIG. 3. Effect of injection of 40 μg levarterenol into the pulmonary artery of a dog on pulmonary wedge–left atrial pressure difference. The difference decreases slightly as the left atrial pressure increases. PA: pulmonary artery pressure; LA: left atrial pressure; PW: pulmonary "wedge" pressure; CA: carotid artery pressure. From Morkin *et al.* (66), by permission of The American Heart Association, Inc.

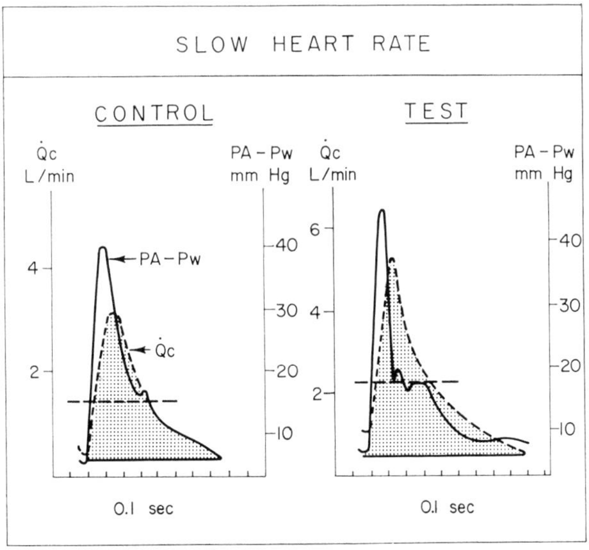

FIG. 4. Relation between pulmonary capillary blood flow (Q_c) and pulmonary vascular pressure gradient ($PA–P_w$) following infusion of levarterenol, 0.8 μg/kg/minute intravenously. The heart rate slowed and increases occurred in the pulmonary artery (PA) and pulmonary wedge (P_w) pressures and in the pressure drop across the pulmonary vascular bed ($PA–P_w$), without blunting of the pulmonary capillary flow. From Morkin *et al.* (66), by permission of the American Heart Association, Inc.

The major problems reside in the complications introduced by the structural changes in the lungs and pulmonary vessels, the performance of the heart, abnormalities in breathing, and abnormal distribution of blood volumes throughout the circulation, so that an accurate distinction between passive mechanical effects and pulmonary vasomotor activity is not easily drawn.

3. *Levarterenol as a Physiological Mediator of Pulmonary Vasomotor Activity*

Until concentrations of levarterenol in the blood could be accurately measured, poorly understood responses of the pulmonary circulation to diverse stimuli could be attributed to levarterenol, either released locally or brought to the lungs from the adrenals. This was the case with acute hypoxia (37). However, circulating levarterenol need not be involved. Thus, Goldring *et al.* (53) have shown that tolerable levels of hypoxia in man are not associated with increases in the quantities of circulating levarterenol even though pulmonary arterial pressure increases; also, the increment in pulmonary arterial "wedge" pressure that characteristically occurs in man during the infusion of levarterenol does not occur during acute hypoxia. On the other hand, during severe (intolerable) hypoxia, a more complicated situation exists because levarterenol is liberated into the circulation and may contribute to the pressor response.

Still unsettled is the role of locally released levarterenol, i.e., from stores within the lungs, in mediating some inexplicable vasoconstrictor responses of the pulmonary circulation. However, the strength of this notion at the present time rests on the fact that a critical test of this idea is difficult to perform.

B. Epinephrine[1]

Epinephrine has been one of the traditional pharmacologic agents for the study of the pulmonary circulation. Indeed, by 1933, there were sufficient reports to warrant a large table in Daly's paper in *Physiological Reviews* (16). However, then as now, interpretation has been handicapped by the dosage-dependence of its effects on the systemic circulation (and possibly on the pulmonary circulation), i.e., vasodilation with minute doses, vasoconstriction with larger doses (52), and by the fact that less is known about the physiological concentrations of epinephrine in the blood of normal animal and man than of levarterenol (53).

[1] Includes epinephrine, USP, as well as mixture of epinephrine and levarterenol, such as Adrenalin.

As with levarterenol, the experiments dealing with the effects of epinephrine on the pulmonary circulation will be divided into two categories: (1) those which disclose potential effects of epinephrine, and (2) those which demonstrate its effects under natural or near-natural conditions.

1. *Potential Effects of Epinephrine*

Pieces of pulmonary vessels that are immersed in solutions containing 0.1–1.0 μg of epinephrine contract in varying degrees (44, 82), although occasional dilatation was observed with immersion in very dilute solutions of epinephrine. Also, in the closed-chest cat, the superficial vessels decrease in caliber following local application of epinephrine (86).

As may be seen in Table III, the experiments using isolated, perfused lungs of dogs also favor vasoconstriction as the primary effect of epinephrine on the pulmonary circulation (1, 2, 18, 19, 35, 40, 47, 48, 49, 55, 58, 71, 72, 76, 77). For example, 5–30 μg of epinephrine injected directly into the pulmonary artery tubing (58) produced a rise in pulmonary artery pressure and an increase in the volume of blood in a venous reservoir, suggesting pulmonary vasoconstriction. The same response seems to be elicited by larger concentrations of epinephrine. However, disparate results have been obtained not only in experiments on the dog (18) but also in rat (40) and cat (48, 71, 72), in which vasodilation was observed when small doses of epinephrine were employed. Whether this vasodilating effect is an artifact or a reflection of epinephrine's dual effect (as on the systemic circulation) is as yet unknown.

That epinephrine can elicit pulmonary vasoconstriction has also been adduced from more intact preparations (Table IV) (4, 6, 7, 24, 30, 31, 34, 36, 45, 50, 54, 63, 79, 85). Borst *et al.* (6), using rotameters in the pulmonary arteries of the dog to measure blood flow through each lung separately, injected 0.17–6.3 μg/kg of epinephrine into the pulmonary inflow tubing of one lung of their preparation. The total blood flow to the lungs remained unchanged; the outflow pressure (left atrial pressure) was identical in both lungs; and the bronchial circulation to each lung was presumably affected equally by the infused epinephrine. As may be seen in Fig. 5, blood flow was diverted from the side that received the epinephrine (the right pulmonary artery), indicating that the drug had produced unilateral pulmonary vasoconstriction. The effect began 6 seconds following injection, reached a maximum in 30 seconds, and lasted for 2–3 minutes.

Experiences with the effect of epinephrine on the pulmonary circulation of open-chest preparations provide additional support for the idea

TABLE III

EFFECT OF EPINEPHRINE[a] ON THE PULMONARY CIRCULATION IN ISOLATED LUNGS

Author and year	Species	Type of preparation, ventilation, injection	Anesthesia	Bronchial circulation intact?	Dose of epinephrine
Gaddum and Holtz (1933)	Dog	Isolated lung, almost completely deflated; no ventilation; single injection	Ether	No	Dogs: 10–50 μg; Cats: 2 μg or 20–200 μg
Alcock *et al.* (1935)	Dog	Isolated lung; negative-pressure ventilation; single injection	Chloroform and ether or pentobarbital 45 mg/kg, i.v., or none	No	2–250 μg
Foggie (1936–1937)	Rat	Isolated lung; positive-pressure respiration; single injection	None	No	0.01–5.0
Alcock *et al.* (1936–1937)	Dog	Isolated lung-thorax-esophagus; negative-pressure ventilation; single injection	Chloroform and ether	Yes	100–200 μg
Daly (1938)	Guinea pig, dog, monkey	Isolated lung; negative pressure ventilation; single injection	None	Yes	1–5 μg
Petrovskaia (1939)	Guinea pig	Isolated lung; positive-pressure ventilation; single injection	None	No	1–10 μg or 15–50 μg
Petrovskaia (1939)	Pig	Isolated lung; negative-pressure ventilation; single injection	None	No	1–10 μg
Daly *et al.* (1940)	Dog	Isolated lung; negative-pressure ventilation; single injection	None	Yes	25–500 μg

[a] Includes epinephrine, U.S.P., and mixtures of epinephrine and levarterenol, such as Adrenalin.

TABLE III (*continued*)

Route of administration	Criteria for response	Interpretation	Remarks
Pulmonary artery cannula	Increase in pressure at constant flow, or decrease in flow at constant pressure	Dogs: pulmonary vasoconstriction at all dose levels; cats: pulmonary vasodilation at 2 μg dose, pulmonary vasoconstriction at high doses (20–200 μg)	Lung volume by plethysmograph; vasoconstrictive effects reversible with ergotoxine
Pulmonary artery tubing	Increase in pulmonary pressure at constant inflow	Small dose decreased lung blood volume without affecting pressure, suggesting vasoconstriction; large dose caused vasoconstriction	Varying lung blood volume (depending on perfusion pressure) caused inaccuracies in gauging dose of drug; changes in lung blood volume measured as difference in blood content of a venous reservoir.
Pulmonary artery cannula	Decrease in pulmonary venous outflow	Pulmonary vasodilatation at small doses (0.01–0.1 μg); pulmonary vasoconstriction at large doses (0.1–5.0 μg)	Vasoconstriction due to large dose (5 μg) reversible with ergotoxine
Bronchial artery	Increase in pulmonary artery pressure at constant flow	Pulmonary vasoconstriction	2 successful experiments: effects on pulmonary artery pressure small, simultaneous profound increase in tidal air; effect on tidal air greater with bronchial arterial injection than with pulmonary arterial injection
Pulmonary artery	Increase in volume of blood in venous reservoir at constant inflow	Pulmonary vasoconstriction in most tests; occasional vasodilation	Vasoconstrictive effects reversible with ergotoxine
Pulmonary artery; "Venous" reservoir	Decrease in pulmonary inflow	Variable results	Tyrode's solution perfused at constant pressure; preparation difficult to work with because of early onset of lung rigidity, requiring 2–5 μg epinephrine for relief
Pulmonary artery	Increase in pulmonary artery pressure at constant volume inflow	Pulmonary vasodilation early in experiment; pulmonary vasoconstriction later on	Pulmonary edema developed after 5–20 min; vasoconstrictive effects reversible with ergotoxine
Pulmonary and bronchial artery	Increase in pulmonary artery pressure and pulmonary venous outflow at constant volume inflow	Pulmonary vasoconstriction at all dose levels	Vasoconstrictive effects reversible with ergotoxine

TABLE III *(continued)*

Author and year	Species	Type of preparation, ventilation, injection	Anesthesia	Bronchial circulation intact?	Dose of levarterenol
Hebb and Konzett (1949)	Dog	Isolated lung; negative- and positive-pressure ventilation; single injection	Chloralose 100 mg/kg or none	No	1–100 μg
Konzett and Hebb (1949)	Dog (8–16 kg)	Same as Table I	None	No	5–30 μg
Nisell (1950)	Cat	Same as Table I	Same as Table I	No	0.5–50 μg
Nisell (1951)	Cat	Isolated lung; positive-pressure respiration; single injection	Ether and Chloralose 50 mg/kg, i.v.	No	10 μg
Gaddum *et al.* (1953)	Cat	Isolated lung; negative- or positive-pressure ventilation; single injection	Chloralose 70 mg/kg intraperitoneally	No	10–50 μg
Ewing *et al.* (1955)	Dog	Isolated lung; artificial ventilation; single injection	Barbiturate	No	Not specified
Gilbert *et al.* (1958)	Dog	Same as Table I	Pentobarbital 30 mg/kg	No	2–50 μg

that epinephrine can elicit pulmonary vasoconstriction, particularly when administered in large dosage. However, when smaller doses are used, the response is less predictable and often more difficult to interpret.

2. *Effects of Epinephrine under Natural or Near-Natural Conditions*

In intact, unanesthetized dogs, both Hamilton *et al.* (54) and Friedberg *et al.* (45) noted that the rise of pulmonary artery pressure fol-

TABLE III *(continued)*

Route of administration	Criteria for response	Interpretation	Remarks
Pulmonary artery tubing	Increase in pulmonary artery pressure and increase in blood volume in venous reservoir	Pulmonary vasoconstriction	None
Pulmonary artery tubing	Increase in pulmonary artery pressure and in blood volume in venous reservoir at constant volume inflow	Pulmonary vasoconstriction	Vasomotor response enhanced by cocaine, reversed by ergotoxine; vasoconstriction also after inhalation of epinephrine
Pulmonary artery	Increase in perfusion pressure at constant flow	Pulmonary vasodilatation in 20 lungs; vasoconstriction in 6 lungs	Cannulae in right ventricle, left atrium, and trachea
Pulmonary artery	Increase in pulmonary artery pressure and increase in pulmonary blood volume	Pulmonary vasoconstriction in some; vasodilatation in others	Recorded blood volume and pulmonary artery pressure
Pulmonary artery cannula	Increase in pulmonary artery pressure at constant flow	Pulmonary vasoconstriction in 4 cats; vasodilatation in 2 cats	Recorded pulmonary artery pressure, venous reservoir volume, and tidal air
Pulmonary artery tubing	Increase in pulmonary artery pressure at constant flow	Pulmonary vasoconstriction	Increase in pulmonary artery pressure occurred prior to onset of increase in carotid artery pressure; pulmonary venous pressure fell, but see Table II for opposite effect in vagotomized open-chest dogs
Pulmonary artery cannula	Same as Table I	Pulmonary venous constriction in doses greater than 4 μg	Increase in pulmonary blood volume measured by increase in lung weight

lowing injections of relatively large doses of epinephrine (100 and 200 μg respectively) was small and could be accounted for by back pressure from the systemic circuit. On the other hand, Hirschman and Boucek (56), using angiography, demonstrated that vessels greater than 0.3–0.5 mm in diameter constricted following injections of 10 μg of epinephrine into the pulmonary arteries of anesthetized dogs.

There are only a few reports dealing with the effects of epinephrine

TABLE IV

EPINEPHRINE[a] EFFECT ON THE PULMONARY CIRCULATION IN OPEN-CHEST AND INTACT ANIMALS

Author and year	Species	Type of preparation, ventilation, injection	Anesthesia	Bronchial circulation intact?	Dose of epinephrine[a]
Hamilton *et al.* (1939)	Dog	Closed chest; single injection	None (trained dogs)	Yes	100 μg
Friedberg *et al.* (1943)	Dog	Closed chest; single injection	None (trained dogs)	Yes	200 μg
Edwards (1951)	Dog (10–20 kg)	Open chest; positive- and negative pressure ventilation; single injection	Morphine and sodium barbital	Yes	150 μg
Tryer (1953)	Sheep	Same as Table I	Sodium barbital, i.v.	Yes	250 μg
Ginzell and Kottegoda (1953)	Cat	Open chest; no ventilation; single injection	Ether	Yes	50–100 μg
Ewing *et al.* (1954)	Dog	Same as Table II	Barbiturate	Yes	Not specified
Luisada *et al.* (1955)	Dog	Same as Table II	Not specified	Yes	100–500 μg
Rose *et al.* (1955)	Dog	Same as Table II	Pentobarbital 25 mg/kg	Yes	3–10 μg/kg
Aviado and Schmidt (1957)	Dog	Isolated left lower lobe; positive-pressure ventilation; single injection	Morphine 2 mg/kg; Chloralose 70 mg/kg, i.v.	Yes	1–3 μg/kg
Borst *et al.* (1956, 1957)	Dog	Same as Table II	Same as Table II	Yes	0.17–6.3 μg/kg

[a] Includes epinepherine, U.S.P., and mixtures of epinephrine and levarterenol such as Adrenalin.

TABLE IV *(continued)*

Route of administration	Criteria for response	Interpretation	Remarks
Pulmonary artery	Sequential changes in mean pulmonary artery pressure compared with simultaneous measurements of mean pulmonary venous pressure	Passive effects predominate	Simultaneous rise in pulmonary artery and pulmonary venous pressure after injection of epinephrine; no measurement of flow
Systemic vein	Sequential changes in pulmonary artery pressure compared with simultaneous measurements of femoral artery pressure	Passive effects predominate	Rise in systemic pressure preceded rise in pulmonary artery pressure
Right lower lobar pulmonary artery	Increase in pulmonary artery pressure	Pulmonary vasoconstriction	Control pressure-flow curve compared with curve for epinephrine at controlled lung inflation
Drug added to system venous reservoir	Increase in pulmonary artery pressure at constant flow	Pulmonary vasoconstriction	Mechanical pumps replaced ventricles, venous reservoirs replaced atria; measured pulmonary artery and aortic pressures
Pulmonary artery cannula	Decreased flow rate from venous reservoir to pulmonary artery	Pulmonary vasoconstriction; occasionally preceded by vasodilation	Vasoconstriction reversible with ergotomine. See Table I
Intravenous	Increase in pulmonary artery pressure before increase in systemic pressure	Passive factors predominate	See Table II
Right jugular vein	Same as Table II	Pulmonary vasoconstriction	See Table II
Pulmonary artery	Same as Table II	Pulmonary vasoconstriction	Same as Table II
Femoral vein or pulmonary artery (perfused lobe)	Increase in pulmonary artery pressure at constant flow	Pulmonary vasoconstriction	Consistent vasoconstriction with lobar perfusion technique; response the same whether or not the drug reached the systemic circulation
Pulmonary artery in flow tubing	Same as Table II	Pulmonary vasoconstriction in test lung	Same as Table II

TABLE IV (*continued*)

Author and year	Species	Type of preparation, ventilation, injection	Anesthesia	Bronchial circulation intact?	Dose of epinephrine[a]
Daly and Luck (1959)	Dog (12.4–21.9 kg)	Same as Table II	Same as Table II	Yes	0.07–2.0 μg/kg
Eliakim and Aviado (1961)	Dog (15–24 kg)	Open chest; positive-pressure ventilation; single injection	Morphine 2 mg/kg; Chloralose 70 mg/kg	Yes	1–10 μg/kg
Feeley *et al.* (1963)	Dog (9.5–16.6 kg)	Same as Table II	Same as Table II	Yes	1 μg/min/kg

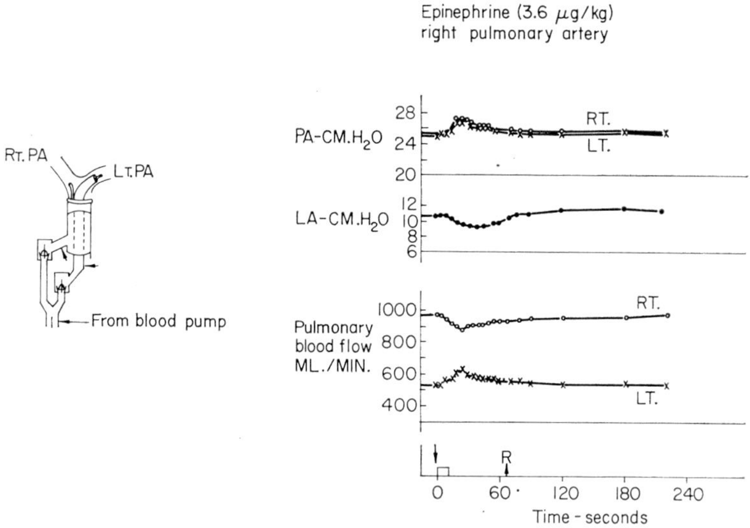

FIG. 5. Effect of epinephrine, 3.6 μg/kg, on pulmonary artery pressure and flow in anesthetized open-chest dog with a mechanical right ventricle and separately ventilated, separately perfused lungs. Injection was commenced at 0 seconds and recirculation was prevented up to point R. The redistribution of blood flow (decreased in the test lung and simultaneously increased in the control lung) denotes vasoconstriction in the pulmonary vascular tree of the test side. PA: pulmonary artery; LA: left atrium. From Borst *et al.* (6), by permission of The American Heart Association, Inc.

TABLE IV (*continued*)

Route of administration	Criteria for response	Interpretation	Remarks
Pulmonary artery	Same as Table II	Same as Table II	Same as Table II
Pulmonary artery	Increase in pulmonary artery pressure at constant flow	Pulmonary vasoconstriction	Increased resistance in pulmonary arteriolar and extrapulmonary venous segments; denervation of lung increased the effect
Inferior vena cava	Same as Table II	Same as Table II	Same as Table II

on the pulmonary circulation in normal man. These are consistent in demonstrating pulmonary arterial hypertension in association with an increase in cardiac output and a decrease in calculated systemic vascular resistance (52). However, they do not settle the mechanisms involved in the pulmonary arterial pressor response because they either omit any measure of pulmonary venous or left atrial pressure (52, 88) or else involve the exhibition of epinephrine by an indirect route, e.g., by nebulizer (3, 25), so that the sites of action of the drug are difficult to define. Nor have studies on patients with cardiac or respiratory disease (88, 89) helped to clarify the mechanism of action of epinephrine on the pulmonary circulation. For the present, it seems likely that epinephrine, like levarterenol, affects the pulmonary circulation in intact animals and man by a combination of mechanisms.

C. The Synthetic Sympathomimetic Amines

The clinical need for systemic vasconstrictor agents has prompted the synthesis of a large number of compounds in which the phenylethylamine nucleus has been the basis of the formulation, but the fact that they all produce systemic vasoconstriction complicates the analysis of their effects on the pulmonary circulation. An extensive survey of the potential effects of 80 such compounds in the pulmonary circulation was conducted by Aviado and Schmidt (4), who found both vasoconstricting and vasodilating effects, depending on the number and location of hydroxyl groups and the nature of the substitutions on the nitrogen atom. A partial list of amines potentially affecting the lesser circulation is appended in Table V, but it is important to note that the number of experimental observations is too few to be conclusive and the effects of these agents in tolerable doses are unknown.

TABLE V

PARTIAL LIST OF SYNTHETIC ADRENERGIC COMPOUNDS WITH POTENTIAL EFFECTS ON THE PULMONARY CIRCULATION[a]

Name		Chemical structure					
				H —C—	H —C—	H —N	
U.S.P.	Commercial[b]						References
		Drugs causing pulmonary vasoconstriction					
Metaraminol	Aramine®	3-OH		OH	CH_3	H_2	4, 34, 56
Phenylephrine	Neo-Synephrine®	3-OH		OH	H	CH_3	4, 57
Epinine		3-OH	4-OH	H	H	CH_3	4
Tyramine			4-OH	H	H	H	4, 17
		Drugs with varying effects on pulmonary circulation					
Hydroxyamphetamine	Paredrine®		4-OH	H	CH_3	H	4, 45
Ephedrine	Ephedrine			OH	CH_3	CH_3	4
Methoxamine	Vasoxyl®	2-CH_3O	5-CH_3O	OH	CH_3	H	4, 34, 73
Pholedrine	Paredrino®		4-OH	H	CH_3	CH_3	4
Synephrin	Sympatol		4-OH	OH	H	CH_3	4
Amphetamine	Benzedrine®			H	CH_3	H	4
Phenylpropanolamine	Propadrine®			OH	CH_3	H	4
		Drugs causing pulmonary vasodilation					
Isoproterenol	Isuprel®	3-OH	4-OH	OH	H	C_3H_7	4, 26, 55
Methamphetamine	Methedrine®			H	CH_3	CH_3	4, 14, 34
Mephentermine	Wyamine®			H	$(CH_3)_2$	CH_3	4, 9
CPD 45–50		2-C_2H_5O	5-C_2H_5O	OH	CH_3	H	4, 5

[a] For a more complete list, see Aviado and Schmidt (4).

[b] In some instances, drugs have two or more commercial names. Limitations of space have precluded listing all of the applicable names.

References

1. Alcock, P., Berry, J. L., and Daly, I. de B., The action of drugs on the pulmonary circulation. *Quart. J. Exptl. Physiol.* **25**, 369 (1935).
2. Alcock, P., Berry, J. L., Daly, I. de B., and Narayana, B., The action on perfused lungs of drugs injected into the bronchial vascular system. *Quart. J. Exptl. Physiol.* **26**, 13 (1936–1937).
3. Alexander, J. K., Mise, J., Dennis, E. W., and Hershberger, R. L., Effects of racemic epinephrine inhalation on cardiopulmonary function in normal man and in patients with chronic pulmonary emphysema. *Circulation* **18**, 235 (1958).
4. Aviado, D. M., and Schmidt, C. F., Effects of sympathomimetic drugs on pulmonary circulation with special reference to a new pulmonary vasodilator. *J. Pharmacol. Exptl. Therap.* **120**, 512 (1957).
5. Barer, G. R., and Gunning, A. J., Action of a sympathomimetic drug and of theophylline ethylene diamine on the pulmonary circulation. *Circulation Res.* **7**, 383 (1959).
6. Borst, H. G., McGregor, M., Whittenberger, J. L., and Berglund, E., Influence of pulmonary arterial and left atrial pressures on pulmonary vascular resistance. *Circulation Res.* **4**, 393 (1956).
7. Borst, H. G., Berglund, E., and McGregor, M., The effects of pharmacologic agents on the pulmonary circulation in the dog. Studies of epinephrine, nor-epinephrine, 5-hydroxytryptamine, acetylcholine, histamine and aminophylline. *J. Clin. Invest.* **36**, 669 (1957).
8. Bousvaros, C. A., Effects of nor-epinephrine on human pulmonary circulation. *Brit. Heart J.* **24**, 738 (1962).
9. Brofman, B. L., Hellerstein, H. K., and Caskey, W. H., Mephentermine—an effective pressor amine. *Am. Heart J.* **44**, 396 (1952).
10. Bruner, H. D., and Schmidt, C. F., Blood flow in the bronchial artery of the anesthetized dog. *Am. J. Physiol.* **148**, 648 (1947).
11. Burch, G. E., DePasquale, N. P., and Hyman, A. L., Pulmonary veins in reversible and irreversible hemorrhagic shock: Response to transfusion. *Circulation* **28**, 698 (1963).
12. Burton, A. C., Relation between pressure and flow in the pulmonary bed. *In* "Pulmonary Circulation. An International Symposium, 1958" (W. Adams and I. Veith, eds.). Grune & Stratton, New York, 1959.
13. Collier, H. D., Meyers, F. H., and Schmitt, C. H., Hemodynamic effects of infusions of epinephrine and arterenol in normal and shocked dogs. *Am. J. Physiol.* **189**, 224 (1957).
14. Cournand, A., Recent observations on the dynamics of the pulmonary circulation. *Bull. N.Y. Acad. Med.* **23**, 27 (1947).
15. Dale, A. S., and Narayana, B., Observations on the perfused lungs of the guinea pig. *Quart. J. Exptl. Physiol.* **25**, 85 (1935).
16. Daly, I. de B., Reactions of the pulmonary and bronchial blood vessels. *Physiol. Rev.* **13**, 149 (1933).
17. Daly, I. de B., Foggie, P., and Von Ludány, G., The potentiation of histamine and tyramine effects by the combined action of ergotoxine and cocaine. *Quart. J. Exptl. Med.* **26**, 235 (1937).
18. Daly, I. de B., Observations on the blood-perfused lungs of the dog, guinea pig, and macacus rhesus, with special reference to "spontaneous" lung movements. *Quart. J. Exptl. Physiol.* **28**, 357 (1938).

19. Daly, I. de B., Foggie, P., and Hebb, C. O., An experimental analysis of the action of adrenaline and histamine on different parts of the pulmonary bed. *Quart. J. Exptl. Physiol.* **30,** 21 (1940).
20. Daly, I. de B., Duke, H., Hebb, C. O., and Weatherall, J., Pulmonary vasomotor fibers in the sympathetic chain and its associated ganglia in the dog. *Quart. J. Exptl. Physiol.* **34,** 285 (1947).
21. Daly, I. de B., and Hebb, C., Pulmonary Vasomotor fibers in the cervical vasosympathetic nerve of the dog. *Quart. J. Exptl. Physiol.* **37,** 19 (1952).
22. Daly, I. de B., Intrinsic mechanisms of the lung. *Quart. J. Exptl. Physiol.* **43,** 2 (1958).
23. Daly, I. de B., and Waaler, B. A., Bronchial circulation and pulmonary vascular resistance (PVR) in isolated perfused lung lobes. *J. Physiol.* (*London*) **153,** 14P (1960).
24. Daly, I. de B., and Luck, C. P., The effects of adrenaline and nor-adrenaline on pulmonary haemodynamics with special reference to the role of reflexes from carotid sinus baroreceptors. *J. Physiol.* (*London*) **145,** 108 (1959).
25. Dirken, M. N. J., and Heemstra, H., Agents acting on the lung circulation. *Quart. J. Exptl. Physiol.* **34,** 227 (1947).
26. Dodge, H. T., and Murdaugh, H. V., Jr., Cardiovascular-renal effects of isoproterenol in congestive heart failure. *Circulation* **16,** 873 (1957).
27. Donald, D. E., A method for perfusion of isolated dog lungs. *J. Appl. Physiol.* **14,** 1053 (1959).
28. Donald, D. E., and Ferguson, D., Pulmonary vascular resistance and duration of perfusion in isolated lung of dog. *J. Appl. Physiol.* **17,** 159 (1962).
29. Edwards, J. E., Functional pathology of the pulmonary vascular tree in congenital cardiac disease. *Circulation* **15, 164** (1957).
30. Edwards, W. S., The effects of lung inflation and epinephrine on pulmonary vascular resistance. *Am. J. Physiol.* **167,** 756 (1951).
31. Eliakim, M., and Aviado, D. M., Effects of nerve stimulation and drugs on the extrapulmonary portion of the pulmonary vein. *J. Pharmacol. Exptl. Therap.* **133,** 304 (1961).
32. Euler, U. S. von, "Noradrenaline—Chemistry, Physiology, Pharmacology and Clinical Aspects." Thomas, Springfield, Illinois, 1956.
33. Euler, U. S. von, and Lishajko, F., Catechol amines in the vascular wall. *Acta Physiol. Scand.* **42,** 333 (1958).
34. Ewing, P. L., Atkinson, G., and Seager, L. D., Effects of sympathomimetic amines on pulmonary circulation. *Federation Proc.* **13,** 353 (1954).
35. Ewing, P. L., Atkinson, G., and Seager, L. D., Pulmonary circulatory effects of sympathomimetic drugs with controlled pulmonary arterial flow. *J. Pharmacol. Exptl. Therap.* **113,** 19 (1955).
36. Feeley, J. W., Lee, T. D., and Milnor, W. R., Active and passive components of pulmonary vascular response to vasoactive drugs in the dog. *Am. J. Physiol.* **205,** 1193 (1963).
37. Fishman, A. P., Respiratory gases in the regulation of the pulmonary circulation. *Physiol. Rev.* **41,** 214 (1961).
38. Fishman, A. P., The clinical significance of the pulmonary collateral circulation. *Circulation* **24,** 677 (1961).
39. Fishman, A. P., Dynamics of the Pulmonary Circulation. *In* "Handbook of Physiology," Circulation II, Chapt. 48. Waverly Press, Baltimore, Maryland. Distributed by Williams & Wilkins, Baltimore, Maryland; Am. Physiol. Soc., Washington, D.C., 1963.

40. Foggie, P., The action of adrenaline, acetylcholine, and histamine on the lungs of the rat. *Quart. J. Exptl. Physiol.* **26,** 225 (1936–1937).
41. Fowler, N. O., Westcott, R. N., Scott, R. C., and McGuire, J., The effect of norepinephrine upon pulmonary arteriolar resistance in man. *J. Clin. Invest.* **30,** 517 (1951).
42. Fowler, N. O., Effects of pharmacologic agents on the pulmonary circulation. *Am. J. Med.* **28,** 927 (1960).
43. Frank, E. D., Frank, H. A., Jacob, S., Weizel, H. A. E., Korman, H., and Fine, J., Effects of norepinephrine on circulation of the dog in hemorrhagic shock. *Am. J. Physiol.* **186,** 74 (1956).
44. Franklin, K. J., The actions of adrenaline and of acetycholine on the isolated pulmonary vessels and azygos vein of the dog. *J. Physiol.* (*London*) **75,** 471 (1932).
45. Friedberg, L., Katz, L. N., and Steinitz, F. S., The effect of drugs on the pulmonary and systemic arterial pressures in the trained, unanesthetized dog. *J. Pharmacol. Exptl. Therap.* **77,** 80 (1943).
46. Fritts, H. W., Jr., and Cournand, A., Physiological factors regulating pressure, flow and distribution of blood in the pulmonary circulation. *In* "Pulmonary Circulation. An International Symposium, 1958" (W. Adams and I. Veith, eds.), p. 62. Grune & Stratton, New York, 1959.
47. Gaddum, J. H., and Holtz, P., The localization of the action of drugs on the pulmonary vessels of dogs and cats. *J. Physiol.* (*London*) **77,** 138 (1933).
48. Gaddum, J. H., Hebb, C. O., Silver, A., and Swan, A. A. B., 5-Hydroxytryptamine. Pharmacological action and destruction in perfused lungs. *Quart. J. Exptl. Physiol.* **38,** 255 (1953).
49. Gilbert, R. P., Hinshaw, L. B., Kuida, H., and Visscher, M. B., Effects of histamine, 5-hydroxytryptamine and epinephrine on pulmonary hemodynamics with particular reference to arterial and venous segment resistances. *Am. J. Physiol.* **194,** 165 (1958).
50. Ginzell, K. H., and Kottegoda, S. R., A study of the vascular actions of 5-hydroxytryptamine, tryptamine, adrenalin and noradrenaline. *Quart. J. Exptl. Physiol.* **38,** 225 (1953).
51. Giuntini, C., Lewis, M. L., Luis, A. S., and Harvey, R. M., A study of the pulmonary blood volume in man by quantitative radiocardiography. *J. Clin. Invest.* **42,** 1589 (1963).
52. Goldenberg, M., Pines, K. L., Baldwin, E. de F., Greene, D. G., and Roh, C. E., The hemodynamic response of man to norepinephrine and epinephrine and its relation to the problem of hypertension. *Am. J. Med.* **5,** 792 (1948).
53. Goldring, R. M., Turino, G. M., Cohen, G., Jameson, A. G., Bass, B. G., and Fishman, A. P., The catecholamines in the pulmonary arterial pressor response to acute hypoxia. *J. Clin. Invest.* **41,** 1211 (1962).
54. Hamilton, W. F., Woodbury, R. A., and Vogt, E., Differential pressures in the lesser circulation of the unanesthetized dog. *Am. J. Physiol.* **125,** 130 (1939).
55. Hebb, C. O., and Konzett, H., Vaso- and Bronchodilator effects of N-Isopropyl norepinephrine in isolated perfused dog lungs. *J. Pharmacol. Exptl. Therap.* **96,** 228 (1949).
56. Hirschman, J. C., and Boucek, R. J., Angiographic evidence of pulmonary vasomotion in the dog. *Brit. Heart J.* **35,** 375 (1963).
57. Horvath, S. M., and Knapp, D. W., Hemodynamic effects of Neo-Synephrine. *Am. J. Physiol.* **178,** 387 (1954).

58. Konzett, H., and Hebb, C. O., Vaso and bronchomotor actions of noradrenalin (arterenol) and of adrenaline in the isolated perfused lungs of the dog. *Arch. Intern. Pharmacodyn.* **78,** 210 (1949).
59. Larsell, O., Ganglia, plexuses, and nerve terminations of the mammalian lung and pleura pulmonalis. *J. Comp. Neurol.* **35,** 97 (1922).
60. Larsell, O., Some aspects of the innervation of the lung. *Northwest Med.* **22,** 311 (1923).
61. Larsell, O., and Dow, S., Innervation of the human lung. *Am. J. Anat.* **52,** 125 (1933).
62. Lilienthal S. L., and Riley, R. L., Diseases of the respiratory system. Circulation through the lung and diffusion of gases. *Ann. Rev. Med.* **5,** 237 (1954).
63. Luisada, A. A., Liu, C. K., Jona, E., and Polli, J. F., Studies of pulmonary vessels. *Angiology* **6,** 503 (1955).
64. McGuire, L. B., Dock, D. S., Hyland, J. W., Harrison, D. C., Haynes, F. W., and Dexter, L., Evaluation of slope method for measuring pulmonary blood volume in man. *J. Appl. Physiol.* **17,** 497 (1962).
65. Miller, W. S., "The Lung." Thomas, Springfield, Illinois, 1937.
66. Morkin, E., Levine, O. R., and Fishman, A. P., The pulmonary capillary flow pulse and the site of pulmonary vasoconstriction in the dog. *Circulation Res.* **15,** 146 (1964).
67. Nahas, G. G., and MacDonald, I., Circulating effects of noradrenaline during apnea in the curarized dog. *Am. J. Physiol.* **187,** 618 (1956).
68. Nahas, G. G., Effects of norepinephine and 5-H.T. on pulmonary circulation of the spinal dog. *Federation Proc.* **17,** 115 (1958).
69. Nahas, G. G., Ligou, J. C., and Nehlman, B., Effects of pH changes on O_2 uptake and plasma catecholamine levels in the dog. *Am. J. Physiol.* **198,** 60 (1960).
70. Nelson, R. A., May, L. G., Bennett, A., Kobayashi, M., and Gregory, R., Comparison of the effects of pressor and depressor agents and influences on pulmonary and systemic pressures of normotensive and hypertensive subjects. *Am. Heart J.* **50,** 172 (1955).
71. Nisell, O. I., The action of oxygen and carbon dioxide on the bronchioles and vessels of the isolated perfused lungs. *Acta Physiol. Scand.* **21,** Suppl. 73 (1950).
72. Nisell, O. I., Reactions of the pulmonary venules of the cat with special reference to the effect on the pulmonary elastance. *Acta Physiol. Scand.* **23,** 361 (1951).
73. Oakley, C., Glick, G., Luria, M. N., Schreiner, B. F., and Yu, P. N., Some regulatory mechanisms of the human pulmonary vascular bed. *Circulation* **26,** 917 (1962).
74. Patel, D. J., and Burton, A. C., Active constriction of small pulmonary arteries in rabbit. *Circulation Res.* **5,** 620 (1957).
75. Patel, D. J., Lange, R. L., and Hecht, H., Some evidence for active constriction in the human pulmonary vascular bed. *Circulation* **18,** 19 (1958).
76. Petrovskaia, B., Broncho and vasomotor responses of guinea pig lungs. *Quart. J. Exptl. Physiol.* **29,** 121 (1939).
77. Petrovskaia, B., The action of drugs on the isolated perfused lungs of the pig. *Quart. J. Exptl. Physiol.* **29,** 277 (1939).
78. Regan, T. J., DeFazio, V., Binak, K., and Hellems, H. K., Norepinephrine induced pulmonary congestion in patients with aortic valve regurgitation. *J. Clin. Invest.* **38,** 1564 (1959).

79. Rose, J. C., Freis, E. D., Hufnagel, C. A., and Massullo, E. A., Effects of epinephrine and norepinephrine in dogs studied with a mechanical left ventricle. *Am. J. Physiol.* **182,** 197 (1955).
80. Rose, J. C., Kot, P. A., Cohn, J. N., Freis, E. D., and Eckart, G. E., Comparison of effects of angiotensin and norepinephrine on pulmonary circulation, systemic arteries and veins, and systemic vascular capacity in the dog. *Circulation* **25,** 247 (1962).
81. Shadle, O. W., Moore, J. C., and Billig, D. M., Effect of *l*-arterenol infusion on "Central Blood Volume" in the dog. *Circulation Res.* **3,** 385 (1955).
82. Smith, D. J., and Coxe, J. W., Reactions of isolated pulmonary blood vessels to anoxia, epinephrine, acetylcholine, and histamine. *Am. J. Physiol.* **167,** 732 (1951).
83. Smith, R. W., Morris, J. A., Manson, W., Beck, R., and Assali, N. S., Effects of chemical mediators on pulmonary and ductus arteriosus circulation in the fetal lamb. *Circulation* **28,** 808 (1963).
84. Takino, M., and Ezaki, Y., Uber die Besonderheiten der Arteriae und Venae pulmonales bei verschiedenen Tieren, besonders beim Menschen V. Mittielung. *Acta Schol Med. Univ. Kioto* **17,** 1 (1935).
85. Tryer, J. H., The actions of *l*-adrenaline and *dl*-noradrenaline on the pulmonary circulation of artificially perfused sheep. *Quart. J. Exptl. Physiol.* **38,** 169 (1953).
86. Wearn, J. T., Ernstene, A. C., Bromer, A. W., Barr, J. S., German, W. J., and Zschiesche, L. J., The normal behavior of the pulmonary blood vessels with observations on the intermittance of the flow of blood in the arterioles and capillaries. *Am. J. Physiol.* **109,** 236 (1934).
87. Williams, M. H., Jr., Relationship between pulmonary artery pressure and blood flow in the dog lung. *Am. J. Physiol.* **179,** 243 (1954).
88. Witham, A. C., and Fleming, J. W., The effect of epinephrine on the pulmonary circulation in man. *J. Clin. Invest.* **30,** 707 (1951).
89. Zimmerman, H. A., A study of the pulmonary circulation in man. *Diseases Chest* **20,** 46 (1951).

D. The Effects of Adrenergic Agents on Smooth Muscles Other Than Those of the Vascular System

P. A. Nasmyth

Department of Pharmacology, St. Mary's Hospital Medical School, Paddington, London, England

I. Introduction 129
II. The Intestine 130
A. The Composition and Quantity of Sympathin Released by Nerve Stimulation 130
B. The Nature of Catecholamines in the Intestine 131
C. Metabolism of Catecholamines in Intestinal Smooth Muscle .. 132
D. Receptors in the Intestine 133
E. Biophysical Effects of Epinephrine and Norepinephrine 134
F. Qualitative and Quantitative Effects of Various Sympathomimetic Amines on the Intestinal Muscle of Various Species 137
G. Mechanism of the Effect of Sympathomimetic Amines on the Intestine 141
H. Effects of Stimulating Nerve Fibers Supplying Intestinal Smooth Muscle 142
I. Tissues Used for the Identification and Assay of Catecholamines 145
III. Uterine Muscle 147
A. The Nature of Catecholamines in the Uterus 147
B. The Effects of Catecholamines on the Uterine Muscle of Various Species 148
C. Biophysical Effects of Catecholamines in the Uterus 157
IV. The Nictitating Membranes 160
A. The Innervation of the Nictitating Membrane 160
B. Drugs and Procedures Which Alter the Sensitivity of the Nictitating Membrane to Catecholamines 164
References 173

I. INTRODUCTION

The sympathetic nervous system and the organs associated with it have exercised the minds and ingenuity of some of the most eminent physiologists and pharmacologists for over half a century. There have been occasions when their functions appeared to have been elucidated and everything could be satisfactorily explained. Such a happy state of affairs never existed for long, and the field has never been more stimulating and controversial than it is at present. The situation is accurately and humorously described by the following comment of Sir John Squire on some lines applied by Alexander Pope to a different scientific discipline and which is quoted by kind permission of Mr. Raglan Squire:

'Nature and Nature's laws, lay hid in night:
God said, Let Newton be! and all was light.'
(Alexander Pope)
It did not last: the Devil, howling Ho!
Let Einstein be! restored the status quo.

Much of the interest has centered around the vascular system, but other sympathetically innervated organs often provide a more convenient model for study.

The organs which make the most satisfactory preparations are the intestine, the uterus, and the nictitating membrane of the cat. It is not surprising, therefore, that apart from the vascular system, these tissues have received the most attention, and in dealing with the effects of sympathomimetic amines on smooth muscle other than that of the vascular system, comment has been confined to them. Conclusions and interpretations based on the results of the experiments described have been limited fairly exclusively to those of the work in question, in an endeavor to avoid conditioning or influencing individual judgments of their relationship to the observations of others.

II. THE INTESTINE

A. The Composition and Quantity of Sympathin Released by Nerve Stimulation

In 1951 Mann and West (76) reported that stimulation of the inferior mesenteric nerve in the cat caused the appearance of both epinephrine and norepinephrine in the mesenteric vein. The mean plasma values in 18 experiments were 0.013 μg/ml of epinephrine and 0.044 μg/ml of norepinephrine. Bearing in mind the relative sensitivity of cat intestine to these two compounds, the authors concluded that they were released in equiactive amounts.

A more detailed investigation was made by Brown *et al.* in 1958 (18). They stimulated the sympathetic nerves to the cat colon with trains of 200–2000 supramaximal shocks at frequencies of 20, 30, and 50 per second. Despite the blanching of the organ produced by these stimuli, no measurable amount of transmitter substance appeared in the colonic venous blood. After 10 mg/kg of the adrenergic blocking agent Dibenzyline®, stimulation produced no visible effect on the tissue blood flow and little effect on the movement of the organ, but transmitter substance now appeared in the effluent from the vein. No attempt was made to differentiate between epinephrine and norepinephrine, total pressor substances being estimated in terms of norepinephrine. Under these circumstances, it was estimated that 295 pg of transmitter was released into the venous effluent per stimulus. Repeated stimulation led to a decline in the amount of transmitter released unless a period of 3 hours was allowed to elapse between trains of stimuli. The fact that the transmitter substance appeared in the venous effluent only after Dibenzyline was interpreted to mean that the transmitter could be destroyed only after combination with the receptor, on the assumption that Dibenzyline prevented this from happening.

The administration of the amine oxidase inhibitors iproniazid, choline-*p*-tolyl ether, or propamidine, did not increase the output of the transmitter whether Dibenzyline was given or not. This suggested what was then suspected and what is now well known, namely, that amine oxidase is not concerned with the *rapid* inactivation of catecholamines.

B. The Nature of Catecholamines in the Intestine

Estimates of the identity and quantity of catecholamines in the intestine are few in number (13, 14, 105). The duodenum, ileum, and colon of the goat, the sheep, and the cow contain more dopamine than epinephrine or norepinephrine. It is generally believed that the norepinephrine is associated with the nerve fibers, since the tissue content of this substance is very much reduced when its sympathetic nerve supply degenerates. By contrast, the epinephrine content is little affected by degeneration of the nerve fibers, so that the proportion of epinephrine to norepinephrine in the tissue rises when the sympathetic nerves are allowed to degenerate. Since chromaffin cells contained in visceral organs continue to produce catecholamines after degeneration of the sympathetic nerves, it is assumed that the epinephrine in the tissue is associated with them. The high dopamine content of the intestine in ruminants correlates well with the distribution of a special kind of chromaffin cell, which is not present in other species. The dopamine is contained in intracellular particles and appears to be bound in a similar way to epinephrine and norepinephrine in the adrenal medulla, since it is released from the particles under similar conditions.

The cat and the rabbit, in contrast with the ruminants, have less dopamine than norepinephrine in the intestine. However, the difference in the norepinephrine content of the cat and the rabbit intestine compared with that of the goat is less marked (33). The actual figures are given in Table I.

According to Holtz (65), the dopamine in the intestines of the ox and the sheep is concentrated in the mucosa, and in both the mucosa and the muscularis it represents about 99% of the catecholamines in the tissue.

TABLE I

NOREPINEPHRINE AND DOPAMINE CONTENT OF INTESTINES OF VARIOUS SPECIES[a]

Species	Tissue	Dopamine (μg/gm)	Norepinephrine (μg/gm)
Ox	Small intestine	17.0	—
	Mucosa	37.0	—
	Muscularis	7.0	—
Sheep	Small intestine	3.5	—
	Mucosa	7.6	—
	Muscularis	2.8	—
Goat	Duodenum	6.3	0.2
Cat	Duodenum	0.2	0.5
Rabbit	Duodenum	0.2	0.4

[a] Compiled from figures quoted by Carlsson (33) and Holtz (65).

C. Metabolism of Catecholamines in Intestinal Smooth Muscle

There appears to be no specific information on the synthesis of catecholamines in the smooth muscle of the intestine, but both Schümann (90) and Holtz (65) have suggested that in some species dopamine may be the end product of biosynthesis. Schümann (90) believes that it is of non-nervous origin in these species and has its own physiological function. In support of his speculation, he points out that the dopamine in the intestine is stored in granules, whereas in the sympathetic nerve fibers, where it is the precursor of norepinephrine, it is found exclusively in the cytoplasm.

As in most other tissues of the body, the enzyme catechol-*o*-methyl transferase plays a considerable part in the metabolism of catecholamines in the intestine. When soluble fractions of the tissue are incubated at 37°C for 1 hour with *l*-epinephrine, 0.3 μmoles of metanephrine are formed (4). This activity is low, however, compared with the liver and the kidney, which form 7.0 and 2.1 μmoles respectively.

The observations of Kirshner (70) suggest that monoamine oxidase may play an important part in the metabolism of catecholamines in the intestine. When 5.0 μmoles of ($\alpha - {}^{14}C$) ($\pm$) epinephrine were infused via the femoral vein of a cat anesthetized with pentobarbitone, the metabolites which appeared in the intestine differed from those in other tissues. They were characterized by a high proportion of 3-methoxy-4-hydroxyphenylethyl glycol and 3-4-dihydroxyphenylethyl glycol. Metanephrine was the other major metabolite, but constituted only 15% of the metabolites present compared with 60% of the other two compounds. The presence of 3-4-dihydroxy mandelic acid and 3-4-dihydroxyphenylethyl glycol among the metabolites in the intestine indicated that monoamine oxidase acts directly on a considerable fraction of the infused epinephrine. As the author indicated, it was not clear to what extent the 3-methoxy derivatives of these neutral and acidic compounds were *o*-methylated prior to their formation from epinephrine.

The rate of formation of metanephrine in the rat intestine after the infusion of epinephrine (71) correlated well with earlier estimates of the tissue content of catechol *o*-methyl transferase (4).

D. Receptors in the Intestine

The pattern for the designation of receptors for catecholamines was set in 1906 by Dale (40), who first differentiated between motor and inhibitor effects and showed that, with few exceptions, the motor effects were blocked by ergot, while the inhibitory effects were not.

Ahlquist (1) compared the ability of various sympathomimetic amines to produce motor and inhibitory effects in various tissues. It was shown quite conclusively that the order of their potency in producing vasoconstriction (a motor effect) was the same as their order of potency in inhibiting the intestine, but not the same as their order of potency in producing other inhibitory effects. Thus, it was concluded that the receptors for producing motor or inhibitory effects were not necessarily different; but a pattern for the relative potencies in different tissues did emerge which led to the suggestion that the receptors should be classified not as motor or inhibitor but as α or β.

More recently Furchgott (52) has reported that Dibenamine® does not block the inhibitory effects of catecholamines on the rabbit intestine. Dihydroergotamine, at a concentration of 10^{-6} gm/ml, blocked the effect of epinephrine at a concentration of 10^{-7} gm/ml. However, the block was overcome by increasing the concentration of epinephrine 20 times. The response then produced by the higher dose of epinephrine could not be blocked by a twentyfold increase in the concentration of dihydroergotamine. This observation threw doubt on the idea that dihydroergotamine blocks by competing for the adrenergic receptors. Furthermore, neither Dibenamine nor dichloroisopropyl norepinephrine (DCI) was very effective in blocking the relaxation of the rabbit duodenum produced by epinephrine, norepinephrine, or isoproterenol. The inference was therefore drawn that the intestinal receptors are neither α nor β, and it was proposed that they should be designated δ receptors. However, the same author (53) reported more recently that DCI alone antagonized the inhibitory action of isoproterenol on the intestine of the intact dog, and that dibozane alone antagonized the inhibition produced by phenylephrine in the same preparation. A combination of both blocking agents antagonized the inhibition produced by epinephrine and norepinephrine in the same preparation. This led to the conclusion that it was unnecessary to postulate δ receptors in the intestine, but simply the presence of both α and β receptors.

Some interesting observations have been made by Vane (103), who reported that epinephrine and norepinephrine relaxed the rat stomach strip bathed in Krebs' solution, whereas it was contracted by (+)-amphetamine and by β-phenylethylamine. They produced a similar effect on the blood-bathed stomach strip from a reserpine-treated rat, but all four compounds relaxed the blood-bathed preparation from a normal rat. It was concluded that (+)-amphetamine and β-phenylethylamine could release norepinephrine from the normal rat stomach strip when it was bathed with blood, but not when it was immersed in Krebs' solution. There remained a need to explain the contractions produced by these compounds when conditions prevented their releasing norepinephrine. The explanation was indicated by the following experiments. When the rat stomach strip was immersed in Tyrode's solution containing 10^{-7} gm/ml of hyoscine, catecholamines relaxed the preparation, amines with one OH group in the nucleus had a biphasic effect, and amines with no OH groups in the nucleus contracted the preparation. The organ was similarly contracted by 5-hydroxytryptamine, and agents which antagonized this effect also antagonized proportionately the actions of the sympathomimetic amines which caused contraction. In addition, amphetamine, epinephrine, and 5-hydroxytryptamine contract the guinea pig ileum. Morphine potentiates this effect of epinephrine but inhibits the actions of 5-hydroxytryptamine and the amphetamine. Thus, the compounds which contracted the rat stomach strip appear to have properties closely allied to those of 5-hydroxytryptamine, and it was concluded that sympathomimetic amines which do not have a catechol nucleus can stimulate tryptamine receptors.

E. Biophysical Effects of Epinephrine and Norepinephrine

In 1940 Bozler (17) reported that epinephrine reduced or abolished the threshold of electrical excitability of the rabbit intestine and reduced the number of action potentials. He also showed that contractions could be induced in cat and dog intestine in response to splanchnic stimulation, when the body temperature was low. He concluded that this effect was due to asphyxia on account of the vasoconstriction, since occlusion of the aortas would produce the same effect. However, Axelsson and Bulbring (6) showed that raising the temperature of the guinea pig taenia coli preparation from 23–27°C to 33–37°C resulted in a transient inhibition or abolition of the spontaneous electrical activity and the conducted response to electrical stimulation was depressed. Conversely, cooling increased electrical activity. It seemed likely, therefore, that the inhibition was caused by an increase in metabolic rate. This possibility was investigated by removing glucose from the external medium, which resulted in increased electrical activity. Restoration of glucose in the medium reversed the effect, and the simultaneous addition of metabolic inhibitors prevented the reversal. The effects of temperature change were also blocked by metabolic inhibitors. It should be noted that the increase in electrical activity produced by removing glucose was not accompanied by a tension response. Indeed, the tension response increased as membrane excitability decreased. Epinephrine also stopped spontaneous spike activity, abolished the conducted response to electrical stimulation, caused hyperpolarization, and increased phosphorylase activity (5). When glucose was removed from the medium, these effects of epinephrine were gradually diminished, and after prolonged exposure they were reversed, depolarization occurred, and spikes were initiated. In the presence of the metabolic inhibitor iodoacetic acid, the inhibitory action of epinephrine was abolished. Epinephrine therefore appears to have a direct depolarizing effect on the membrane, resulting in contraction, which is normally masked by its more powerful inhibitory action. The results suggest that the inhibitory action is caused by increasing the energy available for the stabilizing processes at the cell membrane resulting in hyperpolarization which coincides with an increase in phosphorylase activity.

It is unlikely that epinephrine hyperpolarizes the membrane by changing permeability to potassium ions, because its action is not altered by changes in the external K^+ concentration from 0–30 mM K_0 (21). The fact that epinephrine still produces hyperpolarization in the absence of external potassium, and when the potential is already high, suggests that it does so by increasing the rate of extrusion of sodium.

Later work by Bulbring and Kuriyama (22) showed that epinephrine abolished the spike potentials in the cells of the guinea pig taenia coli before it produced any hyperpolarization. The hyperpolarization was sometimes, but not always followed by block.

The degree of hyperpolarization, when it occurred, depended on the membrane potential prevailing at the time of addition of epinephrine. When the membrane was depolarized to about 25 mV by addition of acetylcholine, epinephrine caused a much greater hyperpolarization. When it was depolarized to about 25 mV by excess K^+, epinephrine produced no hyperpolarization. In the absence of potassium, epinephrine stopped spike discharge and the ensuing hyperpolarization was frequently greater than in normal solutions. Excess sodium depolarized the membrane, but reduced the ability of epinephrine to produce hyperpolarization. Spike activity was not blocked, or only transiently. Excess calcium potentiated the blocking effects of epinephrine. It was concluded that epinephrine produces these effects in the taenia coli by modifying the movement of sodium across the cell membrane.

Gillespie (57) examined the effect of nerve stimulation on preparations of the rabbit colon having parasympathetic (pelvic) nerves and sympathetic (lumbar colonic) nerves attached. The organ was stretched in an isolated organ bath so that, when it relaxed, the tension was practically zero. Under these conditions, the smooth muscle cells exhibited spontaneous mechanical and electrical activity. The membrane potential varied regularly, showing slow waves of change of 5–6 seconds' duration. The depolarization phase of these waves coincided with a short burst of spike potentials followed by repolarization. Coincident with each burst of spike potentials there was a contraction of the smooth muscle. When stretch was applied, the spike potential discharge increased in duration, but the slow waves were still present. As the stretching increased, the interval between discharge of spike potentials was decreased until it finally disappeared and spike potentials occurred at a rate of one per second. Stretching produced a depolarization of about 5.5 mV.

Single stimuli applied to the sympathetic nerves had no effect on either the electrical or the mechanical activity of the preparation. Stimulation at 50 or 20 cps caused a complete loss of both electrical and mechanical activity which outlasted the duration of the stimulus by several seconds. The membrane potential rose to the maximum of the slow waves, but there was no hyperpolarization. Stimulation at 10 cps did not abolish the slow waves or the spike potentials, but the rate of depolarization in the slow waves was reduced, so that it took longer to reach the firing level. Thus the interval between spikes increased. At this low level of stimulation, the correspondence between spike discharge and mechanical contraction disappeared. Both effects occurred, but they were now dissociated. The absence of hyperpolarization was unlike the effect observed by Axelsson *et al.* (5) in the taenia coli. The difference appeared to be due to differences in stretch, for hyperpolarization did occur in the rabbit colon with high rates of stimulation when the preparation was stretched sufficiently to produce continuous spike discharge. Dissociation between spike discharge and contraction at low rates of stimulation was explained by supposing that the observation of electrical activity in one cell does not necessarily reflect what is happening in other cells under these conditions. It is also possible that low concentrations of sympathetic transmitter may interfere with the propagation of activity between cells.

Stimulation of the sympathetic nerves not only suppressed spontaneous electrical activity but also suppressed the effects of stimulating parasympathetic nerves. Thus, it is possible that sympathetic nerve stimulation does stabilize the membrane without producing hyperpolarization. Sometimes a small initial depolarization occurred at the beginning of stimulation. This may be caused by a small amount of acetylcholine released from cholinergic fibers, and it may account for contractions that are sometimes seen, when they are not overcome by subsequent stabilization of the membrane.

F. Qualitative and Quantitative Effects of Various Sympathomimetic Amines on the Intestinal Muscle of Various Species

Most observations of the effects of sympathomimetic amines on the intestine have been made in the rabbit, the guinea pig, the rat, and the cat, with isolated observations on the effect in the horse. In general the compounds inhibit intestinal movement, but there are exceptions to the rule.

West (106) determined the ratio of the doses of *dl*-norepinephrine to equiactive doses of *l*-epinephrine on the ileii of various species. He found both drugs to be inhibitor in the cat, the rabbit, and the rat, and the ratios of activity of *l*-epinephrine to *dl*-norepinephrine on the ileum of each of these species were 1.0, 2.0, and 3.0 respectively. Lockett (74) compared the abilities of epinephrine and isoproterenol to inhibit acetylcholine-induced contractions of the rat ileum and colon. The ratio of activity of epinephrine to isoproterenol on the ileum varied from 1 : 5 to 1 : 50 and on the colon from 1 : 2 to 1 : 3.5. In 1954 McDougal and West (79) compared the abilities of 22 sympathomimetic amines and amino acids to inhibit the peristaltic reflex in the guinea pig ileum. The results are shown in Table II. With the exception of compounds 12, 13, and 14, the dihydroxyphenyl alkylamines were the most active in inhibiting the peristaltic reflex. The dose of these drugs required to inhibit contractions of the guinea pig ileum induced by nicotine had little effect on similar contractions produced by acetylcholine or histamine. This showed that the inhibitory action was not due to any change in the sensitivity of the smooth muscle itself, but suggested that it was due to

TABLE II

RATIO OF DOSES OF SYMPATHOMIMETIC AMINES AND AMINO ACIDS TO EQUIACTIVE DOSE OF (−)-ADRENALINE ON GUINEA PIG ILEUM[a]

No.	Amine	Inhibition of peristalsis	Inhibition of nicotine contraction	No. of experiments
1	(−)-Adrenaline	1	1	30
2	(−)-Noradrenaline	4	2	20
3	(±)-Corbasil	10	5	3
4	Epinine	17	15	3
5	(±)-N-Ethylnoradrenaline	20	8	3
6	Lactyladrenaline	20	20	3
7	Adrenalone	28	20	3
8	Lactylnoradrenaline	40	35	3
9	(±)-α-Ethylnoradrenaline	86	30	3
10	(±)-Isoprenaline	200	200	20
11	Hydroxytyramine	250	100	3
12	Tyramine	1200	1000	3
13	Amphetamine	1200	560	6
14	Ephedrine	1300	540	6
15	Dihydroxyphenylalanine	1500	1500	3
16	Dihydroxyphenylserine	3000	3000	3
17	Propadrine	3000	500	3
18	m-Sympatol	5000	1000	3
19	Sympatol	6000	2000	3
20	m-Norsynephrine	6000	2000	3
21	Paredrine	6000	1000	3
22	p-Norsynephrine	7500	2000	3

[a] Reproduced from McDougal and West (79) by kind permission of the editors.

a ganglion-blocking action or to the suppression of the release of acetylcholine at the nerve ending. The sympatholytic drugs tolazoline, 933F, Dibenamine, SKF® 688A (Dibenzyline), and Sy 28 blocked the inhibitory action of dihydroxyphenyl alkylamines on the guinea pig ileum, but not on the rabbit ileum. The blocking action on the guinea pig ileum could be overcome by increasing the dose of the inhibitory agent. This observation agrees with the results of Furchgott (52) on the effect of dihydroergotamine in blocking the inhibitory action of epinephrine on the rabbit intestine. The concentrations of the sympatholytic drugs required to block the inhibitory effects of the dihydroxyphenyl alkalamines on the guinea pig peristaltic reflex are shown in Table III. The relationship between the structure and activity of the dihydroxyphenyl compounds, whose action on the guinea pig peristaltic reflex and on the rabbit uterus (but not on the rabbit ileum) can be blocked by sympatholytic drugs, is shown in Table IV. The inhibitory action on the

TABLE III

CONCENTRATION OF SYMPATHOLYTIC DRUGS REQUIRED TO ANTAGONIZE THE ACTIONS OF DIHYDROXYPHENYLALKYLAMINES ON THE PERISTALTIC REFLEX OF THE GUINEA PIG AND ON THE RABBIT UTERUS[a]

Drug	Peristaltic reflex	Rabbit uterus	Concentration of sympatholytic drug which itself inhibits peristalsis
Tolazoline	5×10^{-7}	2×10^{-6}	2×10^{-4}
933F	10^{-7}	5×10^{-7}	4×10^{-5}
Dibenamine	2×10^{-7}	2×10^{-7}	2×10^{-6}
SKF 688A (Dibenzyline)	5×10^{-8}	5×10^{-8}	10^{-6}
SY 28	2×10^{-8}	2×10^{-8}	10^{-6}

[a] Reproduced from McDougal and West (79) by kind permission of the editors.

TABLE IV

RELATIONSHIP BETWEEN STRUCTURE AND ACTIVITY OF DIHYDROXYPHENYL COMPOUNDS, THE ACTIONS OF WHICH ON THE GUINEA PIG PERISTALTIC REFLEX AND ON RABBIT UTERUS (BUT NOT ON RABBIT ILEUM) ARE PREVENTED BY SYMPATHOLYTIC DRUGS[a]

Amine no. (see Table II)	Formula 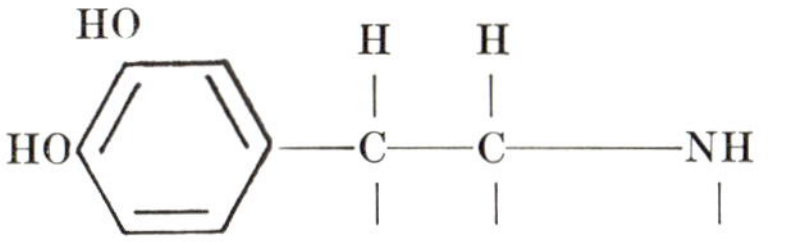			Ratio of dose to equiactive dose of adrenaline: Peristaltic reflex (guinea pig)	Rabbit uterus (excitor)	Rabbit ileum (inhibitor)
2	OH	H	H	4	1	2
1	OH	H	CH_3	1	1	1
5	OH	H	C_2H_5	20	15	8
10	OH	H	$CH(CH_3)_2$	200	—	20
3	OH	CH_3	H	10	30	10
9	OH	C_2H_5	H	86	500	100
16	OH	COOH	H	3000	> 1000	> 10000
11	H	H	H	250	200	200
4	H	H	CH_3	17	30	25
15	H	COOH	H	1500	> 1000	> 10000
7	—C(H)— replaced by —C(=O)—	H	CH_3	28	500	40

[a] Reproduced from McDougal and West (79) by kind permission of the editors.

guinea pig peristaltic reflex of those amines which do not have a catechol nucleus is not blocked by sympatholytic drugs, and the relationship between their structure and activity is shown in Table V. It is clear from these tables that the amines having a catechol nucleus have more potent inhibitory effects than the monohydroxy phenylalkylamines or the phenylalkylamines. Their action can also be blocked by sympatholytic drugs, whereas that of the noncatechol amines cannot.

TABLE V

RELATIONSHIP BETWEEN STRUCTURE AND ACTIVITY OF AMINES, THE ACTIONS OF WHICH ON THE PERISTALTIC REFLEX AND RABBIT ILEUM ARE NOT PREVENTED BY SYMPATHOLYTIC DRUGS[a]

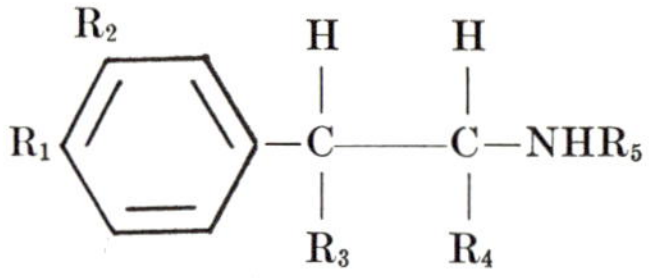

Amine no. (see Table II)	R_1	R_2	R_3	R_4	R_5	Ratio of Dose to equiactive dose of adrenaline: Peristaltic reflex (guinea pig)	Rabbit uterus (excitor)	Rabbit ileum (inhibitor)
12	OH	H	H	H	H	1200	1000	—
21	OH	H	H	CH_3	H	6000	1000	—
22	OH	H	OH	H	H	7500	500	4000
19	OH	H	OH	H	CH_3	6000	100	2000
20	H	OH	OH	H	H	6000	20	50
18	H	OH	OH	H	CH_3	5000	5	10
13	H	H	H	CH_3	H	1200	> 1000	> 10000
17	H	H	OH	CH_3	H	3000	200	> 10000
14	H	H	OH	CH_3	CH_3	1300	1000	> 10000

[a] Reproduced from McDougal and West (79) by kind permission of the editors.

Vane (103) has reported that epinephrine contracts the guinea pig ileum. This effect was also observed by McDougal and West (79) on terminal parts of the ileum. Earlier Munro (82) had made a more detailed investigation of the effect. He found that in adult guinea pigs small doses of epinephrine contracted the ileum if a moderate tone was maintained with histamine at a concentration of 3×10^{-8} gm/ml. Larger doses of epinephrine relaxed the same preparation. The terminal ileum of the guinea pig fetus contracted to epinephrine, the contractions becoming smaller and finally changing to inhibition the more remote was the sample from its junction with the cecum. The adult guinea pig duodenum was relaxed by epinephrine, but the effect in the fetal tissue was commonly biphasic. The cecum and the colon of the fetus were always relaxed, while the stomach was contracted. Atropine usually produced a relaxation of tone and converted the inhibitory response of intermediate sections of the ileum to a contraction. However, atropine did not affect the inhibitory response of the fetal large intestine or that of the adult duodenum. All parts of the fetal intestine of rats and rabbits were relaxed by epinephrine, both before and after exposure to atropine. The inherent tone of the preparation appeared to determine to some extent whether the response was motor or inhibitor.

Alexander (2) reported that the isolated ileum of the horse contracted to epinephrine, but in the intact animal with Thirty-Vella or Biebl loops motility was inhibited, while tone was slightly increased. However, the temperature was decreased in the intact animal, and this factor should be taken into account in interpreting the result.

G. Mechanism of the Effect of Sympathomimetic Amines on the Intestine

Mohme-Lundholm (81) showed that 30 seconds after the inhibition of pendular movement, and the reduction in tone caused by adding 20 μg of epinephrine to rabbit intestine suspended in a 20-ml bath, the lactic acid content of the tissue was increased by a mean value of 36.8 mg/100 gm over the mean control value of 52.9 mg/100 gm. No further increase in the lactic acid content of the tissue occurred with time, but when pendular movement recommenced, the tissue lactic acid level had fallen, so that it was only 13.3 mg/100 gm above the control value. When 1 mg/ml of lactic acid was added to the bathing fluid, the intestine relaxed and pendular movement ceased. The mean lactic acid content of the gut increased, under these conditions, by 26.1 mg/100 gm in 30 seconds. When bicarbonate was added to the bath, more lactic acid or epinephrine was required to produce relaxation. Doses of ergotamine, which blocked the relaxing effect of epinephrine, also blocked the lactic acid production. Ephedrine, which also inhibits the ability of epinephrine to relax the rabbit intestine, blocked the production of lactic acid. Lactic acid formation was also increased by norepinephrine, isoproterenol, 3,4-dihydroxy-norephedrine (corbasil) 3,4-dihydroxyephedrine, and *m*-Sympatol®. All these compounds inhibited the intestine. Agents which inhibit glycolysis were also shown to reduce the inhibitory action and the lactic acid–forming effects of epinephrine. The author cited observations by others that lactic acid inhibits smooth muscle.

By contrast, Bentley (12) was unable to confirm the effects of sodium bicarbonate on the response of the isolated rabbit intestine to epinephrine, even if the sodium chloride in the Tyrode's solution was replaced by sodium bicarbonate, nor was he able to find any evidence for increase in the lactic acid content of the tissue under the influence of epinephrine. However, in a more recent paper, Lundholm and Mohme-Lundholm (75) claimed that Bentley's inability to confirm an increase in tissue lactic acid under the influence of epinephrine was inconclusive, but conceded that it was desirable to demonstrate lactic acid production by a more specific (enzymic) method, and if possible to determine pH changes in the smooth muscle. They expressed the view that epinephrine may, by separate mechanisms, activate either the carbohydrate metabolism or both this and a contractile mechanism in smooth muscle. If only the carbohydrate metabolism is stimulated then relaxation will follow, if the tonus is high. If both mechanisms are stimulated, then contractions will probably result, but the effect will be weakened by lactic acid production.

Whatever may be the truth of the matter, there seems to be considerable evidence that the effects of epinephrine on smooth muscle are related to its effect on carbohydrate metabolism. Bulbring (20) has suggested that epinephrine has a dual action. One is a direct action on the membrane, increasing its permeability to several ions and depolarizing it. The other is a metabolic action making more energy available, which might be used to stabilize the cell membrane and make it less excitable. It is interesting to note that Trendelenburg (96) observed that feeding thyroid to rabbits for 14 days increased the hyperglycemic effects of epinephrine but not those of norepinephrine. This did not affect the ratio of activity of the two drugs on the intestine, but it did increase the sensitivity of the tissue to their action. He also noted that thyroid feeding reduced amine oxidase activity in the liver by 10.4%, but it seems unlikely that this accounted for the change in sensitivity.

A completely different view was expressed by Tidball (95), who showed that the concentration of acetylcholine in the bath fluid surrounding a preparation of the isolated intestine of the rabbit is proportional to the tonus. As epinephrine lowered tonus, so it also lowered the concentration of acetylcholine in the bath fluid. He concluded that epinephrine influenced tonus through an action on the acetylcholine metabolism.

H. Effects of Stimulating Nerve Fibers Supplying Intestinal Smooth Muscle

The standard preparation for observing the effects of stimulating nerve fibers in the isolated intestine was described by Finkleman in 1930 (47). He made preparations of the rabbit duodenum and ileum with mesentery containing blood vessels and nerve fibers attached, and showed that stimulation of the nerve fibers carried in the mesentery and on the blood vessels produced relaxation of intestinal tone and cessation of motility. The effects of nerve stimulation were shown to be similar to those of epinephrine, and, in addition, a transmitter substance with similar properties appeared in the bathing fluid.

Although they did not investigate sympathetic nerves supplying the intestine, Burn and Rand (29) showed that, under certain circumstances, stimulation of the sympathetic nerve fibers supplying various organs produced parasympathetic effects. This led them to suggest that acetylcholine is released at sympathetic nerve endings and that this then releases noradrenaline from stores near the nerve endings. However, Gillespie and Mackenna (58) showed that stimulation of the sympathetic nerves to the rabbit ileum or colon normally produced inhibition. After depletion of the tissue catecholamines by pretreatment with reserpine, stimulation of the same nerve fibers caused the ileum to contract, but it still relaxed on addition of epinephrine or norepinephrine. Concentrations of atropine or hexamethonium which were sufficient to abolish the effects of stimulating the parasympathetic pelvic nerves also abolished the contraction obtained when the sympathetic fibers were stimulated in reserpine-treated preparations. Bathing the reserpine-treated tissues in a high concentration of epinephrine or norepinephrine temporarily restored inhibitory responses to sympathetic nerve stimulation. The authors concluded that depletion of the catecholamines in the sympathetic nerve endings revealed the presence of parasympathetic preganglionic fibers mixed with the sympathetic fibers. In 1961, the same authors (59) showed that, if the pelvic nerves were cut and allowed to degenerate until stimulation of the peripheral cut ends was without effect, then stimulation of the sympathetic nerves in reserpine-pretreated preparations was also without effect. They also showed that, while choline xylyl ether (TM10) blocked the inhibitory action of sympathetic nerve stimulation on the intestine, it did not reveal any parasympathetic effect, despite the fact that the drug did not affect the parasympathetic nerves. They concluded that there could not be any parasympathetic nerves of pelvic origin among the sympathetic fibers of the lumbar colonic nerves. It was suggested that in some unknown way sympathetic nerve stimulation is able to activate the parasympathetic fibers in the reserpine-treated animal.

By contrast, Day and Rand (43) showed that the addition of 1 μg/ml of the sympathetic nerve–blocking agent guanethedine to the solution bathing a Finkleman preparation of the rabbit ileum did convert the inhibition produced upon stimulation of the sympathetic nerves into a contraction. The contraction could be blocked by atropine and sometimes it was reduced by hexamethonium. The contraction was shown not to be due to histamine, 5-hydroxytryptamine, or ATP. The parameters for sympathetic nerve stimulation to produce an optimal motor effect after guanethidine were similar to those required for optimal effects on stimulation of parasympathetic nerves. Similar effects could be produced with the rabbit colon, but required a concentration of 10 μg/ml of guanethidine.

At low frequencies of stimulation, the ilea of young rabbits contracted, while at higher frequencies of stimulation they relaxed. After 61 days of age, however, they relaxed at any frequency of stimulation. Eight to 20 days after sectioning the right vagus in the neck, a motor response could be produced in only 2 out of 5 rabbits. A motor response after guanethidine occurred with similar frequency if both vagi were sectioned in the abdomen.

These authors considered that their results support the view that sympathetic fibers supplying the rabbit intestine are cholinergic. They suggested that guanethidine revealed a motor effect in the gut when the sympathetic nerves were stimulated, because it prevented the released acetylcholine from liberating norepinephrine from the tissue stores.

Bentley (11), using the Finkleman preparation of the rabbit ileum, revealed a small contraction in 5 out of 12 preparations after adding guanethidine to the bathing fluid in concentrations of $1\text{–}2 \times 10^{-6}$ gm/ml. If eserine was added with the guanethidine, contractions were always produced. While Day and Rand reported that the contractions were sometimes reduced by hexamethonium, Bentley found that they were blocked by this ganglion-blocking agent. Bentley also found that hemicholinium did not block the response of the rabbit ileum to stimulation of the periarterial nerves, and he concluded that his results did not support the view that postganglionic sympathetic fibers in the intestine are cholinergic. Paton and Vane (84) examined the effects of stimulating the vagus nerve in *in vitro* preparations of guinea pig, kitten, rat, and mouse stomachs and found that single shocks produced a modest contraction whereas prolonged stimulation caused a bigger contraction followed by relaxation. Transmural stimulation caused similar but larger effects. Periarterial stimulation induced relaxation only. Various tests indicated that the relaxation was produced by an adrenergic mechanism. The relaxation following transmural stimulation was not blocked by hexamethonium, whereas that following vagal stimulation was prevented by this ganglion-blocking agent. It was concluded that the vagus innervates adrenergic as well as cholinergic neurones, and that transmural stimulation excites both pre- and postganglionic cholinergic nerves as well as adrenergic nerves.

I. Tissues Used for the Identification and Assay of Catecholamines

The photofluorimetric method of assay is to some extent replacing biological methods of assessing sympathomimetic amines. However, the photofluorometric technique is a specialized one which is not easily applied to very small quantities of amine. Therefore, it is not inappropriate to list a few preparations of intestinal smooth muscle which have been used for this purpose.

Vane (102) described a preparation of the fundus of the rat stomach for assessing 5-hydroxytryptamine. Later (103) he applied the technique to the detection of sympathomimetic amines in cat's blood. First, he showed that when bathed in Kreb's solution the rat stomach strip responded to the addition of 40 ng/ml of norepinephrine and to 4 ng/ml of epinephrine by relaxing, but it contracted in response to β-phenylethylamine and to amphetamine at a concentration of 0.5 μg/ml and gave a biphasic response to tyramine. When the tissue was superfused with cat blood, the noncatecholamines caused a relaxation, but if the stomach was taken from a reserpine-treated rat its behavior was the same as that when it was bathed with Krebs' solution. It was concluded from this result that, for reasons unknown, the noncatecholamines could release sympathin in the stomach strip prepared from the normal rat when it was bathed with blood, but not when it was bathed with Krebs' solution. These facts make the preparation from the reserpine treated rat very suitable for the detection of epinephrine or norepinephrine released into the circulation by noncatecholamines. It should be noted that Vane found no evidence that tyramine or amphetamine released norepinephrine into the circulating blood of the cat and concluded that if norepinephrine was released in the tissues by these substances it remained local.

In 1964, Armitage and Vane (3) showed that the addition of 0.5 μg/liter of 5-hydroxytryptamine to the fluid bathing an isolated rat stomach strip increased its sensitivity to catecholamines 5–10 times. An optimal increase in sensitivity (10–40 times) was produced by a concentration of 10 μg/liter without changing the ratio of activity of the various catecholamines. Amphetamine and acetylcholine, like 5-hydroxytryptamine, increase the tone of the isolated rat stomach strip, but they do not produce the same degree of sensitization to catecholamines. When the preparation is sensitized in this way, it is even more suitable for the assessment of small quantities of catecholamines.

Table VI shows the ratios of potency of those amines which contract and those which relax the isolated rat stomach strip.

In describing the use of the isolated hen rectal cecum for the assay

TABLE VI

EQUIPOTENT MOLAR RATIOS OF SOME SYMPATHOMIMETIC AMINES ESTIMATED ON THE RAT STOMACH STRIP[a]

Tryptamine-like activity (5-HT = 1) (contraction of rat stomach strip)		Compounds with mixed effects (biphasic response of rat stomach strip)	Noradrenaline-like compounds (noradrenaline = 1) (relaxation of rat stomach strip)	
Name	Equipotent molar ratio	Name	Name	Equipotent molar ratio
β-Phenylethylamine	5,600	Tyramine	Dopamine	250
(+)-Amphetamine	808	(−)-β-Phenylethanolamine	(−)-Noradrenaline	1
(−)-Amphetamine	1,540	Hydroxyamphetamine	(+)-Noradrenaline	250
Mescaline	610	Hydroxyephedrine	Cobefrin (Corbasil)	1.5
Methylamphetamine	25,000		(+)-Cobefrin	740
Pipradol (Meratran)	12,000		(−)-Adrenaline	0.27
Phenmetrazine (Preludin)	7,000		Epinine	33
Tryptamine	400		Isoprenaline	0.03
			Dihydroxyephedrine	0.95

[a] Reproduced from Vane (103) by permission of J. & A. Churchill (London) Ltd.

of adenosine, Barsoum and Gaddum (10) noted that it was also sensitive to epinephrine at a concentration of 10^{-9} gm/ml. Using that part of the cecum next to the rectum bathed in Tyrode's solution containing half the usual concentration of potassium, von Euler (104) adapted the preparation for the assay of catecholamines. He found the tissue to be stable and less subject to variation in sensitivity and spontaneous movement than the rat uterus preparation. Both epinephrine and norepinephrine cause the tissue to relax, but the latter sometimes induces a contraction at the beginning of an experiment. Epinephrine is about 60 times as potent as norepinephrine in relaxing the preparation, but the activity ratio is inclined to be lower in the summer and autumn and higher in the winter and spring. In using the preparation to determine the amount of epinephrine and norepinephrine in a mixture which has not been separated by a chromatographic procedure, it is necessary to conduct a parallel assay on a preparation such as the pithed rat's blood pressure, where the ratio of activity is only of the order of 1 : 2.

III. UTERINE MUSCLE

A. The Nature of Catecholamines in the Uterus

There appears to have been no attempt to measure the amount of epinephrine and norepinephrine in uterine smooth muscle. However, in 1960, Pennefather and Rand (85) performed some experiments to determine the influence of intravenous infusions of various catecholamines on the uterine content of pressor amines estimated as norepinephrine. All the experiments were performed in cats, and the mean values obtained for normal untreated cats in three different groups ranged from 383–690 ng/gm. These figures approximate those given for the cat duodenum in Table I.

Mann and West (76) stimulated the hypogastric nerve of nonpregnant cats and determined the amounts of epinephrine and norepinephrine which appeared in the ovarian vein. The mean value for *l*-epinephrine in 13 cats was 0.005 μg/ml of plasma and that for *l*-norepinephrine was 0.037 μg/ml. These figures represent approximately one-tenth of the total pressor amine content of 1 gm of the cat's uterus, if they are correlated with the figures of Pennefather and Rand. Unfortunately, no figures are available for the blood flow through the uterus, the time for which the plasma level of the amines remains elevated, or for the effect of nerve stimulation on the uterine content of the pressor amines. If this were known, some useful information could be deduced regarding rates of synthesis of catecholamines in the uterus.

B. The Effects of Catecholamines on the Uterine Muscle of Various Species

The effects of the sympathomimetic amines on the uterine muscle varies from species to species and sometimes within the species. When the effect varies within the species, it can usually be correlated with the influence of one or another of the female sex hormones. The mechanism by which these hormones can change the response from a relaxation to a contraction remains somewhat obscure, though the influence they have on the electrophysiology of the muscle may be related to it.

1. *The Cat*

In 1906, Dale (40) reported that the uterus of the virgin or nonpregnant cat usually relaxed in response to an injection of epinephrine or to stimulation of the hypogastric nerve. He commented, however, that the relaxation was sometimes prefaced by a very slight contraction. By contrast, the uterus of the pregnant animal contracted in response to these stimuli. Ergot contracted the cat uterus whether the animal was pregnant or not, and it reversed the effects of epinephrine when they were motor, but did not affect them if they were inhibitor.

Van Dyke and Gustavson (100) made an attempt to determine the cause of the inversion of the uterine response to epinephrine in the pregnant cat. The experiments were made in 1929, before it had been established that the hormone progesterone was elaborated by the corpus luteum, though it was known that it secreted a hormone necessary to maintain pregnancy. They showed that ovariectomy did not alter the inhibitory response of the nonpregnant cat uterus to injections of epinephrine. The effect of ovariectomy in the pregnant cat was to change the motor effect of epinephrine to an inhibitory one provided that fetal resorption was complete. The insertion of strips of sheet rubber into one horn of the nonpregnant uterus produced local hypertrophy after 1–3 weeks, but the inhibitory response to epinephrine remained unchanged. The injection of placental and follicular liquid extracts produced hypertrophy of the nonpregnant uterus but no change in its response to epinephrine. Extracts of early and late vascularized copora lutea, ovarian residue, uterus, and fetus produced no change in the response to epinephrine and produced little or no hypertrophy of the uterus. By contrast, lipoidal extracts of mature corpora lutea caused marked hypertrophy of the uterus in nonpregnant cats and reversed the effect of epinephrine. They concluded that the reversal of the epinephrine response was produced by a substance other than that which provoked estrus. In 1931, the same authors (101) confirmed the finding that the hormone responsible for the inversion of the epinephrine response originated in the mature corpus luteum and that this hormone was not excreted in pregnancy urine.

Bozler (17) observed that in early pregnancy epinephrine still produced inhibition of the cat uterus, but the relaxation was prefaced by a weak contraction. Like Dale, he noted that the initial motor response sometimes occurred in nonpregnant cats and suggested that it was due to their not having quite returned to the resting state following pregnancy. Bozler also reported that the magnitude of the excitatory effect depended largely on body temperature. As the temperature was lowered, the magnitude of the effect was increased and it occurred too quickly to have been due to asphyxia as a result of vasoconstriction. It was concluded that the variation in the response was due to differences in the magnitude of the two phases.

Kennard (68) observed the time course and the relative effects of progestin injections on the response of the uterus to epinephrine and to hypogastric nerve stimulation in mature nonpregnant cats. The animals were spayed 3–10 days before the experiment was commenced. They were then injected with progestin and anesthetized 3–24 hours later. Records of uterine contractions were made *in vivo,* and in 14 out of 17 cats the inhibitor response to nerve stimulation was reversed by the progestin treatment. Reversal of the response to nerve stimulation always preceded reversal of the epinephrine response by several hours. Indeed, if the dose of progestin was kept to the minimum required to reverse the response to nerve stimulation, then the response to epinephrine injection was unaffected. Following a dose of 0.4–1.0 mg/kg of progesterone, there was a latent period of 3–6 hours, after which the response to nerve stimulation became biphasic. From 9–18 hours after the injection, the response became purely motor, but the response to epinephrine remained inhibitor and did not become motor until a further 4–10 hours had elapsed. If no more progestin was given, the responses to both stimuli became inhibitor again, but in this case the epinephrine response reverted before that to nerve stimulation. These experiments were performed in 1937, and, in the light of present knowledge, it seems likely that the different time relationships between the two stimuli were due to the mediator of the nerve impulse being largely norepinephrine.

Graham and Gurd (60) made the interesting observation that when a piece of pregnant cat uterus was suspended in an isolated organ bath together with a piece of nonpregnant uterus the inhibitory response of the latter to epinephrine became a motor response after 2–3 hours. Pseudopregnant uterus from a progesterone-injected animal had the same effect, but pieces of lung or liver, or the addition of progesterone in oil to the bath, were without effect. Reversal of the inhibitory response of the nonpregnant uterus to epinephrine could also be produced by addition to the bath of saline extracts of pregnant or pseudopregnant uterus. These same extracts antagonized the effects of epinephrine on the virgin uterus of immature animals, but did not reverse it. The addition of ergotamine or phenoxybenzamine to the bath prevented the reversal of the epinephrine response by the extracts in uteri from animals in estrus. The suspension of large pieces of nonpregnant uterus in an isolated organ bath in which contractions of the pregnant uterus were being observed was without effect on its motor responses to epinephrine. It was concluded that the substance responsible for the reversal of the uterine response to epinephrine, when the nonpregnant cat becomes pregnant, is water soluble and is presumably different from progesterone. Furthermore, it is incapable of reversing the effect of epinephrine on a uterus which has not been influenced by estrogen. The site of action of the water-soluble substance appears to be such that it can be antagonized by so-called sympatholytic agents.

Labate (72) examined the effect of cocaine on the responses of the cat uterus to epinephrine and to stimulation of the hypogastric nerve. It was found that, in seven out of nine nonpregnant animals, cocaine augmented the relaxation produced by these stimuli, but in the other two the responses were decreased by cocaine. In five pregnant cats, the motor response to nerve stimulation was augmented by cocaine, but the motor response to epinephrine was augmented in only three of them. The motor responses to both stimuli were unaffected in three animals. The conclusion drawn from these experiments together with those on other species was that there is a predominance of adrenergic fibers in the hypogastric nerve of the cat. Bozler (17) objected to the implication that there may be an admixture of cholinergic fibers in the hypogastric nerve on the grounds that the motor responses are not inhibited by atropine. On the other hand, Burn and Rand (29) suggested that the sympathetic nerve impulse is mediated by acetylcholine, which then releases norepinephrine from stores near the nerve ending. They showed that eserine reduced the inhibitory response of the nonpregnant cat uterus to stimulation of the hypogastric nerve and that the subsequent injection of atropine restored it to some extent. When the tissue catecholamines were reduced by reserpine pretreatment, stimulation of the hypogastric nerve produced a small contraction of the uterus which was potentiated by eserine. Atropine then changed the response to a very slight relaxation.

In 1947, West (106) reported that the ratio of activity of *dl*-norepinephrine to *l*-epinephrine in relaxing the nonpregnant cat uterus was 10.0. *dl*-Norepinephrine was more effective than *l*-epinephrine in contracting pregnant uterus, and he gave the ratio of activity as 0.8. Later, in 1950 (107), he confirmed the observation that both *l*-epinephrine and *l*-norepinephrine relaxed the nonpregnant uterus and noted that the action of *l*-norepinephrine was facilitated by the prior injection of *l*-epinephrine. In late pregnancy, when the effect of both drugs was motor, he noted again that the ratio of activity between the two drugs was much reduced and approximated 1.0. Burn and Rand (29) also noted that infusions of epinephrine or norepinephrine increased the inhibitory response of the virgin cat uterus to stimulation of the hypogastric nerve.

There appear to have been no precise quantitative comparisons of the activity of the various sympathomimetic amines on the cat's uterus. However, in 1910, Dale and Barger (41) determined the effect of various sympathomimetic amines on the nonpregnant cat uterus and investigated, in general terms, the influence of chemical structure upon activity. They found that β-phenylethylamine relaxed the virgin cat uterus and that increasing the length of the side chain, as in phenyl propylamine, or decreasing it, as in α-phenylethylamine, only resulted in a decreased effect on the uterus. In other words, the optimum length of the side-chain for sympathomimetic activity was two carbon atoms. Sympathomimetic activity was increased when a hydroxyl group was introduced in the *para* position on the nucleus. Thus *para*-hydroxy phenylethylamine (tyramine) relaxed the virgin cat uterus, and methylation of the amino group did nothing to enhance its effect. The substitution of an ethyl group to give *p*-hydroxyphenylethyl ethylamine weakened the effect on the uterus. If substitution on the amino group was continued until it became a quaternary nitrogen atom, as in *p*-hydroxyphenylethyltrimethylammonium iodide, the compound acquired a nicotinic action and contracted the nonpregnant uterus. Catechol itself had no sympathomimetic activity, for, despite the fact that it produced a rise in blood pressure, it contracted the nonpregnant uterus. However, amines derived from catechol had the most potent sympathomimetic effects. Those derivatives which had a methyl substituent in the amino group were the most powerful in relaxing the uterus, and those with ethyl as the substituent were the next in order of potency. Dose for dose, the amino bases from which these substituted compounds were derived were inactive on the uterus.

2. *The Rabbit*

Unlike the cat uterus, the rabbit uterus responds to sympathomimetic amines with a contraction whether the animal is pregnant or not, though

Labate (72) reported that the contraction following the injection of epinephrine or stimulation of the hypogastric nerve was frequently followed by relaxation. He also noted that cocaine augmented the effects in only two out of 11 nonpregnant rabbits. In the pregnant animal the response to nerve stimulation became weaker as pregnancy progressed, and the effect was not augmented by cocaine in six animals. He concluded that the hypogastric nerves of the rabbit contain a relatively high proportion of cholinergic fibers.

Bozler's comment on this conclusion, namely, that atropine does not block the effect, has already been mentioned. It should also be added that Boura and Green (15) have reported that the sympathetic nerve blocking agent bretylium blocks the response of the isolated rabbit uterus to stimulation of the hypogastric nerve and does not reveal any cholinergic effect. In other situations bretylium blocked the sympathomimetic effect of nerve stimulation and revealed a cholinergic effect. Such was the case with the cardioaccelerans nerve, stimulation of which produced tachycardia before bretylium and bradycardia after the drug. The bradycardia was resistant to further doses of bretylium, but could be blocked by atropine. Labate made his observations of uterine movement with an isotonic lever system. Csapo (38) has since shown that very little gradation of uterine response can be observed with an isotonic recording system, whereas the isometric system gives good gradation of the response. This may have accounted for Labate's failure to observe potentiation of the uterine response to stimulation of the hypogastric nerve by cocaine in many cases. Indeed, most observations of uterine movement have been made with isotonic recording systems, and while such a system may be adequate for recording abolition or reversal of an effect, it seems doubtful if it is of much value in determining changes in the magnitude of a response. Foster *et al.* (50) found that cocaine hydrochloride potentiated the excitor effect of epinephrine on the isolated rabbit uterus, but α-cocaine, which is a much weaker local anesthetic having a similar activity to cocaine in inhibiting amine oxidase, reduced or abolished the effect in four preparations and was without effect in a fifth. This observation together with other experiments led Foster *et al.* to the conclusion that the potentiation of the effects of catecholamines by cocaine is not related to its ability to inhibit amine oxidase.

Comparing the activity of *dl*-norepinephrine with that of *l*-epinephrine, West (106) found that *dl*-norepinephrine had a quarter of the activity of *l*-epinephrine on the pregnant rabbit uterus. Its effect on the nonpregnant uterus was only one-fifth that of *l*-epinephrine. He also remarked that the nonpregnant rabbit uterus showed very little loss of sensitivity to epinephrine when stored in the cold. Later, in 1954, McDougal and West (79) compared the potency of a number of sympathomimetic amines in contracting the rabbit uterus (see Tables II, IV, and V). Generally speaking, the dihydroxyphenylalkylamines were the most potent compounds, except for isoproterenol, which did not contract the rabbit uterus. Of the compounds having only one hydroxyl group on the nucleus, those which have it in the *meta* position are the most potent. The concentrations of various sympatholytic agents required to depress the actions of sympathomimetic amines on the rabbit uterus are given in Table III. It is interesting to note that, while the sympatholytic agents do block the motor effects of the monohydroxyphenyl and the phenylalkylamines on the rabbit uterus, they are ineffective against the actions of these compounds on the peristaltic reflex of the guinea pig.

Schild (89) reported that epinephrine was capable of contracting the rabbit uterus under conditions which suggested that the effect was independent of changes in the membrane potential. When the uterus was immersed in potassium-Ringer's solution at 20°C a contraction occurred which was followed by partial relaxation. Addition of epinephrine then produced contractions which could be antagonized with dihydroergotamine. Schild also produced evidence consistent with the view that the antagonism was due to simple competition. The observations were extended in 1963 when Edman and Schild (45) showed that, if calcium was omitted and EDTA (ethylenediaminetetraacetic acid) added to the bath, the uterine responses to epinephrine declined progressively and were completely abolished in 50 minutes. Addition of calcium at this point restored the responses to about 75% of their original level. When the uterus was immersed in calcium-free KCl-Ringer's solution, it contracted briefly and then relaxed. The addition of calcium to the solution then produced a slowly developing contraction, which persisted as long as the calcium remained in the solution. Epinephrine, at this stage, produced a further increase in tension. The addition of calcium and epinephrine together sometimes produced an effect on the depolarized uterus in excess of that to be expected from the normal uterus in response to the same dose of epinephrine. The authors speculated that the contractile effect of epinephrine in depolarized smooth muscle is produced by some calcium-requiring mechanism probably involving mobilization of bound calcium.

3. *The Guinea Pig*

The effects of sympathomimetic amines on the guinea pig uterus appear to be more confusing than they are in the cat. Bozler (17) reported that in 50% of cases epinephrine raised the threshold of the guinea pig uterus to electrical stimulation during estrus. The preparation never became nonexcitable, and in some epinephrine had no detectable effect. Sometimes the drug even produced a weak contraction. Holtz and Wölpert (66) and Grieff and Holtz (61) reported that epinephrine relaxed the uteri of immature guinea pigs or of adult guinea pigs in anestrus. Treatment of the animals with gonadotropic hormones converted the response to a pure contraction or to a contraction followed by a relaxation. Hermansen (63) compared the effects of epinephrine, norepinephrine, and isoproterenol on the guinea pig uterus. He confirmed the finding that, when the uterus of an immature guinea pig was first isolated, it relaxed in response to a dose of epinephrine. The drug did not, however, inhibit the small amount of spontaneous activity which was present. Isoproterenol relaxed the preparation and inhibited the spontaneous activity in addition. By contrast, norepinephrine contracted the immature guinea pig uterus. When the immature guinea pig uterus was first isolated it exhibited some tone, which gradually declined over several hours, giving place to regular contraction and relaxation. The character of the response elicited by epinephrine appeared to be dependent upon the tone, for the relaxation produced by the drug at the beginning of the experiment gradually changed via a biphasic response to pure contraction about 4 hours after isolation of the uterus. If the isolated uterus was kept overnight at 4°C, it produced a marked contractile response to epinephrine. In support of this supposition was the observation that an immature uterus which responded to epinephrine by relaxation would change its response to contraction if the epinephrine was added in the presence of isoproterenol which had already relaxed the organ. However, if the uterus contracted in response to epinephrine, isoproterenol potentiated the contraction. If epinephrine was added to the bath at the peak of a contractile response to acetylcholine, it produced relaxation; but if the contractile response to acetylcholine was produced in the presence of isoproterenol, then the addition of epinephrine caused a further contraction. At the peak of a contraction produced by norepinephrine, the addition of epinephrine appeared to cause relaxation, but it was without effect if isoproterenol was present as well. If the immature animal was treated with estradiol, then both epinephrine and norepinephrine contracted the uterus, but isoproterenol had no effect because the preparation was already fully relaxed.

The changes in the response to epinephrine did not appear to be related to the Na^+ and K^+ changes, as the uterine content of these ions was the same whatever the response of the organ. During the first 4 hours of isolation, the glycogen content of the uterus declined from 90 to 50 mg/100 ml. There was then no further change in the uterine glycogen content during the ensuing 4 hours. Furthermore, the effect of epinephrine on the glycogen content of the tissue was the same when the tissue was first isolated as it was 8 hours later. However, glycogen determinations were deemed but a very rough estimate of phosphorylase activity. It was therefore suggested that if the relaxant effect was due to an increase in the activity of this enzyme, then one could account for the fact that isoproterenol could reverse the action of epinephrine. Thus, if, as is probable, isoproterenol is more active than epinephrine in increasing phosphorylase activity, it may be impossible for epinephrine to increase it further in the presence of isoproterenol. In such a case the motor effect of epinephrine would predominate. However, the facts were too confusing to permit any definite conclusions.

Mohme-Lundholm (81) reported that epinephrine relaxed the guinea pig uterus in the nonpregnant and early-pregnant state, but contracted it toward the end of gestation. Whether the tissue contracted or relaxed, lactic acid was formed and when the uterus was contracted by epinephrine it was also contracted by lactic acid. Cupric chloride and sodium fluoride added to the bath 5–10 minutes before the dose of epinephrine prevented both the relaxation and the formation of lactic acid. These facts suggested that there was a correlation between the effects of the epinephrine and the lactic acid production. A well-documented account of the effects of epinephrine on carbohydrate metabolism and on the activity of smooth muscle was given by Lundholm and Mohme-Lundholm in 1960 (75).

Singh *et al.* (91) also observed that epinephrine relaxed the adult guinea pig uterus and that it did so without the application of any external force. The oxygen consumption of the tissue was also increased, but the increase lasted only as long as the relaxation. The authors concluded that the relaxation of the guinea pig uterus produced by epinephrine was an active process and that it was related to the increase in oxygen consumption which accompanied it.

Clegg (37) has recently reported that when an isolated guinea pig uterus is bathed in a solution containing neither Ca nor Mg ions, the addition of a small amount of calcium chloride produces an inhibition of spontaneous rhythmical activity in the organ. The effect was blocked by compounds such as bretylium or choline xylyl ether, which prevent the release of the adrenergic transmitter substance. It was therefore concluded that calcium produced its effect by releasing catecholamines from tissue stores. However, the finding of Edman and Schild (45), that epinephrine loses its ability to contract the rabbit uterus in the absence of calcium, suggests that calcium may simply be permissive for the action of the catecholamine. Their observations were made on depolarized tissues, and they did not study the inhibiting effect of epinephrine on the guinea pig uterus. They did observe that epinephrine inhibited the contractile response of the depolarized rat uterus to calcium. It is therefore difficult to be sure what is the correct interpretation of the role of calcium in the uterus, but it would certainly seem that it does not liberate catecholamines from the tissue stores of the depolarized rat uterus.

4. *The Rat*

Like the rabbit, the rat gives unidirectional uterine responses to epinephrine; but unlike the rabbit, its response is an inhibitory one. The uterus of the rat differs greatly from that of other animals in its sensitivity to epinephrine and norepinephrine. Both catecholamines relax it, and West (106) gave the ratio of activity of *dl*-norepinephrine to *l*-epinephrine as 100 : 1 in the nonpregnant rat.

This difference in sensitivity to the two catecholamines provided a means of assessing the amount of each in mixtures. A method for such estimations was described by Gaddum and Lembeck in 1949 (55). It depended upon the ability of epinephrine and norepinephrine to inhibit the contractions exhibited by the isolated nonpregnant rat uterus and the isolated rat colon to carbachol. On the former tissue the ratio of activity was high and on the latter it was low. By the application of a suitable formula to the results it was possible to estimate the amounts of epinephrine and norepinephrine in plasma or extracts containing unknown quantities of the two compounds. As the authors commented, it is more desirable to separate them and assess each component separately. Another question which arises is the specificity of the inhibition of the response to carbachol by epinephrine. Holzbauer and Vogt (67) attempted to find a specific antagonist which could be employed in much the same way as mepyramine is used in histamine assay. They also looked for compounds which would sensitize the uterus to the inhibitory actions of epinephrine, and so overcome the need to discard less sensitive uteri when only small amounts of epinephrine were present in the extract. Out of 27 compounds examined, only nine were effective in modifying the inhibitory action of epinephrine on the rat's uterus. All nine compounds were specific antagonists of hydroxytryptamine on the rat's uterus in the sense that, at concentrations which were without effect on the response of the uterus to choline esters, they inhibited the uterine response to hydroxytryptamine. The following drugs increased the ability of epinephrine to inhibit carbachol contractions: Dibenamine, *N*-(9-fluorenyl)-*N*-ethyl-β-chloroethylamine hydrochloride (SKF® 501), Dibenzyline (*N*-benzyl-*N*-(β-phenoxyisopropyl)-β-chloroethylamine), β-tetrahydronaphthylamine carbonate, and 5-benzyloxygramine. Of these compounds, dibenzyline appeared to be the most effective sensitizing drug. The addition of 0.05 μg to a 2-ml bath followed by 0.075 μg 40 minutes later (each dose being left in the bath for 10 minutes) produced a 20-fold increase in sensitivity to epinephrine and to isoproterenol. It was then possible to measure a response to epinephrine at a concentration of 0.125 ng/ml.

The following drugs decreased the ability of epinephrine to inhibit the contractions of the rat's uterus in response to carbachol: dihydroergotamine methanesulfonate, lysergic acid diethylamide, and 2-methyl-3-ethyl-5-dimethylamino indole (medmain). Veratramine had a temporary effect. Of these, lysergic acid diethylamide was the most specific, diminishing the sensitivity to epinephrine to between one-fifth and one-hundredth of its previous value without interfering with the carbachol-induced contractions and without affecting the inhibitory action of isoproterenol. The blocking agent dichloroisoproterenol more recently described by Powell and Slater (86) is likely to be of no value, because they found that it would not block the inhibitory response of the rat's uterus to isoproterenol except in doses which themselves considerably reduced the tone of the organ. However, its effectiveness in blocking the inhibitory effect of catecholamines on the response of the rat's uterus to carbachol does not appear to have been tested. The value of biological methods for assessing catecholamines may be questioned when a photofluorimetric method is available. However, the physical method involves the use of expensive equipment and it is not easy to obtain accurate estimations by the physical method when extracts contain only very small quantities of amine. Not only does epinephrine relax the normal rat uterus, but Evans *et al.* (46) showed that it also relaxed the depolarized preparation. Later, Edman and Schild (45) noted that epinephrine inhibited the contraction of the depolarized rat uterus to acetylcholine and to calcium, but the concentration required to inhibit the contraction to calcium was much less than that required to inhibit the responses to acetylcholine. The same was true also for isoproterenol. Their speculative interpretation of this phenomenon was that epinephrine prevents the entry of calcium into the cell, whereas they considered it possible that acetylcholine mobilizes calcium from preformed stores. This would account for the noncompetitive nature of the antagonism and for the preferential antagonism toward calcium.

C. Biophysical Effects of Catecholamines in the Uterus

Since it has been shown that depolarization of the membrane is not necessary to initiate a contraction in smooth muscle, it is more difficult to evaluate the role of the membrane potential in relation to drug action in these muscles. However, there appears to be some correlation between contraction and membrane potential at least under normal circumstances. For example, Marshall (78) recorded the membrane potential of the rat uterine muscle cell and showed that in immature or untreated spayed animals it was low at 35 mV and that such uteri were virtually inactive. The administration of estrogen to these animals raised the membrane potential to about 57 mV, and a spontaneous discharge of action potentials began together with rhythmical contraction of the muscle.

Marshall observed that the action potentials were initiated by pacemaker areas which arose where the cell excitability was highest and remarked that they were responsible for the contractions. The action potentials in the pacemaker area arose from slow localized depolarization, just as they do in the sinus node of the heart. Unlike the pacemaker in the heart, the uterine pacemaker did not occupy a fixed position, but moved about from one area to another. By contrast, the progesterone-dominated rat uterus showed weak and irregular contractions, which were not always associated with action potentials. The membrane potential of individual muscle cells rose to 63 mV and the pacemaker areas were more labile than in the estrogen-dominated uterus. Epinephrine hyperpolarized the membrane of the estrogen-dominated rat uterus and abolished the action potentials. It is tempting to associate the hyperpolarization and the loss of action potentials with the relaxation of the smooth muscle, but the depolarized rat uterus also relaxes in response to epinephrine, which fact suggests that the two phenomena are unrelated.

The calcium ion appears to be more certainly associated with the contraction of smooth muscle than depolarization of the membrane, since its omission from Krebs-Ringer solution bathing the isolated rat uterus leads to a failure to contract in response to acetylcholine within 45–60 minutes (42). The strontium ion could substitute for calcium but the cadmium ion could not. So far, however, there is insufficient information to correlate the motor effect of the calcium ion with drug action.

Csapo and Kuriyama (39) investigated the effect of ions and drugs on cell membrane activity and tension in the rat uterus 3–6 hours post partum. Epinephrine at a concentration of 10^{-7} M (as the hydrochloride) hyperpolarized the membrane by about 5–10 mV and decreased the number of spikes in the train. The action potentials were increased from 45–53 mV, the prepotentials were prolonged, and the threshold for spike generation was raised by 3–5 mV. A tenfold increase in the concentration of epinephrine caused a greater degree of hyperpolarization and stopped spike generation. However, after 20–30 minutes in the presence of epinephrine, activity returned though the spikes were few and infrequent. In some cases spikes disappeared before hyperpolarization developed, and there appeared to be no close relationship between the two phenomena. This is similar to the effect of progesterone, but the effect of epinephrine on the contractions of the rat uterus is not similar to that produced by progesterone.

Burnstock *et al.* (32) observed the membrane potentials of quiescent uteri from ovariectomized rats and rabbits and found that in both species it was low at 35.2 mV. Estrogen treatment raised the potential to 52.6 mV in the rat and to 46.0 mV in the rabbit. Treatment with progesterone, after priming with estrogen, further increased the resting potential to 63.8 mV in the rat and to 54.0 mV in the rabbit. The activity of the uteri under these conditions was irregular or reduced. When epinephrine produced inhibition of the uterus it caused hyperpolarization of the membrane; when it caused a contraction it depolarized it. The authors concluded that epinephrine may have excitatory or inhibitory effects according to the muscle and its condition with respect to the resting membrane potential.

Marshall (77) correlated the electrical activity of single uterine muscle fibers of the rat with the development of tension. In the ovariectomized rat pretreated with estradiol benzoate for 5 days, the pacemaker areas, previously referred to, were demonstrated at either the cervical or the ovarian end of the uterus. In these areas, electrical discharge began before any tension developed. As the contraction began, the rate at which action potentials occurred increased for about 10 seconds and then slowly decreased while the contraction was sustained. The discharge finally ceased before the muscle relaxed. In uteri from rats pretreated with estradiol benzoate followed by a reduced dose of estradiol and progesterone, the membrane potential was higher and there was not the same distinct relationship between action potentials and contraction. It was concluded that the muscle fibers do not all contract synchronously as they appear to do in the estrogen-dominated uterus. The effect of epinephrine was to decrease the rate of discharge and finally to abolish the action potentials. The membrane potential rose as the muscle relaxed under the influence of the drug, the picture being the same as that observed in the estrogen-dominated organ.

Bueding *et al.* (19) showed that when the taenia coli of the guinea pig was stretched the creatine phosphate and ATP content of the muscle were decreased significantly. Exposure of the stretched muscle to a low concentration of epinephrine caused a highly significant increase in the concentrations of ATP and creatine phosphate. The effect on the unstretched muscle was smaller. The increase was maximal in 15–90 seconds and could not have been due to the activation of phosphorylase, as this takes longer. It was concluded that by stimulating the formation of energy-rich compounds epinephrine makes more energy available for membrane stabilization.

It seems that, generally speaking, when epinephrine produces an increase in tension the membrane is depolarized, but when its effect is to relax the uterus the membrane is hyperpolarized. If it is permissible to argue from the taenia coli to the uterus, the hyperpolarization could be produced by an increase in the concentration of high-energy compounds in the tissue. On the other hand, when depolarization and a contraction occur, either there must be no increase in the concentration of high-energy compounds, or the energy must be used for a purpose other than that of membrane stabilization. The relationship between the observed electrical changes and the tension response to epinephrine remains obscure, because they are not always consistent and because tension change can occur in depolarized tissues. Indeed, it seems possible that the electrical changes and the tension changes to epinephrine may be secondary to some other action of the drug and therefore not directly related. Any observed relationship may be apparent, not real, and no firm conclusion can be drawn until more information is available.

IV. THE NICTITATING MEMBRANE

The nictitating membrane of the cat holds a unique position in research concerned with the physiology of the sympathetic nervous system and the pharmacology of the sympathomimetic amines. This is because its nerve supply is readily accessible and it is easy to denervate the tissue without much trauma. Investigation of denervation supersensitivity is thus facilitated, and, in consequence, a great deal of work concerned with this phenomenon has been done on the nictitating membrane. Before assessing the results of experiments of this nature, it is of considerable importance to know something of the innervation of the membrane—whether, for example, it is solely innervated by sympathetic fibers or whether there is some admixture of cholinergic nerves; and whether it receives the whole of its postganglionic nerve supply from the superior cervical ganglion. The question of innervation will, therefore, be reviewed first.

A. The Innervation of the Nictitating Membrane

The nictitating membrane is operated by two smooth muscles, the medial and the inferior. They are supplied by separate postganglionic sympathetic nerves, which gain access to the muscles by accompanying branches of the trigeminal nerve. Thompson (94) found no evidence that postganglionic sympathetic fibers to the nictitating membrane are carried in the oculomotor (III), trochlear (IV), or abducens (VI) nerves. He also showed that movements of the nictitating membrane which accompany contraction of the extraocular muscles are probably due to anatomical connections between them.

In 1935, Bacq and Fredericq (8) reported that the contractions of the cat's nictitating membrane in response to epinephrine and nerve stimulation were potentiated by cocaine, the effect on injected epinephrine-being a little greater than the effect on the response to nerve stimulation. However, the effect of the local anesthetic on the responses to norepinephrine and to Epinine® were considerably greater than its effect on the response to nerve stimulation, whereas it potentiated responses to adrenalone and *d*-epinephrine less. The response to nerve stimulation approximated most nearly that induced by injections of *l*-epinephrine, and they deemed this substance to approximate most nearly the physiological mediator. Nevertheless, recent estimations of the catecholamine content of the nictitating membrane by Kirpekar *et al.* (69) indicate that, in common with most other sympathetically innervated tissue, it contains much more norepinephrine than epinephrine. However, the tissue does contain a small percentage of epinephrine, and, in view of the fact that its response to nerve stimulation approximates more nearly that to injected epinephrine, there may be danger in assuming that the nerve mediator is norepinephrine simply because the tissue contains more of the latter compound. Indeed, the same authors show that the superior cervical ganglion contains even more catecholamine than the smooth muscle of the nictitating membrane, but it is generally conceded that acetylcholine is the transmitter in the ganglion.

Bacq and Fredericq (8) also showed that in three out of five cats eserine increased the response to nerve stimulation and atropine reduced it. In two animals, both substances were without effect. They concluded that in 50% of animals there is a small number of cholinergic fibers in the cervical sympathetic. Several authors have since observed that eserine and atropine produce these effects, but the most relevant observations have been made by Thompson (93). Working with the isolated medial muscle of the nictitating membrane, he compared the effects of nicotine and acetylcholine. He confirmed the observations of Westcott and Christiensen (108) that the contraction produced by acetylcholine was blocked by atropine and potentiated by eserine, but the contraction produced by nicotine was affected much less by these drugs. The contraction produced by nicotine could be blocked by hexamethonium bromide, but that produced by acetylcholine could not. High concentration of acetylcholine in the presence of atropine produced a contraction which had the same characteristics as the contraction produced by nicotine. However, the contraction in response to nicotine, which remained in the presence of concentrations of Dibenamine or Dibenzyline sufficient to block responses to adrenaline and noradrenaline, did not display the same characteristics as the contraction in response to acetylcholine. Furthermore, histological investigation failed to reveal any ganglion cells within the muscle. This led to the speculation that nicotine produced its effects in the preparation not by stimulating parasympathetic ganglion cells but by stimulating the large numbers of fine nerve fibers which were demonstrable histologically and which were almost certainly the terminations of the postganglionic sympathetic fibers arising from cells in the superior cervical ganglion.

The fact that hexamethonium antagonized the responses to nicotine was not deemed incompatible with this view, since it also blocks the stimulant action of nicotine on sensory nerve endings (44). Some of the evidence supported the view that there were cholinergic fibers in the nerve supply to the nictitating membrane, but some of the evidence conflicted with such a view. Under these circumstances, Thompson cautiously agreed with the conclusion of Bacq and Fredericq that some cats have a small cholinergic postganglionic nerve supply to the nictitating membrane. However, further work by Thompson together with Burn *et al.* (24) in 1959 showed that the response *in vivo* of the normal nictitating membrane to nicotine was much greater than the response of the denervated membrane, whereas norepinephrine, epinephrine, and acetylcholine all caused a greater contraction in denervated compared with innervated membrane. The same was true for normal and denervated membranes isolated *in vitro* except that the denervated membrane *in vitro* was slightly less sensitive to acetylcholine than the normal membrane. The isolated medial muscle of the nictitating membrane from a reserpine-treated cat was insensitive to nerve stimulation and to nicotine. Reserpine treatment also caused a loss of chromaffin cells from the muscles of the nictitating membrane. Similarly, after denervation the chromaffin cells presented a pyknotic appearance and were apparently dying. The results led the authors to the conclusion that the contraction of the nictitating membrane by nicotine is due to its liberating norepinephrine from a peripheral store possibly contained in chromaffin cells.

This concept of the action of nicotine differed only slightly from the suggestion previously made by Thompson (93) and described above, but the idea that nicotine produced its effect by releasing norepinephrine from peripheral stores was extended by Burn and Rand (29) in the following year. They showed that the remaining response of the nictitating membrane to nerve stimulation in the reserpine-treated cat was practically abolished by atropine and could be partly restored by infusion of norepinephrine. This implied that the contraction remaining in response to nerve stimulation in the reserpine-treated animal was almost wholly due to a release of acetylcholine, and the fact that the response could be increased by infusing norepinephrine into such an animal led to the suggestion that sympathetic postganglionic fibers were originally cholinergic and that in the process of evolution they had come to innervate a store of norepinephrine. Thus, acetylcholine would liberate norepinephrine from the stores. Further development resulted in the production of norepinephrine within the fiber itself and the emergence of a true adrenergic nerve. The response to nerve stimulation could therefore be a compound of the effects of norepinephrine released at the ends of true adrenergic nerves, norepinephrine released from stores by acetylcholine from cholinergic postganglionic sympathetic fibers, and a direct muscarinic action of the acetylcholine. It would be reasonable to suppose, if this hypothesis was correct, that cholinesterase would be present in the smooth muscle supplying the nictitating membrane. Hellmann and Thompson (62) could find none, but they did find large numbers of cholinesterase-containing nerve fibers in the Harderian gland, which is intimately associated with the muscle. Ten days after denervation of the nictitating membrane cholinesterase activity was still present in the Harderian gland but reduced in amount. These results led the authors to conclude that the sympathetic innervation of the cat's nictitating membrane is entirely adrenergic, a conclusion supported by the observation that hemicholinium failed to block the response of the membrane to postganglionic nerve stimulation either *in vivo* or *in vitro*. However, as the authors remark, it does raise the problem of what mechanism is involved when eserine potentiates the effects of acetylcholine on the isolated membrane, if no cholinesterase is present. In a fuller account, Gardiner *et al.* (56) confirmed by a manometric method that there was considerable cholinesterase activity in the Harderian gland but very little in the smooth muscle of the nictitating membrane. Histochemical staining showed a few fine nerve fibers containing acetylcholinesterase running through the smooth muscle of the membrane. Those fibers, which could be traced for any distance, ended on blood vessels, and it was suggested that they were part of a vasodilator nerve supply. The experiments showed that the potentiation of the response of the nictitating membrane to preganglionic nerve stimulation by eserine applied locally to the eye, as observed originally by Bacq and Fredericq (8), was probably due to absorption of sufficient of the eserine to potentiate transmission through the ganglion. The general conclusion of these authors was that the Harderian gland and the blood vessels, but not the smooth muscles, are innervated cholinergically. This view is supported by the observations and conclusions of Cervoni *et al.* (34). They showed that methylatropine, which has antimuscarinic activity equal to that of atropine, was capable of blocking the responses of the isolated inferior muscle of the nictitating membrane to acetylcholine, but it would not block the effects of postganglionic nerve stimulation. Indeed, it enhanced them and potentiated the effects of injected epinephrine.

B. Drugs and Procedures Which Alter the Sensitivity of the Nictitating Membrane to Catecholamines

1. *Denervation*

In 1899, Lewandowsky (73) reported that denervation of the nictitating membrane increased the sensitivity of the organ to injections of adrenal extracts. However, denervation does not have quite the same effect on the response to all sympathomimetic amines. Fleckenstein and Burn (48) investigated the effect of denervation on the sensitivity of the membrane to a number of sympathomimetic amines. Drugs which had either no OH group on the nucleus or only one, and no OH group in the side chain—namely, amphetamine, *N*-methylamphetamine, *p*-hydroxy *N*-methylamphetamine, tyramine, *meta*-tyramine, and β-phenylethylamine—were more effective on the nictitating membrane 19–24 hours after denervation, but less effective 30–40 hours after denervation in all but low doses. At low dose levels, the response of the denervated membrane was greater than that of the innervated organ. From 3–48 days after denervation, the response to these drugs was always much smaller than that of the innervated organ.

Compounds having either no OH groups in the nucleus or only one, but with an OH group attached to the carbon atom next to the nucleus—namely, ephedrine, *p*-hydroxyephedrine, β-phenylethanolamine, and *p*-hydroxy-β-phenylethanolamine—presented a similar picture to that described for drugs having no OH group in the side-chain, except that the response they produced 3–48 days after denervation was less depressed.

Amines with a catechol nucleus—namely, epinephrine, norepinephrine, hydroxytyramine, Epinine, corbasil, and dihydroxyephedrine—all produced greater responses in the denervated organ than they did in the normal membrane.

Norepinephrine was considerably less effective than epinephrine on the normal nictitating membrane, and the rate at which sensitivity developed after denervation was slower for norepinephrine than it was for epinephrine. However, 4 days after denervation the membrane was equally sensitive to both substances. Thus, the actual increase in sensitivity was greater for norepinephrine than for epinephrine. The other compounds in this group all behaved like norepinephrine, showing a great increase in sensitivity 4 days or more after denervation. Neosynephrine, which has a side-chain like that of epinephrine but only one nuclear OH group in the *meta* position, behaved like epinephrine.

Burn and Robinson (30) had shown that denervation of the nictitating membrane caused a variable fall in its content of amine oxidase, and the authors speculated upon the role of this enzyme in the observed effects. However, one year later, Burn and Trendelenburg (31) showed that denervation also increased the sensitivity of the membrane to acetylcholine, pilocarpine, histamine, calcium chloride, and potassium chloride. It seemed, therefore, that the supersensitivity of the membrane was not specific for the humoral transmitter substance unless all these compounds released catecholamines. Their effects were therefore observed in cats whose heads were perfused with Locke's solution by means of a pump. Under these circumstances, only epinephrine and acetylcholine gave good, well-graded responses. Potassium chloride was always without effect on the normal membrane but occasionally produced a small effect on the denervated organ. Calcium chloride had no effect on the normal membrane and produced a 1-mm contraction in only one denervated membrane out of seven. Histamine and pilocarpine sometimes produced contractions in both normal and denervated membranes, but they were always small and only sometimes greater on the denervated side. The results argued that only epinephrine and acetylcholine had direct effects, whereas the other compounds produced their effects indirectly by causing release of an epinephrine-like substance. In support of this view is the observation that cocaine potentiates the effect of histamine upon the nictitating membrane but does not potentiate any of its other effects. Likewise, Ross (87) showed that the adrenergic blocking drugs yohimbine and 933F reduced the responses of the membrane to epinephrine, $CaCl_2$, and KCl, whereas the response to acetylcholine was much less affected. Furthermore, Burn *et al.* (25) showed that degeneration of sympathetic nerve fibers did not cause a fall in the amine oxidase content of the iris or of the foreleg arteries. They argued, therefore, that the earlier experiments of Burn and Robinson (30) were too few in number and had led to an incorrect conclusion. Cholinesterase inhibitors potentiated the nictitating membrane responses but diminished pressor responses. Usually the denervated foreleg was less sensitive to the constrictor action of epinephrine but more sensitive to norepinephrine. Furthermore, there was a correlation between the amount of pseudocholinesterase in the blood vessels of the foreleg and the constrictor response to epinephrine. Thus, if much acetylcholine is present in the foreleg, the arteries would constrict less than normally, but in the nictitating membrane the two compounds would reinforce one another's action. The original argument that denervation supersensitivity was caused by a loss of amine oxidase activity was also shown to be unlikely, because the specific amine oxidase inhibitor iproniazid did not potentiate the actions of epinephrine or norepinephrine on the nictitating membrane. It is now known that amine oxidase plays a less important part in the inactivation of epinephrine and norepinephrine than was thought at this time. The suggestion that acetylcholine in the tissue may be related to the phenomenon does not, as the authors admit, explain why the foreleg is rendered more sensitive to norepinephrine upon denervation. So far as the nictitating membrane is concerned, the idea fits both epinephrine and norepinephrine, except that it does not explain why the sensitivity to norepinephrine should be so much more enhanced than the sensitivity to epinephrine.

An earlier paper by Burn and Hutcheon (23) showed that denervation of the nictitating membrane increased the sensitivity of the organ much more to norepinephrine than to epinephrine. The suggestion offered at this time to explain the phenomenon approximated more closely to present thinking about this problem, because they suggested that some mechanism existed which protected the membrane from circulating catecholamines, and that when the organ was denervated the protection disappeared. The hypothetical protective mechanism was obviously more effective against norepinephrine than it was against epinephrine. In 1961, Herting *et al.* (64) reported that chronic denervation of sympathetic nerves inhibited the uptake of catecholamines by the tissues supplied by them. This, then, could be the hypothetical protective mechanism of Burn and Hutcheon, namely, that under normal circumstances catecholamines may be divided between receptors and storage sites. In denervated organs the catecholamines are denied access to storage sites and therefore more are available to the receptors.

The development of supersensitivity to catecholamines on denervation has been linked with their loss from the tissues which is evoked by the procedure. Thus, Burn and Rand (27) noted that pretreatment with reserpine also produced an increase in sensitivity to catecholamines, and they drew attention to the fact that both denervation and reserpine pretreatment led to a loss of tissue catecholamine.

However, Kirpekar *et al.* (69) showed that the predominant catecholamine in the smooth muscle of the nictitating membrane was norepinephrine. Denervation caused a precipitous fall in the catecholamine content of the organ (about 95%) between 24 and 36 hours after the removal of the superior cervical ganglion. Two weeks after denervation the catecholamine content of the tissue was essentially zero, and no recovery occurred during periods up to 105 days after operation. The procedure increased the sensitivity of the membrane to norepinephrine 200–300 times, but reserpine pretreatment, which caused a 98% fall in the tissue content of catecholamine in 24 hours, caused only a twofold increase in the sensitivity to norepinephrine. By contrast, decentralization of the nictitating membrane did not affect the tissue content of catecholamine, but it did increase its sensitivity to norepinephrine 10–15 times. Thus, increased sensitivity to norepinephrine apparently bore no relation to the tissue content of catecholamines. The difference in the degree of sensitivity to norepinephrine induced by reserpine pretreatment and that induced by denervation could not be ascribed to depression of the smooth muscle by the drug, since the decentralized membrane in the reserpine-treated cat was still 10–15 times more sensitive to norepinephrine. These authors suggest that exogenous norepinephrine is normally taken up by nerve endings. Thus when they degenerate, as in denervation, more of the drug is available to the receptor. However, it does not explain why the decentralized membrane is more sensitive, and the authors speculate that the absence of action potentials for long periods may somehow interfere with the uptake mechanism.

2. *Drugs*

a. Cocaine. In 1910, Frölich and Loewi (51) showed that cocaine potentiated the actions of epinephrine. Tainter and Chang (92), in 1927, demonstrated that it inhibited or abolished the actions of tyramine. In 1939, MacGregor (80) suggested that the potentiation of epinephrine was due to the ability of the local anesthetic to inhibit amine oxidase. This unfortunately did not explain why it inhibited tyramine, so he had to postulate that cocaine prevented it from combining with the receptors. However, Burn and Trendelenburg (31) showed that the specific amine oxidase inhibitor iproniazid did not potentiate the effects of catecholamines, and the possibility that this was the mechanism of the action of cocaine has now been discounted.

The potentiation produced by cocaine must be a peripheral effect, since Thompson (93) has shown that it occurs in the isolated organ. He also demonstrated that the effect was nonspecific, since the contractions produced by acetylcholine and 5-hydroxytryptamine were also potentiated, though the effect on these substances was less marked than that on the catecholamines, and higher concentrations of cocaine were necessary to produce them. More recently Ryall (88) reported that cocaine itself produced a small contraction of the decentralized nictitating membrane. When the nerve was intact the effect was greater. If the preganglionic fiber was cut during the contraction, the membrane immediately relaxed. Paradoxically, epinephrine and norepinephrine also produced relaxation of the membrane contracted by cocaine, and it was suggested that they may produce some ganglion block. The effects were produced in spinal cats, and the author speculated upon the possibility of their being due to potentiation of the effects of norepinephrine circulating as a result of spinalization. However, if this were so, it is difficult to see how injected norepinephrine could relax the contraction.

In an authoritative review of the problem of supersensitivity and subsensitivity to catecholamines, Trendelenburg (98) concluded that the sensitizing action of cocaine is highly selective and is especially pronounced when the sympathomimetic amine possesses a phenolic hydroxyl group in the *meta*-position. He also emphasized that other structural requirements may be of importance and that, while this observation may be true for the nictitating membrane of the spinal cat, it remains to be seen how true it is for other organs and other species. In substantiation of the view that cocaine is highly selective in its action, the point is made that it does not directly sensitize the nictitating membrane to acetylcholine because it fails to potentiate the effects of the latter drug in the reserpine-treated cat. Thus, Trendelenburg suggests that cocaine enables endogenous norepinephrine in close proximity to the receptors to add its effect to that of the acetylcholine, producing an apparent potentiation of the latter drug. This would explain why the effect is absent in the reserpine-treated animal. The same explanation is also offered for the potentiation of 5-hydroxytryptamine.

Trendelenburg (97) and Trendelenburg and Weiner (99) have reported that the subsensitivity to tyramine produced by cocaine and first reported by Tainter and Chang (92) is not a simple matter in the nictitating membrane. Small doses of cocaine potentiated small doses of tyramine but did not much affect large doses of the amine. On the other hand, large doses of cocaine shifted the dose-response curve for tyramine to the right but did not reduce the maximal effect that could be obtained. However, cocaine did not potentiate the response to tyramine in reserpine-treated animals. These observations are consistent with the view that cocaine can inhibit the ability of amines such as tyramine to release norepinephrine, but that the effect can be overcome by increasing the dose of the amine. Thus, with small doses of cocaine, its potentiation of the effects of released norepinephrine would predominate, whereas large doses may very well produce more inhibition of the ability to release norepinephrine.

b. Reserpine. Reserpine depletes the tissues of their store of norepinephrine, and Kirpekar *et al.* (69) showed that as little as 1 mg/kg reduced the norepinephrine content of the nictitating membrane to 2% (or less) of normal within 24 hours of its being injected but did not significantly affect the epinephrine content of the tissue. Burn and Rand (26) reported that in cats pretreated with 2.5–5.0 mg of reserpine on two successive days many sympathomimetic amines which are not derivatives of catechol, such as tyramine phenylethylamine, ephedrine, amphetamine, and (+)-phenylethanolamine, lose their ability to contract the nictitating membrane. On the other hand, norepinephrine, epinephrine, dopamine, and phenylephrine (Neo-Synephrine®) had a greater action in the reserpine-treated animal.

The infusion of norepinephrine restored the activity of the first group of amines and diminished that of the second group. The facts suggested that the first group of amines produced their effects by releasing norepinephrine or epinephrine from the tissues, and amines with this kind of action are now known as "indirect acting."

In 1960, the same authors (28) showed that the response to tyramine in the reserpine-treated cat could be restored not only with an infusion of norepinephrine, but also with its precursors (—)-dopa and dopamine.

Fleming and Trendelenburg (49) made a careful study of the effect of reserpine pretreatment on the sensitivity of the nictitating membrane to norepinephrine. They used doses of reserpine ranging from 0.1–3.0 mg/kg, the animals being taken for experiment 24 hours after the last dose. This kind of treatment produced no significant change in the sensitivity of the membrane to injected norepinephrine, but reduced the response to nerve stimulation in proportion to the dose of reserpine given. When doses of 0.10 mg/kg of reserpine were given daily for up to 14 days, supersensitivity to norepinephrine developed after 7–14 days, but the depletion of tissue stores of norepinephrine (as judged by an indirect method of measurement) was no greater than that observed after single injections of larger amounts of reserpine. It was concluded that there is no direct relationship between supersensitivity to norepinephrine and depletion of the tissue stores of the amine. It was also evident that some time was necessary for the development of supersensitivity.

c. Other Drugs. Chang-Shaw Jang (36) noted that yohimbine blocked the response of the nictitating membrane to injected epinephrine and to nerve stimulation, but 15 minutes later, while the response to injected epinephrine remained blocked, that to nerve stimulation was potentiated. Ergotoxine produced a similar result. It was suggested, in accordance with the views of Gaddum and Dale (54), that the effect of injected epinephrine was blocked more easily than that of nerve stimulation because the antagonists acted at the membrane, barring the access of injected epinephrine more effectively than the access of the transmitter substance released in close proximity to the receptor. However, this does not explain the potentiation. In fact, Thompson (93) reported that, whereas small doses of Dibenamine or Dibenzyline were sufficient to block the effects of epinephrine and norepinephrine on the isolated nictitating membrane, they potentiated the responses to acetylcholine and potassium. If, then, we suppose that some acetylcholine is released when the cervical sympathetic nerve is stimulated, the phenomenon reported by Chang-Shaw Jang can be accounted for.

In 1940 the same author (35) investigated the influence of various sympathomimetic amines on the response of the nictitating membrane to epinephrine and to nerve stimulation. It was found that the responses to both kinds of stimulation were enhanced during and for a few minutes following the effects of adrenalone and sympatol. Tyramine sensitized the membrane to epinephrine for 10–20 minutes and ephedrine had a similar effect, but it was not fully developed until 20–30 minutes had elapsed. The most striking sensitization was produced by amphetamine and by paredrine, which differs from amphetamine in possessing an OH group in the *para*-position. By contrast, the effects of injected epinephrine and nerve stimulation were depressed by epinephrine, norepinephrine, Epinine, and corbasil. The sensitization cannot be satisfactorily explained in terms of amine oxidase inhibition, since corbasil, which is not attacked by the enzyme, is greatly potentiated by ephedrine. Bacq (7) showed that metanephrine, the metabolic product of epinephrine, sensitized the nictitating membrane to nerve stimulation and also to epinephrine and norepinephrine. Normetanephrine had an equally good sensitizing effect, but this does not help to explain the phenomena described by Chang-Shaw Jang, because, in his case, epinephrine and norepinephrine desensitized the membrane. Furthermore, the drugs which produced sensitization in Chang-Shaw Jang's experiments could not (with the possible exception of adrenalone) have reacted with *o*-methyl transferase. It must be concluded that there is, at present, no satisfactory explanation for these phenomena.

Bacq and Renson (9) further investigated the effects of metanephrine. They found that 0.5 mg/kg produced a smaller contraction of the nictitating membrane than 5 μg of epinephrine. Cocaine neither abolished nor augmented the effect of metanephrine, but chronic denervation of the membrane sensitized it to the action of the drug. Metanephrine produced a slow contraction which sometimes lasted as long as 30 minutes. If doses were repeated at intervals of less than 45 minutes, the drug not only sensitized the membrane to the actions of epinephrine, norepinephrine, and nerve stimulation but also to its own action. The sensitization was a peripheral effect, because the response to stimulation is increased whether the stimulus is applied to the pre- or the postganglionic fiber. The drug produces further sensitization of a denervated membrane to norepinephrine, but whereas the effect endures for about 1 hour in the innervated organ it lasts for only 5–10 minutes in the denervated organ. The duration of the sensitization was increased by the amine oxidase inhibitor iproniazid. Dibenzyline inhibited the contraction produced by metanephrine and suppressed its sensitizing effect, but 933F (piperidinomethyl benzodioxane) inhibited only its sympathomimetic action. Normetanephrine had a similar action but was less potent. The authors pointed out that the sensitizing effect of these metabolites of epinephrine and norepinephrine could explain the inconstant responses which occur when doses of the transmitter substances or nerve stimulation itself are applied too frequently or irregularly. The sensitization was not due to inhibition of catechol-*o*-methyl transferase, because it differs from that produced by pyrogallol. They speculated that the effect might be due to conversion of metanephrine to epinephrine or normetarephrine to norepinephrine. Alternatively, metanephrine might occupy nonspecific receptor sites, which could also be normally occupied by the transmitter substances. Under such circumstances the latter would be redirected to the specific sites and produce larger effects than before.

Ryall (88) determined the effect of a number of antidepressant drugs on the response of the nictitating membrane to epinephrine and to norepinephrine. Imipramine and pipradol had little or no effect of their own, but they potentiated the responses to epinephrine and norepinephrine. Unlike cocaine, they did not depress the response to tyramine, nor did they significantly potentiate it. Imipramine still produced a good potentiation after blocking the enzyme *o*-methyl transferase with pyrogallol, and it was concluded that its effect could not be due to inhibition of the methylating enzyme. Nialamide did not cause the membrane to contract, nor did it potentiate responses to epinephrine or norepinephrine, but it did potentiate responses to tyramine. Pheniprazine produced a marked contraction of the nictitating membrane when the preganglionic nerve was cut, or when the superior cervical ganglion was removed. The drug potentiated the responses to epinephrine, norepinephrine, tyramine, and 5-hydroxytryptamine, but had its most marked effect on tyramine. Dexamphetamine also stimulated the membrane directly in the absence of the superior cervical ganglion and potentiated responses to epinephrine, norepinephrine, and tyramine, with its most marked effect on the latter drug.

The author considered that the potentiation of tyramine responses by pheniprazine and nialamide was due to amine oxidase inhibition. However, cocaine also inhibits amine oxidase, but in large doses it depresses tyramine responses.

Thus, it is necessary to invent an explanation for the anomaly. One that has been offered is that cocaine prevents tyramine from releasing norepinephrine. One other disturbing feature of the view that the potentiation is produced as a result of amine oxidase inhibition is the fact that pheniprazine produced much less potentiation of the response to 5-hydroxytryptamine, despite the fact that it is a good substrate for the enzyme. However, it is possible, as the author comments, that there are alternative metabolic pathways open to 5-hydroxytryptamine which are not available to tyramine.

Boura and Green (16) compared the effects of bretylium and guanethidine on the responses of the nictitating membrane to nerve stimulation and various sympathomimetic drugs. Bretylium depressed the slope of the regression lines relating frequency of nerve stimulation to magnitude of contraction, whereas guanethidine preferentially abolished responses to low rates of stimulation and caused a shift of the regression line to the right. Both bretylium and guanethidine increased the sensitivity of the membrane to epinephrine and norepinephrine, the effect being most marked after a series of small daily doses. The development of hypersensitivity to catecholamines went hand in hand with some return of the responses to nerve stimulation despite continued daily administration of guanethidine or bretylium. Both drugs depressed the slope of the dose-response curve to tyramine. However, depending upon the dose of tyramine, the dose of the nerve-blocking agent used, and the duration of its administration, the magnitude of the response to tyramine could be greater than that of the controls. The results suggested that the injection of tyramine produced a progressively smaller release of epinephrine or norepinephrine but that in some situations this was more than compensated for by the increased sensitivity to catecholamines. Corresponding effects were also produced by amphetamine and ephedrine. In an earlier paper (15), cocaine was reported to antagonize the blocking effect of bretylium on the response of the membrane to nerve stimulation. This observation corresponded with that of Nasmyth and Andrews (83) that cocaine prevented blockade by choline xylyl ether of the sympathetic nerve supplying the nictitating membrane. Furthermore, it could restore responses to nerve stimulation even after complete nerve block had been produced by choline xylyl ether. Experiments on the spleen showed that choline xylyl ether practically prevented the appearance of catecholamines in the blood perfusing the spleen when the splenic nerves were stimulated. The injection of cocaine at this time caused an increase in the concentration of catecholamines in the splenic vein blood in response to nerve stimulation. These facts, taken together with the observations of other authors on the action of choline xylyl ether, led to the suggestion that the blocking agent can combine with dopamine and with cocaine. Thus if it combined with dopamine, synthesis of norepinephrine would cease and nerve block would result unless an excess of dopamine was available. Combination of the choline xylyl ether with cocaine would prevent its combination with dopamine and so prevent its blocking action.

References

1. Ahlquist, R. P., A study of the adrenotropic receptors. *Am. J. Physiol.* **153**, 586 (1948).
2. Alexander, F., The effects of some humoral agents on the horse ileum. *Brit. J. Pharmacol.* **7**, 25 (1952).
3. Armitage, A. K., and Vane, J. R., A sensitive method for the assay of catechol amines. *Brit. J. Pharmacol.* **22**, 204 (1964).
4. Axelrod, J., and Tomchick, R., Enzymatic *o*-methylation of epinephrine and other catechols. *J. Biol. Chem.* **233**, 702 (1958).
5. Axelsson, J., Bueding, E., and Bulbring, E., The inhibitory action of adrenaline on intestinal smooth muscle in relation to its action on phosphorylase activity. *J. Physiol.* (*London*) **156**, 357 (1961).
6. Axelsson, J., and Bulbring, E., Metabolic factors affecting the electrical activity of intestinal smooth muscle. *J. Physiol.* (*London*) **156**, 344 (1961).
7. Bacq, Z. M., Rôle physiologique de la métanéphrine et de la normétanéphrine. *Compt. Rend.* **249**, 2398 (1959).
8. Bacq, Z. M., and Fredericq, H., Recherches sur la physiologie et la pharmacologie du système nerveux autonome. XI—Essai d'identification du médiateur chimique libéré dans la membrane nictitante du chat par l'exitation sympathique. *Arch. Intern. Physiol.* **40**, 297 (1935).
9. Bacq, Z. M., and Renson, J., Actions et importance physiologique de la métanéphrine et de la normétanéphrine. *Arch. Intern. Pharmacodyn.* **130**, 385 (1961).
10. Barsoum, G. S., and Gaddum, J. H., The pharmacological estimation of adenosine and histamine in blood. *J. Physiol.* (*London*) **85**, 1 (1935).
11. Bentley, G. A., Studies on sympathetic mechanisms in isolated intestinal and vas deferens preparations. *Brit. J. Pharmacol.* **19**, 85 (1962).
12. Bentley, G. A., A study of the inhibitory action of adrenaline. I. Effects of the carbohydrate metabolism of the isolated rabbit intestine. *Australian J. Exptl. Biol. Sci.* **34**, 485 (1956).
13. Bertler, Å., Falck, B., Hillarp, N. A., Rosengren, E., and Torp, A., Dopamine and chromaffin cells. *Acta Physiol. Scand.* **47**, 251 (1959).
14. Bertler, Å., Hillarp, N. A., and Rosengren, E., Intracellular localization of dopamine in cow intestine. *Acta Physiol. Scand.* **50**, 84 (1960).
15. Boura, A. L. A., and Green, A. F., The actions of bretylium: adrenergic neurone blocking and other effects. *Brit. J. Pharmacol.* **14**, 536 (1959).

16. Boura, A. L. A., and Green, A. F., Comparison of bretylium and guanethidine: tolerance and effects on adrenergic nerve function and responses to sympathomimetic amines. *Brit. J. Pharmacol.* **19,** 13 (1962).

17. Bozler, E., An analysis of the excitatory and inhibitory effects of sympathetic nerve impulses and adrenaline on visceral smooth muscle. *Am. J. Physiol.* **130,** 627 (1940).

18. Brown, G. L., Davies, B. N., and Gillespie, J. S., The release of chemical transmitter from the sympathetic nerves of the intestine of the cat. *J. Physiol. (London)* **143,** 41 (1958).

19. Bueding, E., Bulbring, E., Gerchen, G., and Kuriyama, H., The effect of adrenaline on the adenosine triphosphate and creatine phosphate content of intestinal smooth muscle. *J. Physiol. (London)* **166,** 8P (1963).

20. Bulbring, E., Biophysical changes produced by adrenaline and noradrenaline. *In* "Adrenergic Mechanisms" (J. R. Vane, C. E. W. Wolstenholme, and M. O'Connor, eds.), pp. 275–287. Churchill, London, 1960.

21. Bulbring, E., Electrical activity in intestinal smooth muscle. *Physiol. Rev.* **42,** Suppl. 5, 160 (1962).

22. Bulbring, E., and Kuriyama, H., Effect of change in ionic environment on the action of acetylcholine and adrenaline on the smooth muscle cells of taenia coli. *J. Physiol. (London)* **166,** 59 (1963).

23. Burn, J. H., and Hutcheon, D. E., The action of noradrenaline. *Brit. J. Pharmacol.* **4,** 373 (1949).

24. Burn, J. H., Leach, E. H., Rand, M. J., and Thompson, J. W., Peripheral effects of nicotine and acetylcholine resembling those of sympathetic stimulation. *J. Physiol. (London)* **148,** 332 (1959).

25. Burn, J. H., Philpot, F. J., and Trendelenburg, U., Effect of denervation on enzymes in iris and blood vessels. *Brit. J. Pharmacol.* **9,** 423 (1954).

26. Burn, J. H., and Rand, M. J., The action of sympathomimetic amines in animals treated with reserpine. *J. Physiol. (London)* **144,** 314 (1958).

27. Burn, J. H., and Rand, M. J., The cause of the hypersensitivity of smooth muscle to noradrenaline after sympathetic denervation. *J. Physiol. (London)* **147,** 135 (1959).

28. Burn, J. H., and Rand, M. J., The effect of precursors of noradrenaline on the response to tyramine and sympathetic stimulation. *Brit. J. Pharmacol.* **15,** 47 (1960).

29. Burn, J. H., and Rand, M. J., Sympathetic postganglionic cholinergic fibres. *Brit. J. Pharmacol.* **15,** 56 (1960).

30. Burn, J. H., and Robinson, J. A., Effect of denervation on amine oxidase in structures innervated by the sympathetic. *Brit. J. Pharmacol.* **7,** 304 (1952).

31. Burn, J. H., and Trendelenburg, U., The hypersensitivity of the nictitating membrane to various substances. *Brit. J. Pharmacol.* **9,** 202 (1954).

32. Burnstock, G., Holman, M. E., and Prosser, C. L., Electrophysiology of smooth muscle. *Physiol. Rev.* **43,** 482 (1963).

33. Carlsson, A., The occurrence, distribution and physiological role of catecholamines in the nervous system. *In* "Symposium on Catecholamines" (O. Krayer, ed.), pp. 490–493. Williams & Wilkins, Baltimore, Maryland, 1959.

34. Cervoni, P., West, T. C., and Fink, L. D., Autonomic postganglionic innervation of the nictitating membrane of the cat. *J. Pharmacol. Exptl. Therap.* **116,** 90 (1956).

35. Chang-Shaw Jang, Interaction of sympathomimetic substances on adrenergic transmission. *J. Pharmacol. Exptl. Therap.* **70,** 347 (1940).

36. Chang-Shaw Jang, The potentiation and paralysis of adrenergic effects by ergotoxine and other substances. *J. Pharmacol. Exptl. Therap.* **71,** 87 (1941).
37. Clegg, P. C., Changes in sensitivity to stimulants of the guinea-pig uterus *in vitro* produced by substances which alter the rate of release of adrenergic transmitter. *J. Physiol.* (*London*) **165,** 38P (1963).
38. Csapo, A., Dependence of isometric tension and isotonic shortening of uterine muscle on temperature and on strength of stimulation. *Am. J. Physiol.* **177,** 348 (1954).
39. Csapo, I. A., and Kuriyama, H. A., Effect of ions and drugs on cell membrane activity and tension in the postpartum rat myometrium. *J. Physiol.* (*London*) **165,** 575 (1963).
40. Dale, H. H., On some physiological actions of ergot. *J. Physiol.* (*London*) **34,** 163 (1906).
41. Dale, H. H., and Barger, G., Chemical structure and sympathomimetic action of amines. *J. Physiol.* (*London*) **41,** 19 (1910).
42. Daniel, E. E., Sehdev, H., and Robinson, K., Mechanisms for activation of smooth muscle. *Physiol. Rev.* **42,** Suppl. 5, 228 (1962).
43. Day, M. D., and Rand, M. J., Effect of guanethidine in revealing cholinergic sympathetic fibres. *Brit. J. Pharmacol.* **17,** 245 (1961).
44. Douglas, W. W., and Gray, J. A. B., The excitant action of acetylcholine and other substances on cutaneous sensory pathways and its prevention by hexamethonium and *d*-tubocurarine. *J. Physiol.* (*London*) **119,** 118 (1953).
45. Edman, K. A. P., and Schild, H. O., Calcium and the stimulant and inhibitory effects of adrenaline in depolarized smooth muscle. *J. Physiol.* (*London*) **169,** 404 (1963).
46. Evans, D. H. L., Schild, H. O., and Thesleff, S., Effects of drugs on depolarized plain muscle. *J. Physiol.* (*London*) **143,** 474 (1958).
47. Finkleman, B., On the nature of inhibition in the intestine. *J. Physiol.* (*London*) **70,** 145 (1930).
48. Fleckenstein, A., and Burn, J. H., The effect of denervation on the action of sympathomimetic amines on the nictitating membrane. *Brit. J. Pharmacol.* **8,** 69 (1953).
49. Fleming, W. W., and Trendelenburg, U., The development of supersensitivity to norepinephrine after pre-treatment with reserpine. *J. Pharmacol. Exptl. Therap.* **133,** 41 (1961).
50. Foster, R., Ing, H. R., and Varagić, V., Alpha-cocaine. *Brit. J. Pharmacol.* **10,** 436 (1955).
51. Frölich, A., and Loewi, O., Uber ein steigerung der adrenalinempfindlichkeit durch cocain. *Arch. Exptl. Pathol. Pharmakol.* **62,** 159 (1910).
52. Furchgott, R. F., The receptors for epinephrine and norepinephrine. *In* "Symposium on Catecholamines" (O. Krayer, ed.), pp. 429–441. Williams & Wilkins, Baltimore, Maryland, 1959.
53. Furchgott, R. F., Receptors for sympathomimetic amines. *In* "Adrenergic Mechanisms" (J. R. Vane, G. E. W. Wolstenholme, and M. O'Connor, eds.), pp. 246–252. Churchill, London, 1960.
54. Gaddum, J. H., and Dale, H. H., Reactions of denervated voluntary muscle and their bearing on the mode of action of parasympathetic and related nerves. *J. Physiol.* (*London*) **70,** 109 (1930).
55. Gaddum, J. H., and Lembeck, F., The assay of substances from the adrenal medulla. *Brit. J. Pharmacol.* **4,** 401 (1949).

56. Gardiner, J. E., Hellmann, K., and Thompson, J. W., The nature of the innervation of the smooth muscle, Harderian gland and blood vessels of the cat's nictitating membrane. *J. Physiol.* (*London*) **163**, 436 (1962).
57. Gillespie, J. S., Spontaneous mechanical and electrical activity of stretched and unstretched intestinal smooth muscle cells and their response to sympathetic nerve stimulation. *J. Physiol.* (*London*) **162**, 54 (1962).
58. Gillespie, J. S., and Mackenna, B. R., The effect of reserpine on the response of the rabbit ileum and colon to stimulation of their extrinsic nerves *in vitro*. *J. Physiol.* (*London*) **147,** 31P (1959).
59. Gillespie, J. S., and Mackenna, B. R., The inhibitory action of the sympathetic nerves on the smooth muscle of the rabbit gut, its reversal by reserpine and restoration by catecholamines and by DOPA. *J. Physiol.* (*London*) **156,** 17 (1961).
60. Graham, J. D. P., and Gurd, M. R., Effects of adrenaline on the isolated uterus of the cat. *J. Physiol.* (*London*) **152,** 243 (1960).
61. Grieff, K., and Holtz, P., Uber die uteruswirkung des adrenalins und arterenols. Ein beitrag zum problem der uterus innervation. *Arch. Intern. Pharmacodyn.* **88,** 228 (1951).
62. Hellmann, K., and Thompson, J. W., The nature of the innervation of the nictitating membrane of the cat. *J. Physiol.* (*London*) **159,** 11P (1961).
63. Hermansen, K., The effect of adrenaline, noradrenaline and isoprenaline on the guinea-pig uterus. *Brit. J. Pharmacol.* **16,** 116 (1961).
64. Herting, G., Axelrod, J., Kopin, I. J., and Whitby, L. G., Lack of uptake of catecholamines after chronic denervation of sympathetic nerves. *Nature* **189,** 66 (1961).
65. Holtz, P., Role of L-Dopa decarboxylase in the biosynthesis of catecholamines in nervous tissue and the adrenal medulla. *In* "Symposium on Catecholamines" (O. Krayer, ed.), pp. 317–329. Williams & Wilkins, Baltimore, Maryland, 1959.
66. Holtz, P., and Wölpert, K., Die reaktion des katzen und meerschweinchenuterus auf adrenaline während der verschiedenen stadien des sexualzyklus und ihre hormonal beeinflüssung. *Arch. Exptl. Pathol. Pharmakol.* **185,** 20 (1937).
67. Holzbauer, M., and Vogt, M., Modification by drugs of the response of the rat's uterus to adrenaline. *Brit. J. Pharmacol.* **10,** 186 (1955).
68. Kennard, J. H., The reversal by progestin of responses of the non-pregnant uterus of the cat. *Am. J. Physiol.* **118,** 190 (1937).
69. Kirpekar, S. M., Cervoni, P., and Furchgott, R. F., Catecholamine content of the cat nictitating membrane following procedures sensitizing it to norepinephrine. *J. Pharmacol. Exptl. Therap.* **135,** 180 (1962).
70. Kirshner, N., The metabolism of $[\alpha - {}^{14}C](\pm)$-adrenaline in the cat. *In* "Adrenergic Mechanisms" (J. R. Vane, C. E. W. Wolstenholme, and M. O'Connor, eds.), pp. 45–56. Churchill, London, 1960.
71. Kopin, I. J., Axelrod, J., and Gordon, E., The metabolic fate of H^3 epinephrine and C^{14} metanephrine in the rat. *J. Biol. Chem.* **236,** 2109 (1961).
72. Labate, J. S., Influence of cocaine on the uterine reactions induced by adrenaline and hypogastric nerve stimulation. *J. Pharmacol. Exptl. Therap.* **72,** 370 (1941).
73. Lewandowsky, M., Uber die wirkung des nebennierenextractes auf die glatten muskeln in besonderen des auges. *Arch. Anat. Physiol. Leipzig* 360 (1899).

74. Lockett, M. F., Identification of an isoprenaline-like substance in extracts of adrenal glands. *Brit. J. Pharmacol.* **9,** 498 (1954).

75. Lundholm, L., and Mohme-Lundholm, E., The action of adrenaline on carbohydrate metabolism in relation to some of its pharmacodynamic effects. *In* "Adrenergic Mechanisms" (J. R. Vane, C. E. W. Wolstenholme, and M. O'Connor, eds.), pp. 305–321. Churchill, London, 1960.

76. Mann, M., and West, G. B., The nature of uterine and intestinal sympathin. *Brit. J. Pharmacol.* **6,** 79 (1951).

77. Marshall, J. M., Effects of estrogen and progesterone on single uterine muscle fibers in the rat. *Am. J. Physiol.* **197,** 935 (1959).

78. Marshall, J. M., Regulation of activity in uterine smooth muscle. *Physiol. Rev.* **42,** Suppl. 5, 213 (1962).

79. McDougal, M. D., and West, G. B., The inhibition of the peristaltic reflex by sympathomimetic amines. *Brit. J. Pharmacol.* **9,** 131 (1954).

80. MacGregor, D. F., The relation of cocaine and of procaine to the sympathetic system. *J. Pharmacol. Exptl. Therap.* **66,** 393 (1939).

81. Mohme-Lundholm, E., The mechanism of the relaxing effect of adrenaline on smooth muscle. *Acta Physiol. Scand. Suppl.* **29,** 1 (1953).

82. Munro, A. F., The effect of adrenaline and noradrenaline on the activity of isolated preparations of the gut from the foetal guinea-pig. *Brit. J. Pharmacol.* **8,** 38 (1953).

83. Nasmyth, P. A., and Andrews, W. H. H., The antagonism of cocaine to the action of choline 2,6-xylyl ether bromide at sympathetic nerve endings. *Brit. J. Pharmacol.* **14,** 477 (1959).

84. Paton, W. D. M., and Vane, J. R., An analysis of the responses of the isolated stomach to electrical stimulation and to drugs. *J. Physiol.* (*London*) **165,** 10 (1963).

85. Pennefather, J. N., and Rand, M. J., Increase in noradrenaline content of tissues after infusion of noradrenaline, dopamine and l-dopa. *J. Physiol.* (*London*) **154,** 277 (1960).

86. Powell, C. E., and Slater, I. H., Blocking of inhibitory adrenergic receptors by a dichloro analog of isoproterenol. *J. Pharmacol. Exptl. Therap.* **122,** 480 (1958).

87. Ross, J. F., The effect of piperidinomethylbenzodioxane (933F) and yohimbine upon the action of certain drugs and ions on the nictitating membrane. *Am. J. Physiol.* **116,** 574 (1936).

88. Ryall, R. W., Effects of cocaine and antidepressant drugs on the nictitating membrane of the cat. *Brit. J. Pharmacol.* **17,** 339 (1961).

89. Schild, H. O., Effect of adrenaline on depolarized smooth muscle. *In* "Adrenergic Mechanisms" (J. R. Vane, G. E. W. Wolstenholme, and M. O'Connor, eds.), pp. 288–292. Churchill, London, 1960.

90. Schümann, H. J., Formation of adrenergic transmitter. *In* "Adrenergic Mechanisms" (J. R. Vane, G. E. W. Wolstenholme, and M. O'Connor, eds.), pp. 6–16. Churchill, London, 1960.

91. Singh, I., Singh, S. I., and Dhalla, N. S., Active relaxation of unstriated muscle produced by epinephrine. *Am. J. Physiol.* **200,** 955 (1961).

92. Tainter, M. L., and Chang, D. K., The antagonism of the pressor action of tyramine by cocaine. *J. Pharmacol. Exptl. Therap.* **39,** 193 (1927).

93. Thompson, J. W., Studies on the responses of the isolated nictitating membrane of the cat. *J. Physiol.* (*London*) **141,** 46 (1958).

94. Thompson, J. W., The nerve supply to the nictitating membrane of the cat. *J. Anat.* **95,** 371 (1961).
95. Tidball, M. E., Effect of epinephrine on the relation of acetylcholine to intestinal tonus. *Am. J. Physiol.* **197,** 1327 (1959).
96. Trendelenburg, U., Thyroid and hyperglycaemia produced by adrenaline and noradrenaline. *Brit. J. Pharmacol.* **8,** 454 (1953).
97. Trendelenburg, U., Modification of the effect of tyramine by various agents and procedures. *J. Pharmacol. Exptl. Therap.* **134,** 8 (1961).
98. Trendelenburg, U., Supersensitivity and subsensitivity to sympathomimetic amines. *Pharmacol. Rev.* **15,** 225 (1963).
99. Trendelenburg, U., and Weiner, N., Sensitivity of the nictitating membrane after various procedures and agents. *J. Pharmacol. Exptl. Therap.* **136,** 152 (1962).
100. Van Dyke, H. B., and Gustavson, R. G., On the pregnancy response of the uterus of the cat. *J. Pharmacol. Exptl. Therap.* **37,** 379 (1929).
101. Van Dyke, H. B., and Gustavson, R. G., Further observations on the pregnancy-response of the uterus of the cat. *J. Pharmacol. Exptl. Therap.* **41,** 139 (1931).
102. Vane, J. R., A sensitive method for the assay of 5-hydroxytryptamine. *Brit. J. Pharmacol.* **12,** 344 (1957).
103. Vane, J. R., The actions of sympathomimetic amines on tryptamine receptors. *In* "Adrenergic Mechanisms" (J. R. Vane, G. E. W. Wolstenholme, and M. O'Connor, eds.), pp. 356–372. Churchill, London, 1960.
104. von Euler, U. S., Estimation of adrenaline and noradrenaline in tissue extracts. *Methods Med. Res.* **3,** 131 (1950).
105. von Euler, U. S., "Noradrenaline," p. 141. Thomas, Springfield, Illinois, 1956.
106. West, G. B., Quantitative studies of adrenaline and noradrenaline. *J. Physiol. (London)* **106,** 418 (1947).
107. West, G. B., Further studies on sympathin. *Brit. J. Pharmacol.* **5,** 165 (1950).
108. Westcott, W. C., and Christensen, H. E., Responses of the isolated nictitating membrane (cat). *Am. J. Physiol.* **167,** 836 (1951).

E. The Effects of Sympathomimetic Amines and Adrenergic Blocking Agents on Metabolism

Sydney Ellis*†

Department of Pharmacology, Woman's Medical College of Pennsylvania, Philadelphia, Pennsylvania

I. Introduction ... 179
II. Effects on Carbohydrate Metabolism ... 180
A. General ... 180
B. Blood Glucose ... 182
C. Liver ... 185
D. Blood Lactate and Muscle Glycogenolysis ... 186
E. Heart ... 188
F. Smooth Muscles ... 189
G. Other Tissues ... 191
H. Interpretations ... 191
III. Effects on Fat Metabolism ... 191
A. Fat Metabolism ... 191
B. Fat Transport ... 192
C. Adipose Tissue ... 195
D. Effects of Drugs ... 197
IV. Effects on Oxygen Consumption ... 200
A. Intact Animals ... 200
B. Individual Tissues ... 205
C. Mechanism of the Calorigenic Effect ... 207
D. General Comments ... 207
V. Effects on Cations ... 208
A. Potassium and Sodium ... 208
B. Calcium ... 212
References ... 213

I. INTRODUCTION

The aim of this chapter is to summarize present knowledge of the effects of adrenergic drugs on metabolism with special emphasis on comparative pharmacology in terms of differences related to species, to organs, and to chemical structure. In the past the major attention was on carbohydrate metabolism. Research interest in recent years has been

* The author's research has been supported by grants from the U.S. Public Health Service, National Institutes of Health.

† Present address: Department of Pharmacology and Toxicology, the University of Texas Medical Branch, Galveston, Texas.

focused intensively on fat metabolism. Also, more attention has been given to the calorigenic response to catecholamines and to a possible relation between the effects on fat metabolism and the calorigenic response. Effects of catecholamines on electrolyte metabolism have brought to light important cellular responses that relate to the effects of the catecholamines on bioelectric phenomena and on function.

Information on structure-activity relationships and on the ability of various adrenergic blocking agents to modify the responses to the catecholamines assists in the classification of the receptors (3) for the individual biochemical responses. There is a need for a better understanding of these matters to prevent the misinterpretation of studies using catecholamines and their antagonists as analytical tools in various species.

It is essential to devote some attention to the purely biochemical aspects of cell metabolism in order to place the metabolic response to catecholamines in proper perspective. Questions posed in attempts to understand the effects of epinephrine on metabolism gave much of the impetus for the development of biochemical knowledge, and now more complete knowledge of cellular metabolic control, in turn, leads to a better understanding of the numerous metabolic changes which the catecholamines produce.

The relationship of the metabolic responses to catecholamines to the understanding of the pharmacological effects is not dealt with in detail. Interest in this relationship is high, but many basic questions remain unanswered. The effects of catecholamines on amino acid metabolism are not discussed, since there has been relatively little recent study of this area. The interaction of catecholamines with hormones is such a large and complex topic that space limitations prohibit its inclusion.

To reduce the length of the reference list the reader is referred to a 1956 review (128) and the annotated bibliography compiled by Griffith (166) for the early literature. Some recent reviews have dealt in detail with one or more of the topics covered in this chapter (2, 175, 187, 191, 253, 444, 457, 474). The literature search was completed in March, 1966.

II. EFFECTS ON CARBOHYDRATE METABOLISM

A. General

Attention has been focused on the effects of epinephrine on carbohydrate metabolism since the description in 1901 of "adrenaline diabetes" (42). The work on this topic during the first quarter of the century was presented and interpreted by Cori (78), and the massive literature covering the first half of the century was summarized in 1956

(128). The cellular mechanisms through which epinephrine modifies carbohydrate metabolism have been brought to light only in recent years with the discovery by Sutherland and Cori (443) of the activation of phosphorylase.

Characteristic and important effects of epinephrine on metabolism are the increased blood levels of glucose and lactic acid, derived from glycogen of the liver and skeletal muscles, respectively. Significant increases in pryuvate and citrate also occur, and these may reflect increased formation in tissues. The hyperglycemia is mainly a reflection of glycogenolysis in the liver, where the enzyme glucose-6-phosphatase produces free glucose from the elevated concentration of hexosephosphates produced by rapid glycogenolysis. Stimulation of splanchnic nerves in the rabbit increased liver phosphorylase activity without changing glucose-6-phosphatase activity (415). Hyperglycemia is additionally increased by the effect of epinephrine on skeletal muscle, in which the rate of glucose (199) uptake is reduced compared with the uptake at any given concentration of glucose in the absence of epinephrine (78, 150, 465). Epinephrine decreases the rate at which ^{14}C-glucose is removed from the blood and is converted to $^{14}CO_2$ (110). The blood lactate comes mainly from skeletal muscle, in which epinephrine-induced glycogenolysis cannot release glucose since muscle has no glucose-6-phosphatase activity and since the low fructose-1,6-diphosphatase activity of muscle appears to limit the reversal of the Embden-Meyerhof glycolytic pathway and channels the excess glycogenolysis to lactate (and pyruvate). The lactate supports the hyperglycemia because in several tissues it is utilized in competition with glucose and because epinephrine stimulates its conversion to glucose in hepatic gluconeogenesis (78, 137).

An interesting but very minor source of blood glucose is the kidney (128), which does have significant glucose-6-phosphatase activity.

In the usual studies of the effects of epinephrine on blood glucose and liver glycogen, there is a transient decrease in liver glycogen followed by recovery to normal or elevated levels (78). When epinephrine was infused into rabbits at rates of 0.13–3.6 $\mu g\ kg^{-1}\ min^{-1}$ for many hours, blood glucose was maintained at constant levels for some hours and then fell progressively. Liver and muscle glycogen were low at the conclusion of such prolonged epinephrine administration (50). Under these conditions much of the blood glucose must derive from muscle lactate being converted to glucose in the liver. The amount of lactate converted directly to glycogen appears small (11). Drury and Wick (117) used ^{14}C-labeled lactate and glucose to show that these substances are oxidized mainly during the peak of action of epinephrine. Only as a late effect when ^{14}C-lactate was infused during the action of subcutaneously administered epinephrine could they find as much as 20% of the lactate converted to liver glycogen.

A fascinating, detailed picture of the changes brought about by epinephrine in the enzymatic machinery of carbohydrate metabolism has developed in recent years. The primary discovery of phosphorylase as the rate-limiting enzyme of glycogenolysis and its activation by epinephrine (443) has stimulated a series of important discoveries. The first step in the action of epinephrine is the stimulation of a membrane-bound (99) enzyme system, adenyl cyclase, which converts ATP to adenosine-3′,5′-monophosphate (cyclic AMP). Cyclic AMP appears to be a catalyst for activating several enzymes (446). Cyclic AMP in the presence of ATP and an as yet undefined factor activates the enzyme phosphorylase kinase (255). Then active phosphorlyase kinase, in the presence of ATP, causes the phosphorylation of the relatively inactive form of phosphorylase to active phosphorylase. There are some differences in the details of the active and inactive forms of phosphorylase in liver, skeletal muscle, and heart muscle (255). In addition to activating this series of enzymic changes which promote rapid tissue glycogenolysis, cyclic AMP also appears to inactivate the glycogen synthetase (uridine diphosphate glucose-α-glucan transferase) system in some tissues (12); through this mechanism epinephrine may further reduce tissue glycogen (85, 88). The glycogen synthetase of heart muscle is increased (488) or unchanged (382) by epinephrine.

The rate-limiting enzyme of glycolysis from the hexosephosphates to pyruvate and lactate has been demonstrated to be phosphofructokinase. Since this enzyme is also activated by epinephrine (302) through the "second mediator," cyclic AMP (446), the increased lactate production in the presence of epinephrine is now well explained.

The above facts appear to be well established and have been extensively reviewed (2, 253). This presentation will be concerned especially with tissues other than liver and skeletal muscle, two classic examples of epinephrine-activated tissues. The structure-activity relationships of sympathomimetic agents in their effects on carbohydrate metabolism and the antagonistic effects of adrenergic blocking agents will be brought to bear on the problem of classifying the adrenergic receptors for these responses.

B. Blood Glucose

The hyperglycemic response to epinephrine appears to be common to all the vertebrate animals. There are, however, fairly large variations in sensitivity to this effect of epinephrine. Also, the relative potencies of several sympathomimetic amines and the influences of various adrenergic blocking agents on epinephrine-produced hyperglycemia indicate some marked differences among species in this response.

Studies in which epinephrine was administered by constant intravenous infusion show that in man the blood glucose level is very sensitive to epinephrine, and cats and rabbits are about as sensitive as man. Dogs and rats, however, are several times less sensitive. When epinephrine is given by other routes, more complex factors are involved and the observed differences are as likely to be related to vascular and other changes as to the absolute hepatic sensitivities to epinephrine. The prominent role played by local vasoconstriction in limiting the blood level of subcutaneously administered epinephrine has been nicely demonstrated in a recent paper (209).

To date, without exception in those species tested, norepinephrine has proven to be much less potent than epinephrine for producing hyperglycemia. Norepinephrine, 0.5 mg intramuscularly, was found to produce a similar slight hyperglycemia in normal subjects and in patients with liver disease (225). In the dog (253) and cat (385) isoproterenol is about as potent as epinephrine (79, 438); in the rabbit (194, 292) and rat (127, 208) isoproterenol has a very low relative potency. We shall return to these differences in the discussion of adrenergic blocking agents and the classification of hepatic adrenergic receptors.

With continuous recording of blood glucose levels using the autoanalyzer Marquardt (304) found that epinephrine, 2 μg/kg, in cats anesthetized with Evipal® produced hyperglycemia even in those cats which showed a depressor response. Epinephrine activates phosphorylase in liver slices of several species (349).

1. *Dog*

The order of potencies of the catecholamines on dog blood sugar is ISO $\geqq$ E $>$ NE (E = epinephrine; NE = norepinephrine; ISO = isoproterenol) (69, 314). A similar order of potencies is found in the canine liver cell-free adenylcyclase system (339). Ethylnorepinephrine (Butanephrine®) and its *N*-isopropyl derivative are weak hyperglycemic agents (293). Epinephrine increases the phosphorylase activity of dog liver *in vivo* (48).

Ergot derivatives in high dosage inhibit epinephrine-induced hyperglycemia (244, 294, 314), but other α-adrenergic blocking agents do not affect or may potentiate the hyperglycemic response to epinephrine [phenoxybenzamine (294, 314); azapetine (295)].

The β-adrenergic blocking agents consistently inhibit epinephrine-induced hyperglycemia [dichloroisoproterenol (DCI) (15, 294, 295,

314); pronethalol and MJ-1999 (261); *N*-isopropyl methoxamine (IMA) (392)].

Cocaine potentiates the response to norepinephrine more than the response to epinephrine (181).

2. *Cat*

Norepinephrine is much less potent (429) and ISO is only slightly less potent than epinephrine (136, 305, 385). Moderate doses of methoxamine produce hyperglycemia (136, 305), but ephedrine is almost ineffective (305). A portion of the hyperglycemic response to epinephrine is attributed to an effect on lower brain centers which are more sensitive to small doses of epinephrine than the liver (184, 384, 429, 430).

α-Adrenergic blocking agents do not block epinephrine-induced hyperglycemia [phenoxybenzamine (125); Dibenamine® and phentolamine (130); dibozane (136); yohimbine, azapetine (Ilidar®), Prisoline®, and Hydergine® (305)].

Ergot alkaloids inhibit the hyperglycemic reaction *in vivo* (130, 429). The β-adrenergic blocking agents MJ-1999 and IMA inhibit epinephrine-induced hyperglycemia (136), and DCI inhibits glucose release from liver slices (299).

3. *Rat*

The order of potencies for producing hyperglycemia is: E > NE > ISO (75, 164, 208, 270, 455). Parallel dose-response curves are given by epinephrine and norepinephrine, but ISO produces only a small increase in blood glucose even at high doses (239) and liver slices are unresponsive to ISO (456, 466). The potent effect of ISO on blood lactic acid (164) is suggested as the primary reason for its small effect on blood glucose (147).

Amphetamine and related compounds only reduce blood sugar (354).

α-Adrenergic blocking agents such as phenoxybenzamine do not inhibit epinephrine-induced hyperglycemia (208).

Ergot derivatives in high doses are inhibitory (103, 270).

β-Adrenergic blocking agents, even in high doses, are poor inhibitors of epinephrine-induced hyperglycemia (75, 208, 270).

4. *Rabbit*

The order of hyperglycemic potencies is E > NE > ISO (292, 477) and ISO > sympatol > ephedrine (264). When administered intraperitoneally or into the lateral ventricle epinephrine, 20 μg/kg, produced hyperglycemia, but norepinephrine, 20 μg/kg, did not (184).

α-Adrenergic blocking agents are poor antagonists of epinephrine-induced hyperglycemia [Dibenamine (183, 471), Priscoline (471, 493)].

Ergot derivatives are rather potent antagonists in the rabbit (196, 471, 492).

5. *Man*

Epinephrine is a much more potent hyperglycemic agent than norepinephrine. ISO is much less potent than epinephrine (77, 333). Ephedrine has a weak activity, and norephedrine is inactive (475). α-Methyl-norepinephrine is quite potent; normetanephrine, *N*-methylepinephrine, synephrine, phenylephrine, and dopamine produce some hyperglycemia, but tyramine is ineffective at rates of infusion which increased systolic blood pressure 45 mm Hg (333).

Phenoxybenzamine did not inhibit epinephrine-induced hyperglycemia (364).

Ergokryptine (148) and DHE (dehydroergotamine) (431) appear to be fairly potent antagonists.

Pronethalol is not an effective antagonist (364).

C. Liver

1. *Dog*

Epinephrine stimulates the formation of cyclic AMP (adenosine monophosphate) by subcellular particles of dog liver (371), and the catecholamines (ISO > E > NE) and adrenergic blocking agents, DCI (dichloroisoproterenol) and ergotamine, show the same relative potencies as they do in the intact dog (339). Ergotamine in homogenates of dog (or cat) liver selectively antagonizes the activation of phosphorylase by epinephrine, but not that by glucagon (31). Dihydroergotamine shows this selectivity *in vivo* (153).

2. *Cat*

In liver slices or in subcellular particles of cat liver containing the adenyl cyclase system, DCI and ergotamine are selective inhibitors since they antagonize catecholamines but not glucagon (299).

3. *Rat*

In the intact rat (61, 208) and in the perfused rat liver (277, 421) the relative potencies of the catecholamine for activating phosphorylase and glycogenolysis are E > NE; ISO does not activate phosphorylase or glycogenolysis either *in vivo* (111) or *in vitro* (456). Activation of phosphorylase by epinephrine is blocked by ergotamine, but phenoxybenzamine, phentolamine, DCI, and pronethalol produce only partial blockade. Cyclic AMP (277, 278) and glucagon also activate phosphorylase, but their effects are not inhibited by adrenergic blocking agents, with the exception of DHE, which blocks glucagon (396) and cyclic AMP (351, 352, 353). Other β-adrenergic blocking agents are also poor epinephrine antagonists in the rat liver: pronethalol and IMA (368) and MJ-1999 (236). *In vitro,* activation by epinephrine of phosphorylase in rat liver slices is inhibited by DHE, phentolamine, DCI, and methoxamine in high concentrations (4), but in perfused liver phentolamine inhibited only vasoconstriction and not glycogenolysis (424).

Although anoxia of the liver increases glycogenolysis, it does not increase phosphorylase activity or glucose release (277). Thus, a concentration of phentolamine may be sufficient to prevent the constrictor effect of epinephrine in the perfused rat liver but not to modify glycogenolysis (423).

Ethionine treatment reduces the ATP (adenosine triphosphate) of rat liver, decreases the phosphorylase activity, and prevents the action of epinephrine *in vivo* and of cyclic AMP *in vitro* unless ATP is added (417).

4. *Human*

Epinephrine increases splanchnic glucose output in man along with increases in blood flow and oxygen consumption, but glucagon increases only the glucose production (243). It is reported that glucagon is an effective glycogenolytic agent in hepatic glycogen disease in which epinephrine is not effective (420a), since only glucagon increases blood lactate. However, larger doses of the more potent agent, glucagon, were injected.

5. *Bat*

Epinephrine does not reduce liver glycogen in the hibernating bat, but does in the aroused bat (275).

6. *Classification of Hepatic Adrenergic Receptors*

In Ahlquist's terminology (3), the adrenergic receptors for glycogenolysis in dog and cat liver are of the β type. In rat liver the receptors are not α, but they may be a β subtype (134, 479). On the basis of admittedly incomplete evidence it appears that human, rabbit, and mouse livers have receptors similar to those of the rat liver.

D. Blood Lactate and Muscle Glycogenolysis

1. *Dog*

Norepinephrine is less potent than epinephrine (128) for increasing blood lactate in the dog, but ISO is as potent as or more potent than epinephrine (293). Ethyl-norepinephrine (Butanephrine) and its *N*-isopropyl derivative are much less potent than epinephrine (293).

Catecholamine induced hyperlacticacidemia is partially antagonized by DCI (294, 314) and by MJ-1999 (236).

Ergotamine has some (294) or no (314) antagonistic action.

Phenoxybenzamine potentiates the response to epinephrine (294) or does not affect it (314). Cocaine potentiates the response to norepinephrine more than the response to epinephrine (181).

2. *Cat*

The α-adrenergic blocking agent, dibozane, does not reduce the increase in blood lactate in response to epinephrine, but this response is inhibited by MJ-1999 and IMA (136).

3. *Rat*

Muscle is more sensitive than liver to epinephrine-induced glycogenolysis (422). Muscle glycogenolysis is controlled by a typical β-adrenotropic receptor. The potencies of the catecholamines are ISO > E > NE (61, 132, 209, 217, 235, 370), whether the response measured is the increase in blood lactate (164) or the decrease in muscle glycogen *in vivo* or *in vitro*.

The catecholamines also increase the muscle content of glucose-6-P (26), phosphorylase *a* (27, 208, 273), active phosphorylase *b* kinase (365, 488), and cyclic AMP (366), and they reduce the glycogen synthetase activity (27, 488). Epinephrine (in the presence of insulin) reduced the incorporation of ^{14}C-glucose into glycogen (247). Epinephrine is a more effective inhibitor of glucose uptake by diaphragm when the medium contains a phosphate buffer (199a).

Epinephrine reduces glucose or 2-deoxyglucose phosphorylation by muscle so that more free glucose or free 2-deoxyglucose accumulates intracellularly (245, 246).

ISO and epinephrine are more potent than norepinephrine for lowering serum phosphate, and this response is antagonized by pronethalol (238).

β-Adrenergic blocking agents antagonize the effects of catecholamines on glycogenolysis and phosphorylase. Pronethalol is a more potent antagonist than DCI and closely related derivatives of DCI (208, 218, 324). Methoxamine and ephedrine inhibit effects of epinephrine (4), as does IMA (368).

Phenoxybenzamine appears to potentiate the effects of subcutaneously administered catecholamines (209). Phentolamine and DHE have little effect on muscle glycogenolysis (4, 235).

Theophylline potentiates the effect of epinephrine on phosphorylase (201).

4. *Mouse*

Epinephrine increases the blood lactate level in normal mice and in mice of the I strain, which lack phosphorylase kinase (291).

5. *Frog*

The changes in fructose-6-P and fructose-1,6-P_2 when frog muscle is treated with epinephrine indicate that the reaction catalyzed by phosphofructokinase becomes a limiting step in the Krebs-Meyerhof pathway (359).

In frog sartorius the activation of phosphorylase by epinephrine or norepinephrine is slow compared with the activation induced by electrical stimulation, and only the effect of epinephrine is inhibited by DCI (89). Epinephrine also changes the lactate and glucose-6-P concentrations much more slowly than does electrical stimulation (234).

6. *Human*

The increased release of lactate from the human forearm caused by epinephrine is not reduced by preventing vasoconstriction with phenoxybenzamine (5). Epinephrine also increases the release of pyruvate (165) but reduces the venous phosphate and potassium (104). DCI prevents the increase in lactate in response to epinephrine, but it requires a larger dose than is required for inhibiting the vasodilation (157).

E. Heart

In all species the potency of ISO is found to be greater than that of epinephrine, and the potency of norepinephrine is usually close to that of epinephrine. Epinephrine causes glycogenolysis *in vivo* or *in vitro* in the heart of the dog (72, 387), cat (41) rabbit (41), guinea pig (41), rat (41, 209, 317, 447, 489), and mouse (19). It increases the cardiac oxidation of glucose and lactate (96, 161), decreases its pyruvate and free fatty acid (FFA) uptake (161), and reduces the conversion of glucose to glycogen and glutamate (96).

Epinephrine activates phosphorylase in the heart of the dog (116, 313), cat (25), rabbit (57, 256, 398), rat (24, 116, 188, 209, 257, 262, 276, 304, 489), mouse (291), toad (347), and lamprey eel (346).

It also elevates cardiac cyclic AMP (73, 178, 382), phosphorylase kinase (178), hexosemonophosphates (25, 73, 90, 312), and lactate (372, 490), and it increases glucose phosphorylation in some dog hearts and increases free glucose in others (90) and reduces glucose extraction (372). Glycogen synthetase activity is either unchanged (382) or increased (488).

In addition to epinephrine, norepinephrine, and ISO, the glycogenolytic system of the heart is activated also by the following agents: phenylephrine (188), *p*-sympatol (synephrine) (188), tyramine (263, 276), ephedrine (313), tetrahydropapaveroline (259), and theophylline (201, 464a). The glycogenolytic system and the mechanical activity are not modified by mephentermine, methoxamine, or metanephrine in the rat heart (188), or by methoxamine, naphazoline, or reserpine in the dog heart (313).

Histamine activates phosphorylase in the perfused guinea pig heart, but its effect is not antagonized by β-adrenergic blocking agents, including pronethalol (259).

Norepinephrine or epinephrine effects are potentiated by theophylline (201), cocaine (180, 297), and some antihistamines (297), but not by pretreatment with reserpine (297).

Blockade of catecholamine effects is observed with DCI [dog (259, 313), guinea pig (259, 464a), rabbit (256), rat (209)], pronethalol (258, 368, 382), propranolol (297), and with Kö 592 (258), but not with IMA (368, 382) nor with the α-adrenergic blocking agents phenoxybenzamine (209, 313), phentolamine (235), or dibozane (235).

Blockade of catecholamine effects by β-adrenergic blocking agents is considered selective because these agents do not inhibit the action of theophylline (259).

F. Smooth Muscles

1. *Blood Vessels*

In bovine mesenteric arteries *in vitro* under anaerobic conditions epinephrine or potassium cause contraction and an increase in lactate production; Dibenamine prevents both effects of epinephrine, but not those of potassium (287). DHE also inhibits the effect of epinephrine on lactate production in the absence of glucose, but not in the presence of glucose (284, 284a). Epinephrine does not increase mesenteric artery phosphorylase (322) or glycogenolysis (32). It does increase the content of glucose-6-P, fructose-6-P, fructose-1,6-diphosphate, and dihydroxyacetonephosphate, and these changes are not inhibited by DHE, which inhibits contraction of the mesenteric artery (32, 33). Even in the presence of O_2 and glucose epinephrine increases lactic acid production (286).

Epinephrine does not increase the activity of the adenyl cyclase system of dog aorta or femoral artery (248).

Epinephrine reduces mucopolysaccharide formation by human aorta *in vitro* (203a), but when administered twice daily for 5 days to rabbits it increases the incorporation of ^{35}S-sulfate in the aorta (318).

2. *Tracheal Muscle*

Epinephrine produces a small increase in phosphorylase activity in bovine tracheal muscle (322).

3. *Intestinal Muscle*

Epinephrine causes an increased lactate formation by stomach muscle whether the muscle contracts or relaxes after Dibenamine treatment (323). In rabbit jejunum epinephrine causes increased glycogenolysis and lactate formation (321).

Taenia coli muscle of the guinea pig is relaxed by epinephrine whether or not DCI is present, but DCI prevented the activation of phosphorylase (448). An improvement in the technique of handling the preparation changed the response to one in which cyclic AMP is increased by epinephrine but phosphorylase is unchanged (56). Other investigators report that epinephrine increases phosphorylase in the taenia coli and this response is inhibited by β-adrenergic blocking agents but not by α-adrenergic blocking agents (52).

4. *Uterus*

Catecholamines are reported to decrease (271) or increase (108) rat uterine phosphorylase *in vivo* and to decrease its glycogen *in vitro* (272) and *in vivo* (108). *In vivo,* phenoxybenzamine is a more effective antagonist against norepinephrine and epinephrine than against ISO, and DCI and pronethalol are more effective against ISO (108). *In vitro,* the catecholamine activation of phosphorylase is antagonized by β-adrenergic blocking agents but not by α-adrenergic blocking agents (52). Phenoxybenzamine prevented the 5-hydroxytryptamine-induced contraction and activation of phosphorylase of the rat uterus *in vitro* (109).

5. *Ductus deferens*

In vivo, epinephrine decreases the glycogen content and phosphorylase activity of the rat ductus deferens, but *in vitro* it increases the phosphorylase activity of tissue from castrate but not from intact rats (274).

G. Other Tissues

1. *Kidney*

Epinephrine either does not change (367) or increases (252) kidney glycogen. Lactate production by the kidney (120) is increased.

2. *Brain*

Epinephrine and amphetamine reduce rat brain phosphorylase (219). Adenylic cyclase preparations of dog brain are stimulated to produce cyclic AMP by ISO > E > NE (248).

3. *Glands*

Catecholamines increase the oxidation of glucose to CO_2 in thyroid gland slices (360) and in rat submaxillary gland if calcium is present (393, 394).

4. *Erythrocytes*

Catecholamines (ISO > E > NE) increase the cyclic AMP of nucleated pigeon red cells, and the effect of epinephrine is prevented by DCI, reduced by ergotamine, and not influenced by phenoxybenzamine (98).

5. *Bone*

Epinephrine produces glycogenolysis in mouse parietal bone (237).

H. Interpretations

It is now proposed (446) that the cyclase system in most tissues is responsive to catecholamines and that, where this is true, the receptor behaves as a β-adrenotropic receptor in terms of relative potencies of the catecholamines and the antagonistic effects of the α- and β-adrenergic blocking agents. There is a growing body of evidence that the activation of the glycogenolytic system by catecholamines occurs in many tissues. It may be that only β-receptors are involved in this response, but the evidence is too limited and, in some cases, it is contradictory, so that this hypothesis must be critically tested in many tissues.

III. EFFECTS ON FAT METABOLISM

A. Fat Metabolism

In early work it was apparent that fat was the major fuel when metabolism was stimulated by epinephrine (78) and that the sympathetic nervous system and catecholamines had prominent effects on fat metabolism (483, 189, 190). Effects of catecholamines on fat transport were supported by observations that epinephrine decreased "white" adipose tissue lipid and increased liver triglycerides (16, 76). The observations of Dole (112) and Gordon and Cherkes (160a) that the catecholamines increase plasma free fatty acids gave the impetus for the important work of recent years on the effect of catecholamines on fat transport and utilization. An excellent extensive summary of the physiology and pharmacology of adipose tissue is now available (375).

There is now a well-established scheme of the control of fat transport and utilization. Activation of sympathetic nerves (152, 241) or administration of catecholamines (191) activates lipolysis in adipose tissue. Hydrolysis of triglycerides releases free fatty acids (FFA) and glycerol. The FFA are complexed with plasma albumin and the plasma FFA level is increased. Some of the FFA may be resynthesized in the adipose cells to triglycerides (462). The released glycerol cannot be reutilized for this synthesis because glycerol kinase is deficient in adipose tissue. Glucose is essential as a source of glycerophosphate for the resynthesis of triglycerides. Lactate or pyruvate infusions in dogs appear to inhibit the effect of norepinephrine on plasma FFA more strongly than does glucose (319). Utilization of FFA by liver (426), muscle (427), heart (410), and other tissues (122, 410) is increased when the plasma level of FFA is increased by catecholamines or by other mechanisms, but the increased utilization appears closely related to the plasma concentration (13) rather than to a direct effect of the catecholamines on FFA utilization (123). Although catecholamines do not increase the extraction of fatty acids by the isolated heart, the oxidation to CO_2 is increased in proportion to the increased O_2 consumption (162).

B. Fat Transport

1. *Plasma FFA and Glycerol*

Increased plasma FFA and/or glycerol is an indication of lipid mobilization from fat depots for storage or utilization by the liver and other tissues. Some species of animals are very sensitive to this effect of catecholamines, whereas other species appear more or less resistant to this action. Man (112, 160a, 408, 436, 496), dog (141, 158), rat (133), and horse (64) are quite sensitive to the FFA-mobilizing effect of catecholamines; cat (136) is much less sensitive; rabbit, guinea pig, and pig (390) respond poorly; the chicken is unresponsive and so is its adipose tissue *in vitro* (66). In man, plasma FFA is more sensitive to ISO than are plasma lactate and glucose or O_2 consumption (54). Norepinephrine increases plasma oleic and linoleic acids more than stearic and palmitic acids (386, 425), and chronic treatment of rabbits with epinephrine increased their plasma unsaturated fatty acids (350). Epinephrine decreases triglycerides and increases di- and monoglycerides of rabbit adipose tissue (468).

Depletion of rat epididymal fat during a 12-hour fast is not influenced by hexamethonium, phenoxybenzamine, or ergotamine (278a).

Catecholamines are implicated in the increased plasma FFA during fasting by the observations that reserpine treatment reduces the response in intact animals (124) and prevents it in adrenodemedullated animals (139).

The availability of glucose regulates the resynthesis of adipose tissue FFA into triglycerides. Thus, agents which elevate plasma glucose reduce the release of FFA into the blood (414). Differences in the potencies of norepinephrine and epinephrine in the maintenance of high plasma FFA levels during continuous infusions of catecholamines (141) are related to the much lower hyperglycemic potency of norepinephrine (193). Epinephrine produces a larger and more prolonged increase in plasma FFA in patients with hepatic glycogenosis, which prevents epinephrine-induced hyperglycemia, than in normal subjects (412). The FFA response to epinephrine is not influenced by the level of thyroid function in humans (177), by obesity (358), or by toxemia of pregnancy (496).

Cold-acclimated rats produce a greater increase in plasma FFA and their adipose tissues *in vitro* release more FFA in response to norepinephrine (179), but their hyperglycemic responses are lower (379).

Insulin administration reduces the effect of epinephrine on plasma FFA (55, 362, 369). Although insulin lowers plasma FFA, a marked, prolonged hypoglycemia induced by insulin in dogs (14) and in man (470) causes a sympathetically activated "rebound" increase in plasma FFA.

Aging of rats does not influence the plasma FFA response to norepinephrine, but adipose tissue of old rats is less responsive (28, 221). Fed obese mice (307) and adipose tissue of obese mice *in vitro* (308) are less responsive to epinephrine.

Some rather selective antagonists to catecholamine-induced FFA release have been reported. Prostaglandin is a very potent inhibitor of the increase in plasma FFA in response to epinephrine or norepinephrine. It does not antagonize the hyperglycemic response (29), but, through its own depressor activity, it produces a "physiological" antagonism to the catecholamine pressor effects (435). Prostaglandin is a complex fatty acid. Other organic acids such as nicotinic (63, 65, 67, 151, 348), salicylic, and benzoic acids (34) inhibit norepinephrine-induced increase in FFA, but nicotinamide (121), *p*-aminosalicylic acid, and salicylamide are not inhibitory (34). The mechanism of the inhibitory action of nicotinic acid (36) and of prostaglandin (436) is a selective antagonism against the activation of adipose tissue lipase; they do not depress the unstimulated release of FFA and glycerol (63). Nicotinic acid in modifying FFA does not affect the blood pressure or pulse rate in man (67, 348) or pressor responses to epinephrine and norepinephrine in dogs (65, 151).

Plasma FFA is not increased by epinephrine in scorbutic guinea pigs, but treatment with ascorbic acid restores the response (331).

Plasma glycerol is increased by epinephrine and norepinephrine in rabbit (101, 174), in dog (68), and in man (68, 332, 408, 411), and by ISO in rat (207). Glucose reduces plasma glycerol as it reduces plasma FFA (411).

2. *Blood Lipid*

A large dose of epinephrine in oil increases serum triglycerides, cholesterol, and phospholipids in rabbits (119) and in dogs (230), but in rats, after 24 hours, total and free cholesterol and phospholipid are elevated, although triglycerides are not (414a), and in dogs chronic treatment with epinephrine elevates plasma cholesterol (154). The delayed increase in cholesterol in dogs treated with norepinephrine is not prevented by doses of nicotinic acid or MJ-1999 which inhibit the increase in plasma FFA (260).

Increased triglyceride uptake by the dog heart during the infusion of epinephrine (373) may cause catecholamine-induced fatty changes in the dog heart (300).

3. *Interaction of FFA with Carbohydrate Metabolism*

When tissue utilization of FFA is increased by a higher plasma FFA, glucose tolerance is reduced (400) and oxidation of glucose is diminished, so that more glycogen is stored and more glucose may be converted to lactate. A greater conversion of glucose to pyruvate and lactate occurs when glucose is administered with norepinephrine in a dose which only increases plasma FFA (473). It has been suggested that this result indicates that a rise in plasma FFA directs the metabolism of glucose to a greater extent into pyruvate and lactate. Conversely, infusion of lactate (or exercise) reduces plasma FFA (159).

4. *Liver*

The liver (and other tissues) remove FFA in proportion to its concentration in the plasma (143, 426, 427). Partial hepatectomy slows the return of plasma FFA to the control level following the administration of epinephrine; CCl_4 poisoning prevents the epinephrine-induced increase in FFA, presumably by increasing the liver uptake of FFA (228). Some of the FFA is oxidized in the liver, but most is converted into triglycerides and eventually released as lipoproteins into the blood. Increased utilization for synthesis of FFA into triglycerides may explain the reduced amount of α-glycerophosphate in the liver after epinephrine, alcohol, or starvation (454). Norepinephrine in dogs (141) and rats (16, 149) increases liver triglycerides, but not liver cholesterol or phospholipid. When norepinephrine is infused into the portal vein, liver glycerides are not increased (141). In the perfused rat liver epinephrine and norepinephrine reduce the release of triglycerides even when phenoxybenzamine prevents vasoconstriction (197). Epinephrine increases the incorporation of palmitate-^{14}C into triglycerides without increasing the specific activity of the triglycerides (145), presumably because there is also an increased oxidation of fatty acids to ketone bodies (175, 181a).

C. Adipose Tissue

Most studies of the effects of catecholamines on adipose tissue *in vitro* have been done on rat epididymal fat pads. This tissue responds to epinephrine and norepinephrine with an increase in tissue FFA and a release of FFA when albumin is present for binding the FFA (173). Lipid peroxides are also increased by epinephrine (39).

In the isolated, perfused epididymal fat pad epinephrine increases the release of FFA (202), but not the release of lipase into the perfusate as heparin does (203).

Rat mesenteric fat also increases its FFA release in response to epinephrine (376), but brown adipose tissue does not (345). Brown adipose tissue increases its O_2 consumption in response to epinephrine (223).

Perirenal adipose tissues of rat, dog, or hamster produce more FFA when exposed to epinephrine or norepinephrine, but tissues of rabbit, guinea pig, or pig do not (390).

Human subcutaneous tissue *in vitro* increases its FFA release when exposed to epinephrine, but not its O_2 consumption (35).

The composition of the released FFA resembles that of the tissue triglycerides, but palmitic and palmitoleic acids appear in higher concentrations and oleic and linoleic acids in lower concentrations (204, 315).

Epinephrine also increases the FFA in rat diaphragm (155) and in rat heart (70) *in vitro.*

1. *Effects on Enzymes and Metabolism of Adipose Tissue*

Epinephrine activates glycogenolysis (458, 459) and lipolysis (460) of rat adipose tissue. The effect on lipolysis appears separable from the effect on glycogenolysis, because serotonin activates phosphorylase and glycogenolysis without affecting FFA release, while epinephrine activates both (458), and there are quantitative differences between the two processes activated by glucagon or by epinephrine (171). Epinephrine does not influence the glycogen synthetase activity of adipose tissue (169).

The mechanisms for the activation by epinephrine of glycogenolysis and lipolysis in adipose tissue are now known in considerable detail. The phosphorylase (458) and the lipase (205, 380, 388) activities are increased in homogenates of adipose tissue previously exposed to epinephrine. The lipase activated by epinephrine is not a lipoprotein lipase (205, 388), and unlike heparin, which activates the lipoprotein lipase and releases this activity into the medium, epinephrine only activates a special lipase in the tissue and does not release lipase activity into the medium (37).

Epinephrine does not release the lipemia clearing factor (heparin-released) into the plasma of dogs or humans (135), but it has a late effect on human plasma lipolytic activity (374) and on rat cardiac lipoprotein lipase (6).

The epinephrine-activated lipase is found in the oil fraction and fat cake, not in the aqueous layer or in the sediment of the centrifuged homogenate of adipose tissue (206). A similar lipase is activated by epinephrine in rabbit adipose tissue, but to a much smaller extent than in rat tissue (461), and in the rat heart (38), but not in rabbit aorta (495).

Later, it was found (381) that the lipase activity in a cell-free adipose tissue preparation could be activated by incubation with ATP plus epinephrine; activation also occurs with cyclic AMP, and caffeine or theophylline potentiate the effect of cyclic AMP; activation is produced by calcium in place of cyclic AMP. Epinephrine activates lipase in the adipose tissue homogenate, but adrenocorticotropic hormone (ACTH), thyroid stimulating hormone (TSH), and growth hormone (GH) do not (389). The cell-free homogenate of the epididymal fat pad catalyzes the synthesis of cyclic AMP, and epinephrine stimulates this process. The mechanism of action of epinephrine on adipose tissue lipase resembles the activation of phosphorylase in several tissues, as demonstrated by recent studies (60) in which low concentrations of epinephrine increased the concentration of cyclic AMP in adipose tissue and a lipid-soluble dibutyl ester of cyclic AMP was able to activate the lipase in the intact cell. The effect of epinephrine on cyclic AMP content of adipose tissue was potentiated by caffeine and antagonized by DCI and to some extent by phentolamine. Thus, the correlation of the activation of lipolysis with changes in cyclic AMP levels indicates that the latter does act as a "second mediator" in this process (446).

Epinephrine increases the glucose uptake as well as the FFA and glycerol release of adipose tissue *in vitro* (267), but added glucose inhibits the release of FFA (55) but not the release of glycerol (240, 413). Oxygen consumption is also increased by epinephrine, but if the suspending medium does not contain albumin to bind the FFA or glucose (plus insulin) to increase reesterification of the released FFA, an inhibition of oxygen uptake supervenes, an effect attributed to the increased cellular concentration of FFA which may inhibit various metabolic processes (18, 173, 227). Epinephrine, in addition to increasing the FFA release and O_2 consumption, also increases CO_2 production, lactate and glycerophosphate formation, and fatty acid synthesis in the presence of glucose and insulin (138, 146, 290). Epinephrine reduces the conversion of pyruvate-2-^{14}C to lactate, glyceride-glycerol, fatty acids, and protein (138) and of acetate-1-^{14}C to lipid and $^{14}CO_2$ (357) and of glucose-U-^{14}C to fatty acids (172), but it increases the conversion of glucose-U-^{14}C to CO_2 and glyceride-glycerol (383). Epinephrine reduces the incorporation of palmitate-1-^{14}C into triglycerides of adipose tissue 290, 432, 434).

The increase in glucose uptake, conversion to glyceride-glycerol, and oxidation induced in adipose tissue by exposure to epinephrine could be produced by exposure to palmitate (62). Thus, the effects of epinephrine on glucose metabolism are interpreted as effects resulting from the release of FFA (62). Opposed to this view are the facts that a low concentration of epinephrine causes only an increased FFA release without a change in glucose uptake, and that serotonin increases glucose uptake without changing FFA release (460). Under some conditions epinephrine or norepinephrine reduces glucose uptake (463, 464).

Epinephrine also stimulates reesterification of FFA, but after the early period (413) the rate of lipolysis is far greater than the rate of reesterification (462).

Although calcium does not appear essential for the effect of epinephrine on FFA release (279) or on glucose uptake (463), NaF, 10^{-2} *M*, prevents the lipolytic effect of epinephrine (462).

D. Effects of Drugs

1. *Sympathomimetic Amines*

The relative lipolytic potencies of epinephrine, norepinephrine, and ISO are quite similar in man (43, 86, 333, 361), and rat (102, 140, 207,

281, 282, 334, 482, 487), but in hamster adipose tissue the relative potencies are ISO > E > NE (390). Some differences in the potencies of epinephrine and norepinephrine are attributable to differences in hyperglycemic potencies (404).

In man weak lipolytic activity is reported for α-methylnorepinephrine and synephrine (333), but many other common sympathomimetic amines are not effective (43, 333). Amphetamine (242), and tyramine are effective in normal but not in reserpine-pretreated rats (140). Rat adipose tissue *in vitro* does not respond to ephedrine, amphetamine, dopamine, or tyramine (403, 482). Phenylephrine is effective in rat adipose tissue *in vitro* (482). In fact, ephedrine, amphetamine, and tyramine may be better antagonists than phentolamine against norepinephrine *in vitro* (482).

2. *Interaction of Autonomic Drugs with Catecholamines*

FFA release from rat adipose tissue *in vitro* is not changed by acetylcholine (plus physostigmine) or by carbachol, and these agents do not antagonize the response to epinephrine (74).

Cocaine, in dogs, potentiates the effect of norepinephrine on plasma FFA (163, 181), an effect not dependent on an intact liver circulation, but the effect of epinephrine is only slightly influenced. In the rat, cocaine prevents the tyramine-induced increase in plasma FFA (484). Cocaine does not potentiate the effect of norepinephrine on rat adipose tissue *in vitro* (338), but under these conditions tyramine alone is inactive (482). Caffeine, 100 mg/kg, increases rat plasma FFA for hours (242), and *in vitro* caffeine potentiates the epinephrine-induced release of glycerol (462).

Reserpine pretreatment potentiates the plasma FFA response to epinephrine and norepinephrine in dogs (1). Guanethidine reduces these responses in rabbits (251). α-Methyltyrosine pretreatment in rats prevents the increase in plasma FFA in response to tyramine, but not in response to norepinephrine (330, 486). The observation that α-methyldopa does not prevent the action of tyramine is explained by the fact that the decarboxylated derivative α-methylnorepinephrine is about as potent as norepinephrine on rat adipose tissue (330, 485).

3. *Adrenergic Blocking Agents*

In general, α-adrenotropic blocking agents are poor antagonists against catecholamine-induced lipolysis. Ergotamine in rats has been reported to be an effective antagonist (160) or to be ineffective (278a); a large dose of dihydroergotamine is an effective antagonist (133). Ergotamine is ineffective in the dog (296), and hydergine is ineffective in man (167).

Studies on the effects of adrenergic blocking agents on FFA are complicated by the intrinsic action of some of the blocking agents on FFA release.

Dibenamine (193), phenoxybenzamine (296), and phentolamine (44, 45, 46, 249) produce FFA release by a mechanism which appears to involve the release of catecholamines (47). Phenoxybenzamine also increases serum cholesterol in rabbits (7). Several β-adrenergic blocking agents behave as competitive dualists in releasing FFA and then blocking the response to catecholamines. DCI, other dihalophenylethylamine derivatives, and pronethalol (254, 406) release FFA by their own effect on adipose tissue, but MJ-1999 and propranolol are free of this activity (261).

Although some reports (193, 405) indicate that a large dose of Dibenamine or phenoxybenzamine suppresses the catecholamine-induced increase in plasma FFA, most studies in dog (296, 301), in man (364), and in rat (79, 437) indicate that these agents are weak or ineffective antagonists against catecholamine activation of lipolysis. It is suggested that the adrenergic blocking agents prevent the FFA release by rat adipose tissue but allow the activation of lipase by norepinephrine (53).

Phentolamine also is not an effective antagonist in dogs (151) or in man (168); it is effective in high doses in rats (336, 403, 482) or on rat adipose tissue *in vitro* (405).

Dibozane is not an effective antagonist of epinephrine-induced lipolysis in either the rat (133) or the cat (136).

β-Adrenotropic blocking agents are good antagonists to catecholamine-induced increases in plasma FFA in several species. The catecholamine effect is suppressed in dogs by DCI (13, 15, 151, 314), pronethalol (151, 260), MJ-1999 (261), and IMA and other methoxamine derivatives (58, 298, 301, 392); in cats by MJ-1999 and IMA (136); and in man by pronethalol (364, 433), IMA (392), and *N*-*t*-butylmethoxamine (215).

In rats only slight or no antagonism is obtained with DCI (133) and pronethalol (236); MJ-1999 (133, 261) is inactive; Kö 592 [1-(3-methylphenoxy)-3-isopropylaminopropanol-2] produces only partial antagonism (437); and IMA (133) is inactive.

In rat adipose tissue *in vitro* high concentrations of DCI inhibit catecholamine-induced FFA release (15, 281, 283, 335, 336), but this effect is not selective for only catecholamine actions on FFA. Other compounds closely related to DCI have similar characteristics (281, 282). IMA in high concentrations is also antagonistic (58, 298).

DCI is also an antagonist in adipose tissue of the hamster (391).

FFA release by catecholamines appears to be mediated by β-receptors in man, dog, and cat. In the rat the situation is somewhat complicated. β-Adrenergic blocking drugs are not effective *in vivo. In vitro* both α- and β-adrenergic blocking drugs are effective in relatively high concentrations (480, 481). It has been found (479) that blockade by phentolamine is noncompetitive, but β-adrenergic blockers (337) produce a blockade of the competitive, reversible type, although the receptor has a somewhat different character in the rat adipose tissue than the β-receptor in other tissues. The "second mediator" has been demonstrated to be cyclic AMP in the rat adipose tissue. Therefore, it may well be that in rat adipose tissue the adrenotropic receptor resembles the β-receptor in biochemical function but has a different structure-activity spectrum.

IV. EFFECTS ON OXYGEN CONSUMPTION

A. Intact Animals

The calorigenic action of epinephrine is most commonly measured in terms of oxygen consumption, an indirect estimate of heat production. The calorigenic response to epinephrine has been demonstrated in many animal species (128, 233, 320). Large doses of epinephrine or norepinephrine, however, reduce oxygen consumption or cause a diphasic effect, a reduction followed by an increase in oxygen consumption. Reports that epinephrine produces only a reduction in oxygen consumption in pigeons (397) and in fishes may be explained by more complete dose-response data. For example, in mice epinephrine, in a dose of 1–2 mg/kg subcutaneously, increases O_2 consumption, while 4–5 mg/kg reduces O_2 consumption (395).

The effect of epinephrine on the oxygen utilization in the whole animal cannot be attributed to an effect on any single organ. Several organs increase their oxygen use in response to epinephrine. The effect is somewhat complex in that organs *in situ* appear to show this response, whereas most investigators using resting tissue segments or slices have observed little or no effects of epinephrine on oxygen metabolism. More recent studies, however, indicate that epinephrine increases the oxygen utilization of some resting tissues under suitable conditions.

For several reasons investigators have been seeking an action of epinephrine that would account for the calorigenic effect through an indirect effect, rather than through an effect exerted directly on the metabolic machinery of a particular organ. Some of the proposed mechanisms include: an increase in work of the heart which would increase the oxygen use of the heart; an increase in protein metabolism which would invoke the specific dynamic effect; an increase in plasma glucose, lactic acid, or free fatty acids (FFA) which might cause an increase in the oxygen uptake of several tissues.

Recent interest in the calorigenic effect of the catecholamines was stimulated by the hypothesis that the increased oxygen use in acute cold exposure or in cold-acclimated animals may be referable to increased sympathetic activity. Since cold exposure does release catecholamines into the circulating blood, the effects of catecholamines on metabolism may explain the acute response to cold. There is some doubt, however, that the catecholamines play a role in the increased oxygen metabolism of cold-acclimated animals. The differences between the thermogenesis of cold exposure (not attributable to shivering) and catecholamine effects are discussed in several papers (40, 100, 106, 212, 268, 310, 325, 326, 327, 328).

Of some importance in the general mechanisms for cold adaptation is the observation that the interscapular brown adipose tissue of cold-adapted rats (6°C for 40 days) has about twice the O_2 consumption *in vitro* as the tissue of warm-adapted rats (420).

An interesting mechanism is proposed (266) for the sensitization to norepinephrine-induced calorigenesis in cold-acclimated animals. Since daily administration of norepinephrine in oil for 45 days increased the response to norepinephrine almost as much as did exposure to 6°C for 45 days, in both situations the sensitization may be explained by a saturation of norepinephrine stores so that the acutely administered norepinephrine reaches the tissue receptors in higher concentration (266). If this hypothesis is correct, cocaine should not potentiate the effect of norepinephrine in cold-adapted or norepinephrine-adapted rats.

The fact that norepinephrine in a dose of about 2 mg/kg decreases the oxygen consumption of control rats but increases that of cold-acclimated rats (402) raises questions concerning differences in circulation or in circulatory reactivity to catecholamines to explain some of the unusual effects occurring in cold-adapted animals. One such phenomenon is the reversal of relative potencies of epinephrine and norepinephrine that occurs after cold acclimation. The decrease in O_2 consumption and in body temperature is attributed to the vasoconstrictor action of norepinephrine, since these effects of norepinephrine are antagonized by phenoxybenzamine or dihydroergotamine but not by DCI (402). Also, in cats norepinephrine is less potent than epinephrine and the diphasic effect of higher doses of norepinephrine is converted by dibenamine into a pure increase in O_2 consumption (428).

At relatively high rates of infusion, 10 μg kg^{-1} min^{-1}, epinephrine, norepinephrine, and ISO almost double the oxygen consumption of anesthetized rats, but only epinephrine and norepinephrine reduce the respiratory quotient (RQ) (9). A single large dose of ISO produces a transient increase in RQ (440). Even with prolonged infusions of epinephrine which maintain high blood sugar levels the RQ is reduced (50). Since all three catecholamines raise the plasma FFA and since ISO raises the plasma lactic acid level with but a small effect on blood glucose, the difference in effect of ISO on the RQ may be explained by lactate competing more effectively than glucose with FFA for oxidation. At higher rates of infusion of epinephrine in rats oxygen consumption is reduced, but phentolamine converts the effect of epinephrine into a large increase of oxygen consumption (10). Hull (212) found that pronethalol potentiates the decrease in O_2 use with epinephrine. These findings taken together indicate that the vasoconstrictor effect of larger doses of epinephrine must be the cause of the reduced oxygen consumption. These results also suggest that the effect of epinephrine on oxygen consumption is not mediated by α-receptors.

1. *Dog*

Epinephrine, norepinephrine, or ISO infused at a rate of 1 μg kg^{-1} min^{-1} increase the oxygen consumption of dogs when the blood pH is normal or alkaline, but not when it is reduced below 7.3 (343). A similar inhibition of activation by norepinephrine of lipolysis by low pH is attributed to an inhibition of the cyclase system by acidity (451).

Tolazoline is about 50 times less potent than norepinephrine for increasing the O_2 consumption in the anesthetized dog (231).

2. *Cat*

In adult cats epinephrine, 1 μg kg^{-1} min^{-1}, increases O_2 consumption 15–20% (176). In cats (198) norepinephrine is more active than epinephrine in increasing O_2 use, and cold acclimation sensitizes to the calorigenic effect.

Epinephrine or norepinephrine, 4 μg kg^{-1} min^{-1} for 5 minutes, increases oxygen consumption about equally. A secondary increase in O_2 use after the first 15 minutes is absent in eviscerated cats and is attributed, therefore, to hepatic metabolism (419).

In newborn cats, epinephrine and norepinephrine, 0.4 mg/kg subcutaneously, are reported to be equally potent calorigenic agents even after pretreatment with Dibenzyline®, 25 mg/kg (23), or to be very different in effect (NE $>$ E) (326, 409). In young cats also norepinephrine is much more effective than epinephrine for increasing O_2 consumption (325, 328). The data (326a) indicate the following order of potencies: NE = ISO > E = phenylephrine; dopamine has some effect, but novadral (*m*-hydroxyphenylethanolamine), normetanephrine, and metanephrine are inactive at 0.4 mg/kg subcutaneously. Blood glucose and lactate vary independently from O_2 use in neonate cats when metabolism is stimulated by epinephrine or norepinephrine (22). Furthermore, the action of norepinephrine on O_2 consumption is not stimulated by infusing lactate, glucose, or glucose plus insulin.

Cold acclimation increases the sensitivity of the cat to norepinephrine more than to epinephrine (198).

The calorigenic effect of epinephrine in cats is not inhibited by phenoxybenzamine (428).

3. *Rabbit*

The potency ratios for both the increases in lactic acid and O_2 consumption were calculated to be *l*-ISO: *l*-E: *l*-NE, 1:9:120 (289). In newborn rabbits, norepinephrine has a greater calorigenic effect than epinephrine (100, 326a, 409).

Rabbits are less sensitive to the calorigenic effects of epinephrine and norepinephrine than are rats (80). At 5 $\mu g\ kg^{-1}\ min^{-1}$, epinephrine is more effective than norepinephrine in warm- and cold-adapted rabbits. Rabbits, unlike rats, show slight evidence of cold sensitization to catecholamines, but cold adaptation does increase the rate of response of O_2 metabolism (80).

DCI inhibits the calorigenic and hyperlacticacidemic effects of epinephrine and ISO in adult rabbits (288), and pronethalol inhibits the calorigenic effect of catecholamines in newborn rabbits (212).

Cocaine increases the O_2 consumption more than the blood lactate and also increases these responses to epinephrine (285).

Oxygen consumption in newborn rabbits at 35°C is increased by 2 $\mu g\ kg^{-1}\ min^{-1}$ of norepinephrine and ISO more than by epinephrine. These effects are reduced by exposure to an ambient temperature of 25°C, which increases the basal O_2 consumption, or by hypoxia (10% O_2) at either 35°C or 25°C (40).

4. *Guinea Pig*

In newborn guinea pigs norepinephrine and epinephrine are equally effective in elevating O_2 consumption (100, 326).

5. *Rat*

The relative potencies for increasing O_2 consumption in rats are ISO > E = NE, and, furthermore, the effect of norepinephrine, 0.5 mg/kg subcutaneously, on O_2 consumption occurs with negligible changes in blood glucose and lactate and in liver and muscle glycogen (164). In newborn of most species, including the rat, norepinephrine is more effective than epinephrine (212, 326).

In rats the potencies on oxygen consumption of ISO : metaproterenol : DCI are 20 : 3 : 1 (441). ISO or metaproterenol are effective also in rats pretreated with reserpine, indicating a direct effect of these amines, but a small dose of DCI, 0.5 mg/kg, does not prevent the action of ISO (441). Other more potent β-adrenergic blocking agents (propranolol, etc.) inhibit the calorigenic effects of ISO, epinephrine, and norepinephrine (442). The calorigenic effect of epinephrine in rats is inhibited by ergotamine (355) or DHE (399), but not by phenoxybenzamine (224, 407).

Amphetamine, 5 mg/kg, increases O_2 use in control anesthetized rats, but not in rats pretreated with reserpine (363). DOPA, 50 mg/kg, is effective in raising oxygen consumption in rats, but 5-HTP is not (363).

Cold acclimation sensitizes rats to the calorigenic effects of catecholamines, especially norepinephrine (105, 200, 210, 211).

Adrenocortical hormones allow the full expression of epinephrine's calorigenic effect in rats (95). In cold-adapted (10°C) rats urinary excretion of epinephrine and norepinephrine increased over four times that of control (25°C) rats (265). The cold-adapted rat does not appear more sensitive to the calorigenic effect of norepinephrine than the warm-adapted rat when the tests are done at 30°C and 5°C in rats anesthetized with pentobarbital, treated with Flaxedil®, and artificially ventilated (340).

6. *Mouse*

Norepinephrine is more potent than epinephrine for increasing the O_2 metabolism of newborn mice (326). Methamphetamine, 20 mg/kg, produces parallel increases in O_2 consumption and body temperature (113).

7. *Man*

In man at 0.1 $\mu g\ kg^{-1}\ min^{-1}$, ISO is about as effective as epinephrine in increasing O_2 consumption. Norepinephrine is less potent than epinephrine for producing the calorigenic effect (77, 232). Also, norepinephrine has less effect on blood lactate than epinephrine or ISO (77) and less effect on blood glucose than epinephrine (232). An increase in the effect on O_2 use of norepinephrine, 0.15 $\mu g\ kg^{-1}\ min^{-1}$, was observed in cold-exposed humans (226).

In man, sympatol, 180 mg subcutaneously, produces insignificant changes in O_2 consumption and in blood glucose and lactate compared to the marked effects on all three produced by epinephrine, 1 mg subcutaneously (49).

Pronethalol inhibits the calorigenic effect of norepinephrine (433).

B. Individual Tissues

Oxygen utilization is increased by epinephrine in several tissues.

1. *Liver*

Epinephrine increases oxygen use of the perfused canine liver (8).

2. *Muscle*

In confirmation of many earlier studies, it is found that epinephrine or norepinephrine does not increase the O_2 consumption of the kitten isolated diaphragm whether the catecholamines are given *in vivo* before the removal of the diaphragm or added to the diaphragm *in vitro* (21). Neither epinephrine nor norepinephrine modifies the O_2 consumption of the intact rat leg, a preparation which includes a large muscle mass (182).

3. *Heart*

The blood-perfused dog heart increases its O_2 use in response to epinephrine, norepinephrine, or ISO (186). DCI inhibits the effects on O_2 consumption of all three catecholamines, but phenoxybenzamine does not (185). Mephentermine (478) also increases the oxygen consumption of the dog heart, but methoxamine decreases it (185).

Despite earlier reports that epinephrine does not increase the O_2 consumption of heart slices (128), it is reported (447) that epinephrine produces a 20% increase in O_2 consumption of rat heart slices and a 50% increase in slices obtained from hearts of rats subjected to hypoxia. Another study (311) supports earlier findings in that epinephrine produces only a slight decrease in O_2 consumption of rat heart slices, but significantly reduces the oxidation of exogenous glucose and palmitate.

Although several studies on "resting" cardiac muscle preparations have demonstrated no significant increase (269) or reduction (311, 161) in O_2 use, there are now indications that epinephrine can increase O_2 consumption in "nonworking" cardiac muscle. In one study (30) it was found that epinephrine or norepinephrine increased O_2 use in fibrillating or in potassium-arrested dog hearts *in situ,* but in a more recent study only small effects of catecholamines were found in the potassium-arrested dog heart (250). Epinephrine increased O_2 consumption to a significant degree in the perfused, potassium-arrested rat heart (70). During the increased O_2 use in the presence of epinephrine there was also an increased release of glycerol not associated with an increase in FFA release. The later findings were interpreted as evidence that the increased O_2 use was secondary to the epinephrine-induced lipolysis and the activation of O_2 consumption by the metabolized FFA or their reconversion to triglycerides (70). In the perfused beating or potassium-arrested rat heart oxidizable FFA at concentrations found in intact rats produce large increases in qO_2 of the heart (71).

Epinephrine doubled the O_2 uptake of perfused hearts even in the absence of exogenous substrates, but the effect lasted only 30 minutes; in the presence of glucose, the effect on O_2 use was present for over 2 hours (144).

The earlier controversial reports on the effect of epinephrine on cardiac efficiency (128) are explained by recent detailed studies. In papillary muscle epinephrine increases the efficiency of hypodynamic muscles, but the efficiency is unchanged by epinephrine or norepinephrine in well-functioning papillary muscles (269). In the intact heart, epinephrine reduces the efficiency at low filling pressure, does not change the efficiency at moderate filling pressure, and increases the efficiency only at high filling pressure (increased fiber length) possibly as a result of a decrease in the fiber length (478). In other studies on the isolated, supported dog heart, low doses of norepinephrine increased contraction with little effect on O_2 consumption and only at high doses did it produce "oxygen wasting" (476).

An apparent antagonism by nitroglycerin of the effect of norepinephrine on the O_2 use of the dog heart has been shown to be an effect of nitroglycerin on the total work of the heart (303).

4. *Smooth Muscle*

Relaxation of frog stomach muscle and guinea pig uterus by epinephrine is associated with increased oxygen utilization (418).

5. *Salivary Glands*

Epinephrine increases the O_2 use and amylase secretion of mouse parotid glands *in vitro,* but the effect on O_2 use was not observed in the absence of serum globulin, in the presence of Dibenamine or of *d*-tartrate, or in glands of mice sacrificed with ether (170). The O_2 consumption of cat submaxillary gland slices also is increased by a low concentration of epinephrine or norepinephrine (439).

6. *Kidney*

Epinephrine does not increase the O_2 use of the rat kidney (182).

C. Mechanism of the Calorigenic Effect

The calorigenic effect of the catecholamines cannot be attributed to an indirect response to the elevation of blood glucose or of blood lactate. The relative potencies of epinephrine, norepinephrine, and ISO for increasing O_2, consumption, for increasing blood glucose, and for increasing blood lactate in various mammalian species show sufficiently wide differences to justify this conclusion. Furthermore, the infusion of glucose does not raise O_2 consumption and the infusion of lactic acid produces only small increases in O_2 consumption. In newborn kittens norepinephrine elevates O_2 use without increasing the blood level of lactate or ketone bodies, and also the O_2 use of these animals is not increased by infusions of lactate (409). Whether the calorigenic effect of the catecholamines can be attributed to the indirect effect of the elevation of plasma FFA is not completely settled by available evidence. Havel *et al.* (192) find that in man norepinephrine increases O_2 consumption, blood glucose, glycerol, and FFA and that pretreatment with nicotinic acid prevents the effect of norepinephrine on blood glycerol and FFA but only reduces its effect on O_2 consumption. They interpret these results and other information as evidence that O_2 consumption is increased through the effect of catecholamines on fat metabolism. Opposed to these findings are the observations in the dog which indicate that nicotinic acid inhibits almost completely the catecholamine-induced increase in FFA without significantly inhibiting the increase in O_2 consumption and the observations in the rat which indicate that nicotinic acid and adrenergic blocking agents differentially influence the epinephrine-induced increase in FFA and the increase in O_2 consumption (236).

Hull and associates (101, 214) place more weight on the O_2 consumption of brown fat induced by exposure to cold or by norepinephrine than on the rise in plasma FFA. They based their interpretation on experiments in which removal of much of the brown fat of the newborn rabbit almost completely inhibited the effect of norepinephrine on O_2 consumption (214) and their observation of only a slight rise in FFA induced by norepinephrine in newborn rabbits (101).

D. General Comments

It would appear that the calorigenic effect of the catecholamines cannot be explained on the basis of a direct stimulation of large masses of muscle, liver, or heart. The hypotheses relating the calorigenic effect to indirect stimulation of oxygen consumption induced by elevation of such metabolic substrates as glucose, lactate, or free fatty acids do not fare well in the face of unfavorable experimental evidence.

The hypothesis that the calorigenic effect is related to the stimulation of heat production by special tissues such as brown adipose tissue must be tested further. The report by Hull and Segall (213, 214) that excision of a major portion of the brown adipose tissue of the newborn rabbit inhibits the calorigenic effect of norepinephrine injection or of cold exposure appears to be strong evidence that the major portion of the calorigenic effect occurs through the response of this tissue. Since the brown adipose tissue does not release much FFA in response to catecholamines, some of the separation of the calorigenic effect from rises in free fatty acids with adrenergic drugs and their antagonists may not be inconsistent with this proposed mechanism of the calorigenic effect.

V. EFFECTS ON CATIONS

Interest in the effects of sympathomimetic agents on electrolytes has increased much in recent years (129). Changes in plasma and tissue concentrations have been measured and fluxes have been estimated with radioisotopes. Major attention has been on potassium, but many reports on sodium, calcium, and other electrolytes have appeared.

A. Potassium and Sodium

1. *Plasma and Liver*

Epinephrine and closely related substances elevate plasma potassium (107) when they are administered rapidly intravenously in moderate to large doses, or when they are infused at relatively high rates. When epinephrine is administered subcutaneously, as in its usual clinical use, it reduces the plasma potassium concentration. The principal source of the increased plasma potassium following an intravenous injection of epinephrine is the liver, but a small amount comes from other tissues (97). The "afterfall" in plasma potassium following the brief rise, or the lowering of plasma potassium following subcutaneous administration of epinephrine, can be accounted for by the increased uptake by muscle and the reversal of the hepatic change. The difference between portal vein and hepatic vein plasma potassium levels indicates that during the early phase of the action of intravenously administered epinephrine there is a large outpouring of potassium from the liver; this is followed by a much longer period during which the portal-hepatic difference is reversed and the liver appears to restore its lost potassium and even to surpass the resting level.

The mechanism of the epinephrine-activated potassium release from the liver has concerned many investigators. Some have tried to relate potassium release to vasoconstriction or to hepatic glycogenolysis and glucose release (84). Time-response data on the rise in plasma potassium and the rise in blood pressure or the rise in blood glucose have been used to draw conclusions in favor of or against these relationships. Present evidence suggests that these two responses are not essential for the hyperkalemic response to epinephrine. In the dog and cat, glucagon elevates plasma potassium in all animals (131, 416) and ISO does so in a fraction of the animals (115, 132a, 316), but neither elevates blood pressure or produces constriction in the hepatic circulation. In the perfused rat liver, epinephrine produces a rapid elevation in glucose and a retention of potassium for the first 3 minutes followed by an increase to a maximum at 5–6 minutes (83). Separation of the hyperglycemic response from the hyperkalemic response has been accomplished by first depleting liver glycogen with repeated administrations of glucagon (130). During a 20-minute infusion of epinephrine at 5 μg kg^{-1} min^{-1} the hyperglycemia is maintained while the potassium reaches its peak at 1 minute and decreases to below the control level at 15 minutes (84).

The concentration of cyclic AMP and the activation of phosphorylase do not appear related to the release of potassium since in the dog (453) and the cat (132a) the injection of cyclic AMP increases the plasma glucose (and liver phosphorylase) to the same extent as epinephrine does, but only the latter produces a large increase in plasma potassium. The time-response effects of epinephrine on liver phosphorylase activity and potassium release suggest to some (452) a common mechanism, but others (142) find the potassium release more rapid than the activation of phosphorylase.

More recent evidence from experiments with dogs (316) and cats (132a) have shown that most α-adrenergic blocking agents prevent epinephrine-induced-hyperkalemia without inhibiting the hyperglycemia, and, contrariwise, that β-adrenergic blocking agents prevent epinephrine-induced hyperglycemia without influencing the hyperkalemia. Thus, the adrenergic blocking agents clearly separate the potassium release from the activation of the glycogenolytic system and the subsequent liberation of glucose. In addition, these results clearly establish that in the dog and the cat the receptor mediating the potassium release is an α-adrenergic receptor. The relative potencies of catecholamines for producing hyperkalemia in the cat and the dog are E $>$ NE; the potency of ISO has been shown in one experiment in the cat (306) to be equal to that of epinephrine, but others have found that in the dog (115, 316) and in the cat (132a) only a minority of the animals showed a significant potassium effect in response to ISO. Some additional information on the mechanism of the potassium response derives from the findings that glucagon in dogs (153) and cats (132a) increases plasma potassium and glucose and that these responses are not inhibited by selective adrenergic blocking agents (dibenamine is an exception). Also, angiotensin II in the cat produces hyperglycemia and hyperkalemia and chlorpromazine inhibits the hyperkalemic response to epinephrine without modifying the hyperkalemic response to angiotensin (306) nor the hyperglycemic response to epinephrine (305).

The pharmacological importance of the α-receptor in relation to hepatic release of potassium will be discussed in a subsequent section (4. Smooth Muscle) on the catecholamine-induced changes in muscular organ potassium. A depolarizing effect of epinephrine on rat liver cell membrane potential has been observed (450).

Catecholamine-induced potassium release from the liver may be a reaction in which sodium is exchanged for the released potassium. The anions of lactic, keto, and phosphoric acids are not released in amounts equivalent to the potassium release (82). Since the sodium change would be small relative to the high plasma concentration of sodium, several reports have stated that no significant change occurs in response to catecholamines. Continuous recording of plasma concentrations with glass electrodes differently sensitive to potassium or to sodium (220) demonstrates a fall in plasma sodium accompanying the increase in potassium which follows the injection of epinephrine or norepinephrine; ISO, 1–2.5 μg/kg, has no effect on potassium and elevates sodium only slightly. Sodium uptake accompanies potassium release in the response of the perfused hypothermic rabbit liver to epinephrine (126). Measurements of epinephrine-induced changes in the perfused frog liver, however, indicate a lower sodium along with a decreased potassium concentration (81).

2. *Erythrocytes*

Uptake of potassium by human red cells is not influenced by epinephrine (229), but catecholamines increase the potassium uptake of nucleated frog and pigeon erythrocytes (356). If these contrasting results are confirmed, they might be related to the report (445) that the cyclase system is not found in the non-nucleated red cell but is present in nucleated red cells. The cyclase system might then be explored in relation to the activation by epinephrine of the sodium pump and potassium influx (59).

3. *Heart*

Norepinephrine causes a dose-dependent uptake of potassium by the heart (87). The increased resting potential of dog auricle caused by epinephrine or norepinephrine is interpreted as a possible increase in active Na transport (118). Later studies (156) in stimulated and in quiescent frog atrial strips showed that epinephrine causes a 10–20% increase in ^{24}Na efflux without a significant change in influx and a somewhat greater increase in ^{42}K influx (32%) than in efflux (25%). Similarly, in contracting or quiescent rabbit auricle preparations the greater increase in influx of potassium than efflux resulted in an increased tissue potassium level (467, 469). Norepinephrine increased the turnover of potassium and uptake of ^{86}Rb by dog heart (280). During the early action of epinephrine infused into dogs' left coronary arteries, there is an uptake of potassium (and phosphate) (372).

4. *Smooth Muscle*

Effects of catecholamines on potassium and sodium concentration changes and fluxes have been reported for some tissues containing smooth muscle. Daniel (91) has reviewed these aspects in relation to contractions of vertebrate smooth muscles.

Since these data are complex and somewhat confusing, they will be presented in a frame of reference which may be helpful, even though it may eventually be proved to be biased or even completely wrong.

When a smooth muscle is contracted by catecholamines, there is some reduction in the membrane potential which may result from increased membrane permeability to sodium and potassium. When a smooth muscle is relaxed by catecholamines, there is usually hyperpolarization of the membrane potential, and this is thought by some to indicate an increased output of sodium in exchange for potassium as an effect of "sodium pumping." Another mechanism which might cause hyperpolarization and relaxation is a selective increase in permeability to potassium alone.

Analysis of the mechanism of epinephrine-induced potassium release from the liver clearly indicates that this effect involves α-adrenotropic receptors (*vide supra*). In the taenia coli muscle of the guinea pig, potassium efflux occurs in response to norepinephrine but not to ISO, and phentolamine prevents the response to norepinephrine whereas pronethalol does not (222). These observations of Jenkinson and Morton (222) obviously show an increased potassium permeability mediated by α-receptors. Since the response through these receptors in the intestinal muscle is relaxation, there must be hyperpolarization due to selective increase in potassium permeability. Nagasawa (341) also observed that epinephrine increased potassium efflux in the taenia coli muscle without modifying sodium fluxes.

It has also been suggested that relaxation of smooth muscle could be brought about by increased activity of the sodium pump and membrane hyperpolarization (59). This would necessitate an "electrogenic" pump. Increased potassium uptake in response to epinephrine in taenia coli muscle is also reported (216). The use of selective α- and β-adrenergic blocking agents to analyze this response might demonstrate whether this increased potassium uptake is a function of a β-receptor.

In hormone-primed uterine tissue of rabbits and cats, epinephrine and norepinephrine produce contractions and potassium loss; dibenamine prevents the potassium loss. ISO does not increase potassium loss. In the cat uterus, epinephrine increases potassium loss when the tissue is contracted, relaxed, or unchanged (92). In the rat uterus which is relaxed by epinephrine, epinephrine produces an increase in potassium content.

The dog femoral artery (449) and rat aorta (92, 93) respond to catecholamines with a decrease in potassium concentration in keeping with their known α-receptor responses, but the dog carotid artery increased its potassium content slightly (195). An analysis of the receptors involved might help to explain the contrasting results.

Small doses of norepinephrine (93) and ISO (94) do not modify the potassium content of rat stomach muscle.

The rates of sodium and glucose transport from the mucosal to the serosal side of everted segments of rat small intestine are increased about 50% by epinephrine or norepinephrine, but are not changed by dopamine, glucagon, cyclic AMP, DCI, or ergotamine; DCI blocked the effect of epinephrine on glucose movement completely and on sodium partially; ergotamine in high concentrations blocked both (17).

B. Calcium

Recent work on the effects of epinephrine on calcium tends to support an old hypothesis, the Zondek theory (494), which suggested that epinephrine might act by increasing the cellular concentration of ionized calcium (472). In electrically stimulated rabbit atria epinephrine reduces the ^{45}Ca influx at normal levels of calcium and does not influence influx at 0.3 mM calcium; it was suggested that epinephrine might increase influx at still lower calcium levels (51). Epinephrine does increase ^{45}Ca influx into guinea pig atria in a low calcium medium (377), and, since epinephrine increases calcium influx, efflux, and exchange, it was suggested that it influences atrial muscle permeability to calcium (378).

Smooth muscle studies indicate that epinephrine does not change Ca uptake by guinea pig taenia coli (401), that high concentrations of epinephrine increase Ca release by strips of longitudinal muscle of guinea pig ileum (20) or by taenia coli (342), and that epinephrine causes a small increase in Ca influx in the rat uterus (491).

In the cat submaxillary gland, epinephrine increases secretion and permeability to sucrose, but ISO does not; phenoxybenzamine and DHE antagonize the effects of epinephrine (309). A large dose of ISO decreases the calcium of the salivary glands and increases salivary calcium; on repeated administration glandular calcium and weight increase (114).

It has been suggested (329) that there is a sympathetic influence through the parathyroid on calcium metabolism, since recovery from oxalate-induced hypocalcemia is speeded by stimulation of sympathetic nerves or by epinephrine and is retarded by phentolamine; also sympathetic stimulation and epinephrine were ineffective in thyroparathyroidectomized dogs. In parathyroidectomized rats ISO increases serum calcium (238).

Recent reports present evidence that epinephrine stimulates glucose oxidation in salivary gland slices through the Embden-Meyerhof-Krebs system only in the presence of calcium (393, 394).

Acknowledgments

The author is indebted to Dr. Barbara L. Kennedy for assistance with the search of the literature, to Miss Mildred Ezekiel for careful reorganization of the bibliography, and to Mrs. Patricia Oswald for painstaking work in preparing the typescript.

References

1. Abboud, F. M., Wendling, M. G., and Eckstein, J. W., Effect of norepinephrine on plasma free fatty acids in dogs treated with reserpine. *Am. J. Physiol.* **205,** 57–59 (1963).
2. Acheson, G. H., ed., 2nd *Catecholamine Symp. Pharmacol. Rev.* **18,** 1–804 (1966).
3. Ahlquist, R. P., The adrenotropic receptor-detector. *Arch. Intern. Pharmacodyn.* **139,** 38–41 (1962).
4. Ali, H. I. E. S., Antonio, A., and Haugaard, N., The action of sympathomimetic amines and adrenergic blocking agents on tissue phosphorylase activity. *J. Pharmacol. Exptl. Therap.* **145,** 142–150 (1964).
5. Allwood, M. J., and Cobbold, A. F., Lactic acid release by intra-arterial adrenaline infusions before and after dibenyline, and its relationship to blood flow changes in the human forearm. *J. Physiol. (London)* **157,** 328–334 (1961).
6. Alousi, A. A., and Mallov, S., Effects of hyperthyroidism, epinephrine, and diet on heart lipoprotein lipase activity. *Am. J. Physiol.* **206,** 603–609 (1964).

7. Amemori, T., Effect of Dibenzyline on serum cholesterol in rabbits. *Experientia* **18,** 331–332 (1962).
8. Andrews, W. H. H., and Glockling, B., Oxygen utilization of the perfused canine liver and its modification by adrenaline, acetylcholine and histamine. *J. Physiol.* (*London*) **132,** 522–528 (1958).
9. Ankermann, H., Die Wirkungen des Adrenalin, Noradrenalin und Isoproterenol auf den Gasstoffwechsel und die Korpertemperatur narcotisierter Ratten bei intravenöser Dauerinfusion. *Acta Biol. Med. Ger.* **8,** 489–510 (1962).
10. Ankermann, H., Zum Problem der stoffwechselsenkenden Wirkung des Adrenalins. *Acta Biol. Med. Ger.* **8,** 609–616 (1962).
11. Annison, E. F., Lindsay, D. B., and White, R. R., Metabolic interrelations of glucose and lactate in sheep. *Biochem. J.* **88,** 243–248 (1963).
12. Appleman, M. M., Belocopitow, E., and Torres, H. N., Factors affecting the activity of muscle glycogen synthetase. *Biochem. Biophys. Res. Commun.* **14,** 550–554 (1964).
13. Armstrong, D. T., Steele, R., Altszuler, N., Dunn, A., Bishop, J. S., and deBodo, R. C., Regulation of plasma free fatty acid turnover. *Am. J. Physiol.* **201,** 9–15 (1961).
14. Armstrong, D. T., Steele, R., Altszuler, N., Dunn, A., Bishop, J. S., and deBodo, R. C., Plasma free fatty acid turnover during insulin-induced hypoglycemia. *Am. J. Physiol.* **201,** 535–539 (1961).
15. Ashmore, J., Preston, J. E., and Love, W. C., Effects of dichloroisoproterenol on blood sugar and plasma free fatty acids. *Proc. Soc. Exptl. Biol. Med.* **109,** 291–294 (1962).
16. Aujard, C., Influence d'une sécrétion prolongée de noradrénaline ou d'un séjour de longue durée à basse température sur les lipides du foie chez le rat. *Compt. Rend. Soc. Biol.* **147,** 965–968 (1953).
17. Aulsebrook, K. A., Intestinal absorption of glucose and sodium: Effects of epinephrine and norepinephrine. *Biochem. Biophys. Res. Commun.* **18,** 165–169 (1965).
18. Ball, E. G., and Jungas, R. L., On the action of hormones which accelerate the rate of oxygen consumption and fatty acid release in rat adipose tissue *in vitro*. *Proc. Natl. Acad. Sci. U.S.* **47,** 932–941 (1961).
19. Balzer, H., and Palm, D., Über den Mechanismus der Wirkung des Reserpins auf den Glykogengehalt der Organe. *Arch. Exptl. Pathol. Pharmakol.* **243,** 65–84 (1962).
20. Bannerjee, A. K., and Lewis, J. J., Influence of drugs on $^{47}Ca^{2+}$ release from depolarized intestinal smooth muscle. *J. Pharm. Pharmacol.* **16,** 702–703 (1964).
21. Baum, H., El-Khanagry, H. A., and Moore, R. E., Catecholamine-stimulated thermogenesis: Some factors influencing the pattern of respiration of isolated kitten diaphragms. *J. Physiol.* (*London*) **169,** 237–248 (1963).
22. Baum, H., Moore, R. E., and El-Khanagry, H. A., The role of glycolysis in the acute stimulation of oxygen consumption in the whole animal by noradrenaline and adrenaline. *Biochem. J.* **79,** 2P–3P (1961).
23. Baum, H., Moore, R. E., and Underwood, M. C., Stimulation of heat production in new-born cats and adult rats by adrenaline and noradrenaline. *J. Physiol.* (*London*) **154,** 49P–50P (1960).

24. Belford, J., and Feinleib, M. R., Phosphorylase activity of heart muscle under various conditions affecting force of contraction. *J. Pharmacol. Exptl. Therap.* **127,** 257–264 (1959).
25. Belford, J., and Feinleib, M. R., The increase in glucose-6-phosphate content of the heart after the administration of inotropic catecholamines, calcium, and aminophylline. *Biochem. Pharmacol.* **11,** 987–994 (1962).
26. Belford, J., and Feinleib, M. R., Effect of stimulation and catecholamines on glucose-6-phosphate content of intact skeletal muscle. *Biochem. Pharmacol.* **13,** 125–127 (1964).
27. Belocopitow, E., The action of epinephrine on glycogen synthetase. *Arch. Biochem. Biophys.* **93,** 457–458 (1961).
28. Benjamin, W., Gellhorn, A., Wagner, M., and Kundel, H., Effect of aging on lipid composition and metabolism in the adipose tissue of the rat. *Am. J. Physiol.* **201,** 540–546 (1961).
29. Bergström, S., Carlson, L. A., and Orö, L., Effect of prostaglandins on catecholamine induced changes in the free fatty acids of plasma and in blood pressure in the dog. Prostaglandin and related factors 22. *Acta Physiol. Scand.* **60,** 170–180 (1964).
30. Berne, R. M., Effect of epinephrine and norepinephrine on coronary circulation. *Circulation Res.* **6,** 644–654 (1958).
31. Berthet, J., Sutherland, E. W., and Rall, T. W., The assay of glucagon and epinephrine with use of liver homogenates. *J. Biol. Chem.* **229,** 351 (1957).
32. Beviz, A., and Mohme-Lundholm, E., The effect of adrenalin on the hexosephosphate content of vascular smooth muscle. *Acta Physiol. Scand.* **62,** 109–114 (1694).
33. Beviz, A., and Mohme-Lundholm, E., Influence of dihydroergotamine and adrenaline on the concentration of glucose-6-phosphate, fructose-6-phosphate, adenosinetriphosphate and creatinephosphate in bovine mesenteric artery. *Acta Physiol. Scand.* **65,** 289–291 (1965).
34. Bizzi, A., Codegoni, A. M., and Garattini, S., Salicylate, a powerful inhibitor of free fatty acid release. *Nature* **204,** 1205 (1964).
35. Björntorp, P., The fatty acid release and lipolysis of human subcutaneous tissue *in vitro. Metab. Clin. Exptl.* **13,** 1318–1326 (1964).
36. Björntorp, P., The effect of nicotinic acid on adipose tissue metabolism *in vitro. Metab. Clin. Exptl.* **14,** 836–839 (1965).
37. Björntorp, P., and Furman, R. H., Lipolytic activity in rat epididymal fat pads. *Am. J. Physiol.* **203,** 316–322 (1962).
38. Björntorp, P., and Furman, R. H., Lipolytic activity in rat heart. *Am. J. Physiol.* **203,** 323–326 (1962).
39. Blackard, W. G., Ball, M. F., and Engel, F. L., Some hormonal, metabolic, and nutritional factors influencing lipid peroxidation by rat adipose tissue *in vitro. J. Clin. Invest.* **41,** 1288–1296 (1962).
40. Blatteis, C. M., Hypoxia and the metabolic response to cold in new-born rabbits. *J. Physiol.* (*London*) **172,** 358–368 (1964).
41. Blukoo-Allotey, J. A., and Vincent, N. H., Inhibitory effect of acetylcholine upon glycogenolysis induced by epinephrine in isolated mammalian hearts. *Pharmacologist* **7,** 140 (1965).
42. Blum, F., Ueber Nebennierendiabetes. *Deut. Arch. Klin. Med.* **71,** 146–167 (1901).

43. Bogdonoff, M. D., Linhart, J. W., Klein, R. J., and Estes, E. H., Jr., The specific structure of compounds effecting fat mobilization in man. *J. Clin. Invest.* **40,** 1993–1996 (1961).

44. Boshart, C. R., Smith, T. C., Will, L., Perrine, J., and Ringler, I., Effect of phentolamine on body fat. *Nature* **189,** 405–406 (1961).

45. Boshart, C. R., Smith, T. C., Will, L., Pirré, A., Perrine, J., and Ringler, I., Action of phentolamine on rat adipose tissue. *J. Pharmacol. Exptl. Therap.* **143,** 221–229 (1964).

46. Boshart, C. R., Will, L., Pirré, A., and Ringler, I., Metabolic effects of phentolamine compared to epinephrine. *Federation Proc.* **20,** 276 (1961).

47. Boshart, C. R., Will, L., Pirré, A., and Ringler, I., The effects of reserpine, guanethidine and other autonomic drugs on free fatty acid mobilization induced by phentolamine. *J. Pharmacol. Exptl. Therap.* **149,** 57–64 (1965).

48. Bot, Gy., Szilágyi, T., and Szabó, E., Wirkung von Zuckerbelastung und Adrenalin auf die Phosphorylase- und Glukose-6-Phosphatase-Aktivität der Leber. *Acta Physiol. Acad. Sci. Hung.* **11,** 421–426 (1957).

49. Brentano, C., and Pflug, E., Der Einfluss des Sympatols auf den Kohlehydrat- und Gasstoff-Wechsel des Menschen. *Klin. Wochschr.* **28,** 979–981 (1938).

50. Bridge, E. M., and Noltie, H. R., The action of adrenaline on the respiratory quotient. *J. Physiol.* (*London*) **85,** 334–342 (1935).

51. Briggs, A. H., and Holland, W. C., Effects of epinephrine and Ca on contractile strength and Ca^{45} exchange in rabbit atria. *Am. J. Physiol.* **199,** 609–612 (1960).

52. Brody, T. M., and Diamond, J., Effect of catecholamines on uterine motility and phosphorylase activity. *Pharmacologist* **7,** 140 (1965).

53. Brooker, W. D., and Calvert, D. N., Comparative effects of adrenergic blocking agents upon catecholamine stimulated release of free fatty acids. *Federation Proc.* **23,** 541 (1964).

54. Bruce, R. A., Cobb, L. A., and Williams, R. H., Effects of exercise and isoproterenol on free fatty acids and carbohydrates in cardiac patients. *Am. J. Med. Sci.* **241,** 59–67 (1961).

55. Buckle, R. M., and Beck, J. C., Modifying influence of glucose on fatty acid-mobilizing activities of epinephrine, ACTH and growth hormone *in vitro. Metab. Clin. Exptl.* **11,** 235–244 (1962).

56. Bueding, E., and Bülbring, E., The inhibitory action of adrenaline. Biochemical and biophysical observations. *In* "Pharmacology of Smooth Muscle" (E. Bülbring, ed.), pp. 37–56. Macmillan, New York, 1964.

57. Buffoni, F., and Giotti, A., L'azione della noradrenalina sulla contrazione frequenza e attività fosforilasica degli atri di cavia normali e trattati con reserpina. *Boll. Soc. Ital. Biol. Sper.* **37,** 672–675 (1961).

58. Burns, J. J., Colville, K. I., Lindsay, L. A., and Salvador, R. A., Blockade of some metabolic effects of catecholamines by *N*-isopropyl methoxamine (B. W. 61–43). *J. Pharmacol. Exptl. Therap.* **144,** 163–171 (1964).

59. Burnstock, G., The action of adrenaline on excitability and membrane potential in the taenia coli of the guinea-pig and the effect of DNP on this action and on the action of acetylcholine. *J. Physiol.* (*London*) **143,** 183–194 (1958).

60. Butcher, R. W., Ho, R. J., Meng, H. C., and Sutherland, E. W., Adenosine 3′,5′-monophosphate in biological materials. II. The measurement of adenosine 3′,5′-monophosphate in tissues and the role of the cyclic nucleotide in the lipolytic response of fat to epinephrine. *J. Biol. Chem.* **240,** 4515–4523 (1965).

61. Byushuk, N. S., Comparative study of glycogen content changes in liver and skeletal muscle under the influence of adrenaline and noradrenaline. *Vopr. Med. Khim.* **9**, 411–414 (1963).
62. Cahill, G. F., Jr., Leboeuf, B., and Flinn, R. B., Studies on rat adipose tissue *in vitro*. VI. Effect of epinephrine on glucose metabolism. *J. Biol. Chem.* **235**, 1246–1250 (1960).
63. Carlson, L. A., Studies on the effect of nicotinic acid on catecholamine stimulated lipolysis in adipose tissue *in vitro*. *Acta Med. Scand.* **173**, 719–722 (1963).
64. Carlson, L. A., Fröberg, S., and Persson, S., Concentration and turnover of the free fatty acids of plasma and concentration of blood glucose during exercise in horses. *Acta Physiol. Scand.* **63**, 434–441 (1965).
65. Carlson, L. A., and Liljedahl, S.-O., Lipid metabolism and trauma. II. Studies on the effect of nicotinic acid on norepinephrine induced fatty liver. *Acta Med. Scand.* **173**, 787–791 (1963).
66. Carlson, L. A., Liljedahl, S.-O., Verdy, M., and Wirsén, C., Unresponsiveness to the lipid mobilizing action of catecholamines *in vivo* and *in vitro* in the domestic fowl. *Metab. Clin. Exptl.* **13**, 227–231 (1964).
67. Carlson, L. A., and Orö, L., The effect of nicotinic acid on the plasma free fatty acids. Demonstration of a metabolic type of sympathicolysis. *Acta Med. Scand.* **172**, 641–645 (1962).
68. Carlson, L. A., and Orö, L., Studies on the relationship between the concentration of plasma free fatty acids and glycerol *in vivo*. *Metab. Clin. Exptl.* **12**, 132–142 (1963).
69. Cavalca, L., and Gilardi, F., Struttura molecolare ed effetto iperglicemizzante delle catecholamine. *Atti Soc. Lombarda Sci. Med. Biol.* **10**, 154–158 (1955).
70. Challoner, D. R., and Steinberg, D., Metabolic effect of epinephrine on the Q_{O_2} of the arrested isolated perfused rat heart. *Nature* **205**, 602–603 (1965).
71. Challoner, D. R., and Steinberg, D., Effect of free fatty acid on the oxygen consumption of perfused rat heart. *Am. J. Physiol.* **210**, 280–286 (1966).
72. Cherkes, A. I. (Tscherkess, A. J.), Herzmittel wirkung und Herzstoffwechsel. *Acta Med. URSS* **3**, 155–169 (1940).
73. Cheung, W. Y., and Williamson, J. R., Kinetics of cyclic adenosine monophosphate changes in rat heart following epinephrine administration. *Nature* **207**, 979–981 (1965).
74. Chlouverakis, C., Parasympathomimetic agents and the metabolism of rat adipose tissue. *Metab. Clin. Exptl.* **12**, 936–940 (1963).
75. Claassen, V., and Noach, E. L., Dichloro-isuprel inhibition of sympathomimetic hyperglycemia. *Arch. Intern. Pharmacodyn.* **126**, 332–340 (1960).
76. Clément, G., and Schaeffer, G., Démonstration de l'effet mobilisateur de l'adrénaline sur les graisses de réserve. Rôle du système nerveux sympathique. *Compt. Rend. Soc. Biol.* **141**, 320–322 (1947).
77. Cobbold, A. F., Ginsburg, J., and Paton, A., Circulatory, respiratory and metabolic responses to isopropylnoradrenaline in man. *J. Physiol.* (*London*) **151**, 539–550 (1960).
78. Cori, C. F., Mammalian carbohydrate metabolism. *Physiol. Rev.* **11**, 143–275 (1931).
79. Correll, J. W., Mobilization of unesterified fatty acids (UFA) from isolated rat adipose tissue by nerve stimulation *in vitro*. *Federation Proc.* **20**, 275 (1961).
80. Cottle, W. H., Calorigenic response of cold-adapted rabbits to adrenaline and to noradrenaline. *Can. J. Biochem. Physiol.* **41**, 1334–1337 (1963).

81. Craig, A. B., Jr., Observations on epinephrine and glucagon-induced glycogenolysis and potassium loss in the isolated perfused frog liver. *Am. J. Physiol.* **193,** 425–430 (1958).
82. Craig, A. B., Jr., Effects of epinephrine on lactic and keto-acid production, phosphate balance and pH changes in the isolated perfused frog liver. *Am. J. Physiol.* **196,** 969–971 (1959).
83. Craig, A. B., Jr., Vascular and metabolic effects of epinephrine in the isolated perfused rat liver. *J. Pharmacol. Exptl. Therap.* **149,** 346–350 (1965).
84. Craig, A. B., Jr., and Honig, C. R., Hepatic metabolic and vascular responses to epinephrine: A unifying hypothesis. *Am. J. Physiol.* **205,** 1132–1138 (1963).
85. Craig, J. W., and Larner, J., Influence of epinephrine and insulin on uridine diphosphate glucose-a-glucan transferase and phosphorylase in muscle. *Nature* **202,** 971–973 (1964).
86. Cucurachi, L., Castello, S., Ambanelli, U., and Strata, A., Modificazioni umorali lipidiche e glicidiche conseguenti alla infusione di noradrenalina (confronto con le azioni dell'adrenalina). *Med. Clin. Sper.* **13,** 83–95 (1963).
87. Daggett, W. M., Mansfield, P. R., and Sarnoff, S. J., Myocardial K^+ changes resulting from inotropic agents. *Federation Proc.* **23,** 357 (1964).
88. Danforth, H., Glycogen synthetase activity in skeletal muscle. Interconversion of two forms and control of glycogen synthesis. *J. Biol. Chem.* **240,** 588–593 (1965).
89. Danforth, W. H., Helmreich, E., and Cori, C. F., The effect of contraction and epinephrine on the phosphorylase activity of frog sartorius muscle. *Proc. Natl. Acad. Sci. U.S.* **48,** 1191–1199 (1962).
90. Danforth, W. H., McKinsey, J. J., and Stewart, J. T., Transport and phosphorylation of glucose in dog heart. *J. Physiol.* (*London*) **162,** 367–384 (1962).
91. Daniel, E. E., Effect of drugs on contractions of vertebrate smooth muscle. *Ann. Rev. Pharmacol.* **4,** 189–222 (1964).
92. Daniel, E. E., and Daniel, B. N., Effects of contractile stimuli on exchanges of electrolytes between uterine tissues and a saline-bicarbonate medium. *Can. J. Biochem. Physiol.* **37,** 127–148 (1959).
93. Daniel, E. E., Dawkins, O., and Hunt, J., Selective depletion of rat aorta potassium by small pressor doses of norepinephrine. *Am. J. Physiol.* **190,** 67–70 (1957).
94. Daniel, E. E., Dodd, A., and Hunt, J., Effects of Pitressin and isoproterenol on aorta electrolytes. *Arch. Intern. Pharmacodyn.* **119,** 43–55 (1959).
95. Davidson, I. W. F., Salter, J. M., and Best, C. H., The effect of glucagon on the metabolic rate of rats. *Am. J. Clin. Nutr.* **8,** 540–546 (1960).
96. Davis, E. J., The effects of insulin and adrenalin on the metabolism of glucose and lactate by perfused guinea pig hearts. *Can. J. Biochem.* **43,** 1001–1009 (1965).
97. Davis, L. D., Helmer, P. R., and Murphy, Q. R., Role of potassium in cyclopropane-epinephrine ventricular tachycardia. *Anesthesiology* **25,** 54–58 (1964).
98. Davoren, P. R., and Sutherland, E. W., The effect of l-epinephrine and other agents on the synthesis and release of adenosine 3′,5′-phosphate by whole pigeon erythrocytes. *J. Biol. Chem.* **238,** 3009–3015 (1963).
99. Davoren, P. R., and Sutherland, E. W., The cellular localization of adenyl cyclase in the pigeon erythrocyte. *J. Biol. Chem.* **238,** 3016–3023 (1963).

100. Dawes, G. S., and Mestyán, G., Changes in the oxygen consumption of new-born guinea-pigs and rabbits on exposure to cold. *J. Physiol. (London)* **168**, 22–42 (1963).
101. Dawkins, M. J. R., and Hull, D., Brown adipose tissue and the cold response of new-born rabbits to cold. *J. Physiol. (London)* **172**, 216–238 (1964).
102. De Caro, L. G., Buniva, G., and Gorini, M., Confronto tra l'azione della (−) adrenalina e della noradrenalina sul livello plasmatico degli acidi grassi non esterificati. *Boll. Soc. Ital. Biol. Sper.* **39**, 1127–1130 (1963).
103. DeGroot, C. A., Cobaltous chloride and blood glucose levels. *Arch. Intern. Pharmacodyn.* **130**, 374–384 (1961).
104. de la Lande, I. S., Manson, J., Parks, V. J., Sandison, A. G., Skinner, S. L., and Whelan, R. F., The local metabolic action of adrenaline on skeletal muscle in man. *J. Physiol. (London)* **157**, 177–184 (1961).
105. Depocas, F., The calorigenic response of cold-acclimated white rats to infused noradrenaline. *Can. J. Biochem. Physiol.* **38**, 107–114 (1960).
106. Depocas, F., Biochemical changes in exposure and acclimation to cold environments. *Brit. Med. Bull.* **17**, 25–31 (1961).
107. D'Silva, J. L., The action of adrenaline on serum potassium. *J. Physiol. (London)* **82**, 393–398 (1934).
108. Diamond, J., and Brody, T. M., Phosphorylase activity in rat uterus after catecholamine administration. *Biochem. Pharmacol.* **14**, 7–16 (1965).
109. Diamond, J., and Brody, T. M., Relationship between uterine contraction and phosphorylase activation. *Pharmacologist* **7**, 140 (1965).
110. Dickman, S. R., Wiest, W. G., and Eik-Nes, K., Effects of epinephrine on metabolism of glucose of normal dogs. *Am. J. Physiol.* **194**, 327–332 (1958).
111. Dixon, R. L., Rogers, L. A., and Fouts, J. R., The effects of norepinephrine treatment on drug metabolism by liver microsomes from rats. *Biochem. Pharmacol.* **13**, 623–631 (1964).
112. Dole, V. P., A relation between non-esterfied fatty acids in plasma and the metabolism of glucose. *J. Clin. Invest.* **35**, 150–154 (1956).
113. Doss, D., Müller-Beissenhirtz, P., and Ohnesorge, F. K., Mortalität, Körpertemperatur und Sauerstoffverbrach von Mäusen nach Methamphetamin unter dem Einfluss verschiedener Umgebungstemperaturen. *Arch. Exptl. Pathol. Pharmakol.* **245**, 108–109 (1963).
114. Dreisbach, R. H., Effect of isoproterenol on calcium metabolism in rat salivary gland. *Proc. Soc. Exptl. Biol. Med.* **116**, 953–956 (1964).
115. Dresel, P. E., and Nickerson, M., The role of potassium in epinephrine-induced cardiac arrhythmias. *J. Pharmacol. Exptl. Therap.* **125**, 142–149 (1959).
116. Drummond, G. I., Valadares, J. R. E., and Duncan, L., Effect of epinephrine on contractile tension and phosphorylase activation in rat and dog hearts. *Proc. Soc. Exptl. Biol. Med.* **117**, 307–309 (1964).
117. Drury, D. R., and Wick, A. N., Epinephrine and carbohydrate metabolism. *Am. J. Physiol.* **194**, 465–468 (1958).
118. Dudel, J., and Trautwein, W., Die Wirkung von Adrenalin auf das Ruhepotential von Myokardfasern des Vorhofs. *Experientia* **12**, 396–398 (1956).
119. Dury, A., Effects of epinephrine on lipid partition and metabolism in the rabbit. *Circulation Res.* **5**, 47–53 (1957).
120. Dzúrik, R., Krajči-Lazáry, B., and Niederland, T. R., Glucose metabolism in rat kidney: Influence of insulin and adrenalin. *J. Physiol. (London)* **168**, 782–786 (1963).

121. Eaton, R. P., *In vitro* inhibition of the fat-mobilizing action of norepinephrine. *Proc. Soc. Exptl. Biol. Med.* **114**, 599–600 (1963).
122. Eaton, R. P., Catecholamine stimulation of oxygen consumption *in vitro. Federation Proc.* **23**, 270 (1964).
123. Eaton, P., and Steinberg, D., Effects of medium fatty acid concentration, epinephrine, and glucose on palmitate-1-C^{14} oxidation and incorporation into neutral lipids by skeletal muscle *in vitro. J. Lipid Res.* **2**, 376–382 (1961).
124. Edmondson, J. H., and Goodman, H. M., Effect of reserpine on fatty acid mobilization. *Proc. Soc. Exptl. Biol. Med.* **110**, 761–764 (1962).
125. Elder, J. T., Antagonism of lysergic acid diethylamide (LSD)-induced hyperglycemia. *Intern. J. Neuropharmacol.* **3**, 295–300 (1964).
126. Elliott, F. S., Levin, F. M., and Shoemaker, W. C., Hepatic electrolyte and glucose responses to epinephrine. *J. Pharmacol. Exptl. Therap.* **150**, 61–66 (1965).
127. Ellis, S., The effect of amines on the blood sugar of the rat. *J. Pharmacol. Exptl. Therap.* **101**, 92–100 (1951).
128. Ellis, S., The metabolic effects of epinephrine and related amines. *Pharmacol. Rev.* **8**, 485–562 (1956).
129. Ellis, S., Relation of biochemical effects of epinephrine to its muscular effects. *Pharmacol. Rev.* **11**, 469–479 (1959).
130. Ellis, S., and Beckett, S. B., Mechanism of the potassium mobilizing action of epinephrine and glucagon. *J. Pharmacol. Exptl. Therap.* **142**, 318–326 (1963).
131. Ellis, S., Beckett, S. B., and Boutwell, J. H., Dibenamine blockade of epinephrine and glucagon hyperkalemias. *Proc. Soc. Exptl. Biol. Med.* **94**, 343–345 (1957).
132. Ellis, S., Davis, A. H., and Anderson, H. L., Jr., Effects of epinephrine and related amines on contraction and glycogenolysis of the rat's diaphragm. *J. Pharmacol. Exptl. Therap.* **115**, 120–125 (1955).
132a. Ellis, S., and Eusebi, A. J., Dissociation of epinephrine-induced hyperkalemia and hyperglycemia by adrenergic blocking drugs and theophylline: Role of cyclic 3′,5′-AMP. *Federation Proc.* **24**, 151 (1965).
133. Ellis, S., and Kennedy, B. L., Interactions of sympathomimetic amines and adrenergic blocking agents at receptor sites mediating lipolysis in the intact rat. *Pharmacologist* **7**, 137 (1965).
134. Ellis, S., Kennedy, B. L., Eusebi, A. J., and Vincent, N. H., Autonomic control of metabolism. *In* "New Adrenergic Blocking Drugs: Their Pharmacological, Biochemical and Clinical Actions" (N. C. Moran, ed.); *Ann. N.Y. Acad. Sci.* **139** (3), 826–832 (1967).
135. Engelberg, H., Effect of epinephrine upon plasma optical density, unesterified fatty acids, lipemia clearing and heparin levels. *Proc. Soc. Exptl. Biol. Med.* **100**, 492–494 (1959).
136. Eusebi, A. J., and Ellis, S., Receptors mediating epinephrine-induced increases in plasma glucose, lactate, and free fatty acids in the cat. *Pharmacologist* **7**, 136 (1965).
137. Exton, J. H., and Park, C. R., The stimualtion of gluconeogenesis from lactate by epinephrine, glucagon, and cyclic 3′,5′-adenylate in the perfused rat liver. *Pharmacol. Rev.* **18**, 181–188 (1966).

138. Fain, J. N., Effect of puromycin on incubated adipose tissue and its response to dexamethasone, insulin, and epinephrine. *Biochim. Biophys. Acta* **84**, 636–642 (1964).

139. Farkas, T., Vertua, R., Usardi, M. M., and Paoletti, R., Investigations on the mechanism of action of nicotinic acid. *Life Sci.* **3**, 821–827 (1964).

140. Fassina, G., d-Ampfetamina e acidi grassi plasmatici. *Arch. Intern. Pharmacodyn.* **152**, 298–306 (1964).

141. Feigelson, E. B., Pfaff, W. W., Karmen, A., and Steinberg, D., The role of plasma free fatty acids in development of fatty liver. *J. Clin. Invest.* **40**, 2171–2179 (1961).

142. Finder, A. G., Boyme, T., and Shoemaker, W. C., Relationship of hepatic potassium efflux to phosphorylase activation induced by glucagon. *Am. J. Physiol.* **206**, 738–742 (1964).

143. Fine, M. B., and Williams, R. H., Effect of fasting, epinephrine and glucose and insulin on hepatic uptake of nonesterified fatty acids. *Am. J. Physiol.* **199**, 403–406 (1960).

144. Fisher, R. B., and Williamson, J. R., The effects of insulin, adrenaline and nutrients on the oxygen uptake of the perfused rat heart. *J. Physiol.* (*London*) **158**, 102–112 (1961).

145. Fizette, N. B., and Heimberg, M., The effect of 1-epinephrine (E) on incorporation of palmitate-1-C^{14} into liver and serum triglycerides (TG). *Pharmacologist* **6**, 172 (1964).

146. Flatt, J. P., and Ball, E. G., Studies on the metabolism of adipose tissue. XV. An evaluation of the major pathways of glucose catabolism as influenced by insulin and epinephrine. *J. Biol. Chem.* **239**, 675–685 (1964).

147. Fleming, W. W., and Kenny, A. D., The effect of fasting on the hyperglycemic responses to catecholamines in rats. *Brit. J. Pharmacol.* **22**, 267–274 (1964).

148. Freis, E. D., Stanton, J. R., and Wilkins, R. W., The effects of certain dihydrogenated alkaloids of ergot in hypertensive patients. *Am. J. Med. Sci.* **216**, 163–171 (1948).

149. Friedman, M., and Byers, S. O., Effects of epinephrine and norepinephrine on lipid metabolism of the rat. *Am. J. Physiol.* **199**, 995–999 (1960).

150. Fritz, I. B., Shatton, J., Morton, J. V., and Levine, R., Effects of epinephrine and insulin on glucose disappearance in eviscerated dogs. *Am. J. Physiol.* **189**, 57–62 (1956).

151. Fröberg, S., and Orö, L., The effects of nicotinic acid, phentolamine and nethalide on the plasma free fatty acids and the blood pressure in the dog. *Acta Med. Scand.* **174**, 635–641 (1963).

152. Fröberg, S., and Orö, L., The effect of carotid occlusion and central vagal stimulation on the free fatty acids of plasma and the blood pressure in the dog. *Acta Med. Scand.* **176**, 65–71 (1964).

153. Galansino, G., d'Amico, G., Kanameishi, D., Berlinger, F. G., and Foà, P. P., Hyperglycemic substances originating in the pancreatoduodenal area. *Am. J. Physiol.* **198**, 1059–1062 (1960).

154. Gans, J. H., Epinephrine and cholesterol metabolism in the dog. *Pharmacologist* **6**, 173 (1964).

155. Garland, R. B., and Randle, P. J., Effects of alloxan diabetes and adrenaline on concentrations of free fatty acids in rat heart and diaphragm muscles. *Nature* **199**, 381–382 (1963).

156. Glitsch, H. G., Haas, H. G., and Trautwein, W., The effect of adrenaline on the K and Na fluxes in the frog's atrium. *Arch. Exptl. Pathol. Pharmakol.* **250**, 59–71 (1965).
157. Glover, W. E., and Shanks, R. G., Observations on the relation between the vasodilator and metabolic actions of adrenaline in the human forearm. *J. Physiol.* (*London*) **167**, 280–287 (1963).
158. Gold, M., Attar, H. J., Spitzer, J. J., and Scott, J. C., Effect of norepinephrine on myocardial free fatty acid uptake and oxidation. *Proc. Soc. Exptl. Biol. Med.* **118**, 876–879 (1965).
159. Gold, M., Miller, H. I., Issekutz, B., Jr., and Spitzer, J. J., Effect of exercise and lactic acid infusion on individual free fatty acids of plasma. *Am. J. Physiol.* **205**, 902–904 (1963).
160. Goodman, H. M., and Knobil, E., Effect of adrenergic blocking agents on fatty acid mobilization during fasting. *Proc. Soc. Exptl. Biol. Med.* **102**, 493–495 (1959).
160a. Gordon, R. S., Jr., and Cherkes, A., Production of unesterified fatty acids from isolated rat adipose tissue incubated *in vitro*. *Proc. Soc. Exptl. Biol. Med.* **97**, 150–151 (1958).
161. Goto, Y., The fatty metabolism in the heart muscle. *Japan Circ. J.* (English Ed.) **26**, 121–127 (1962).
162. Gousios, A., Felts, J. M., and Havel, R. J., Effect of catecholamines, glucose, insulin, and changes of flow on the metabolism of free fatty acids by the myocardium. *Metab. Clin. Exptl.* **14**, 826–831 (1965).
163. Graham, M. H., Abboud, F. M., and Eckstein, J. W., Effect of norepinephrine on plasma nonesterified fatty acid concentrations after administration of cocaine. *J. Pharmacol. Exptl. Therap.* **143**, 340–343 (1964).
164. Grana, E., Cappelli, V., and Lilla, L., Sull' attività metabolica della (−)N-isopropilnoradrenalina. *Farmaco* (*Pavia*) *Ed. Sci.* **15**, 689–699 (1960).
165. Greene, N. M., Effect of epinephrine on lactate, pyruvate, and excess lactate production in normal human subjects. *J. Lab. Clin. Med.* **58**, 682–686 (1961).
166. Griffith, F. R., "Adrenaline, Adrenergic-Sympathomimetic and Adrenolytic-Sympatholytic Drugs. An Index and Annotated Bibliography." Univ. of Buffalo, Buffalo, New York, 1956.
167. Guarnieri, E., and Giardina, A., Contributo allo studio dei rapporti tra metabolismo lipidico e glucidico e alla loro regolazione nervosa. Nota I. -Effetti di un farmaco ad azione simpaticolitica sull'iperglicemia e sull'aumento dei NEFA plasmatici da carico adrenalinico. *Rassegna Neurolog. Vegativa* **18**, 239–252 (1964).
168. Guarnieri, E., and Giardina, A. Contributo allo studio dei rapporti tra metabolismo lipidico e glucidico e alla loro regolazione nervosa. Nota. II. -Effetti di un farmaco ad azione adrenolitica sull'iperglicemia e sull'aumento dei NEFA plasmatici da carico adrenalinico. *Rass. Neur. Veg.* **18**, 253–260 (1964).
169. Gutman, A., and Shafrir, E., Metabolic influences on enzymes of glycogen synthesis and breakdown in adipose tissue. *Am. J. Physiol.* **207**, 1215–1220 (1963).
170. Hagen, J. H., Stimulation of secretion and metabolism in mouse parotid glands *in vitro*. *Biochem. Pharmacol.* **2**, 206–214 (1959).

171. Hagen, J. H., Effect of glucagon on the metabolism of adipose tissue. *J. Biol. Chem.* **236,** 1023–1027 (1961).

172. Hagen, J. H., and Ball, E. G., Studies on the metabolism of adipose tissue. IV. Effect of insulin and adrenaline on glucose utilization, lactate production, and net gas exchange. *J. Biol. Chem.* **235,** 1545–1549 (1960).

173. Hagen, J. H., and Ball, E. G., Studies on the metabolism of adipose tissue: the effect of adrenaline on oxygen consumption and glucose utilization. *Endocrinology* **69,** 752–760 (1961).

174. Hagen, J. H., and Hagen, P. B., An enzymatic method for the estimation of glycerol in blood and its use to determine the effect of noradrenaline on the concentration of glycerol in blood. *Can. J. Biochem. Physiol.* **40,** 1129–1139 (1962).

175. Hagen, J. H., and Hagen, P. B., Actions of adrenalin and noradrenalin on metabolic systems. *In* "Actions of Hormones on Molecular Processes" (G. Litwack and D. Kritchevsky, eds.), pp. 268–319. Wiley, New York, 1964.

176. Hall, V. E., and Chamberlin, P. E., The synergic calorigenic action of epinephrine and dinitrophenol. *J. Pharmacol. Exptl. Therap.* **59,** 451–457 (1937).

177. Hamburger, J., Smith, R. W., Jr., and Miller, J. M., Effects of epinephrine on free fatty acid mobilization in hyperthyroid and hypothyroid subjects. *Metab. Clin. Exptl.* **12,** 821–832 (1963).

178. Hammermeister, K. E., Yunis, A. A., and Krebs, E. G., Studies on phosphorylase activation in the heart. *J. Biol. Chem.* **240,** 986–991 (1965).

179. Hannon, J. P., and Larson, A. M., The site and mechanism of norepinephrine-calorigenesis in the cold-acclimatized rat. *Federation Proc.* **20,** 209 (1961).

180. Hardman, J. G., Mayer, S. E., and Clark, B., Cocaine potentiation of the cardiac inotropic and phosphorylase responses to catecholamines as related to the uptake of ^{3}H-catecholamines. *J. Pharmacol. Exptl. Therap.* **150,** 341–348 (1965).

181. Hardman, J. G., and Mayer, S. E., The influence of cocaine on some metabolic effects and the distribution of catecholamines. *J. Pharmacol. Exptl. Therap.* **148,** 29–31 (1965).

181a. Harel, L., Mode d'action de l'adrénaline sur l'oxydation des acides gras. *Arch. Sci. Physiol.* **13,** 151–160 (1959).

182. Hart, J. S., and Jansky, L., Participation of muscle and kidney in non shivering thermogenesis, measured *in vivo. Federation Proc.* **21,** 224 (1962).

183. Harvey, S. C., Wang, C. Y., and Nickerson, M., Blockade of epinephrine-induced hyperglycemia. *J. Pharmacol. Exptl. Therap.* **104,** 363–376 (1952).

184. Hasselblatt, A., and Sproull, D. H., Hyperglycemia induced by drugs. *J. Physiol.* (*London*) **157,** 124–136 (1961).

185. Hashimoto, K., Shigei, T., Imai, S., Saito, Y., Yago, N., Uei, I., and Clark, R. E., Oxygen consumption and coronary vascular tone in the isolated fibrillating dog heart. *Am. J. Physiol.* **198,** 965–970 (1960).

186. Hashimoto, K., Studies on the coronary flow and the oxygen consumption of the isolated dog heart in ventricular fibrillation and the effects of epinephrine, levarterenol, isoproterenol, acetylcholine, 5-hydroxytryptamine, ATP, theophyllinethylenediamine, nitroglycerin, and papaverine on it. *Japan Circulation J.* (English Ed.) **21,** 1–7 (1957).

187. Haugaard, N., and Hess, M. E., Actions of autonomic drugs on phosphorylase activity and function. *Pharmacol. Rev.* **17,** 27–69 (1965).

188. Haugaard, N., Kukovetz, W. R., and Hess, M. E., The effect of sympathomimetic amines on phosphorylase activity of the isolated rat heart. *Pharmacol. Rev.* **11**, 466–468 (1959).

189. Hausberger, F. X., Über die Innervation der Fettorgane. *Z. Mikroskop. Anat. Forsch.* **36**, 231–266 (1934).

190. Hausberger, F. X., Effect of denervation on brown adipose tissue. *Federation Proc.* **21**, 397 (1962).

191. Havel, R. J., Catecholamines. *Med. Chem. Ser. Monographs* **2**, 357–380 (1964).

192. Havel, R. J., Carlson, L. A., Ekelund, L. -G., and Holmgren, A., Studies on the relation between mobilization of free fatty acids and energy metabolism in man: effects of norepinephrine and nicotinic acid. *Metab. Clin. Exptl.* **13**, 1402–1412 (1964).

193. Havel, R. J., and Goldfien, A., The role of the sympathetic nervous system in the metabolism of free fatty acids. *J. Lipid Res.* **1**, 102–108 (1959).

194. Hazard, R., and Mouillé, P., Relations entre les fonctions amine et alcool de l'adrénaline et son action hyperglycémiante. Actions comparées chez le lapin (voie intraveineuse) de la noradrénaline, de l'éthylnoradrénaline et de l'isoprénaline; de l'adrénalone, de l'hydroxytyramine et de l'épinine. *J. Physiol.* (*Paris*) **57**, 399–406 (1965).

195. Headings, V. E., and Rondell, P. A., Arterial muscle contraction and potassium movement *in vitro*. *Am. J. Physiol.* **202**, 17–20 (1962).

196. Heidenreich, O., Kook, Y., Baumeister, L., and Reus, E., Stoffwechselwirkungen von synthetischem angiotensin II. *Arch. Intern. Pharmacodyn.* **148**, 309–319 (1964).

197. Heimberg, M., and Fizette, N. B., The action of norepinephrine on the transport of fatty acids and triglycerides by the isolated perfused rat liver. *Biochem. Pharmacol.* **12**, 393–394 (1963).

198. Hemingway, A., Price, W. M., and Stuart, D., The calorigenic action of catecholamines in warm acclimated and cold acclimated non-shivering cats. *Intern. J. Neuropharmacol.* **3**, 495–503 (1964).

199. Henneman, D. H., and Shoemaker, W. C., Effect of glucagon and epinephrine on regional metabolism of glucose, pyruvate, lactate, and citrate in normal conscious dogs. *Endocrinology* **68**, 889–898 (1961).

199a. Herman, M. S., and Ramey, E. R., Epinephrine action on glucose uptake by rat diaphragm; effect of ionic composition. *Am. J. Physiol.* **199**, 226–228 (1960).

200. Héroux, O., Effect of guanethidine on metabolic response to noradrenaline and cold resistance in warm-acclimated rats. *Can. J. Physiol. Pharmacol.* **42**, 265–267 (1964).

201. Hess, M. E., Hottenstein, D., Shanfeld, J., and Haugaard, N., Metabolic effects of theophylline in cardiac and skeletal muscle. *J. Pharmacol. Exptl. Therap.* **141**, 274–279 (1963).

202. Ho, R. J., and Meng, H. C., A technique for the cannulation and perfusion of isolated rat epididymal fat pad. *J. Lipid Res.* **5**, 203–209 (1964).

203. Ho, S. J., and Meng, H. C., Tissue and medium lipolytic activity and free fatty acid content of heparin- and epinephrine-perfused rat epididymal fat pad *in vitro*. *Federation Proc.* **23**, 270 (1964).

203a. Hollander, W., The inhibitory effects of catecholamines on mucopolysaccharide and lipid synthesis by the arterial wall. *Federation Proc.* **22**, 210 (1963).

204. Hollenberg, C. H., and Douglas, D. E., Effect of adrenaline, corticotropin, fasting, and diabetes on the composition of the long-chain fatty acids of rat epididymal fat. *Nature* **193**, 1074–1075 (1962).

205. Hollenberg, C. H., Raben, M. S., and Astwood, E. B., The lipolytic response to corticotropin. *Endocrinology* **68**, 589–598 (1961).

206. Hollett, C. R., Adipose tissue: hormonal influence on distribution of lipolytic activity in homogenate fractions. *Biochem. Biophys. Res. Commun.* **15**, 575–580 (1964).

207. Holtz, P., Stock, K., and Westermann, E., Pharmakologie des Tetrahydropapaverolins und seine Entstehung aus Dopamin. *Arch. Exptl. Pathol. Pharmakol.* **248**, 387–405 (1964).

208. Hornbrook, K. R., and Brody, T. M., Phosphorylase activity in rat liver and skeletal muscle after catecholamines. *Biochem. Pharmacol.* **12**, 1407–1415 (1963).

209. Hornbrook, K. R., and Brody, T. M., The effect of catecholamines on muscle glycogen and phosphorylase activity. *J. Pharmacol. Exptl. Therap.* **140**, 295–307 (1963).

210. Hsieh, A. C. L., and Carlson, L. D., Role of adrenaline and noradrenaline in chemical regulation of heat production. *Am. J. Physiol.* **190**, 243–246 (1957).

211. Hsieh, A. C. L., Carlson, L. D., and Gray, G., Role of the sympathetic nervous system in the control of chemical regulation of heat production. *Am. J. Physiol.* **190**, 247–251 (1957).

212. Hull, D., Pronethalol and the oxygen consumption of new-born rabbits. *J. Physiol.* (*London*) **173**, 13 (1963).

213. Hull, D., and Segall, M. M., The effect of removing brown adipose tissue on heat production in the new-born rabbit. *J. Physiol.* (*London*) **175**, 58P (1964).

214. Hull, D., and Segall, M. M., The contribution of brown adipose tissue to heat production in the new-born rabbit. *J. Physiol.* (*London*) **181**, 449–457 (1965).

215. Hunninghake, D. B., Azarnoff, D. L., and Waxman, D., Inhibition of fatty acid mobilization in humans by N-tertiary butyl methoxamine. *Pharmacologist* **7**, 136 (1965).

216. Hüter, J., Bauer, H., and Goodford, P. J., Die Wirkung von Adrenalin auf Kalium-Austausch und Kalium-Konzentration im glatten Muskel (Taenia coli des Meerschweinchens). *Arch. Exptl. Pathol. Pharmakol.* **246**, 75–76 (1963).

217. Hynie, S., Mühlbachová, E., Elisová, K., and Wenke, M., Influence of some β-sympathotropic agents on muscle glycogen content *in vitro*. *Intern. J. Neuropharmacol.* **3**, 189–196 (1964).

218. Hynie, S., Wenke, M., Mühlbachová, E., and Dolejšová, K., Metabolische veranderungen nach chronischer applikation von isoproterenol. *Arch. Exptl. Pathol. Pharmakol.* **245**, 101–102 (1963).

219. Iriye, T. T., Kuna, A., and Simmonds, F., Effects of various agents *in vivo* on phosphorylase activity of rat brain. *Biochem. Pharmacol.* **11**, 803–807 (1965).

220. Jamieson, J. D., and Friedman, S. M., Sodium and potassium shifts associated with peripheral resistance changes in the dog. *Circulation Res.* **9**, 996–1004 (1961).

221. Jelinkova, M., and Hruza, Z., Decreased effect of norepinephrine and growth hormone on the release of free fatty acids in old rats. *Physiol. Bohemoslov.* **13**, 327–332 (1964).

222. Jenkinson, D. H., and Morton, I. K. M., Effects of noradrenaline and isoprenaline on the permeability of depolarized intestinal smooth muscle to inorganic ions. *Nature* **205,** 505–506 (1965).

223. Joel, C. D., and Shackney, S. E., Respiratory metabolism of rat brown adipose tissue *in vitro*. *Federation Proc.* **21,** 184 (1962).

224. Johnson, G. E., and Sellers, E. A., The effect of reserpine on the metabolic rate of rats. *Can. J. Biochem. Physiol.* **39,** 279–285 (1961).

225. Jörgensen, G., and Noelle, H., Zur Frage des Blutzuckeranstieges nach 1-Noradrenalin bei Gesunden und Leberkranken. *Aertzl. Wochschr.* **11,** 844 (1956).

226. Joy, R. J. T., Response of normal men to infused norepinephrine before and after chronic cold exposure. *Physiologist* **5,** 164 (1962).

227. Jungas, R. L., and Ball, E. G., Studies on the metabolism of adipose tissue. XII. The effects of insulin and epinephrine on free fatty acid and glycerol production in the presence and absence of glucose. *Biochemistry* **2,** 383–388 (1963).

228. Kabal, J., and Ramey, E. R., Effect of liver damage on plasma FFA response to epinephrine. *Proc. Soc. Exptl. Biol. Med.* **119,** 708–710 (1965).

229. Kahn, J. B., Jr., and Acheson, G. H., Effects of cardiac glycosides and other lactones, and of certain other compounds, on cation transfer in human erythrocytes. *J. Pharmacol. Exptl. Therap.* **115,** 305–318 (1955).

230. Kaplan, A., Jacques, S., and Gant, M., Effect of long-lasting epinephrine on serum lipid levels. *Am. J. Physiol.* **191,** 8–12 (1957).

231. Kappey, F., Die Wirkung von 2-Benzyl-imidazolin und Noradrenalin auf den Sauerstoffverbrach des Hundes bei gleichzeitiger Warmebelastung. *Arzneimittel -Forsch.* **14,** 169–171 (1964).

232. Kappert, A., Sutton, G. C., Reale, A., Skoglund, K.-H., and Nylin, G., The clinical response of human beings to *l*-noradrenaline and its clinical applicability. *Acta Cardiol.* **5,** 121–136 (1950).

233. Karlberg, P., Moore, R. E., and Oliver, T. K., Jr., The thermogenic response of the newborn infant to noradrenaline. *Acta Paediat.* **51,** 284–292 (1962).

234. Karpatkin, S., Helmreich, E., and Cori, C. F., Regulation of glycolysis in muscle. II. Effect of stimulation and epinephrine in isolated frog sartorius muscle. *J. Biol. Chem.* **239,** 3139–3145 (1964).

235. Kennedy, B. L., and Ellis, S., Interactions of sympathomimetic amines and adrenergic blocking agents at receptor sites mediating glycogenolysis. *Federation Proc.* **22,** 449 (1963).

236. Kennedy, B. L., and Ellis, S., Dissociation of catecholamine-induced calorigenesis from lipolysis and glycogenolysis in intact animals. *Pharmacologist* **7,** 137 (1965).

237. Kenny, A. D., Glycogenolytic action of epinephrine on mouse parietal bone. *Endocrinology* **71,** 901 (1962).

238. Kenny, A. D., Effect of catecholamines on serum calcium and phosphorus levels in intact and parathyroidectomized rats. *Arch. Exptl. Pathol. Pharmakol.* **248,** 144–152 (1964).

239. Kenny, A. D., and Fleming, W. W., Effect of adrenalectomy on hyperglycemic responses of fed and fasted rats to catecholamines. *Proc. Soc. Exptl. Biol. Med.* **119,** 255–258 (1965).

240. Kerpel, S., and Shafrir, E., Relation of glucose metabolism to fatty acid esterification and lipolysis in adipose tissue. *Bull. Res. Council Israel* **A11,** 92–93 (1962).
241. Khan, A. U., Forney, R. B., and Hughes, F. W., Stress of shocking stimulus on plasma free fatty acids in rats. *Arch. Intern. Pharmacodyn.* **151,** 459–464 (1964).
242. Khan, A. U., Forney, R. B., and Hughes, F. W., Plasma free fatty acids in rats after shock as modified by centrally active drugs. *Arch. Intern. Pharmacodyn.* **151,** 466–473 (1964).
243. Kibler, R. F., Taylor, W. J., and Myers, J. D., The effect of glucagon on net splanchnic balances of glucose, amino acid nitrogen, urea, ketones, and oxygen in man. *J. Clin. Invest.* **43,** 904–915 (1964).
244. Kilburn, K. H., Effect of adrenergic blockade with Hydergine on hyperglycemia accompanying hypothermia in dogs. *Am. J. Physiol.* **199,** 955–958 (1960).
245. Kipnis, D. M., and Cori, C. F., Studies of tissue permeability. V. The penetration and phosphorylation of 2-deoxyglucose in the rat diaphragm. *J. Biol. Chem.* **234,** 171–177 (1959).
246. Kipnis, D. M., Helmreich, E., and Cori, C. F., Studies of tissue permeability. IV. The distribution of glucose between plasma and muscle. *J. Biol. Chem.* **234,** 165–170 (1959).
247. Kits van Heijningen, A. J. M., The influence of insulin and adrenaline on the incorporation of C^{14}-labeled glucose into glycogen fractions of the isolated rat diaphragm. *Arch. Biochem. Biophys.* **102,** 456–462 (1963).
248. Klainer, L. M., Chi, Y.-M., Friedberg, S. L., Rall, T. W., and Sutherland, E. W., Adenyl Cyclase. IV. The effects of neurohormones on the formation of adenosine 3′,5′-phosphate by preparations from brain and other tissues. *J. Biol. Chem.* **237,** 1239–1243 (1962).
249. Klein, R. F., and Bogdonoff, M. D., Effect of phentolamine (Regitine®) infusion upon serum nonesterified fatty acid. *Clin. Res.* **8,** 58 (1960).
250. Klocke, F. J., Kaiser, G. A., Ross, J., Jr., and Braunwald, E., Mechanism of increase of myocardial oxygen uptake produced by catecholamines. *Am. J. Physiol.* **209,** 913–918 (1965).
251. Konttinen, A., and Rajasalmi, M., Effect of sympathetic blocking agent on plasma FFA and on the response evoked by catecholamines. *Proc. Soc. Exptl. Biol. Med.* **112,** 723–725 (1963).
252. Krajči-Lazáry, B., Dzúrik, R., and Niederland, T. R., Vliv adrenalínu na metabolické procesy v obličkách. *Cesk. Fysiol.* **11,** 196 (1962).
253. Krayer, O., ed., *Symp. Catecholamines. Pharmacol. Rev.* **11,** 233–566 (1959).
254. Krčíková, D., Hynie, S., Schusterová, D., and Mühlbachová, E., Influence of some new β-sympathotropic agents on lipid mobilization *in vitro. Biochem. Pharmacol.* **12,** Suppl., 86 (1963).
255. Krebs, E. G., DeLange, R. J., Kemp, R. G., and Riley, W. D., Activation of skeletal muscle phosphorylase. *Pharmacol. Rev.* **18,** 163–171 (1966).
256. Kukovetz, W. R., Kontraktilität und Phosphorylaseaktivität des Herzens bei gänglionarer Erregung nach adrenerger Blockade und unter Atropin. *Arch. Exptl. Pathol. Pharmakol.* **243,** 291–406 (1962).
257. Kukovetz, W. R., Hess, M. E., Shanfeld, J., and Haugaard, N., The action of sympathomimetic amines on isometric contraction and phosphorylase activity of the isolated rat heart. *J. Pharmacol. Exptl. Therap.* **127,** 122–127 (1959).

258. Kukovetz, W. R., and Pöch, G., Zur Frage des Angriffspunktes der Herzwirkung von Methylxanthinen. *Arch. Exptl. Pathol. Pharmakol.* **243**, 343–344 (1962).

259. Kukovetz, W. R., and Pöch, G., Zur Frage der Trennbarkeit adrenerger Wirkung auf die Kontraktilität und Phosphorylaseaktivität des Herzmuskels durch β-Adrenolytica. *Arch. Exptl. Pathol. Pharmakol.* **251**, 127 (1965).

260. Kvam, D. C., Effect of β-adrenergic blockade or nicotinic acid on norepinephrine-induced increases in plasma free fatty acids and total cholesterol in the dog. *Life Sci.* **4**, 479–485 (1965).

261. Kvam, D. C., Riggilo, D. A., and Lish, P. M., Effect of some new β-adrenergic blocking agents on certain metabolic responses to catecholamines. *J. Pharmacol. Exptl. Therap.* **140**, 183–192 (1965).

262. Lacroix, E., and Leusen, I., Influences of sympathomimetic amines on phosphorylase activity of isolated perfused rat hearts. *Arch. Intern. Pharmacodyn.* **126**, 482–485 (1960).

263. Lacroix, E., and Leusen, I., Action inotrope des amines sympathomimétiques et activité phosphorylasique du coeur de rat isolé. *Arch. Intern. Pharmacodyn.* **133**, 89–100 (1961).

264. Laubender, W., and Presser, C., Der Einfluss der Desoxydation des Benzolkerns in Stoffen von Adrenalin-Grundstruktur auf die Blutzuckersteigernde Wirking. *Arzneimittel -Forsch.* **7**, 298–301 (1957).

265. Leblanc, J. A., and Nadeau, G., Urinary excretion of adrenaline and noradrenaline in normal and cold-adapted animals. *Can. J. Biochem. Physiol.* **39**, 215–217 (1961).

266. Leblanc, J., and Pouliot, M., Importance of noradrenaline in cold adaptation. *Am. J. Physiol.* **207**, 853–856 (1964).

267. Leboeuf, B., Flinn, R. B., and Cahill, G. F., Jr., Effect of epinephrine on glucose uptake and glycerol release by adipose tissue *in vitro*. *Proc. Soc. Exptl. Biol. Med.* **102**, 527–529 (1959).

268. Leduc, J., Catecholamine production and release in exposure and acclimation to cold. *Acta Physiol. Scand.* **53**, Suppl. 183, 1–101 (1961).

269. Lee, K. S., and Yu, D. H., Effect of epinephrine on metabolism and contraction of cat papillary muscle. *Am. J. Physiol.* **206**, 525–530 (1964).

270. Lei, B. W., and McCutcheon, R. S., Influence of adrenergic receptors on blood sugar and lactic acid levels in the rat. *J. Pharm. Sci.* **53**, 503–506 (1964).

271. Leonard, S. L., Hormonal effects on phosphorylase activity in the rat uterus. *Endocrinology* **63**, 853–859 (1958).

272. Leonard, S. L., and Crandall, M., Hormonal stimulation of phosphorylase activity in the rat uterus *in vitro*. *Endocrinology* **73**, 807–815 (1963).

273. Leonard, S. L., and Day, H. T., Effect of 5-hydroxytryptamine on phosphorylase and glycogen levels in muscle tissue. *Proc. Soc. Exptl. Biol. Med.* **104**, 338–341 (1960).

274. Leonard, S. L., and Schane, H. P., Hormonal effects on phosphorylase activity and glycogen levels in the rat ductus deferens. *Endocrinology* **76**, 870–875 (1965).

275. Leonard, S. L., and Wimsatt, W. A., Phosphorylase and glycogen levels in skeletal muscle and liver of hibernating and nonhibernating bats. *Am. J. Physiol.* **197**, 1059–1062 (1959).

276. Leusen, I., and Lacroix, E., Inotropismus des Herzens und Phosphorylase a-Aktivität. *Verhandl. Deutsch. Ges. Kreislaufforsch.* **27**, 265–270 (1961).

277. Levine, R. A., Effect of glycogenolytic agents on phosphorylase activity of perfused rat liver. *Am. J. Physiol.* **208,** 317–323 (1965).

278. Levine, R. A., Pesch, L. A., Klatskin, G., and Giarman, N. J., Effect of serotonin on glycogen metabolism in isolated rat liver. *J. Clin. Invest.* 43, 797–809 (1964).

278a. Levy, A. C., and Ramey, E. R., Effect of autonomic blocking agents on depot fat mobilization in normal and adrenalectomized animals. *Proc. Soc. Exptl. Biol. Med.* **99,** 637–639 (1958).

279. Lopez, E., White, J. E., and Engel, F. L., Contrasting requirements for the lipolytic action of corticotropin and epinephrine on adipose tissue *in vitro. J. Biol. Chem.* **234,** 2254–2258 (1959).

280. Love, W. C., and Burch, G. E., Differences in the rate of Rb^{86} uptake by several regions of the myocardium of control dogs and dogs receiving *l*-noradrenaline or pitressin®. *J. Clin. Invest.* **36,** 479–484 (1957).

281. Love, W. C., Carr, L., and Ashmore, J., Lipolysis in adipose tissue: effects of dl-3,4-dichloroisoproterenol and related compounds. *J. Pharmacol. Exptl. Therap.* **140,** 287–294 (1963).

282. Love, W. C., Carr, L., and Ashmore. J., Influence of isoproterenol and 1-(2′,4′-dichlorophenyl)-2-*t*-butylaminoethanol (DCB) on free fatty acid release and glucose metabolism in adipose tissue. *J. Pharmacol. Exptl. Therap.* **142,** 137–140 (1963).

283. Love, W. C., Stoelting, R., and Johnson, R., Studies on the regulation of adipose tissue metabolism. *Federation Proc.* **21,** 193 (1962).

284. Lundholm, L., and Mohme-Lundholm, E., Dissociation of contraction and stimulation of lactic acid production in experiments on smooth muscle under anaerobic conditions. *Acta Physiol. Scand.* **57,** 111–124 (1959).

284a. Lundholm, L., and Mohme-Lundholm, E., Contraction and glycogenolysis of smooth muscle. *Acta Physiol. Scand.* **57,** 125–129 (1959).

285. Lundholm, L., and Mohme-Lundholm, E., The effect of cocaine and adrenaline on blood lactic acid and oxygen consumption in rabbits. *Acta Pharmacol. Toxicol.* **15,** 257–264 (1959).

286. Lundholm, L., and Mohme-Lundholm, E., Studies on the effects of drugs upon the lactic acid metabolism and contraction of vascular smooth muscle. *Acta Physiol. Scand.* **55,** 45–63 (1962).

287. Lundholm, L., and Mohme-Lundholm, E., Energetics of isometric and isotonic contraction in isolated smooth muscle under anaerobic conditions. *Acta Physiol. Scand.* **64,** 275–282 (1965).

288. Lundholm, L., and Svedmyr, N., Blockade of the lactic acid-stimulating and calorigenic effects of adrenaline or isoprenaline by chloroisoprenaline. *Acta Pharmacol. Toxicol.* **20,** 303–308 (1963).

289. Lundholm, L., and Svedmyr, N., Comparative investigation of the calorigenic and lactic acid stimulating effects of isoprenaline and adrenaline in experiments on rabbits. *Acta Physiol. Scand.* **62,** 60–67 (1964).

290. Lynn, W. S., MacLeod, R. M., and Brown, R. H., Effects of epinephrine, insulin, and corticotropin on the metabolism of rat adipose tissue. *J. Biol. Chem.* **235,** 1904–1911 (1960).

291. Lyon, J. B., Jr., and Porter, J., The relation of phosphorylase to glycogenolysis in skeletal muscle and heart of mice. *J. Biol. Chem.* **238,** 1–11 (1963).

292. McChesney, E. W., McAuliff, J. P., and Blumberg, H., The hyperglycemic action of some analogs of epinephrine. *Proc. Soc. Exptl. Biol. Med.* **71,** 220–223 (1949).
293. McCutcheon, R. S., Canine blood sugar and lactic acid responses to adrenergic amines after ganglionic block. *J. Am. Pharm. Assoc., Sci. Ed.* **49,** 714–716 (1960).
294. McCutcheon, R. S., Canine blood sugar and lactic acid responses to adrenergic amines after adrenergic block. *J. Pharmacol. Exptl. Therap.* **136,** 209–212 (1962).
295. McClure, D. A., Dichloroisoproterenol (DCI) inhibition of sympathomimetic-induced hyperglycemia. *Pharmacologist* **2,** 94 (1960).
296. McElroy, W. T., Jr., and Spitzer, J. J., Effects of adrenergic blocking agents on plasma free fatty acid concentrations. *Am. J. Physiol.* **200,** 318–322 (1961).
297. McNeill, J. H., and Brody, T. M., The potentiating effect of various drugs on norepinephrine induced phosphorylase activation in rat heart. *Pharmacologist* **7,** 140 (1965).
298. Mahler, R., Preston, J. E., and Ashmore, J., Effects of an adrenergic blocking agent (N-isopropylmethoxamine) on blood glucose and plasma free fatty acids of normal and alloxan-diabetic dogs. *Federation Proc.* **23,** 541 (1964).
299. Makman, M. H., and Sutherland, E. W., Jr., Use of liver adenyl cyclase for assay of glucagon in human gastro-intestinal tract and pancreas. *Endocrinology* **75,** 127–134 (1964).
300. Maling, H. M., and Highman, B., Exaggerated ventricular arrhythmias and myocardial fatty changes after large doses of norepinephrine and epinephrine in unanesthetized dogs. *Am. J. Physiol.* **194,** 590–596 (1958).
301. Maling, H. M., Williams, M. A., Highman, B., Garbus, J., and Hunter, J., The influence of phenoxybenzamine and isopropylmethoxamine (BW 61-43) on some cardiovascular, metabolic, and histopathologic effects of norepinephrine infusions in dogs. *Arch. Exptl. Pathol. Pharmakol.* **248,** 54–72 (1964).
302. Mansour, T. E., Changes in the structure and activity of heart phosphofructokinase (PFK). *Federation Proc.* **23,** 171 (1964).
303. Marchett, G. V., Merlo, L., and Antognetti, R. M., The effects of nitroglycerin on the coronary blood flow and oxygen consumption of the myocardium in anesthetized dogs. *Am. J. Cardiol.* **13,** 51–57 (1964).
304. Marquardt, P. Blutzuckersteigerung bei blutdrucksenkender Wirkung des Adrenalins. *Arzneimittel -Forsch.* **12,** 728–729 (1962).
305. Marquardt, P., and Krause, I., Die Blutzucker-Wirkung des Adrenalins nach Vorbehandlung mit Sympathicolytica. *Arzneimittel -Forsch.* **12,** 843–846 (1962).
306. Marquardt, P., Schmidt, H. A., and Späth, M., Kontinuierliche Registrierung der Kaliumveränderung im Vollblut der Katze durch Phenylalkylamine und Peptide. *Med. Exptl.* **10,** 291–302 (1964).
307. Marshall, N. B., Influence of epinephrine and fasting on free fatty acid mobilization in goldthioglucose-induced obesity. *Proc. Soc. Exptl. Biol. Med.* **107,** 941–943 (1961).
308. Marshall, N. B., and Engel, F. L., The influence of epinephrine and fasting on adipose tissue content and release of free fatty acids in obese-hyperglycemic and lean mice. *J. Lipid Res.* **1,** 339–342 (1959–1960).
309. Martin, K., Observations on the increase in permeability induced by adrenaline in the submaxillary gland. *J. Physiol.* (*London*) **172,** 50–60 (1964).

310. Masoro, E. J., Effect of cold on metabolic use of lipids. *Physiol. Rev.* **46**, 67–101 (1966).

311. Matsumoto, S., Metabolism of the heart muscle. Effects of epinephrine, insulin and hydrocortisone on the C^{14}-labeled glucose and palmitate-1-C^{14} metabolism of the normal rat heart muscle. *Japan Heart J.* **4**, 131–140 (1963).

312. Mayer, S. E., Action of epinephrine on glucose uptake and glucose-6-phosphate in the dog heart *in situ. Biochem. Pharmacol.* **12**, 193–201 (1963).

313. Mayer, S. E., and Moran, N. C., Relation between pharmacologic augmentation of cardiac contractile force and the activation of myocardial glycogen phosphorylase. *J. Pharmacol. Exptl. Therap.* **129**, 271–281 (1960).

314. Mayer, S., Moran, N. C., and Fain, J., The effect of adrenergic blocking agents on some metabolic actions of catecholamines. *J. Pharmacol. Exptl. Therap.* **134**, 18–27 (1961).

315. Meinertz, H., The differential release of fatty acids from adipose tissue *in vitro. Federation Proc.* **21**, 284 (1962).

316. Mendez, C., Erlij, D., and Moe, G. K., Indirect action of epinephrine on intraventricular conduction time. *Circulation Res.* **14**, 318–326 (1964).

317. Merrick, A. W., Responses of cardiac tissue to certain stimulants and inhibitors. *Am. J. Physiol.* **200**, 229–232 (1961).

318. Milch, L. J., and Loxterman, P. B., Aortal mucopolysaccharide changes after epinephrine administration in rabbits. *Proc. Soc. Exptl. Biol. Med.* **116**, 1125–1126 (1964).

319. Miller, H. I., Issekutz, B., Jr., Paul, P., and Rodahl, K., Effect of lactic acid on plasma free fatty acids in pancreatectomized dogs. *Am. J. Physiol.* **207**, 1226–1230 (1964).

320. Miller, W. L., and Krake, J. J., Comparative expiratory and oxidative effects of glucagon and epinephrine in mice. *Proc. Soc. Exptl. Biol. Med.* **113**, 784–788 (1963).

321. Mohme-Lundholm, E., The association between the relaxing and the lactic-acid stimulating effects of adrenaline in smooth muscle. *Acta Physiol. Scand.* **48**, 268–275 (1960).

322. Mohme-Lundholm, E., Phosphorylase activity of smooth muscle. *Acta Physiol. Scand.* **54**, 200–208 (1962).

323. Mohme-Lundholm, E., Lactic acid production and adrenaline reversal in experiments on isolated smooth muscle. *Acta Physiol. Scand.* **55**, 225–230 (1962).

324. Mohme-Lundholm, E., and Svedmyr, N., Influence of nethalide on the phosphorylase activating effects of adrenaline and isoprenaline in experiments on isolated rat diaphragm. *Acta Physiol. Scand.* **61**, 192–194 (1964).

325. Moore, R. E., Control of heat production in newborn mammals: role of noradrenaline and mode of action. *Federation Proc.* **22**, 920–929 (1963).

326. Moore, R. E., and Underwood, M. C., Possible role of noradrenaline in control of heat production in the newborn animal. *Lancet* **1**, 1277–1278 (1960).

326a. Moore, R. E., and Underwood, M. C., Noradrenaline as a possible regulator of heat production in the new-born kitten. *J. Physiol.* (*London*) **150**, 13P–14P (1960).

327. Moore, R. E., and Underwood, M. C., Hexamethonium, hypoxia and heat production in new-born and infant kittens and puppies. *J. Physiol.* (*London*) **161**, 30–53 (1962).

328. Moore, R. E., and Underwood, M. C., The thermogenic effects of noradrenaline in new-born and infant kittens and other small mammals. A possible hormonal mechanism in the control of heat production. *J. Physiol. (London)* **168,** 290–317 (1963).

329. Morii, H., Fujita, T., Orimo, H., Okinaka, S., and Nakao, K., Effect of sympathetic stimulation, epinephrine and phentolamine on recovery from induced hypocalcemia. *Endocrinology* **76,** 58–62 (1965).

330. Moutschen, J., Moës, A., and Gilot, J., Effect of α-methyldopa and α-methyl-*m*-tyrosine on the mobilization of free fatty acids. *Experientia* **20,** 495–496 (1964).

331. Mueller, P. S., The absence of plasma free fatty acid response to epinephrine in vitamin-C-deprived guinea pigs. *J. Lipid Res.* **3,** 92–94 (1962).

332. Mueller, P. S., and Evans, W. H., Responses of plasma glycerol concentrations to epinephrine, norepinephrine, glucose, insulin, and prolonged fasting in man. *J. Lab. Clin. Med.* **61,** 953–961 (1963).

333. Mueller, P. S., and Horwitz, D., Plasma free fatty acid and blood glucose responses to analogues of norepinephrine in man. *J. Lipid Res.* **3,** 251–255 (1962).

334. Mühlbachová, E., Wenke, M., and Hynie, S., The effect of adrenaline on depot adipose tissue. *Physiol. Bohemoslov.* **10,** 44–49 (1961).

335. Mühlbachová, E., Wenke, M., and Hynie, S., The effect of some sympathotropic substances on lipid metabolism. *Physiol. Bohemoslov.* **10,** 181–186 (1961).

336. Mühlbachová, E., Wenke, M., Hynie, S., and Dolejšová, K., Interactions of some sympathicotropic agents affecting lipid mobilisation. *Arch. Intern. Pharmacodyn.* **144,** 454–463 (1963).

337. Mühlbachová, E., Wenke, M., Hynie, S., and Dolejšová, K., Die Beeinflussung der Lipolyse im Fettgewebe durch Isoproterenol. *Arch. Exptl. Pathol. Pharmakol.* **245,** 104 (1963).

338. Mühlbachová, E., Wenke, M., Schusterová, D., Krčíková, D., and Elisová, K., Indirectly acting sympathotropic drugs and lipid mobilization. *Intern. J. Neuropharmacol.* **3,** 217–225 (1964).

339. Murad, F., Chi, Y.-M., Rall, T. W., and Sutherland, E. W., Adenyl cyclase. III. The effect of catecholamines and choline esters on the formation of adenosine 3′,5′-phosphate by preparations from cardiac muscle and liver. *J. Biol. Chem.* **237,** 1233–1238 (1962).

340. Nagasaka, T., and Carlson, L. D., Responses of cold- and warm-adapted dogs to infused norepinephrine and acute body cooling. *Am. J. Physiol.* **209,** 227–230 (1965).

341. Nagasawa, J., The effects of temperature and some drugs on the ionic movements in the smooth muscle of guinea-pig taenia coli. *Tohoku J. Exptl. Med.* **81,** 222–236 (1963).

342. Nagasawa, J., Calcium movement in the smooth muscle of guinea-pig taenia coli. *Tohoku J. Exptl. Med.* **85,** 72–82 (1965).

343. Nahas, G. G., Ligou, J. C., and Mehlman, B., Effects of pH changes on O_2 uptake and plasma catecholamine levels in the dog. *Am. J. Physiol.* **198,** 60–66 (1960).

344. Nakatani, G., The effect of adrenaline on the phosphorylase activity of the heart in the open-chest rat. *Japan. J. Pharmacol.* **13,** 282–291 (1963).

345. Napolitano, L., McNary, J. E., and Kloep, L. P., The release of free fatty acids from brown and white adipose tissues after incubation with ACTH or epinephrine. *Metab. Clin. Exptl.* **14,** 1076–1082 (1965).
346. Nayler, W. G., and Howells, J. E., Phosphorylase a/b ratio in the lamprey heart. *Nature* **207,** 81 (1965).
347. Nayler, W. G., and Wright, J. E., Effects of epinephrine on the mechanical and phosphorylase activity of normo- and hypothermic hearts. *Circulation Res.* **13,** 199–206 (1963).
348. Nestle, P. J., Plasma triglyceride concentration and plasma free fatty acid changes in response to norepinephrine in man. *J. Clin. Invest.* **43,** 77–82 (1964).
349. Niemeyer, H., Radojković, J., and Pérez, N., The influence of diet on liver phosphorylase. III. Role of inactivation on the decrease of phosphorylase under certain dietary conditions. *Arch. Biochem.* **97,** 285–291 (1962).
350. Norcia, L. N., and Evans, J. D., Composition of rabbit plasma free fatty acids. *Federation Proc.* **21,** 290 (1962).
351. Northrop, G., and Parks, R. E., Jr., 3′,5′-AMP-induced hyperglycemia in intact rats and in the isolated perfused rat liver. *Biochem. Pharmacol.* **13,** 120–123 (1964).
352. Northrop, G., and Parks, R. E., Jr., The effects of adrenergic blocking agents and theophylline on the 3′,5′-AMP-induced hyperglycemia. *J. Pharmacol. Exptl. Therap.* **145,** 87–91 (1964).
353. Northrop, G., and Parks, R. E., Jr., Studies on epinephrine and 3′,5′-AMP-induced hyperglycemia employing the isolated perfused rat liver preparation. *J. Pharmacol. Exptl. Therap.* **145,** 135–141 (1964).
354. Opitz, K., Wirkungen einiger Anorektica auf den Kohlenhydrat- und Fettsäurestoffwechsel. *Arch. Exptl. Pathol. Pharmakol.* **250,** 279 (1965).
355. Orestano, G., Azione dei farmaci simpatico e parasimpatico-mimetici sugli scambi gassosi. V. Influenza della ergotamina sull'azione eccitometabolica della adrenalina. *Boll. Soc. Ital. Biol. Sper.* **8,** 1148–1156 (1933).
356. Orskov, S. L., Experiments on the influence of adrenaline and noradrenaline on the potassium absorption of red blood cells from pigeons and frogs. *Acta Physiol. Scand.* **37,** 299–306 (1956).
357. Orth, R. D., Odell, W. D., and Williams, R. H., Some hormonal effects on the metabolism of acetate-1-C^{14} by rat adipose tissue. *Am. J. Physiol.* **198,** 640–644 (1960).
358. Orth, R. D., and Williams, R. H., Response of plasma NEFA levels to epinephrine infusions in normal and obese women. *Proc. Soc. Exptl. Biol. Med.* **104,** 119–120 (1960).
359. Özand, P., and Narahara, H. T., Regulation of glycolysis in muscle. III. Influence of insulin, epinephrine, and contraction on phosphofructokinase activity in frog skeletal muscle. *J. Biol. Chem.* **239,** 3146–3152 (1964).
360. Pastan, I., Herring, B., Johnson, P., and Field, J. B., Studies on the mechanism by which epinephrine stimulates glucose oxidation in the thyroid. *J. Biol. Chem.* **237,** 287–290 (1962).
361. Penick, S. B., and Hinkle, L. E., Jr., The effect of glucagon, phenmetrazine, and epinephrine on hunger, food intake and plasma nonesterified fatty acids. *Am. J. Clin. Nutr.* **13,** 110–114 (1963).

362. Perry, W. F., and Bowen, H. F., Factors affecting the *in vitro* production of nonesterified fatty acid from adipose tissue. *Can. J. Biochem. Physiol.* **40,** 749–755 (1962).

363. Pfeifer, A. K., Vizi, E. Sz., Sátory, É., and Galambos, É., Effect of reserpine on the metabolic centers. *Arch. Intern. Pharmacodyn.* **149,** 126–135 (1964).

364. Pilkington, T. R. E., Lowe, R. D., Robinson, B. F., and Titterington, E., Effect of adrenergic blockade on glucose and fatty-acid mobilization in man. *Lancet* **2,** 316–317 (1962).

365. Posner, J. B., Stern, R., and Krebs, E. G., *In vivo* response of skeletal muscle glycogen phosphorylase, phosphorylase *b* kinase and cyclic AMP to epinephrine administration. *Biochem. Biophys. Res. Commun.* **9,** 293–296 (1962).

366. Posner, J. B., Stern, R., and Krebs, E. G., Effects of electrical stimulation and epinephrine on muscle phosphorylase, phosphorylase *b* kinase, and adenosine 3′,5′-phosphate. *J. Biol. Chem.* **240,** 982–985 (1965).

367. Pytasz, M., Zarzycki, J., and Taborska, J., Wplyw adrenaliny na glikogen i glikoze nerki. *Acta Physiol. Polon.* **11,** 865–866 (1960).

368. Quinn, P. V., Hornbrook, K. R., and Brody, T. M., Blockade of catecholamine-induced phosphorylase activation by *N*-isopropyl methoxamine (B. W. 61–43) in certain tissues. *Pharmacologist* **7,** 140 (1965).

369. Raben, M. S., and Hollenberg, C. H., Effect of growth hormone on plasma fatty acids. *J. Clin. Invest.* **37,** 922–923 (1958).

370. Rafaelsen, O. J., Glycogen content of rat diaphragm after intraperitoneal injection of insulin and other hormones. *Acta Physiol. Scand.* **61,** 314–322 (1964).

371. Rall, T. W., and Sutherland, E. W., Formation of a cyclic adenine ribonucleotide by tissue particles. *J. Biol. Chem.* **232,** 1065–1076 (1958).

372. Regan, T. J., cited in Bunker, J. P., and Vandam, L. D., Effects of anesthesia on metabolism and cellular functions. *Pharmacol. Rev.* **17,** 183–263 (1965).

373. Regan, T. J., and Moschos, C. B., Lipid transport alteration in the heart during epinephrine infusions. *Federation Proc.* **22,** 518 (1963).

374. Regazzini, A., L'attività lipolitica plasmatica dopo somministrazione di adrenalina. *Giorn. Clin. Med. (Bologna)* **44,** 1006–1014 (1963).

375. Renold, A. E., and Cahill, G. F., Jr., sect. eds., "Handbook of Physiology, Sect. 5: Adipose Tissue," 684 pp., 4109 refs. Am. Physiol. Soc., Washington, D.C., 1965.

376. Reshef, L., and Shapiro, B., Effect of epinephrine, cortisone and growth hormone on release of unesterified fatty acids by adipose tissue *in vitro.* Metab. *Clin. Exptl.* **9,** 551–555 (1960).

377. Reuter, H., Über den Ca-Umsatz der Meerschweinchenvorhofs unter der Einwirkung von Adrenalin. *Arch. Exptl. Pathol. Pharmakol.* **247,** 230–231 (1964).

378. Reuter, H., Über die Wirkung von Adrenalin auf den cellulären Ca-Umsatz des Meerschweinchenvorhofs. *Arch. Exptl. Pathol. Pharmakol.* **251,** 401–412 (1965).

379. Rimmer, A. D., Schönbaum, E., and Sellers, E. A., Effects of norepinephrine on blood glucose and free fatty acids in cold-adapted rats. *Am. J. Physiol.* **203,** 95–97 (1958).

380. Rizack, M. A., An epinephrine-sensitive lipolytic activity in adipose tissue. *J. Biol. Chem.* **236,** 657–662 (1961).

381. Rizack, M. A., Activation of an epinephrine-sensitive lipolytic activity from adipose tissue by adenosine 3′,5′-phosphate. *J. Biol. Chem.* **239,** 392–394 (1964).

382. Robison, G. A., Butcher, R. W., Øye, I., Morgan, H. E., and Sutherland, E. W., The effect of epinephrine on adenosine 3′,5′-phosphate levels in the isolated perfused rat heart. *Mol. Pharmacol.* **1,** 168–177 (1965).

383. Rodbell, M., Metabolism of isolated fat cells. I. Effects of hormones on glucose metabolism and lipolysis. *J. Biol. Chem.* **239,** 375–380 (1964).

384. Rosenberg, F. J., and DiStefano, V., A central nervous system component of epinephrine hyperglycemia. *Am. J. Physiol.* **203,** 782–788 (1962).

385. Rosenblum, I., Wohl, A., and Stein, A. A., Studies in cardiac necrosis. III. Metabolic effects of sympathomimetic amines producing cardiac lesions. *Toxicol. Appl. Pharmacol.* **7,** 344–351 (1965).

386. Rothlin, M. E., Rothlin, C. B., and Wendt, V. E., Free fatty acid concentration and composition in arterial blood. *Am. J. Physiol.* **203,** 306–310 (1962).

387. Rozovskaya, E. S., Changes in chemical composition of cardiac muscle under the influence of adrenaline and acetylcholine. *Farm. Toks.* **8,** 11–14 (1945).

388. Rubenstein, D., Chiu, S., Naylor, J., and Beck, J. C., Lipolytic action of epinephrine in adipose tissue homogenates. *Am. J. Physiol.* **206,** 149–152 (1964).

389. Rubenstein, D., Daniel, A., Chiu, S., and Beck, J. C., The effect of glucose and epinephrine upon lipolysis and esterification in adipose tissue. *Clin. Res.* **10,** 234 (1962).

390. Rudman, D., Brown, S. J., and Malkin, M. F., Adipokinetic actions of adrenocorticotropin, thyroid-stimulating hormone, vasopressin, α- and β-melanocyte-stimulating hormones, fraction H, epinephrine and norepinephrine in the rabbit, guinea pig, hamster, rat, pig and dog. *Endocrinology* **72,** 527–543 (1963).

391. Rudman, D., Garcia, L. A., Brown, S. J., Malkin, M. F., and Perl, W., Dose-response curves for the adipokinetic action of aromatic amines and adrenocorticotropin upon the isolated adipose tissue of the hamster. *J. Lipid Res.* **5,** 28–37 (1964).

392. Salvador, R. A., Colville, K. I., April, S. A., and Burns, J. J., Inhibition of lipid mobilization by N-isopropyl methoxamine (B.W. 61–43). *J. Pharmacol. Exptl. Therap.* **144,** 172–180 (1964).

393. Sandhu, R. S., Gessert, C. F., and McIntyre, A. R., Stimulation by acetylcholine and norepinephrine of glucose oxidation in rat submaxillary gland slices, as influenced by calcium. *Biochem. Pharmacol.* **13,** 1100–1103 (1964).

394. Sandhu, R., Gessert, C. F., and McIntyre, A. R., Effects of norepinephrine, acetylcholine and calcium on the oxidation of glucose in the submaxillary gland of the rat. *Biochem. Pharmacol.* **14,** 1289–1291 (1965).

395. Santaló, R. C., Consumo de oxigeno: Adrenalina y potasio. *Rev. Clin. Esp.* **57,** 10–17 (1955).

396. Sarcione, E. J., Sokal, J. E., and Gerszi, K. E., Relationship of the adrenal medulla to the hyperglycemic effect of glucagon. *Endocrinology* **67,** 337–346 (1960).

397. Sarzana, G., Rubino, F., and Cascio, G., Sul alcuni aspetti dell'azione dell'-adrenalina sul metabolismo. *Arch. Fisiol.* **53,** 200–223 (1953).

398. Satchell, D. G., Cairncross, K. D., and Freeman, S. E., The effects of amitriptyline on glycogen phosphorylase in cardiac muscle. *Biochem. Pharmacol.* **13,** 1683–1685 (1964).

399. Sawyer, H. K., Jr., and Lipner, H. J., Effects of dihydroergotamine in athyroid and thyroxinized rats. *Am. J. Physiol.* **201,** 264–266 (1961).

400. Schalch, D. S., and Kipnis, D. M., The impairment of carbohydrate tolerance by elevated plasma free fatty acids. *J. Clin. Invest.* **43,** 1283–1284 (1964).

401. Schatzmann, H. J., Calciumaufnahme und Abgabe am Darmmuskel des Meerschweinchens. *Arch. Ges. Physiol.* **274,** 295–310 (1961).

402. Schönbaum, E., Sellers, E. A., and Johnson, G. E., Noradrenaline and survival of rats in a cold environment. *Can. J. Biochem. Physiol.* **41,** 975–983 (1963).

403. Schotz, M. C., and Page, I. H., Effect of norepinephrine on plasma non-esterified fatty acids (NEFA) and the release of NEFA from epididymal adipose tissue. *Federation Proc.* **18,** 139 (1959).

404. Schotz, M. C., and Page, I. H., Effect of norepinephrine and epinephrine on nonesterified fatty acid concentration in plasma. *Proc. Soc. Exptl. Biol. Med.* **101,** 624–626 (1959).

405. Schotz, M. C., and Page, I. H., Effect of adrenergic blocking agents on the release of free fatty acids from rat adipose tissue. *J. Lipid Res.* **1,** 466–468 (1960).

406. Schusterová, D., Krčíková, D., Mühlbachová, E., Hynie, S., and Wenke, M., Influence of some new beta-sympathotropic agents on lipid mobilization *in vitro. Intern. J. Neuropharmacol.* **3,** 129–134 (1964).

407. Schwartz, N. B., Effect of Dibenzyline on the metabolic actions of epinephrine and thyroxine. *Am. J. Physiol.* **203,** 523–531 (1962).

408. Schwarz, K., Eymer, K. P., Kopetz, K., and Weinges, K. F., Normalwerte des Glycerins in menschlichen Serum und deren Veränderungen nach Arterenol-Injectionen. *Klin. Wochschr.* **39,** 975–976 (1961).

409. Scopes, J. W., and Tizard, J. P. M., The effect of intravenous noradrenaline on the oxygen consumption of new-born mammals. *J. Physiol. (London)* **165,** 305–326 (1963).

410. Scott, J. C., Finkelstein, J. L., and Spitzer, J. J., Myocardial removal of free fatty acids under normal and pathological conditions. *Am. J. Physiol.* **203,** 482–486 (1962).

411. Shafrir, E., and Gorin, E., Release of glycerol in conditions of fat mobilization and deposition. *Metab. Clin. Exptl.* **12,** 580–587 (1963).

412. Shafrir, E., and Gutman, A., Prolonged elevation of serum free fatty acids following epinephrine administration to patients with glycogenosis. *Israel J. Med. Sci.* **1,** 84–86 (1965).

413. Shafrir, E., and Kerpel, S., Fatty acid esterification and release as related to the carbohydrate metabolism of adipose tissue: effect of epinephrine, cortisol, and adrenalectomy. *Arch. Biochem. Biophys.* **105,** 237–246 (1964).

414. Shafrir, E., Sussman, K. E., and Steinberg, D., The nature of the epinephrine-induced hyperlipidermia in dogs and its modification by glucose. *J. Lipid Res.* **1,** 109–117 (1959).

414a. Shafrir, E., Sussman, K. E., and Steinberg, D., Role of the pituitary and the adrenal in the mobilization of free fatty acids and lipoprotein. *J. Lipid Res.* **1,** 459–465 (1959).

415. Shimazu, T., and Fukuda, A., Increased activities of glycogenolytic enzymes of liver after splanchnic-nerve stimulation. *Science* **150,** 1607–1608 (1965).

416. Shoemaker, W. C., and Finder, A. G., Relation of potassium and glucose release from the liver in the unanesthetized dog. *Proc. Soc. Exptl. Biol. Med.* **108,** 248–252 (1961).

417. Shull, K. H., Hepatic phosphorylase and adenosine triphosphate levels in ethionine-treated rats. *J. Biol. Chem.* **237**, PC1734–PC1735 (1962).

418. Singh, I., Singh, S. I., and Dhalla, N. S., Active relaxation of unstriated muscle produced by epinephrine. *Am. J. Physiol.* **200**, 955–958 (1961).

419. Skarin, A. T., Lockwood, M. A., and Griffith, F. R., Jr., Role of the liver in calorigenic action of epinephrine and norepinephrine. *Am. J. Physiol.* **203**, 49–52 (1963).

420. Smith, R. E., and Hoijer, D. J., Metabolism and cellular function in cold acclimation. *Physiol. Rev.* **42**, 60–142 (1962).

420a. Sokal, J. E., Lowe, C. V., Sarcione, E. J., Mosovich, L. L., and Doray, B. H., Studies of glycogen metabolism in liver glycogen disease (von Gierke's disease): Six cases with similar metabolic abnormalities and responses to glucagon. *J. Clin. Invest.* **40**, 364–374 (1961).

421. Sokal, J. E., Miller, L. L., and Sarcione, E. J., Glycogen metabolism in the isolated liver. *Am. J. Physiol.* **195**, 295–300 (1958).

422. Sokal, J. E., and Sarcione, E. J., Effect of epinephrine on glycogen stores. *Am. J. Physiol.* **196**, 1253–1257 (1959).

423. Sokal, J. E., and Sarcione, E. J., Failure of physiological concentrations of epinephrine to affect glycogen-levels in the isolated rat liver. *Nature* **204**, 881–882 (1964).

424. Sokal, J. E., Sarcione, E. J., and Henderson, A. M., Relative potency of glucagon and epinephrine as hepatic glycogenolytic agents: studies with the isolated perfused rat liver. *Endocrinology* **74**, 930–938 (1964).

425. Spitzer, J. J., and Gold, M., Effect of catecholamines on the individual free fatty acids of plasma. *Proc. Soc. Exptl. Biol. Med.* **110**, 645–647 (1962).

426. Spitzer, J. J., and McElroy, W. T., Jr., Some hormonal effects on uptake of free fatty acids by the liver. *Am. J. Physiol.* **199**, 876–878 (1960).

427. Spitzer, J. J., and McElroy, W. T., Jr., Some hormonal influences on the hepatic uptake of free fatty acids in diabetic dogs. *Diabetes* **11**, 222–226 (1962).

428. Spoelstra, A. J.-G., Recherches sur l'effet calorigène de l'adrénaline et de la noradrénaline. *J. Physiol.* (*Paris*) **55**, 677–696 (1963).

429. Sproull, D. H., Hyperglycaemia produced by intracisternal injection of adrenaline in cats. *J. Physiol.* (*London*) **169**, 527–537 (1963).

430. Sproull, D. H., The origin of the hyperglycaemic response to intracisternal adrenaline in the cat: the site of systemic absorption and of central action of adrenaline from the subarachnoid space. *J. Physiol.* (*London*) **169**, 538–552 (1963).

431. Spühler, O., Die experimentelle Untersuchung eines neuen Sympathicolyticums, des Dihydroergotamins (DHE 45). *Schweiz. Med. Wochschr.* **77**, 28–32 (1947).

432. Stein, Y., and Stein, O., Metabolic activity of rat epididymal fat pad labeled selectively by an *in vivo* incubation technique. *Biochim. Biophys. Acta* **54**, 555–571 (1962).

433. Steinberg, D., Nestel, P. J., Buskirk, E. R., and Thompson, R. H., Calorigenic effect of norepinephrine correlated with plasma free fatty acid turnover and oxidation. *J. Clin. Invest.* **43**, 167–176 (1964).

434. Steinberg, D., Vaughan, M., and Margolis, S., Control of fatty acid release from adipose tissue through control of the rate of triglyceride synthesis. *J. Biol. Chem.* **235**, 38–39 (1960).

435. Steinberg, D., Vaughan, M., Nestel, P. J., and Bergström, S., Effect of prostaglandin E opposing those of catecholamines on blood pressure and on triglyceride breakdown in adipose tissue. *Biochem. Pharmacol.* **12**, 764–766 (1963).
436. Steinberg, D., Vaughan, M., Nestel, P. J., Strand, O., and Bergström, S., Effects of the prostaglandin on hormone-induced mobilization of free fatty acids. *J. Clin. Invest.* **43**, 1533–1540 (1964).
437. Stock, K., and Westermann, E., Effects of adrenergic blockade and nicotinic acid on the mobilization of free fatty acids. *Life Sci.* **4**, 1115–1124 (1965).
438. Stoltzenberger-Seidel, M., Klinische Untersuchungen zur Behandlung des Asthma bronchiale. *Klin. Wochschr.* **51**, 1306–1310 (1940).
439. Strömblad, B. C. R., Oxygen consumption of the normal and denervated submaxillary gland *in vitro*. *Acta Physiol. Scand.* **40**, 130–145 (1957).
440. Strubelt, O., Sauerstoffverbrauch und Coenzym A-Aktivität nach Dinitrophenol und Isoproterenol bei Ratten. *Biochem. Pharmacol.* **13**, 845–848 (1964).
441. Strubelt, O., Zur stoffwechselsteigernden Wirkung von Isoproterenol und Metaproterenol und ihrer Beeinflussung durch Dichloroisoproterenol und Reserpin. *Arch. Exptl. Pathol. Pharmakol.* **247**, 301–302 (1964).
442. Strubelt, O., Die Bedeutung der adrenergischen β-Receptoren für die kalorigene Wirkung sympathicomimetischer Amine. *Arch. Exptl. Pathol. Pharmakol.* **251**, 126 (1965).
443. Sutherland, E. W., and Cori, C. F., Influence of insulin preparations on glycogenolysis in liver slices. *J. Biol. Chem.* **172**, 737–750 (1948).
444. Sutherland, E. W., and Rall, T. W., The relation of adenosine-3′,5′-phosphate and phosphorylase to the actions of catecholamines and other hormones. *Pharmacol. Rev.* **12**, 265–299 (1960).
445. Sutherland, E. W., Rall, T. W., and Menon, T., Adenyl cyclase. I. Distribution, preparation, and properties. *J. Biol. Chem.* **273**, 1220–1227 (1962).
446. Sutherland, E. W., and Robison, G. A., The role of cyclic-3′,5′-AMP in responses to catecholamines and other hormones. *Pharmacol. Rev.* **18**, 145–161 (1966).
447. Szekeres, L., Lénárd, G., Bánhidy, F., and Török, T., The effect of epinephrine on myocardial metabolism of normal and hypoxic rats. *Arch. Intern. Pharmacodyn.* **115**, 150–156 (1958).
448. Timms, A. R., Bueding, E., Hawkins, J. T., and Fisher, J., The effect of adrenaline on phosphorylase activity, glycogen content, and isotonic tension of intestinal smooth muscle (taenia coli) of the guinea-pig. *Biochem. J.* **84**, 80P (1962).
449. Tobian, L., and Fox, A., The effect of nor-epinephrine on the electrolyte composition of arterial smooth muscle. *J. Clin. Invest.* **35**, 297–301 (1956).
450. Toida, N., Tamai, T., and Takagisi, T., Electrophysiological studies of the liver by intracellular recording with a microelectrode. Part I. Electrical potential from a rat liver *in situ*. *Kyushu J. Med. Sci.* **9**, 163–176 (1958).
451. Triner, L., and Nahas, G. G., Effect of pH on the lipolytic action of catecholamines. *Pharmacologist* **7**, 137 (1965).
452. Tsujimoto, A., Tanino, S., Kaniike, K., Seto, K., and Kurogochi, Y., Relationship of hyperkalemic response to hepatic phosphorylase activation induced by adrenaline. *Japan. J. Pharmacol.* **15**, 423–428 (1965).

453. Tsujimoto, A., Tanino, S., Nishiue, T., and Kurogochi, Y., Potassium mobilizing action of 3′,5′-cyclic adenosine monophosphate. *Japan. J. Pharmacol.* **15,** 441–443 (1965).

454. Tzur, R., Tal, E., and Shapiro, B., α-Glycerophosphate as regulatory factor in fatty acid esterification. *Biochim. Biophys. Acta* **84,** 18–23 (1964).

455. Van Der Pol, M. C., The effect of some sympathicomimetics in relation to the two receptor-theory. III. The effect on the blood sugar content. *Acta Physiol. Pharmacol. Neerl.* **4,** 541–546 (1956).

456. Van Roy, F. P., and Schulhof, L. W., The effect of sympathomimetics on glycogenolysis of rat liver slices *in vitro. Arch. Intern. Pharmacodyn.* **130,** 368–373 (1961).

457. Vane, J. R., ed., "Adrenergic Mechanisms." Little, Brown, Boston, Massachusetts, 1960.

458. Vaughan, M., Effect of hormones on phosphorylase activity in adipose tissue. *J. Biol. Chem.* **235,** 3049–3053 (1960).

459. Vaughan, M., Effect of hormones on glucose metabolism in adipose tissue. *J. Biol. Chem.* **236,** 2196–2199 (1961).

460. Vaughan, M., The metabolism of adipose tissue *in vitro. J. Lipid Res.* **2,** 293–316 (1961).

461. Vaughan, M., Berger, J. E., and Steinberg, D., Hormone sensitive lipase and monoglyceride lipase activities in adipose tissue. *J. Biol. Chem.* **239,** 401–409 (1964).

462. Vaughan, M., and Steinberg, D., Effects of hormones on lipolysis and esterification of free fatty acids during incubation of adipose tissue *in vitro. J. Lipid Res.* **4,** 193–199 (1963).

463. Verner, J. V., Jr., Blackard, W. G., and Engel, F. L., Some factors modifying actions of hormones on glucose uptake by adipose tissue *in vitro. Endocrinology* **70,** 420–428 (1962).

464. Verner, J. V., Jr., and Engel, F. L., The blocking effect of ACTH and the catecholamines on glucose uptake by adipose tissue. *Am. J. Med.* **27,** 329 (1959).

464a. Vincent, N. H., and Ellis, S., Inhibitory effect of acetylcholine on glycogenolysis in the isolated guinea-pig heart. *J. Pharmacol. Exptl. Therap.* **139,** 60–68 (1963).

465. Vogel, U., Vogel, G., and Winter, G., Der Einfluss von Adrenalin und Acetylcholin auf die arteriovenöse Blutzuckerdifferenz der Katzenextremität. *Z. Ges. Inn. Med. Ihre Grenzgebiete* **8,** 447–456 (1953).

466. Vrij, Jzn. C., Gho, B. K., de Groot, C. A., and Weber, J. F., The effect of isopropyl-nor-adrenaline and nor-adrenaline on the glycogen content of skeletal muscle and liver of the rat. *Acta Physiol. Phramacol. Neerl.* **4,** 547–554 (1956).

467. Waddell, A. W., Adrenaline, noradrenaline and potassium fluxes in rabbit auricles. *J. Physiol.* (*London*) **155,** 209–220 (1961).

468. Wadström, L. B., Lipolytic effect of the injection of adrenaline on fat depots. *Nature* **179,** 259–260 (1957).

469. Walker, J. M. G., and Weatherall, M., Calcium in relation to the actions of ouabain and adrenaline on the heart. *Brit. J. Pharmacol.* **23,** 66–79 (1964).

470. Wallace, J. M., and Harlan, W. R., Significance of epinephrine in insulin hypoglycemia in man. *Am. J. Med.* **38,** 531–539 (1965).

471. Watts, D. T., Inhibition of ether hyperglycemia by adrenergic blocking agents. *Current Res. Anesthesia Analgesia* **33,** 343–345 (1954).

472. Waugh, W. H., Role of calcium in contractile excitation of vascular smooth muscle by epinephrine and potassium. *Circulation Res.* **11,** 927–940 (1962).

473. Weil, R., Ho, P.-P., and Altszuler, N., Effect of free fatty acids on metabolism of pyruvic and lactic acids. *Am. J. Physiol.* **208,** 887–890 (1965).

474. Weiner, N., The catecholamines: biosynthesis, storage and release, metabolism, and metabolic effects. *In* "The Hormones" (G. Pincus, K. V. Thimann, and E. B. Astwood, eds.), Vol. IV, pp. 403–479. Academic Press, New York, 1964.

475. Weise, H., Die Wirkung des Ephedrins und des Norephedrins auf den Blutzuckerspiegel Stoffwechselgesunder und Diabetiker. *Aerztl. Wochschr.* **11,** 417–419 (1956).

476. Weisfeldt, M. L., and Gilmore, J. P., Apparent dissociation of the inotropic and O_2 consumption effect of norepinephrine. *Federation Proc.* **23,** 357 (1964).

477. Weiszbecker, L., and Koneczny, O., Die Hyperglykämie nach Adrenalin und Noradrenalin unter der Wirkung von Atropin. *Arzneimittel-Forsch.* **145,** 485 (1961).

478. Welch, G. H., Braunwald, E., Case, R. B., and Sarnoff, S. J., The effect of mephentermine sulfate on myocardial oxygen consumption, myocardial efficiency, and peripheral vascular resistance. *Am. J. Med.* **24,** 871–881 (1958).

479. Wenke, M., Lincová, D., Čepelík, J., Černohorský, M., Hynie, S., Some aspects of the action of *beta* adrenergic blocking drugs on adrenergic lipid mobilization. *In* "New Adrenergic Blocking Drugs: Their Pharmacological, Biochemical and Clinical Actions" (N. C. Moran, ed.), *Ann. N.Y. Acad. Sci.* **139** (3), 860–878 (1967).

480. Wenke, M., Mühlbachová, E., and Hynie, S., Effects of some sympathicotropic agents on the lipid metabolism. *Arch. Intern. Pharmacodyn.* **136,** 104–112 (1962).

481. Wenke, M., Mühlbachová, E., Hynie, S., and Dolejšová, K., Metabolic effects of catecholamines. *Physiol. Bohemoslov.* **12,** 43–50 (1963).

481a. Wenke, M., Mühlbachová, E., Hynie, S., and Dolejšová, K., Metabolické účinky katecholaminú. *Acta Univ. Carolinae Med.* **17,** 123–130 (1963).

482. Wenke, M., Mühlbachová, E., Schusterová, D., Elisová, K., and Hynie, S., Effect of directly acting sympathomimetic drugs on lipid metabolism *in vitro*. *Intern. J. Neuropharmacol.* **3,** 283–292 (1964).

483. Wertheimer, E., and Shapiro, B., The physiology of adipose tissue. *Physiol. Rev.* **28,** 451–464 (1948).

484. Westermann, E., and Stock, K., Untersuchungen über die Bedeutung des Sympathicus für die Mobilisation freier Settsäuren. *Arch. Exptl. Pathol. Pharmakol.* **245,** 102–103 (1963).

485. Westermann, E., and Stock, K., Wirkung von α-Methyl-Dopa und α-Methyl-*m*-Tyrosin auf den Fettsoffwechsel der Ratte. *Arch. Exptl. Pathol. Pharmakol.* **247,** 299–300 (1963).

486. Westermann, E., and Stock, K., Über die Wirkung von β-Sympatholytica auf die Lipolyse. *Arch. Exptl. Pathol. Pharmakol.* **250,** 290 (1965).

487. White, J. E., and Engel, F. L., A lipolytic action of epinephrine and norepinephrine on rat adipose tissue *in vitro*. *Proc. Soc. Exptl. Biol. Med.* **99,** 375–378 (1958).

488. Williams, B. J., and Mayer, S. E., Glycogen synthetase of heart muscle: effect of hormones. *Federation Proc.* **24,** 151 (1965).

489. Williamson, J. R., Metabolic effects of epinephrine in the isolated, perfused rat heart. I. Dissociation of the glycogenolytic from the metabolic stimulatory effect. *J. Biol. Chem.* **239**, 2721–2729 (1964).
490. Winterscheid, L. C., Bruce, R. A., Blumberg, J. B., and Merendino, K. A., Effects of isoproterenol on carbohydrate metabolism of isolated canine heart. *Circulation Res.* **12**, 76–84 (1963).
491. Woolley, D. W., and Gommi, B. W., Transport of calcium into muscle in response to serotonin and other hormones. *Biochim. Biophys. Acta* **74**, 781–782 (1963).
492. Wright, P. A., Jordan, E. J., and Haight, A. S., Effectiveness of DHE in blocking epinephrine-induced hyperglycemia in rabbits and bullfrogs. *Endocrinology* **62**, 696–698 (1958).
493. Yasuo, A., Studies on relationship between blood-sugar reaction and sympathetic blocking drugs. *Nippon Seirigaku Zasshi* **23**, 596–607 (1961).
494. Zondek, S. G., Die Bedeutung des Antagonismus von Kalium und Calcium für die Physiologie und Pathologie. *Klin. Wochschr.* **2**, 382–385 (1923).
495. Zsoldes, S. J., and Heinemann, H. O., Lipolytic activity of rabbit aorta *in vitro*. *Am. J. Physiol.* **206**, 615–617 (1964).
496. Zuspan, F. P., Nelson, G. H., and Ahlquist, R. P., Epinephrine infusions in normal and toxemic pregnancy. *Am. J. Obstet. Gynecol.* **90**, 88–98 (1964).

IV. ADRENERGIC BLOCKING DRUGS

A. Blockade of α-Adrenergic Receptors*

Mark Nickerson and Norman K. Hollenberg†

Department of Pharmacology and Therapeutics, University of Manitoba, Faculty of Medicine, Winnipeg, Manitoba, Canada

I. Introduction 243
II. Major Groups of α-Adrenergic Blocking Agents 245
A. Haloalkylamines 245
B. Ergot Alkaloids 249
C. Imidazolines 252
D. Dibenzazepines 255
E. Benzodioxans 255
F. Other Agents 257
III. Responses of Various Effector Systems to α-Adrenergic Blockade 257
A. Heart 258
B. Vasculature 260
C. Central Nervous System 272
D. Metabolic Responses 277
E. Other Effector Systems 279
IV. Therapeutic Use of α-Adrenergic Blockade 283
A. Pheochromocytoma 283
B. Essential Hypertension 285
C. Peripheral Vascular Disease 286
D. Shock 289
E. Other Conditions 290
References 291

I. INTRODUCTION

It has long been recognized that the relative potencies of sympathomimetic amines vary widely when tested on different tissues and organs (9), and that pharmacologically active materials can completely inhibit

* Work from this laboratory included in this article has been supported by grants-in-aid from the Medical Research Council of Canada, the Defense Research Board of Canada, the Manitoba Heart Foundation, and the Life Insurance Medical Research Fund.

† Present address: Cardiorenal Unit, Peter Bent Brigham Hospital, Boston, Massachusetts.

some responses to a sympathomimetic agent without affecting others (39). Attempts have been made to explain and categorize these differentials in several ways, but it is now generally accepted that they are due to the involvement of at least two distinct populations of adrenergic tissue receptors. These receptors may be defined as the structures on or in a cell with which a sympathomimetic substance (agonist) reacts to produce its characteristic effects. A specific blocking agent (antagonist) appears to interact with the same sites, preventing the action of the agonist without itself producing an observable response. Ahlquist (4) studied the relative potencies of several catecholamines in evoking a variety of responses, and found two distinct patterns of activity. In terms of the three most important and best known agonists, these were: adrenaline > noradrenaline ≫ isoproterenol, which he termed α, and isoproterenol > adrenaline ≫ noradrenaline, which he termed β. The α-adrenergic receptors subserve predominantly excitation of smooth muscle and gland cells and intestinal relaxation, the β-receptors predominantly inhibition of smooth muscle tone, including that of the intestine, and stimulation of the myocardium.

Although the concept that the effects of catecholamines and other sympathomimetic agents are mediated by two distinct types of adrenergic receptors is of relatively recent origin, Dale (39) clearly demonstrated the blockade of what are now termed α-adrenergic receptors by preparations of ergot 60 years ago, and correctly distinguished responses mediated by the two types in observing that cardiac stimulation and certain "inhibitory" effects of adrenaline are resistant to blockade. Since that time, many groups of natural and synthetic drugs have been shown to possess blocking properties qualitatively similar to those of ergot (α-adrenergic blocking agents) (19, 177), but only the most effective and thoroughly studied of these will be discussed in the present article. It can be assumed that equal magnitudes and durations of α adrenergic blockade will produce comparable physiological and pharmacological effects, irrespective of the agent involved. Differences in net responses are due to properties of the individual drugs distinct from the blockade of α-adrenergic receptors. All α-adrenergic blocking agents more effectively inhibit responses to circulating sympathomimetic amines than those to sympathetic nerve activity, and this differential can be very large, as in the case of some of the benzodioxans.

Until quite recently, blockade of α-adrenergic receptors was referred to simply as adrenergic blockade, with recognition that cardiac stimulation and inhibitory responses of smooth muscle were immune. However, with the introduction of dichloroisoproterenol (DCI), the first agent shown to produce a specific blockade of β-adrenergic receptors (203), it became necessary to distinguish between the two types of blocking agents. It is interesting to note that the blockade of adrenergic receptors is much more selective than their activation. Although relative effectiveness may vary considerably, almost all sympathomimetic agents have some effect on both types, whereas the action of a blocking agent appears to be almost entirely limited to one or the other (187).

Adrenergic blocking agents, both α and β, produce their effects by preventing the actions of adrenaline, noradrenaline, and other sympathomimetic amines on the adrenergic receptors of effector cells. Agents of this type should be clearly distinguished from others which can reduce the effects of sympathetic nerve activity and of certain sympathomimetic agents by actions on afferent receptors, the central nervous system, ganglia, or peripheral adrenergic nerve endings. Such drugs may greatly reduce responses dependent on sympathetic nerve function, but they do not clearly distinguish between those mediated by α- and those mediated by β-receptors, and they do not inhibit responses to injected catecholamines.

II. MAJOR GROUPS OF α-ADRENERGIC BLOCKING AGENTS

A. Haloalkylamines

The pharmacology of this group of agents, of which Dibenamine® (*N,N*-dibenzyl-β-chloroethylamine) is the prototype, was first reported in 1945 (188), and has been the subject of several extensive reviews (88, 177, 180, 181, 258). The haloalkylamines produce a blockade of α-adrenergic receptors which is more complete and persistent than that due to any other type of agent studied to date. In the doses usually employed to block α-adrenergic receptors, the haloalkylamines produce few obvious effects in man or laboratory animals not attributable to this action and, thus, provide a clearer picture of the results of α-adrenergic blockade than do agents of other chemical classes.

Chemical requirements for α-adrenergic blocking activity among the over 1500 haloalkylamines studied to date are quite rigid (88, 177, 192, 258). The most important of these are as follows: (*a*) The compound usually must be a tertiary alkylamine; some activity of a secondary amine structure has been reported in one series of compounds. (*b*) It must have a halogen or an alkyl- or arylsulfonate in the β-position of the alkyl group that can be displaced during formation of an intermediate ethylenimonium ion. (*c*) It must have at least one unsaturated ring structure in proper relation to the nitrogen. If these requirements are met, the third substituent on the nitrogen usually has only a minor influence on activity.

Substitution of a phenoxyethyl for one of the benzyl groups of Dibenamine considerably increases potency (195), and an alkyl-methyl substitution increases intestinal absorption. Both of these alterations are found in phenoxybenzamine (Dibenzyline®, Dibenyline®, *N*-phenoxyisopropyl-*N*-benzyl-β-chloroethylamine), which has a potency six to eight times that of Dibenamine and is considerably better absorbed after oral administration. It is now the haloalkylamine most commonly used, and it is the only member of the series which has been extensively investigated in man. Haloalkylamines which form ethylenimonium intermediates most rapidly are the most potent when given intravenously, i.e., bromine, iodine, and sulfonate compounds are more active than their chlorine congeners. However, this relationship is reversed for oral administration (157), presumably because much of a rapidly reacting compound forms inactive products prior to absorption.

The highly reactive β-haloalkyl moiety is common to this group of adrenergic blocking agents and the nitrogen mustards, but the toxicities of most members of the former group are much less than those of the latter, largely because they contain only one rather than two or three such substituents. In both series the halogen, or halogenoid, is released and an unstable cyclic ethylenimonium intermediate is formed. The molecular species directly responsible for blockade is probably the highly reactive carbonium ion formed when this unstable three-membered ring breaks (13). The relatively slow onset of action of the haloalkylamine blocking agents, even after intravenous administration, is probably due to the time required for the formation of these reactive intermediates, which can then alkylate a variety of nucleophilic groupings found in biological systems (12, 113). The persistence and completeness of the blockade produced appear to be dependent upon this relatively stable bonding to tissue constituents (182, 189). The exact nature of the groupings on or near α-adrenergic receptors with which the haloalkylamines react has not been established. *In vitro* studies have shown a preferential reaction of Dibenamine with sulfhydryl groups and somewhat less reactivity toward amino and carboxyl groups (113). However, theoretical arguments have been presented in favor of an anionic site of attack (12). Although reaction with phosphate *in vitro* is limited, formation of a phosphate ester was suggested because a simple carboxylic acid ester probably would not be sufficiently stable to account for the very prolonged blockade produced by most members of this series.

Adrenergic blockade by a haloalkylamine appears to develop in two stages, an initial relatively loose attachment to the site of action (receptor), during which the drug is in mass action equilibrium with other compounds which can interact with the same site, and a later stable bonding, alkylation (180). The presence of a catecholamine or a competitive α-adrenergic blocking agent during the first stage can decrease the degree of blockade by the haloalkylamine (78, 192, 227). The fact that occupancy of a specific type of receptor by an agonist or competitive antagonist during the first stage of action of a haloalkylamine inhibits the blockade of this, but not of other types of receptors provides the basis for a relatively specific method to determine the type of receptor with which a given agent interacts (78, 125, 126, 179).

After blockade by a haloalkylamine has developed fully it is unaltered by the presence of a sympathomimetic amine or of a competitive α-adrenergic blocking agent, indicating that the drug is no longer in equilibrium with the receptors. Thus, the action may be referred to as "nonequilibrium blockade," in that although the blocking agent interacts with the specific α-adrenergic receptors, its stable attachment precludes a mass action equilibrium between agonist and antagonist for the receptor site (180). Stable bonding of the drug to receptors rather than continued release from fat or other depots is responsible for both the persistence and completeness of the blockade produced by agents of this series (3, 182, 189; cf. 24).

Blockade by most haloalkylamines develops relatively slowly. The peak effect of Dibenamine is reached 1 to 2 hours after intravenous administration, and, although phenoxybenzamine acts somewhat more rapidly, its blockade probably is not maximal in less than 1 hour. After a single dose the blockade disappears with a half-life of roughly 24 hours in intact laboratory animals and man and can be readily detected for 3 to 4 days. A corollary of this persistent action is that the effects of daily administration are cumulative over periods of at least a week.

In vitro studies have shown that the agonist log dose-response curve is shifted progressively to the right by increasing doses of a haloalkylamine blocking agent, without reduction of the slope or asymptote, as in characteristic of competitive antagonists. This is possible with a nonequilibrium agent because normal tissues contain receptors in excess of the number required for a maximal response to most agonists, the "spare receptors" (179, 243), and a considerable proportion can be inactivated before the tissue is incapable of a maximal response when exposed to an adequate concentration of agonist. However, when the remaining functional receptors have been reduced below a limiting number, no concentration of agonist can produce a full response, and both the slope and the asymptote of the agonist log dose-response curve are reduced (179, 180).

In addition to α-adrenergic receptors, haloalkylamines can block receptors mediating responses to 5-hydroxytryptamine (5-HT, serotonin), histamine, and acetylcholine. When produced, blockade of responses to these other types of agonists has the same general pharmacological characteristics as the α-adrenergic blockade. Inhibition of responses to histamine and 5-HT requires the same basic chemical configuration as does α-adrenergic blockade. However, potency with respect to these properties may vary widely. Dibenamine has relatively low antihistaminic activity, but phenoxybenzamine and a number of phenoxyethyl and 1-naphthylmethyl congeners have potencies similar to those of antihistaminics now employed clinically (140). Effective blockade of muscarinic responses to acetylcholine usually requires exposure to a haloalkylamine in relatively high concentration or for extended periods (15, 78) but does represent a specific reaction with cholinergic receptors. In the blockade of vagal effects on the heart, phenoxybenzamine has about 1/500 the activity of atropine (14), and large doses of Dibenamine do not appear to interfere with cholinergic vasodilatation in skeletal muscle (68). However, anticholinergic activity has been reported to be somewhat greater under certain *in vitro* conditions (23). Possible involvement of nonadrenergic receptors should be checked before definitive conclusions are drawn in experiments in which the haloalkylamines are used as pharmacological tools, but, in general, this factor complicates the result much less than do the direct actions of other available α-adrenergic blocking agents. Inhibition of the nicotinic responses of ganglia and skeletal muscle to acetylcholine by the haloalkylamines has not been reported.

Haloalkylamines can stimulate the myocardium *in vitro,* and in some circumstances may produce an initial pressor response in intact animals, apparently by release of endogenous catecholamines (87, 187). Phenoxybenzamine also increases the amount of noradrenaline released into the venous effluent per stimulus delivered to the splenic nerve at low but not at high frequencies (27). The mechanism of this effect is not clear, and the increase in blood levels and urinary excretion of catecholamines which haloalkylamines may produce in intact animals is even more difficult to interpret because of the marked increase in sympathetic nerve activity induced reflexly by the peripheral blockade (49).

When administered rapidly intravenously, most haloalkylamines produce central nervous system stimulation, but slow infusion of phenoxybenzamine usually produces sedation and lethargy in man, and some congeners appear to have considerable central nervous system depressant activity. The mechanisms involved in the central effects of these agents are not well understood, but the stimulant effect clearly is not due to α-adrenergic blockade (178), and no central effect has been shown to involve this mechanism.

Dibenamine, phenoxybenzamine, and most other haloalkylamine adrenergic blocking agents are highly lipid soluble at body pH, and considerable amounts may accumulate in fat after administration of large doses (24). Such accumulation is not found after doses of phenoxybenzamine in the range required to produce α-adrenergic blockade. The metabolic fate of these highly unstable compounds is poorly understood. Over 50% of the radioactivity of intravenously administered phenoxybenzamine is excreted in 12 hours and over 80% in 24 hours, but small amounts remain in various tissues for at least a week (182).

The routes of administration of haloalkylamines are limited by their irritant properties and their instability in neutral or alkaline aqueous solution. Some 20–30% of orally administered phenoxybenzamine, and a considerably lower percentage of Dibenamine, appears to reach the blood stream in active form after oral administration, and a moderate level of α-adrenergic blockade can be produced in man by tolerated oral doses of the former. However, full blockade of responses to adrenergic stimuli is only practicable with intravenous administration, usually by slow infusion to avoid central nervous system stimulation and to minimize the fall in blood pressure which may result from the blockade of reflex vasoconstriction. Extensive α-adrenergic blockade which develops slowly produces little fall in blood pressure in normovolemic recumbent laboratory animals or man, but it can cause a sharp drop in pressure in any situation involving compensatory sympathetic vasoconstriction, such as upright posture or hypovolemia. The haloalkylamine adrenergic blocking agents have not been reported to have significant acute or chronic toxic effects other than central nervous system stimulation and local tissue damage. Most of the "side effects" produced are expressions of α-adrenergic blockade per se.

Haloalkylamines with α-adrenergic blocking activity have very low aqueous solubilities, except in the presence of high acidity, and undergo rapid hydrolysis in neutral or alkaline aqueous solutions to form inactive alcohol derivatives. They are usually prepared as stable stock solutions in acidified propylene glycol or alcohol and, because of their irritant properties, should be well diluted immediately prior to intravenous administration. The usual dose of phenoxybenzamine by this route is 1.0–5.0 mg/kg in laboratory animals and 1.0 mg/kg in man.

B. Ergot Alkaloids

The ergot alkaloids were the first adrenergic blocking agents discovered, and most aspects of their general pharmacology were described in the classical report of Dale (39). They still have not been surpassed in absolute potency, but unfortunately they have many other important pharmacological actions which are prominent with doses equal to or smaller than those required to produce α-adrenergic blockade. These frequently have been overlooked in the interpretation of experimental results because the ergot alkaloids have been classified as adrenergic blocking agents and attention has been focused on this property. The most important of these "side effects" are direct stimulation of smooth muscle and complex excitant and depressant actions on the central nervous system.

Many pharmacologically active substances have been isolated from ergot, but only those containing a lysergic acid nucleus are conventionally referred to as the "ergot alkaloids." Of these, only those with a peptide side chain have α-adrenergic blocking activity: ergotamine and ergotoxine, the latter being a mixture of three closely related alkaloids—ergocornine, ergocristine, and ergokryptine (245). Dihydroderivatives of ergotamine and of members of the ergotoxine complex have been prepared by partial reduction of the lysergic acid nucleus (246). Such hydrogenation decreases ability to stimulate smooth muscle and increases adrenergic blocking activity. The best known of these derivatives are dihydroergotamine (DHE 45) and Hydergine®, a mixture of the dihydro derivatives of alkaloids of the ergotoxine group. The active forms of all of the ergot alkaloids are levorotatory. They are relatively unstable and are readily converted to the much less active dextro isomers in solution.

The ergot alkaloids produce a competitive blockade of α-adrenergic receptors which tends to be more complete and persistent than that produced by other competitive antagonists, but much less than that induced by nonequilibrium agents (haloalkylamines). All members of the ergotoxine complex are more potent α-adrenergic blocking agents than is ergotamine, and hydrogenation increases the potency of all severalfold without major alterations in their relative activities. The blockade produced in animals anesthetized with a barbiturate is much less than that in other preparations, a difference which has been recognized for many years but has never been satisfactorily explained. The blocking actions of the ergot alkaloids have been studied primarily in experiments on laboratory animals; side effects prevent the administration of doses which could produce extensive α-adrenergic blockade in man.

The ergot alkaloids may alter responses to certain sympathomimetics, such as isoproterenol, from depressor to pressor. This effect is most readily demonstrable under conditions which minimize α-adrenergic blockade, e.g., with ergotamine in barbiturate-anesthetized animals. The original explanation which postulated a more extensive blockade of inhibitory (β-receptor) than of excitatory (α-receptor) vascular responses is now untenable. A more recent interpretation is that the pressor response is due to increased cardiac output in the presence of a peripheral vascular bed already constricted by the alkaloid (139). A similar reversal can be produced by several sympathomimetic amines (263).

The most important direct peripheral action of all the ergot alkaloids, including those devoid of α-adrenergic blocking activity, is stimulation of smooth muscle. In at least some organs this appears to be due to an action on the same receptors involved in responses to catecholamines (124, 218). Thus, the ergot alkaloids can be considered to be "partial agonists," among which intrinsic activity decreases and blocking activity increases from ergotamine to the dihydrogenated derivatives of ergotoxine.

The natural ergot alkaloids very effectively stimulate many smooth muscle structures, and the most important effects of this action, those on the uterus and blood vessels, were known long before the first demonstration of their adrenergic blocking activity. The vasoconstriction produced can cause a considerable rise in blood pressure and provides the basis for their use in the treatment of migraine. The coronary vessels are included in this action, and the ergot alkaloids hasten the development of pain in patients subject to angina pectoris when they exercise or breathe a gas mixture low in oxygen, and can induce anginal pain and, perhaps, myocardial infarction in susceptible subjects at rest (84, 254). Hydrogenation reduces but does not eliminate the direct action on smooth muscle. Dihydroergotamine is effective in the relief of migraine because of this property, and when given for this purpose has been observed to induce labor in a pregnant woman (254). Hydrogenated derivatives of the ergotoxine group are much less effective smooth muscle stimulants than is dihydroergotamine, but are not devoid of this action, which has been observed as a pressor effect in pithed cats (217), and as an increase in vascular resistance in sympathectomized human limbs (73). They also have a demonstrable oxytocic effect on the human uterus at term (127). The smooth muscle of veins may be particularly susceptible to the direct constrictor action of ergot. Hydergine increases right atrial and systemic venous pressures while lowering the systemic arterial pressure (107).

The ergot alkaloids produce a complex mixture of stimulation and depression of the central nervous system. Toxic doses induce general sedation and somnolence, and injection of ergotamine base into the third ventricle of cats leads to prolonged and apparently normal sleep. Respiration is depressed both in anesthetized laboratory animals and in unanesthetized man. Central depression, perhaps a direct effect on the vasomotor center, appears to be responsible for the decreased peripheral sympathetic tone, the vasodilatation and the fall in blood pressure induced by hydrogenated alkaloids in laboratory animals (135), and for the vasodilatation, fall in blood pressure, postural hypotension, and depressed vasomotor reflexes observed in man (8). The natural alkaloids probably produce a similar central vasomotor depression, but the effects of this action are usually obscured by the peripheral vasoconstriction produced. Both the natural and hydrogenated alkaloids also induce a bradycardia, which appears to be due predominantly to stimulation of vagal centers rather than to inhibition of sympathetic activity, since it persists after high spinal cord section or sympathetic cardiac denervation, but is markedly reduced by vagotomy. However, a component of sympathetic inhibition is indicated by the fact that ergotamine reduces the maximum tachycardia induced by struggle in vagotomized cats with intact cardiac sympathetic innervation (165).

The effects of carbon dioxide on blood pressure and respiration are readily inhibited by the ergot alkaloids, apparently as a result of decreased responsiveness of medullary centers. Cardiovascular responses to carotid baroreceptor and chemoreceptor stimulation are also inhibited, in that order of sensitivity, by the central effects of doses which do not produce significant peripheral adrenergic blockade; the rate of firing of the afferent nerve fibers involved is unaffected. The ergot alkaloids also cause generalized impairment of temperature regulation, presumably by an action on the hypothalamus (234). Potency in producing these central effects is not correlated with α-adrenergic blocking activity. (Central effects of the ergot alkaloids are discussed in 64, 143, 217, 250, 270.)

The peptide ergot alkaloids are poorly absorbed after oral administration. They appear to be rapidly degraded in the body, and insignificant amounts of active drug are excreted in the urine. Penetration into the brain and cerebrospinal fluid has not been demonstrated, although there is no doubt that the ergot alkaloids have major effects on the central nervous system (217).

C. Imidazolines

Many substituted imidazolines have been synthesized and studied pharmacologically. The group may be considered a pharmacologist's paradise or a nightmare, depending on one's point of view. A very high percentage of the compounds studied have pharmacological activity, often with high potency, and only slight changes in structure produce compounds with quite different major effects. At the present time agents of this chemical group are marketed for their antihistaminic, sympathomimetic, α-adrenergic blocking, and vasodilator effects. Unfortunately, these properties, and several others, including histamine-like, cholinergic, sedative, etc., are not mutually exclusive, and most of the imidazoline derivatives lack specificity in that they produce several of these effects at comparable doses. Many studies of the pharmacology of compounds of this series have failed to establish which of several possible actions was responsible for the effects observed, e.g., whether vasodilatation was due to α-adrenergic blockade or to a direct relaxant effect on vascular smooth muscle.

Only two substituted imidazolines have been studied extensively for their α-adrenergic blocking activity, tolazoline (Priscoline®, 2-benzyl-2-imidazoline) and phentolamine [Regitine®, Rogitine®, 2-(*N′*,*p*-tolyl-*N′*-(*m*-hydroxyphenyl)-aminomethyl)-imidazoline]. These agents produce a competitive blockade of α-adrenergic receptors which is relatively weak and of short duration. The drugs are readily washed out of isolated tissues and have a short duration of action *in vivo*. Priscoline is rapidly cleared by the kidney, whereas phentolamine is predominantly inactivated by metabolic degradation. In some circumstances responses to 5-hydroxytryptamine and to histamine, as well as those to sympathomimetics, may be blocked, but antihistaminic activity is limited, and antagonism of responses to 5-HT has not been studied extensively. Important qualitative differences between the two agents have not been demonstrated, but phentolamine is a considerably more active adrenergic blocking agent, at least six times as potent as tolazoline, and its other actions are somewhat less prominent (100, 211).

Effects other than α-adrenergic blockade have been studied much more adequately for tolazoline than for phentolamine, and have been characterized as "sympathomimetic," "parasympathomimetic," and "histamine-like" (5), although in many cases the precise mechanisms of action have not been established. One of the most important effects of both tolazoline and phentolamine is vasodilatation due to a direct action on vascular smooth muscle, which is exerted by doses lower than those required to produce effective α-adrenergic blockade (5, 211). Indeed, tolazoline was first reported as a vasodilator with properties similar to those of histamine, and its α-adrenergic blocking activity was only demonstrated in later studies. This vasodilatation is not blocked by atropine and may be "histamine-like," although the effects of antihistaminics on it have not been studied. Other effects which may be "histamine-like" include vasoconstriction in the rabbit, stimulation of isolated intestine which is not blocked by atropine, stimulation of the uteri of dogs, cats, and rabbits *in vivo* and *in vitro* (5), and stimulation of the intestine of intact cats (86). Tolazoline potentiates the effects of histamine on several of these structures, but the effects of antihistaminic drugs on the responses have not been reported. Tolazoline stimulates gastric secretion of both acid and pepsin in laboratory animals and man (86, 253). It is only slightly less effective than is histamine for this purpose and has been successfully substituted for the latter in a clinical test of gastric secretory capacity (253).

Several properties of tolazoline have been classified as "sympathomimetic." Tachycardia, increased cardiac output, and coronary dilatation have been described in isolated hearts (5, 86). Increased cardiac output in intact dogs is due to both tachycardia and increased stroke volume (10). Tachycardia is a common response to therapeutic doses in man and is a prominent sign of tolazoline toxicity. This agent may increase the blood pressure in dogs, probably because the effect on cardiac output is more marked than the decrease in peripheral resistance (5). This is particularly marked after the first injection of a series, and may be associated with cardiac arrhythmias (146). Therapeutic doses of tolazoline have also been noted to produce an alarming hypertension in man. Tolazoline stimulates the denervated nictitating membrane (86), potentiates the myocardial stimulation and coronary dilatation due to adrenaline, and may also induce transient relaxation of gastrointestinal musculature (5). Evidence for classifying these effects as sympathomimetic is largely indirect and negative, i.e., their similarity to those evoked by adrenaline and their resistance to atropine.

The imidazoline group of tolazoline and phentolamine provides some chemical similarity to pilocarpine, but it is not clear whether this is responsible for their parasympathomimetic properties. Cardiac slowing in the rabbit and stimulation of the intact gastrointestinal tract are effects of tolazoline which have been shown to be blocked by atropine (5). Miosis and stimulation of salivary, pancreatic, and respiratory tract secretion and accentuation of the effects of acetylcholine on isolated intestine (33, 86, 117) are other acetylcholine-like effects which have been reported. However, the influence of atropine on these responses has not been studied, and superficial resemblances can be deceiving, e.g., the profuse sweating induced in cattle by tolazoline probably is not "cholinergic" (252). Effects which may be related to cholinergic nicotinic actions include potentiation of acetylcholine-induced contractions of the frog rectus abdominis, a curariform effect on skeletal muscle, and stimulation of the perfused superior cervical ganglion (86).

The side effects encountered in the therapeutic use of the imidazolines reflect their multiple pharmacological properties. Important cardiac effects are tachycardia, arrhythmias, and anginal pain. Gastrointestinal stimulation may result in abdominal pain, nausea, vomiting, diarrhea, and production or exacerbation of peptic ulcer. Piloerection, chilliness, and apprehension are also not uncommon.

D. Dibenzazepines

Several dibenzazepine derivatives have been shown to have α-adrenergic blocking activity (205). Of these, azapetine (Ilidar®, 6-allyl-6,7-dihydro-5H-dibenz(c,e)azepine) is the most effective, and the only one studied extensively. It produces a competitive blockade of α-adrenergic receptors very similar to that produced by tolazoline, but of somewhat greater duration (129, 164). Responses of most smooth muscle structures mediated by α-receptors are blocked by comparable doses of the two agents, but the intrinsic eye muscles appear to be less resistant to azapetine than to tolazoline. Like the latter, azapetine produces vasodilatation more by a direct action on vascular smooth muscle than as a result of α-adrenergic blockade (129, 164). It tends to reduce the blood pressure somewhat more than does tolazoline, probably because it causes less cardiac stimulation. However, palpitation is a not uncommon side effect of large doses in man (93).

Azapetine has not been carefully studied for the multitude of other effects which tolazoline has been shown to produce, but many responses to the two agents are similar. Azapetine appears to increase gastrointestinal motility less than does tolazoline; its effect on gastric secretion has not been studied. However, diarrhea and reactivation of peptic ulcers have been reported in patients receiving the drug, and a causal relationship cannot be ruled out. Many of the frequent but rarely dangerous side effects observed during azapetine therapy, including drowsiness, weakness, dizziness, confusion, and perhaps some cases of anorexia, nausea, and vomiting (93), are referable to the central nervous system, but detailed studies of the central effects of this agent have not been reported.

E. Benzodioxans

Members of the benzodioxan series were among the first synthetic adrenergic blocking agents to be studied (70). However, they have many actions other than α-adrenergic blockade, and consequently have been largely replaced by other agents as pharmacological tools and have received only desultory clinical trial. The blockade of α-adrenergic receptors is competitive and relatively transient. In common with other adrenergic blocking agents the benzodioxans inhibit responses to circulating adrenergic mediators more readily than those to sympathetic nerve activity. This differential is similar to that of other α-adrenergic blocking agents such as the haloalkylamines or ergot alkaloids for some members of the series, such as prosympal [883F, 2-(diethylaminomethyl)-1,4-benzodioxan], but is much larger for others, such as piperoxan

[Benodaine®, 933F, 2-(1-piperidylmethyl)-1,4-benzodioxan], which provides the basis for its use as a test for pheochromocytoma (83). Many intermediate ratios are also found within the series (20). The levorotatory form of prosympal is about six times as active as its *d*-isomer. Dibozane [1,4-(*bis*-1,4-benzodioxan-2yl methyl) piperazine] is a much more recent addition to this series, which has been used in experiments to differentiate between α- and β-adrenergic receptors in various tissues (6).

The benzodioxans directly stimulate the smooth muscle of many different organs, including that of uteri, gastrointestinal tract, bronchi, and nictitating membrane (20) and of peripheral and coronary blood vessels (41, 134). The direct peripheral vasoconstriction is responsible for the pressor effect in pithed dogs or animals under complete spinal anesthesia, and it probably combines with central nervous system stimulation to raise the blood pressure in unanesthetized man (131, 133).

The benzodioxans directly depress the myocardium, piperoxan being approximately three times as potent as quinidine in this regard (43). Their effects on the mammalian heart are quite nonspecific. Electrically induced fibrillation and $BaCl_2$-induced ectopic rhythms are inhibited as readily by piperoxan as are adrenaline-induced arrhythmyias (48), and the cardiac response to vagal stimulation is reduced almost parallel to that to accelerator nerve stimulation (260).

The benzodioxans have both stimulant and depressant effects on the central nervous system, which frequently complicate interpretation of the effects of peripheral α-adrenergic blockade. Inhibition of responses to carotid occlusion and to stimulation of the central stump of the severed vagus nerve by doses of 883F which do not inhibit responses to splanchnic nerve stimulation appears to be due to brain stem depression (260). Other manifestations of central nervous system depression include analgesia, suppression of vomiting due to digitalis or apomorphine, and prolongation of the action of several central nervous system depressants (21). Large doses of piperoxan may produce anesthesia. A number of quite varied responses to the benzodioxans can be attributed to central nervous system stimulation. They may produce a vagal bradycardia in anesthetized dogs despite systemic hypotension, followed by a tachycardia which is prevented by cardiac denervation or ganglionic blockade (260). The hyperglycemic response to a benzodioxan is also probably due to central nervous system stimulation (20), as is at least a part of their pressor effect in unanesthetized dogs and man.

The multiple actions of the benzodioxans are reflected in the side effects encountered in attempts to use them clinically. These are common, even with minimal effective doses, and include nausea and vomiting, headache, nervousness, dizziness, fright, hyperpnea, flushing, coldness and clamminess of the extremities, hypertension, palpitation, tachycardia, and precordial pain.

F. Other Agents

The list of agents which have been studied for their α-adrenergic blocking activity is long (19, 177), but most of these have received little recent attention. Yohimbine, an alkaloid related chemically to reserpine, has been known to have adrenergic blocking activity since 1925 (206). This alkaloid, and several naturally occurring or semisynthetic congeners such as corynanthine and ethyl yohimbine, produce a competitive α-adrenergic blockade of relatively short duration. However, the recent limited interest in yohimbine has been because of possible endocrine effects rather than as an α-adrenergic blocking agent. It has been sporadically promoted as an aphrodisiac, but there is no convincing evidence to support this claim.

Many drugs which are of pharmacological interest and therapeutic usefulness because of other, unrelated properties depress responses to adrenergic stimuli. In most cases this action is weak and of questionable specificity. However, certain phenothiazines, which are of interest primarily because of their effects on the central nervous system, can produce considerable blockade of α-adrenergic receptors. This action varies widely and is not well correlated with other properties within this group of compounds. There is no convincing evidence that they produce adrenergic blockade within the central nervous system or that any of their central effects are due to inhibition of responses to endogenous catecholamines. Chlorpromazine is one of the more effective α-adrenergic blocking agents among the phenothiazines, and this action has been implicated in both the postural hypotension which it produces and its protective effect in shock. However, both of these effects probably also involve central inhibition of vasomotor reflexes, and the relative contributions of the two mechanisms is quite unclear. Chlorpromazine produces a characteristic α-adrenergic blockade, comparable to that due to tolazoline or azapetine, *in vitro,* but *in vivo* it can prolong and, under appropriate conditions, enhance pressor responses to noradrenaline (152). The basis for this unexpected behavior is unclear.

III. RESPONSES OF VARIOUS EFFECTOR SYSTEMS TO α-ADRENERGIC BLOCKADE

The effects of administration of an α-adrenergic blocking agent on any tissue, organ or system are determined by three major factors: (*a*) the degree and duration of the blockade, (*b*) the nature and magnitude of the effects mediated through α-adrenergic receptors at the time of observation, and (*c*) actions of the agent administered in addition to adrenergic blockade. Failure to consider or to evaluate correctly factors *b* and *c* has frequently led to misinterpretation of *a*, and has made a major contribution to the many apparently conflicting reports which have been published. The present discussion will be directed primarily to the effects of α-adrenergic blockade per se, but it will be necessary to assess the control over various functions exerted by the sympathetic nervous system in order to define the conditions of an observed response to blockade, and other effects of the agents will be mentioned where they provide a useful comparison or simply cannot be fully dissociated from the results of blockade. Because they produce fewer obvious effects unrelated to α-adrenergic blockade than do other available agents, examples will be chosen from observations on the haloalkylamines wherever possible.

A. Heart

Adrenergic effects on the mammalian myocardium may be classified into two major types, "physiological" and "pathological." The most important of the former are the inotropic and chronotropic responses, and of the latter, the arrhythmias, induced particularly in the presence of certain sensitizing agents. Blockade of inotropic and chronotropic responses by various α-adrenergic blocking agents has been claimed by several workers (37), but many of these reports have been shown to be in error, and it has now been convincingly established that the major "physiological" responses of the myocardium are resistant to α-adrenergic blockade (168, 177, 187), in confirmation of Dale's early observation that they are not blocked by ergot (39). These responses appear to be mediated entirely by β-receptors (50, 167). The tachycardia induced by sympathomimetics is usually accentuated by α-adrenergic blockade because the pressor response is inhibited. In addition, sympathetic stimulation of the myocardium is a common reflex response to the blockade of peripheral vasomotor tone.

In contrast to their failure to block physiological responses of the mammalian myocardium, the α-adrenergic blocking agents effectively inhibit cardiac arrhythmias induced by catecholamines and other sympathomimetics. These occur particularly in the presence of certain hydrocarbons and halogenated hydrocarbons, the most important of which are anesthetics. Almost all α-adrenergic blocking agents tested in adequate dosage have been found to inhibit adrenaline-induced arrhythmias in dogs (2, 123, 169, 177, 194, 196, 200). In addition, Dibenamine has been shown to prevent "spontaneous" arrhythmias in patients under deep cyclopropane anesthesia (185), which indicates that adrenergic stimuli are involved in their pathogenesis.

The mechanisms of protection against cardiac arrhythmias by α-adrenergic blocking agents have not been completely elucidated. In general, the protection parallels blocking activity, but among agents of some chemical classes other pharmacological properties probably play a very important role. This is always suggested when a drug has a similar protective effect against arrhythmias induced by very different procedures. It is well known that nonspecific myocardial depressants such as quinidine provide significant protection against most types of cardiac arrhythmias (44, 123, 196), and the benzodioxans have been shown to be several times as potent as quinidine in depressing the myocardium (43). Involvement of nonspecific myocardial effects is also suggested by the fact that dihydroergotamine is less than half as potent as ergotamine in preventing cyclopropane-adrenaline arrhythmias (200), although it is a more effective α-adrenergic blocking agent. The haloalkylamines also exert a quinidine-like effect, but it probably is not an important component of their effect on cardiac arrhythmias. Although highly effective against arrhythmias involving adrenergic stimuli, these agents do not prevent, and may accentuate, those induced by electrical stimulation or acute coronary occlusion. In addition, their myocardial depressant and antiarrhythmic properties have been separated both temporally and on the basis of chemical structure. Protection by Dibenamine against cyclopropane-adrenaline arrhythmias lasts for up to 5 days, whereas the quinidine-like effect is evanescent, and 2-dibenzylaminoethanol, a hydrolysis product of Dibenamine lacking adrenergic blocking activity, has a quinidine-like action similar to that of the parent compound (2), but does not protect against cyclopropane-adrenaline arrhythmias.

Adrenaline-hydrocarbon arrhythmias can be modified considerably by changes in arterial pressure (51, 53, 161, 194), and it has been demonstrated that part of the protective effect of adrenergic blockade is due to inhibition of the peripheral vasoconstriction responsible for the usual pressor response to sympathomimetic amines (161, 194). However, a direct effect on the heart appears also to be involved since blockade of the pressor response and protection against arrhythmias can be dissociated (81, 123, 194).

A possible relationship between hyperkalemia and the increased ventricular excitability induced by adrenaline and noradrenaline has been reported (235), and it has been suggested that the transient hyperkalemia induced by adrenaline is an important factor in the induction of arrhythmias, since hepatectomy, ergot alkaloids, and Dibenamine all can prevent both (198). However, subsequent observations appear to exclude a causal relationship between the hyperkalemia and arrhythmia induction. These include the observations that (*a*) the hyperkalemic response to adrenaline is not quantitatively related to the induction of arrhythmias, (*b*) injection of potassium does not enhance the ability of subthreshold doses of adrenaline to induce arrhythmias, (*c*) prevention of hyperkalemia by vascular isolation of the liver does not prevent the arrhythmias, and (*d*) the infusion of potassium to provide blood levels comparable to those produced by previously arrhythmia-inducing doses of adrenaline does not facilitate the production of arrhythmias by this agent after Dibenamine blockade (52).

The effects of α-adrenergic blocking agents on cardiac arrhythmias due to conditions which do not involve adrenergic stimuli are quite variable, and appear to be dependent upon direct myocardial depression rather than adrenergic blockade (177). Ergotamine and dihydroergotamine protect significantly against fatal ventricular fibrillation after acute coronary artery occlusion in dogs (149), but their effectiveness does not parallel α-adrenergic blocking potency and Dibenamine is ineffective (177). The benzodioxans 883F and 933F (piperoxan) have been reported to inhibit cardiac arrhythmias due to electrical stimulation in cats (48), but they appear to be entirely ineffective against the arrhythmias induced by digitalis overdosage (62).

Although they much more commonly produce myocardial depression, certain drugs classified as α-adrenergic blocking agents can directly stimulate the myocardium. This is particularly true of tolazoline, which can produce severe tachycardia and an increase in cardiac output of sufficient magnitude to give a net pressor response in both dogs and man (5, 99). The rise in blood pressure may be accompanied by cardiac arrhythmias (146). Tolazoline has been found to be useful in the treatment of some cases of left heart failure and paroxysmal nocturnal dyspnea (265), but this effect is probably due predominantly to peripheral vasodilatation rather than to myocardial stimulation.

B. Vasculature

The effect of α-adrenergic blockade on any portion of the vascular system is a function of the level of sympathetic nervous system activity to that segment, and this can alter markedly during physiological activity or stress. Thus, although extensive α-adrenergic blockade usually causes little fall in blood pressure when induced slowly in normovolemic, recumbent laboratory animals or man, the pressure may fall precipitously in the presence of a high level of compensatory sympathetic vasoconstrictor activity, as in hypovolemia or in man in an upright position.

Most segments of the vasculature containing smooth muscle are innervated by sympathetic adrenergic nerves and respond both to noradrenaline released locally and to circulating sympathomimetic amines, the former being by far the most important in responses to endogenous materials (32). Responses to noradrenaline are almost entirely constrictor, mediated by α-receptors. Adrenaline can also act on β-receptors to relax the smooth muscle of some vascular beds, particularly in skeletal muscle, but endogenous adrenaline is rarely released in sufficient amounts to have important vascular effects.

Since both competitive and nonequilibrium blocking agents act to reduce the number of α-adrenergic receptors available for reaction with an agonist, they should inhibit equally the responses to all sympathomimetic amines which act on such receptors. Many apparent exceptions to this have been reported, but they can be ascribed to properties of the agonists other than their action on α-adrenergic receptors and to the complex nature of the responses measured. For example, a dose of a haloalkylamine which eliminates the pressor response to injected adrenaline or converts it to depressor may reduce the response to noradrenaline 50% or less. This difference is due to the fact that the blood pressure response involves both vasoconstriction (α-receptors) and vasodilatation (β-receptors). Adrenaline acts effectively on both types of receptors, and moderate inhibition of the former may allow vasodilatation, mediated by the latter, to predominate. Noradrenaline has very little vasodilator action, and consequently, almost all of the residual vasoconstriction is reflected in the pressor response (193).

Reversal of any response by α-adrenergic blockade requires that the parameter measured be a composite of two opposing actions. Reversal of the pressor response to an injected sympathomimetic is slight or absent when the capacity for adrenergic vasodilatation is severely limited by any factor, e.g., the species (rabbits), the sympathomimetic agent used (phenylephrine or noradrenaline), or the preparation (pithed animals or isolated perfused limbs, in which vasodilation is already nearly maximal). Responses to sympathetic adrenergic nerve activity usually are not reversed. However, if the total response involves a vasodilating influence of any type, reversal may occur, e.g., the vasoconstriction in a skeletal muscle vascular bed in response to sympathetic nerve stimulation is readily reversed by Dibenamine because of the involvement of cholinergic vasodilator fibers (68). The vasodilator, hypotensive effects of hypercapnea and of many drugs are unmasked by α-adrenergic blockade because the reflex vasoconstriction which normally compensates for them is prevented.

The peripheral vascular tree can be compared to an electrical circuit with many parallel resistances, each of which is made up of a number of resistances in series (67). The parallel resistances are related to various tissues, organs, and body areas (skeletal muscle, kidneys, skin, etc.) and determine the distribution of cardiac output. The resistance within each vascular bed is the sum of the resistances of several different types of vessels, which can be conveniently divided into those proximal to and those distal to the capillaries. The relative tonus, and resultant resistance, of these two groups of vessels controls capillary hydrostatic pressure and, thus, net transcapillary fluid exchange and plasma volume. In the kidney this balance is reflected in the glomerular filtration rate. The precapillary resistance, predominantly that of arterioles and metarterioles, represents the major part of the total peripheral resistance, and most studies of peripheral blood flow measure this component.

1. *Renal Vascular Bed*

Responses to sympathomimetic amines administered intravenously or intra-arterially indicate that the renal vessels of the dog, cat, and man have predominantly α-receptor, constrictor responses (32, 154, 247). Slight renal vasodilatation attributable to β-receptor activation has been shown in response to isoproterenol and to large doses of noradrenaline given after very large doses of phenoxybenzamine (4, 158). Renal sympathetic nerve stimulation decreases blood flow as a direct function of the stimulus frequency in dogs and cats (32, 247). However, sympathetic tone to the renal vessels at rest appears to be minimal. Phenoxybenzamine, ergot alkaloids, imidazolines, or azapetine administered to laboratory animals in doses adequate to block renal vasoconstriction due to injected sympathomimetic amines or the increased sympathetic nerve activity induced by hemorrhage have little effect on resting renal blood flow (110, 111, 172, 240). Similarly, tolazoline and phenoxybenzamine appear to have little effect on renal blood flow in human subjects with essential hypertension (69, 257).

The interpretation of small changes in renal vascular resistance in response to α-adrenergic blockade is complicated by the very effective autoregulation in the renal circulation and the fact that in most experiments systemic administration of the blocking drug caused some fall in blood pressure. However, local administration of phenoxybenzamine into one renal artery, which did not alter the systemic arterial pressure, was also reported to have no consistent effect on renal blood flow, although the vasoconstrictor responses to infused adrenaline and to hemorrhage were effectively blocked (111). The limited or absent vasodilator responses of the renal vascular bed at rest to sympathomimetic amines which activate β-receptors and to α-adrenergic blocking agents is not due to the fact that it is already maximally dilated. Hydralazine (Apresoline®) or typhoid vaccine can produce a considerable increase in resting renal blood flow even in the face of a decreased blood pressure (154, 173).

Unilateral denervation has been reported to increase slightly the renal blood flow measured in unanesthetized dogs and rabbits (132, 136). However, the renal vascular bed is very sensitive to any stress, and it is quite possible that sympathetic tone was somewhat above the true resting level under the conditions of these flow measurements. The effects of adrenergic blocking agents on renal blood flow in the presence of increased sympathetic vasoconstrictor activity is much more dramatic. Intense renal vasoconstriction is a prominent feature of the response to hemorrhage and shock (1, 111, 118, 202, 228). Phenoxybenzamine has been reported to reduce considerably the fall in renal blood flow induced by hemorrhage (111), and pretreatment with this blocking agent allows renal blood flows at least 50% greater than those of control dogs to persist during the development of hemorrhagic shock (118).

Differential effects of sympathetic nervous system activity and, consequently, of α-adrenergic blockade on various components of the intrarenal vasculature may play an important role in the response of the kidney to sympathetic nervous system activity. However, the evidence for such differential effects is fragmentary and, in many instances, conflicting. A diversion of blood flow from cortical to medullary areas in response to sympathetic nerve activity or injected catecholamines has been suggested (256). However, direct evidence of functionally significant diversion is lacking (153). Changes in Diodrast® extraction compatible with this hypothesis have been observed (247), but these results are also compatible with alternative explanations. Although reductions in cortical and medullary flow may be similar, it is becoming clear that the latter is reduced much less than is glomerular filtration during the development of shock. This imbalance leads to a washout of the osmotic gradient in the renal papillae and prevents concentration of urine (138, 229). Much additional information is required before it will be possible to assess the contribution of differential effects to responses such as the prevention by phenoxybenzamine of the high renal vascular resistance and oliguria which otherwise persist after the return of shed blood and reestablishment of an arterial pressure adequate for glomerular filtration in hemorrhagic shock (118).

The effects of adrenergic blockade on renal parameters other than hemodynamic are very complex, and there are many discrepancies and apparent contradictions among the published observations on this subject. Adrenaline and noradrenaline induce sodium and potassium retention in man, with little change or an actual increase in urine volume (176), and renal denervation has been reported to increase the rate of sodium and water excretion (132). The noradrenaline-induced alterations in electrolyte excretion occur in patients with Addison's disease or with diabetes insipidus and thus appear to be primary rather than mediated via adrenal steroids or posterior pituitary hormones (176). Despite minimal effects on renal plasma flow and glomerular filtration rate, phenoxybenzamine usually produces a diuresis, with or without an associated natriuresis, in normal man. The drug also blocks the effects of noradrenaline on sodium and water excretion in the dog. The prompt increase in plasma volume which phenoxybenzamine may induce and inhibition of the noradrenaline-induced reduction in plasma volume may be involved in these renal effects, but this possibility has not been adequately investigated (118, 191, 249, 266).

2. *Cutaneous Vascular Bed*

Most studies of skin vessels have been carried out on the hand or foot, with the implicit assumption that these areas are representative of the entire cutaneous vascular bed. This obviously is invalid for some responses, e.g., blushing, and it is possible that the effects of catecholamines and, consequently, of α-adrenergic blockade may vary in different regions of the body. Responses of the smooth muscle of cutaneous vessels to sympathomimetic amines and to sympathetic nerve stimulation are mediated almost exclusively by α-receptors. Constrictor responses are blocked but rarely reversed by α-adrenergic blocking agents. Isoproterenol given intra-arterially has been reported to produce only limited vasodilatation (95, 262), and even this may represent a contribution of other tissues in the area of flow measurement. The preponderance of α-receptors is illustrated by the fact that even isoproterenol can cause blanching, a reflection of net vasoconstriction, when injected intracutaneously. The vasoconstrictor effects of adrenaline or sympathetic nerve stimulation on cutaneous vessels are not reversed by α-adrenergic blockade (97).

The magnitude of the effect of adrenergic blockade on skin blood flow is highly dependent on ambient temperature, reflecting the role of sympathetic vasomotor tone to this vascular bed in temperature regulation. Every α-adrenergic blocking agent tested can produce cutaneous vasodilatation in man in a cool environment (18, 54, 90, 116), and an increase in finger or toe temperature is one of the earliest signs of developing α-adrenergic blockade (42). The cutaneous vascular bed is intensely constricted during asphyxia (32, 120), hemorrhage, and shock

(220), and a dramatic warming of the extremities is often apparent less than an hour after the administration of phenoxybenzamine to patients in shock.

Several factors which complicate interpretation of responses to α-adrenergic blocking agents are well illustrated by observations on cutaneous vessels. The naturally occurring ergot alkaloids directly constrict these vessels and, thus, can mask any dilator effects of adrenergic blockade (18), but dihydrogenated derivatives of alkaloids of the ergotoxine group consistently dilate cutaneous vessels in the hand and foot. The latter produce relatively much more adrenergic blockade and much less direct vasoconstriction than do the parent compounds. However, the vasodilatation still cannot be attributed to α-adrenergic blockade because they decrease sympathetic vasoconstrictor tone by an action on the central nervous system which is prominent with doses even lower than those required to produce significant α-adrenergic blockade. This central action probably is responsible for most of the vasodilatation induced by doses of Hydergine tolerated by man (8). Another complication is illustrated by the report that 1 and 2 mg/kg of azapetine or tolazoline, respectively, given intravenously produced greater increases in digital skin temperature in man than did 0.2 mg/kg of phenoxybenzamine (90). However, the phenoxybenzamine produced more nasal stuffiness and postural hypotension, effects which are generally well correlated with the blockade of sympathetic vasoconstrictor control of peripheral vessels, and it appears likely that much of the increase in digital temperature induced by the tolazoline and azapetine was due to their direct vasodilator effects (5, 129) rather than to α-adrenergic blockade. In man 1 mg/kg of phenoxybenzamine given intravenously can increase skin blood flow almost as much as local anesthetic nerve block or spinal anesthesia (269), and this entire response probably is due to blockade per se.

3. *Splanchnic Vascular Bed*

The mesenteric vessels are effectively constricted by splanchnic nerve stimulation or by infused adrenaline or noradrenaline (32, 45). A small dilator response to splanchnic nerve stimulation has been observed after α-adrenergic blockade with Dibenamine, phenoxybenzamine, or azapetine (45, 189); it is not blocked by atropine. However, splanchnic vascular resistance can be altered by changes in gastrointestinal smooth muscle tone, and it is not entirely clear that this is due to a direct effect on the blood vessels. The resistance of the mesenteric bed is increased markedly by asphyxia (11, 120), hemorrhage, and shock (1, 118). Superior mesenteric flow at rest is moderately increased by phenoxybenzamine, and the flow in blocked animals is more than double that of control dogs during the development of hemorrhagic shock (118). Hepatic artery flow appears to decrease in parallel with mesenteric flow during splanchnic nerve stimulation, and this effect can be blocked by moderate doses of phenoxybenzamine or azapetine (94).

Splanchnic nerve stimulation and injected adrenaline contract the spleen in cats and dogs (32, 98). The response to nerve stimulation can be blocked and that to adrenaline slightly reversed by phenoxybenzamine (98). Ergot also blocks splenic contractions induced by adrenaline or by sympathetic nerve stimulation in cats, as demonstrated in the very early studies of Dale (39). Blockade of the splenic contraction induced by increased sympathetic nerve activity is probably the mechanism by which haloalkylamines prevent the increase in hematocrit produced by excitement in cats (189) and that occurring early in the course of hemorrhage in dogs (118).

It has been reported that the hepatotoxicity of carbon tetrachloride, as measured by both morphological and biochemical criteria, can be prevented in the rat by α-adrenergic blockade with phenoxybenzamine, ergotamine, or phentolamine (26, 31), and the same investigators have presented considerable additional evidence for the involvement of endogenous catecholamines in this toxic effect (244). It has been suggested that the pathogenesis involves an intense vasoconstriction mediated by the α-receptors of visceral vascular smooth muscle, resulting in ischemia and hypoxia of sufficient severity to produce the centrilobular necrosis characteristic of this condition. However, it appears unlikely that the toxic effect of the primary agent is mediated entirely by catecholamines. Death following administration of single large doses of adrenaline is due to respiratory arrest, pulmonary edema, or cardiac arrhythmias (184). More prolonged infusion of a catecholamine reduces the circulating blood volume and induces shock (63, 272). Hepatic damage has not been reported as an important component of catecholamine toxicity in animals, or as a complication of pheochromocytoma in man.

4. *Skeletal Muscle Vascular Bed*

The vasculature of skeletal muscle is constricted by stimulation of the paravertebral sympathetic chain and by injected noradrenaline (32, 92), and these responses are inhibited by various agents with the relative effectiveness expected on the basis of their general α-adrenergic blocking activity, i.e., phenoxybenzamine > phentolamine > azapetine or tolazoline (92). Adrenaline produces dilatation (mediated by β-receptors) as well as constriction of vessels in skeletal muscle, and the net effect is a function of both the preexisting state of the vessels and the concentration of adrenaline reaching them. Maximal dilatation is induced by amounts considerably smaller than those required to produce maximal constriction (189), but the net response to large doses is always vasoconstriction. A predominantly constrictor response to adrenaline in the skeletal muscle vascular bed of the dog hind limb can be reversed to predominantly vasodilator by a dose of α-adrenergic blocking agent less than one-third that required to block the constrictor response to sympathetic nerve stimulation. In addition to the effects of α-adrenergic blockade, phentolamine, tolazoline, and azapetine all dilate muscle vessels by a direct action on the vascular smooth muscle (129, 164).

Vasoconstriction in skeletal muscle beds is a prominent response to asphyxia (16, 40) and to hemorrhage and shock (1, 58, 216), but it was recognized many years ago that "essential" muscles, such as those involved in respiration, which remain active during hemorrhage, are much less ischemic than others (220). It is now well known that the smooth muscle of vessels in skeletal muscle is very responsive to local metabolic activity and that vigorous exercise can overcome sympathetic vasoconstriction in these beds and induce a "functional sympathectomy" (36). Consequently, an α-adrenergic blocking agent cannot be expected to augment the muscle blood flow during maximal tolerated exercise. Although such an increase has been frequently suggested on the basis of clinical observations, there appear to be no published measurements to support this contention for any α-adrenergic blocking agent, or other "vasodilator," in either normal subjects or patients with vascular disease.

5. *Cerebral Vascular Bed*

There has been much controversy regarding the effects of sympathetic nervous system activity and of sympathomimetic amines on the cerebral circulation (96, 238). The abundance of conflicting reports may be related to the fact that the major vessels involved serve both cerebral and extracerebral tissues. However, the results of studies which carefully separated these components seem to agree that catecholamines have little action on cerebral vessels (91). Thus, there is no basis for an effect of α-adrenergic blockade on cerebral vascular resistance per se. However, a reduction in systemic arterial pressure due to blockade in other areas can cause cerebral vasodilatation. This probably is a reflection of the regulatory effect of changes in pCO_2, which is so sensitive and effective that there is little change in cerebral blood flow over a considerable range of pressures. When flow begins to decrease, venous oxygen saturation tends to fall in parallel, and cerebral oxygen consumption remains relatively constant over a further considerable range of hypotension. Jugular pO_2 values indicating adequate cerebral oxygenation have been found uniformly in patients under general anesthesia with cerebral systolic arterial pressures below 32 mm Hg for considerable periods of time, and as low as 17 mm Hg (56). Mild signs of central nervous system depression may appear in conscious subjects when the cerebral blood flow has fallen to approximately 50% of control values (66). The adaptability of the cerebral circulation is reflected in the fact that the only cerebral complication noted in one group of 407 patients whose systolic pressures were held below 80 mm Hg, usually at 50 to 65 mm, for periods of about an hour during orthopedic surgery, was transient confusion in 9, all over 70 years of age (121).

6. *Coronary Vascular Bed*

Interpretation of the responses of coronary vessels is complicated by the fact that their tone is intimately related to myocardial activity and metabolism. There appears to be universal agreement that adrenaline, noradrenaline, and sympathetic nerve activity increase coronary blood flow (96). This response probably reflects the dominance of the effects of increased myocardial activity over the limited primary vasoconstrictor action of noradrenaline or sympathetic nerve stimulation (251). The myocardial effects are mediated by β-adrenergic receptors and, as would be expected, Dibenamine has been shown not to affect coronary flow (141). It is probable that the reported inhibition of adrenaline- and noradrenaline-induced coronary dilatation by massive doses of azapetine was due to some nonspecific depression of vascular or myocardial reactivity rather than to adrenergic blockade per se (47). The ergot alkaloids and benzodioxans can increase coronary resistance and decrease flow as a result of their direct actions on the vascular smooth muscle.

7. *Pulmonary Vascular Bed*

There is general agreement regarding the effects of sympathomimetics and of α-adrenergic blocking agents on pulmonary vascular pressures and blood flow (7), but there is difference of opinion regarding the mechanisms involved. The pulmonary vessels convey the entire cardiac output in series with the systemic vasculature, but in general have considerably less smooth muscle in their walls than do comparable systemic vessels. Consequently, the pulmonary circulation is quite sensitive to changes in cardiovascular parameters elsewhere in the body. Adrenaline or noradrenaline given intravenously increases pulmonary artery pressure, with either an increase or no change in total blood flow. Increased cardiac output (268) and increased left atrial pressure (175) have both been implicated as contributing to the increased pulmonary pressure in intact laboratory animals and man. Increased left atrial pressure may result, at least in part, from a shift of blood from the systemic to the pulmonary circuit (74, 213, 231). An opposite shift of blood volume, due predominantly to blockade of adrenergic vasoconstriction, particularly venoconstriction, in systemic beds rather than to an effect on pulmonary vessels per se, may be a major factor in the reduction in systemic venous and pulmonary pressures and the relief of pulmonary edema which α-adrenergic and ganglionic blocking agents can induce in both experimental animals and man (60, 107, 108, 265).

An effect on pulmonary vessels probably is involved in the transient reduction in pulmonary artery pressure and pulmonary vascular resistance induced by tolazoline given intravenously or directly into the pulmonary artery (103, 221). This response is variable, but is of considerable magnitude in some patients with elevated pulmonary pressures. A differential effect on parallel vascular beds within the lung is suggested by the fact that decreased total resistance may be accompanied by decreased arterial oxygen saturation. Direct involvement of α-adrenergic blockade in this effect of tolazoline on pulmonary vessels has not been established. Adrenaline and noradrenaline constrict the vessels of isolated, perfused lungs, and this action is blocked by ergot alkaloids, piperoxan, or Dibenamine (7, 197), but the contribution of blockade of adrenergic pulmonary vasoconstriction to responses of the pulmonary circulation in intact laboratory animals or man is unclear.

The pulmonary lesions and mortality induced by exposure to high pressures of oxygen can be prevented by haloalkylamines (130), but the pulmonary hypertension associated with hypoxia or an increase in the inspired pCO_2 is resistant to adrenergic or ganglionic blockade and apparently does not involve adrenergic or other nervous mechanisms (7, 197).

8. *Nutrient Blood Flow*

The precapillary resistance has two important functional components, the major resistance of arterioles and metarterioles, which controls total flow through a given vascular bed, and that of precapillary sphincters, which is much smaller but is important in determining the local distribution of flow through alternative channels. The distribution between true capillaries, which provide effective exchange of metabolites with tissue cells, the "nutrient" flow, and "thoroughfare" or "shunt" pathways, from which relatively less exchange occurs, is a major factor in determining the functional adequacy of the circulation (29). Total vascular resistance and the distribution of flow between nutrient and other channels can change independently in innervated limbs (209) and, presumably, elsewhere in the body. Control of the local distribution of blood flow appears to be predominantly adrenergic and to involve α receptors. Using ^{86}Rb and oxygen uptakes as indices, it has been shown that sympathetic nerve stimulation decreases nutrient flow in skeletal muscle as a function of the stimulus frequency. This effect persists during prolonged stimulation and is of considerable magnitude even at low, physiological frequencies (209). Infusion of noradrenaline can also considerably reduce the relative nutrient blood flow in the mesenteric vascular bed (191). The precapillary sphincters appear to have significant resting neurogenic tone, since reflex inhibition of vasomotor tone increases both ^{86}Rb and oxygen extraction in skeletal muscle vascular beds of dogs and cats (210). The effect of α-adrenergic blockade on precapillary sphincters at rest has not been reported, but it should be very similar to that of reflex release of vasomotor tone, as it is on other segments of the vascular system. That α-adrenergic blockade can relax precapillary sphincters effectively is shown by the observation that pretreatment with phenoxybenzamine can prevent the decrease in nutrient flow fraction (^{86}Rb uptake) which occurs in the mesenteric bed of dogs in hemorrhagic shock or during noradrenaline infusion (191).

9. *Postcapillary Vessels*

Postcapillary vessels contain the major part of the total blood volume and can function as a reservoir of intravascular fluid to buffer changes in volume or to meet special requirements, as in sustaining the increased cardiac output associated with exercise (160). In addition, these vessels play an important role in regulating the total intravascular fluid volume. Although they contribute only a small part of the total peripheral resistance, this component is very important in regulating capillary pressure and, thus, the exchange of fluid between the intravascular and interstitial compartments (160). Venules and very small veins probably contribute most to the postcapillary resistance, whereas the major capacity resides in somewhat larger veins. However, this is not a qualitative distinction, and the same vessels may be important in determining both postcapillary resistance and total vascular capacity. The postcapillary vessels are very sensitive to many drug effects. For example, in patients with chronic congestive heart failure, Dibenamine can reduce systemic venous and right atrial pressures without significant changes in arterial pressure or cardiac output, and the ergot alkaloids, including Hydergine, can increase venous and right atrial pressures and the gradient between them without altering or while decreasing cardiac output and arterial pressure (107). The effects of the ergot alkaloids are probably due to a direct action on the smooth muscle of veins and are less marked with Hydergine than with ergotamine or dihydroergotamine.

Blood vessels subserving both resistance and capacitance functions are consistently constricted by adrenaline, noradrenaline, and sympathetic nerve activity in both laboratory animals and man (57, 105, 160, 233). Phentolamine appears to block this effect of noradrenaline in the human forearm (57). In contrast, it has been suggested that phenoxybenzamine given intra-arterially does not reach the α-receptors of veins in man because subsequent infusion of adrenaline causes a marked increase in forearm blood flow and an apparent parallel increase in venous tone, quantitated by a pressure-volume index derived by venous occlusion plethysmography (232). However, a careful examination of this indirect method of measuring venous tone revealed that the apparent distensibility of limb veins in man is highly dependent on the flow, or filling rate (119). Thus, the reported venoconstriction appears to have been an artifact due to the sharp increase in blood flow associated with the arteriolar dilatation induced by adrenaline in the skeletal muscle vascular bed after blockade by phenoxybenzamine of the constrictor component of its action. It has not yet been possible to obtain an independent measure of the effect of α-adrenergic blockade on venous tone in man, but the high tone of small veins in dogs subjected to hemorrhagic hypotension is rapidly reduced by phenoxybenzamine given intra-arterially (118), and there is no reason to assume that the α-receptors of human veins are more resistant to blockade.

Adrenergic blockade with phenoxybenzamine produces hemodilution and a parallel increase in plasma volume in both chicks and dogs (191, 266), and delays or prevents the decrease in plasma volume associated with the decompensatory phase of hemorrhagic shock (118) or with noradrenaline infusion (249). These effects appear to involve a decrease or prevention of a rise in capillary pressure and a consequent shift in net transcapillary fluid movement toward the intravascular compartment. The decrease in capillary pressure cannot be due to a lower arterial blood pressure. This was kept constant in the shock experiments, and even where some fall occurred or a rise in pressure was prevented, these changes were secondary to decreased peripheral resistance (predominantly precapillary), which would allow greater transmission of the arterial pressure to the capillary bed. The hemodilution induced by phenoxybenzamine probably is due to a reduction in the tone of postcapillary vessels. Phenoxybenzamine administered to dogs during the development of hemorrhagic shock causes a sharp decrease in small vein wedge pressure, despite a considerable decrease in precapillary resistance and increase in blood flow (118). Blockade of the sympathetic control of capacitance vessels is also indicated by the postural hypotension which is one of the most prominent signs of α-adrenergic blockade in man.

C. Central Nervous System

The effects of α-adrenergic blockade on central nervous system functions and responses are quite unclear. The complexity of the effector system, which allows a primary depressant action to appear as gross stimulation and *vice versa,* lack of knowledge regarding the physiological role, if any, of endogenous catecholamines, and uncertainties regarding penetration of drugs into and their distribution within the central nervous system all contribute to the difficulty of obtaining definitive information. The most prominent gross central effects of adrenaline, noradrenaline, and other sympathomimetic amines are stimulant, whereas the best-studied local effects are depressant.

A major difficulty in establishing the effects of α-adrenergic blockade per se is the fact that all adequately studied α-adrenergic blocking agents appear to influence central nervous system activity by mechanisms other than blockade. The observed central effects of these agents do not form a consistent pattern and are rarely well correlated with blocking activity as determined on peripheral structures. The ergot alkaloids and benzodioxans have particularly prominent and relatively specific effects on the central nervous system. Major central effects of the former include inhibition of sympathetic and stimulation of vagal activity and stimulation of the chemoreceptor trigger zone for emesis. In contrast, the benzodioxans act centrally to increase sympathetic nervous system activity, a major component of their pressor effect in unanesthetized laboratory animals and man (83, 112). The haloalkylamines, in common with many other drugs of diverse types, produce mild sedation and a feeling of lethargy, and Dibenamine has been noted to produce various temporal lobe symptoms, including a relatively specific derangement of time sense, and perseverations, often with full insight (116, 212). These relatively specific psychic reactions have not been observed with phenoxybenzamine, which because of its greater adrenergic blocking potency is administered to man in considerably smaller doses than Dibenamine. The two drugs may not differ qualitatively in this regard, but it is clear that production of these psychic responses does not parallel peripheral α-adrenergic blocking activity.

Dibenamine has been reported to have a "tranquilizing" effect, reducing anxiety, increasing the contact of schizophrenics with their surroundings, reducing catatonia, etc., and to inhibit apomorphine-induced emesis, both with the slow onset and long duration characteristic of its peripheral blockade (71, 159, 212). These observations point to participation of the reactive imonium intermediates formed from haloalkylamines in certain of their central actions, but, in view of the many components of biological systems with which these may react (113), cannot be taken as evidence that α-adrenergic receptors are involved. Haloalkylamines can stimulate the central nervous system to cause nausea, vomiting, hyperventilation, motor excitability, and even convulsions, particularly when a relatively large dose is injected rapidly intravenously (116, 212). These effects are rarely seen with the usual therapeutic doses of phenoxybenzamine and are clearly unrelated to adrenergic blockade (178).

Investigations predicated on the assumption that ataractic activity is related to "central adrenergic blockade" led to the development of ethoxybutamoxane (8-ethoxy-2-butylaminomethyl-1,4-benzodioxan), which is an effective "tranquilizer" in laboratory tests (236). It antagonizes adrenaline-induced arousal of cats with pontomesencephalic junction lesions, prevents apomorphine-induced emesis, and reduces spontaneous activity and aggression. However, its peripheral adrenergic blocking activity appears to be weak; indeed, no conclusive evidence that it has α-adrenergic blocking activity has been published. Thus, the data presently available on this compound are inadequate to support either a role of catecholamines in emotional processes or α-adrenergic blockade as the mechanism of its effects on the central nervous system.

The results of studies of blockade of central effects of exogenous sympathomimetic amines have been inconclusive. Few of these attempts have utilized simplified systems amenable to neurophysiological techniques. Indeed, there appears to have been a preoccupation with complexity, often without full recognition of the parallel increase in the difficulty of interpreting results. [See Rothballer (215) for examples.] In one study in which phenoxybenzamine was shown to prevent adrenaline suppression of a conditioned avoidance response, both the effect of the catecholamine and its inhibition could be quite clearly attributed to peripheral actions (137). Unfortunately, many of the pitfalls in interpreting behavioral changes are much less obvious.

One early study demonstrated that chlorpromazine can antagonize adrenaline-induced inhibition of synaptic transmission in the relatively simple transcallosal system (151). Unfortunately, more specific and effective α-adrenergic blocking agents were not tested, and it is difficult to attribute this effect to the adrenergic blocking activity of the phenothiazine because reserpine and azacyclonol (Frenquel®), which have little or no α-adrenergic blocking activity in the usual tests on peripheral structures, were also effective.

Some very interesting observations regarding the effects of α-adrenergic blocking agents on a specific synapse in the central nervous system have come from studies of the inhibitory effects of lateral olfactory tract (LOT) stimulation and of possible chemical mediators on mitral cells of the olfactory bulb (17, 222). In addition to LOT stimulation, acetylcholine, 5-hydroxytryptamine (5-HT), and, particularly, noradrenaline applied locally could reduce the firing rate of these cells. Agonists and antagonists were applied electrophoretically through the same multibarreled micropipette that was used for recording unit discharge. With this technique, Dibenamine and phentolamine were shown to block the inhibitory effect of noradrenaline without affecting responses to acetylcholine or to 5-HT. Dibenamine also considerably shortened the inhibition due to LOT stimulation and in some cases increased the rate of "spontaneous" firing. The effect of noradrenaline was not inhibited by cholinergic blocking agents or by dichloroisoproterenol (DCI), a β-adrenergic blocking agent, but it was antagonized, at least as effectively as was the effect of 5-HT, by LSD-25 and BOL-148, lysergic acid derivatives with predominantly 5-HT blocking actions on peripheral structures. The blockade produced by Dibenamine appeared to be relatively slow in onset but of shorter duration than expected from studies on peripheral α-adrenergic systems. These studies appear to provide considerable, but not definitive, support for specific α-adrenergic blockade at a central synapse. They also suggest that the characteristics and specificities of blockade within the central nervous system may differ considerably from those of peripheral blockade.

Only a few of the many reports of studies involving more complex central nervous system responses can be mentioned here. Most contain discrepancies or omissions which preclude a definitive conclusion that α-adrenergic receptors were involved in the observed effects (215). Dibenamine does not alter appreciably adrenaline-induced respiratory stimulation in laboratory animals or in man (116, 189), or the transient apnea produced in anesthetized animals (190), but this adrenergic blocking agent and several others of diverse chemical structure have been reported to antagonize the stimulation of motor activity by methamphetamine in mice (255). Many nonspecific central and peripheral factors can influence spontaneous activity, and it is difficult to attribute this effect to central α-adrenergic blockade. The relative potencies of the agents in this test and in the blockade of peripheral α-adrenergic receptors varied tremendously, and adrenaline and noradrenaline themselves similarly antagonized the methamphetamine-induced activity.

Phenoxybenzamine has been shown to block and adrenaline infusion to restore bulbar inhibition of the patellar reflex (38). However, the onset appears to be faster and the duration of this effect much shorter than is characteristic of the blockade of peripheral α-adrenergic receptors by this agent. In addition, complete abolition of the phenoxybenzamine effect by infusion of adrenaline would be incompatible with a non-equilibrium blockade unless it was considerably less than complete, which cannot be assessed in the absence of dose-response data.

Phenoxybenzamine, Dibenamine, and chlorpromazine have all been reported to decrease EEG activity and to inhibit the analeptic effect of amphetamine, but not that of caffeine or pentylenetetrazol, in barbiturate-depressed rabbits. However, phentolamine, dihydroergotamine, and azapetine, administered in doses adequate to block peripheral α-receptors, did not have comparable effects (174). A similar difference was found in the effects of various α-adrenergic blocking agents on the EEG stimulation (activation) induced by adrenaline, noradrenaline, or methoxamine. The stimulant effects of these sympathomimetics were enhanced by dichloroisoproterenol and effectively inhibited by small doses of phenoxybenzamine or chlorpromazine. However, relatively large doses of phentolamine, dihydroergotamine, or azapetine had no inhibitory effect (85). The significance of these observations in terms of specific α-adrenergic blockade is uncertain. In particular, the fact that chlorpromazine was effective whereas phentolamine was not requires explanation. Chlorpromazine is a less effective α-adrenergic blocking agent than is phentolamine, with much more prominent "nonadrenergic" effects on the central nervous system, and this difference suggests involvement of the latter in the observed effects.

An effect of α-adrenergic blockade on complex behavior is suggested by the report that ethoxybutamoxane or phenoxybenzamine, given locally or systemically, antagonized the feeding induced in satiated rats by the introduction of small amounts of adrenaline or noradrenaline into an area of the lateral hypothalamus, and the spontaneous food intake of fasted animals (101). Water intake by dehydrated rats and that induced in satiated animals by cholinergic substances applied to the same brain stem area were much less affected. Phenoxybenzamine placed in the ventral amygdala has also been reported to decrease food intake and increase water intake in deprived rats (102). These results suggest an involvement of α-adrenergic receptors, but several problems remain to be resolved. Phenoxybenzamine was effective 4 but not 24 hours after systemic administration of 5 mg/kg, a dose which should have provided considerable α-adrenergic blockade after 24 hours, and ethoxybutamoxane appeared to be more potent than the haloalkylamine, although the very limited information available indicates that it is a much less active α-adrenergic blocking agent. Indeed, no unequivocal evidence that it has this action has been published. It is most unfortunate for a drug to become a critical tool in complex experiments before its basic pharmacology has been established.

Blocking agents have been utilized by many workers in attempts to demonstrate an adrenergic link in the processes leading to secretion of anterior pituitary hormones in response to stimuli transmitted via the central nervous system. It is now quite clear that release of adrenocorticotropin (ACTH) is not specifically inhibited by α-adrenergic blockade (104, 199, 224), but observations on the release of gonadotropic hormone are controversial. Several relatively specific haloalkylamine blocking agents have been shown to inhibit ovulation induced in rabbits by adrenaline or noradrenaline injected into the third ventricle or by coitus, and spontaneous ovulation in rats and fowl (150, 223). A certain specificity of this effect was suggested by the fact that 2-dibenzylaminoethanol, a hydrolysis product of Dibenamine devoid of α-adrenergic blocking activity, was ineffective in doses which produced comparable central nervous system stimulation. However, several important observations are difficult to reconcile with the conclusion that ovulation is inhibited by specific α-adrenergic blockade. Phentolamine is ineffective, even when administered in very large doses, and the temporal pattern of effectiveness of the haloalkylamines does not appear to correspond to the characteristic slow onset of their blocking action. However, this is difficult to assess accurately in the absence of at least some information regarding the minimal doses required to block ovulation shortly after injection (less than 1 minute in the rabbit coital test) and after an interval commensurate with development of the full α-adrenergic blockade. A most important observation is that properly timed single injections of Dibenamine or phenoxybenzamine can prevent ovulation in rats, but do not do so during a sequence of daily injections (166), although the α-adrenergic blockade is maximal under the latter conditions. The haloalkylamines are ideally suited for experiments involving the less stressful procedure of chronic administration, and it is unfortunate that these experiments were not done much earlier in the investigation of this phenomenon and have not been extended to other experimental situations in which single injections were effective.

There is an urgent need for critical studies of the effects of α-adrenergic blocking agents on central actions of adrenaline and noradrenaline which can be measured objectively in simplified effector systems. In their absence, it is not even entirely clear how to identify central α-adrenergic blockade if it does occur in experiments on more complex systems. It may be that adrenergic receptors in the central nervous system differ from both of the well-characterized peripheral types and that it is incorrect to assess experimental results in terms of known patterns of peripheral blockade. However, peripheral blockade is the only yardstick now available, and it seems unlikely that a more accurate one will arise from observations on complex responses issuing from a "black box." It must be concluded that specific "central adrenergic blockade" involving receptors similar to peripheral α-adrenergic receptors has not yet been conclusively demonstrated. Although many "suggestive" observations have been reported, each must be assessed separately. The many apparently direct effects of α-adrenergic blocking agents on the central nervous system make it hazardous to lump these very diverse observations together under the "where there is smoke there must be fire" philosophy.

D. Metabolic Responses

Over-all metabolic responses to catecholamines are made up of many interdependent factors, including alteration of heat loss, activation of compensatory mechanisms, and interaction with hormones, particularly those of the thyroid gland. It is not surprising that reports of the effects of α-adrenergic blockade on metabolic rate are conflicting. However, it appears that blockade per se does not markedly alter the stimulation produced by either adrenaline or thyroxine (226).

The more prominent discrete metabolic responses to sympathomimetic agents include liver and skeletal muscle glycogenolysis, leading to increased blood glucose and lactate, respectively, release of free fatty acids from adipose tissue, and a transient hyperkalemia followed by a more prolonged hypokalemia. Several α-adrenergic blocking agents, particularly ergot alkaloids, inhibit adrenaline-induced hyperglycemia, but potency in this regard does not parallel blockade of other responses mediated by α-receptors, even among the ergot alkaloids (114). Ergotamine is considerably more effective than is dihydroergocornine, although the latter is a much more potent α-adrenergic blocking agent when tested on other systems, and ergonovine, which is devoid of α-adrenergic blocking activity, also inhibits adrenaline-induced hyperglycemia. Phenoxybenzamine has a relatively weak effect in rabbits and was found to be ineffective in dogs under conditions in which dichloroisoproterenol (DCI), a β-adrenergic blocking agent, effectively inhibited adrenaline-induced hyperglycemia (155). In some situations phenoxybenzamine can itself increase blood glucose or enhance adrenaline-induced hyperglycemia, probably secondary to release of endogenous catecholamines (115, 116, 189). Dihydroergotamine pretreatment has been reported to potentiate and phenoxybenzamine pretreatment to inhibit the hypoglycemia induced in rats by tolbutamide (115).

Catecholamines appear to promote liver glycogenolysis via the production of cyclic 3′,5′-AMP, and dihydroergotamine and the β-receptor blocking agent DCI can inhibit adrenaline stimulation of its production in broken cell adenyl cyclase preparations of dog liver (248). Stimulation by glucagon is unaffected. Other adrenergic blocking agents have not been tested in this system, but it is reasonable to assume that their effects would parallel those on adrenaline-induced hyperglycemia. Obviously, inhibition of liver glycogenolysis does not conform to the pattern of α-adrenergic blockade characteristic of most other effector systems, and it appears reasonable to assume that this effect is not due to α-adrenergic blockade per se.

Adrenaline-induced glycogenolysis in skeletal muscle and the resultant lactacidemia are almost completely resistant to all α-adrenergic blocking agents (177). However, adrenaline-induced lactate production by intestinal smooth muscle has been reported to be blocked by both ergotamine and ephedrine (162).

Catecholamines share with many other substances the ability to promote the release of free fatty acids from adipose tissue both *in vivo* and *in vitro*. This effect involves activation of adipose tissue lipase and, like glycogenolysis, appears to be mediated by cyclic 3′,5′-AMP. Both DCI and phentolamine have been reported to inhibit the adrenaline-induced increase in its concentration in rat epididymal fat pads (248). Similarly, Dibenamine, phenoxybenzamine, and phentolamine can block the adrenaline-evoked release of free fatty acid from rat epididymal fat pads *in vitro* (225). The accumulation of triglycerides in liver in response to stimuli such as cold and alcohol appears to involve increased production of free fatty acid in adipose tissue and can be blocked by Dibenamine, phenoxybenzamine, or ergotamine in rats (25). However, in the dog, the increase in plasma free fatty acid induced by adrenaline is inhibited by β-adrenergic blocking agents such as DCI and pronethalol (nethalide, Alderlin®), but not by phenoxybenzamine or phentolamine (77, 155). Thus, although catecholamine-induced lipolysis and release of free fatty acid from adipose tissue is somewhat more susceptible to inhibition by α-adrenergic blocking agents than is glycogenolysis in liver or skeletal muscle, this response does not appear to conform consistently to the pattern characteristic of responses mediated by α-adrenergic receptors.

Injected adrenaline evokes a transient hyperkalemia by releasing potassium from the liver (52, 61, 198, 235). This response is prevented by ergot alkaloids or Dibenamine, roughly in parallel with their inhibition of α-receptor responses of smooth muscle. It is not clear why Dibenamine should also block the hyperkalemic response to glucagon, but the inhibition of the potassium release, but not of the associated glycogenolysis and release of glucose, provides convincing evidence that the two responses are not causally related (61). Although the haloalkylamines do not alter normal blood levels of potassium, Dibenamine increases tolerance to infused potassium by increasing its apparent "volume of distribution" (122), probably as a result of increased uptake by various tissues. The mechanism involved in this effect has not been elucidated, but something more than blockade-induced increases in blood flow is probably involved.

Haloalkylamines have also been reported to inhibit the anticurare effect of adrenaline (148) and to reduce the work output and inhibit the sodium-potassium exchange associated with skeletal muscle activity (241).

E. Other Effector Systems

1. *Eye*

In his initial paper on the actions of ergot (39), Dale noted that ergot inhibited the effects of sympathetic stimulation and of adrenaline on the dog dilator pupillae. In intact cats, Dibenamine produces ptosis, extension of the nictitating membrane, and a decrease in the mydriasis induced by dim light (189). The iris is not immobilized, and the size of the pupil can still vary considerably as a result of the parasympathetic (cholinergic) innervation of the circular smooth muscle. Mydriasis, widening of the palpebral fissure, and retraction of the nictitating membrane in response to stimulation of the cervical sympathetic trunk or to adrenaline are also abolished or greatly reduced by Dibenamine or phenoxybenzamine. Miosis is one of the earliest signs of α-adrenergic blockade in man, but accommodation appears to be little affected. The radial fibers of the iris have been reported to be resistant to blockade by tolazoline and yohimbine, which do not inhibit mydriasis induced by adrenaline or by cervical sympathetic nerve stimulation in doses which reverse the pressor effect of adrenaline (33).

Dibenamine and phenoxybenzamine effectively lower the elevated intraocular pressure in some cases of glaucoma, although they have little effect on the pressure of normal eyes (34, 204). Ergot alkaloids and piperoxan have been reported to have no consistent effect (89), probably because only very limited blockade is produced by the maximal doses tolerated by man. Reduction in the intraocular pressure by α-adrenergic blockade is not dependent on the relatively mild miosis produced and can occur in the presence of a persistent mydriasis due to belladonna overdosage. The mechanism responsible for the reduced pressure has not been definitively established, but Dibenamine has been shown to reduce (46) and adrenergic stimuli to increase (75) the rate of formation of aqueous humor. Blockade of a direct effect of adrenergic stimuli on some aspect of aqueous formation may be adequate to account for the observed reduction in pressure in glaucomatous eyes, but it has also been suggested that the effect may be secondary to the relief of spasm of uveal vessels (35).

2. *Uterus*

The effect of α-adrenergic blockade on the uterus is dependent on species and hormonal factors which determine the response of this organ to adrenergic stimuli. Uterine relaxation in response to sympathomimetics is mediated by β-adrenergic receptors in all circumstances in which it has been adequately studied, and is resistant to blockade, as was noted by Dale in his early studies on ergot (39). Dibenamine can block and reverse adrenaline-induced contraction of the nonpregnant rabbit uterus, both *in vivo* and *in vitro,* but it does not prevent the inhibitory effect of adrenaline on the nonpregnant cat uterus (189). Where a response is the result of effects mediated by both types of adrenergic receptors, the gross effect of blockade will depend on the nature of the control response. If this is a contraction (predominance of α-receptor activation), adequate α-adrenergic blockade can produce a "reversal," i.e., unmask the inhibitory (β-receptor) response, but the blocking agent can only augment the response of an organ in which the net effect is already relaxant. The uteri of various species and under various hormonal conditions are stimluated by many α-adrenergic blocking agents. The ergot alkaloids are best known for this property, but it is shared by benzodioxans, imidazolines, and agents of a number of less well known groups (19, 177). These stimulant effects are due to direct actions on uterine smooth muscle unrelated to α-adrenergic blockade.

3. *Intestine*

Until recently the responses of intestinal smooth muscle to sympathomimetic agents and to adrenergic blocking agents defied classification. Intestinal relaxation in response to various members of a series of catecholamines appeared to follow more closely the pattern of α- than that of β-receptor activation (4). However, the effect is not consistently blocked by either α- or β-adrenergic blocking agents, which led some workers to give the adrenergic receptors of gastrointestinal smooth muscle a separate position in the Greek alphabet series (79). However, it has now been demonstrated that, although neither type of blocking agent prevents relaxation in response to adrenaline, complete blockade can be achieved by a combination of the two (6, 80). As would be expected, an α-adrenergic blocking agent can alone inhibit relaxation induced by a sympathomimetic substance with little effect on β-receptors, e.g., phenylephrine, and, conversely, a β-receptor blocking agent can alone antagonize the effect of a sympathomimetic agent which has little effect on α-receptors. Thus, the earlier anomalous position of this tissue appears to have been due to the presence of both α- and β-receptors, both subserving the same function, relaxation.

Dibenamine has been reported to block effectively suppression by sympathomimetic agents of the peristaltic response of isolated intestine to increased intraluminal pressure (156). The finding that nicotine stimulation is also antagonized suggests either that this effect is not due to specific α-receptor blockade, or that the receptors involved are in intramural ganglia. The latter appears to be the more likely explanation, since the effects of adrenaline on ganglia are blocked by Dibenamine (55) and by dihydroergotamine (147) in doses comparable to those required to block other responses mediated by α-adrenergic receptors.

Certain older observations on the blockade of adrenaline-induced intestinal relaxation by α-adrenergic blocking agents are difficult to explain. Indeed, the finding that this response is mediated by both α- and β-receptors (6, 80) appears to preclude its inhibition by α-adrenergic blockade alone. In addition, if such blockade did have a significant effect, it should inhibit responses to noradrenaline somewhat more than those to adrenaline, the exact opposite of the relative effectiveness reported for the ergot alkaloids (219). Agents frequently reported to inhibit adrenaline-induced relaxation of intestinal smooth muscle, ergot alkaloids, nonhalogenated phenoxyethylamines, benzodioxans, etc. (177, 219), have in common important effects on smooth muscle other than α-adrenergic blockade. However, the effect does not appear to be entirely nonspecific, since the relaxation induced by papaverine is unaffected. In addition, inhibition of relaxation by ergot alkaloids is not modified appreciably by either hexamethonium or atropine, indicating that it is not dependent on intramural ganglia or cholinergic receptors (219). It appears that the mass of confusing data on the inhibition of adrenaline-induced intestinal relaxation by certain α-adrenergic blocking agents may now be explicable on the basis of the observation of Furchgott (79) that the blockade of this response by dihydroergotamine is noncompetitive and, thus, does not directly involve specific adrenergic receptors of any type.

Like most other smooth muscle, that of the gastrointestinal tract is stimulated by the ergot alkaloids. Ergotamine increases peristaltic activity and the rate of passage of solid material along the gastrointestinal tract, and doses which are ineffective alone markedly potentiate the stimulant effect of neostigmine.

4. *Glands*

Adrenergic stimuli can induce salivary secretion, although they are much less effective than are cholinergic mechanisms. The relative potencies of several sympathomimetic amines (adrenaline > noradrenaline > synephrine > isoproterenol) suggests that the adrenergic receptors involved are similar to the α-receptors of smooth muscle (30). This is confirmed by the effects of α-adrenergic blocking agents. Ergot, tolazoline, and Dibenamine all effectively prevent secretion by the cat submaxillary gland in response to sympathetic nerve stimulation or to adrenaline (33, 39, 259).

Sweating is predominantly under cholinergic control, but adrenergic sweating does occur in certain body areas in man, particularly the hands and feet, and in some individuals it can be induced in other areas by the intracutaneous injection of a sympathomimetic amine (106, 239). It is always much less profuse than sweating induced by cholinergic stimuli. Adrenaline and noradrenaline evoke sweating considerably more effectively than does isoproterenol, indicating the involvement of α-adrenergic receptors. Dibenamine, administered either intravenously or locally by iontophoresis, effectively blocks "spontaneous" palmar and plantar sweating and the response to injected sympathomimetic agents, but not that to acetylcholine or methacholine (106, 239).

In contrast to man, sweating in the horse and in cattle is almost entirely adrenergic and, at least in the former, appears to be due to circulating catecholamines rather than to direct innervation of the glands (65, 252). However, presently available data suggest that the adrenergic receptors involved may be very different in the two species. Both adrenaline and noradrenaline can induce sweating in cattle, and this response is effectively blocked by Dibenamine (252), indicating that it is mediated by α-receptors. In the horse, adrenaline, administered either locally or intravenously, or isoproterenol causes profuse sweating, whereas noradrenaline induces piloerection, but not sweating. Dibenamine has been shown to inhibit the piloerection evoked by noradrenaline, but sweating due to adrenaline in this species is unaffected by Dibenamine, phenoxybenzamine, phentolamine, dihydroergotamine, and several other α-adrenergic blocking agents (65). Thus, sweating in the horse appears to involve β- rather than α-receptors. Unfortunately, the effects of β-adrenergic blocking agents on this response have not been reported.

Observations on sweating have added one final item to the already confusing pharmacology of tolazoline. Overdosage with this agent has been noted to induce generalized sweating in man (163). This appeared to be too profuse and generalized to be adrenergic, and seemed most likely to be an expression of the cholinergic properties of this agent. However, tolazoline also causes sweating in cattle, although their sweat glands appear to be entirely noncholinergic, sweat production being unaffected by either atropine or acetylcholine (252).

IV. THERAPEUTIC USE OF α-ADRENERGIC BLOCKADE

There is an important distinction between the therapeutic use of adrenergic blockade and the therapeutic use of an adrenergic blocking agent. As indicated in previous sections, most of the available α-adrenergic blocking agents have important actions other than blockade, and these have complicated therapeutic trials even more than they have laboratory experiments. The list of conditions in which adrenergic blocking agents have been tried is most impressive, but the majority lack any sound theoretical basis for success in either the pathological physiology of the condition treated or the pharmacology of the drug used. It is not surprising that in most cases the reproducible results were not impressive and, in spite of initial enthusiasm, interest rapidly declined.

The therapeutic objective in the use of α-adrenergic blockade per se is usually to inhibit excitatory responses of smooth muscle structures, particularly those of components of the vascular system. The situations in which such blockade can be utilized and the degree of blockade tolerated are sharply limited by the fact that efferent adrenergic pathways play a critical role in the cardiovascular reflexes which allow man to function as a biped. Consequently, the therapeutic benefits of blockade in ambulatory patients are often severely limited by the disadvantages of disrupting postural cardiovascular reflexes.

A. Pheochromocytoma

The most fully established use of α-adrenergic blocking agents is in the diagnosis of catecholamine-releasing tumors of the adrenal medulla or other chromaffin tissue. Phentolamine is the agent most commonly employed. It is usually given intravenously in a dose of 5.0 mg, and a fall in blood pressure of 35/25 mm Hg from a stable resting baseline within 3 to 4 minutes after injection usually is considered a positive diagnostic response (128, 214). The test is valid only if the drug is administered while the patient's blood pressure is elevated considerably above normal and, thus, is most useful in cases where there is sustained hypertension. False-negative results can occur, probably because of the limited, competitive nature of the α-adrenergic blockade produced by this agent, but the standard dose selected for the test is such that these are rare. They also may be caused by the concomitant administration of antihypertensive drugs. False-positive responses are much more common, and their incidence is increased in patients who are azotemic or are receiving sedatives, narcotics, or other central nervous system depressants (237). Both the direct vasodilator action of phentolamine and some blockade of sympathetic vasomotor tone may be involved in the fall in blood pressure in the absence of excess circulating catecholamines, but the former is probably the more important. Central nervous system depressants accentuate the fall in blood pressure by depressing compensatory reflexes. The phentolamine test is basically a screening procedure in which a positive response is an indication for further investigation, particularly determination of blood levels or urinary excretion of catecholamines or their metabolites. Tachycardia and transient dizziness may develop, but more serious side effects are extremely rare, and the test is commonly carried out as an office procedure.

The first α-adrenergic blocking agent to be used as a test for pheochromocytoma was piperoxan (83). If the blood pressure is elevated by the presence of excess circulating catecholamines, this agent usually causes a fall, but otherwise it increases the blood pressure in both normotensive and hypertensive subjects. Any response which is predominantly depressor is considered positive. Because of the qualitative distinction between positive and negative responses, fewer false-positive results are produced by piperoxan than by phentolamine. However, even with careful infusion the side effects of piperoxan are much more common and severe than with phentolamine, the most feared being an acute hypertensive crisis culminating in pulmonary edema or convulsions. Because of the incidence and severity of side effects, piperoxan has been largely replaced by other agents and procedures as a diagnostic test, and the drug is no longer generally available for clinical use.

Adrenergic blocking agents are also useful in the preoperative management of cases of pheochromocytoma, in the prolonged treatment of cases not amenable to surgery, and to minimize operative and postoperative complications. Oral phenoxybenzamine is probably the agent of choice in the first two situations. The drug has been shown to be capable of controlling the blood pressure for extended periods, and the stable, persistent blockade minimizes fluctuations. Such blockade may allow major improvement in the cardiovascular status of a patient prior to operation. Because responses to circulating catecholamines are blocked more readily than those to sympathetic nerve activity, only relatively small doses are required and postural hypotension is usually not a problem.

Many of the complications which contribute to the frequently stormy operative and postoperative courses of patients with pheochromocytoma can be attributed to effects of released catecholamines mediated by α-receptors (230), and blockade with phentolamine or phenoxybenzamine has been used during operation in attempts to minimize them. The former is given intravenously in divided doses or as an infusion as required during the surgical procedure, but often provides only partial control of the paroxysmal hypertension induced by catecholamines released during operative manipulation of the tumor. Because of its slow onset of action, phenoxybenzamine must be administered prior to operation, but the more complete and stable α-adrenergic blockade produced appears to offer greater protection against both operative and postoperative complications, and pretreatment may provide the additional benefit of allowing physiological adjustments, particularly in blood volume, to occur prior to the operative stress. In patients pretreated with phenoxybenzamine, the blood pressure cannot be raised postoperatively by sympathomimetic agents, but this does not appear to be a serious problem. Postoperative hypotension, which requires infusion of noradrenaline for periods of 6 to 72 hours to correct, occurs in almost all patients not receiving phenoxybenzamine (214), but it is rare or absent in patients pretreated with this drug. The fall in blood pressure appears to be predominantly a result of the inadequate plasma volume which results from periods of severe adrenergic vasoconstriction prior to and during operation rather than to a sudden decrease in circulating catecholamines per se (28, 128).

B. Essential Hypertension

Although the pathogenesis of essential (or primary) hypertension is obscure, it is unlikely that sympathoadrenal overactivity plays an important role in sustaining the elevated blood pressure. However, this has not prevented the extensive use of agents which interfere with adrenergic nerve function in the therapy of this condition, e.g., ganglionic blocking agents, antiadrenergic agents such as guanethidine, etc. Although the results obtained with these drugs are frequently far from ideal, they can lower the blood pressure, particularly the systolic pressure in the erect position, and an effective α-adrenergic blocking agent can produce a similar result (171, 207). Phenoxybenzamine administered intravenously can lower the blood pressure as much as any other agent which interferes with adrenergic vasomotor tone. The blockade is associated with much the same spectrum of side effects as is therapy with antiadrenergic agents such as guanethidine, including postural hypotension, nasal stuffiness, miosis, failure of ejaculation, and subjective lethargy and weakness. However, in contrast to the effect of antiadrenergic agents, responses mediated by β-receptors are unaffected by α-adrenergic blockade, and reflex stimulation of the myocardium may be quite disturbing, particularly when cardiovascular reflexes are called into play by postural changes, exercise, etc. Since the α-adrenergic blocking agents do not appear to have positive advantages over a drug such as guanethidine, and the most effective available agents of this class are not fully effective after oral administration, their use in the long-term, ambulatory treatment of essential hypertension has been largely abandoned.

Phenoxybenzamine is used occasionally to reduce the blood pressure in hypertensive crises, where the necessity for intravenous administration is not a serious disadvantage. Occasional cases of accelerated hypertension show a regression of sequelae, such as encephalopathy and depressed renal function, which appears to be out of proportion to the reduction in arterial blood pressure (271). This suggests that sympathetically mediated vasoconstriction may be a significant factor in some cases or at some stage of severe hypertension. Unfortunately, it is not possible at the present time to identify the cases which will respond most favorably prior to a trial of therapy.

C. Peripheral Vascular Disease

Adrenergic blocking agents have been used extensively for the treatment of peripheral vascular dysfunction, but often without due consideration of either the pathological physiology involved or the pharmacology of the drugs employed. Peripheral vascular disease can be subdivided in two different ways as a basis for assessing the possible effects of drug therapy: (*a*) the organs and tissues compromised, and (*b*) the mechanism limiting flow. The major areas involved may be skin or skeletal muscle, and, at least in the case of the former, flow may be limited by either organic structural changes, usually in larger vessels, or vasoconstriction, usually arteriolar and mediated at least in part by the sympathetic nervous system. Vasoconstriction rarely if ever is responsible for a serious deficit of blood flow to skeletal muscle, because this vascular bed is predominantly under the control of local metabolic factors, which can produce essentially maximal vasodilatation of small vessels during exercise to tolerance.

As would be expected on the basis of pathogenesis, the most favorable clinical responses to α-adrenergic blockade are in conditions in which the deleterious effects of inadequate blood flow are predominantly in the skin and in which adrenergic vasoconstriction contributes significantly to the deficiency (59, 76). Unfortunately, these represent only a small fraction of the clinically important cases of peripheral vascular disease, organic obstruction due to atherosclerosis being a much more common cause of inadequate blood flow. In Raynaud's syndrome before major trophic changes have developed, acrocyanosis and chronic chilblains, administration of an appropriate adrenergic blocking agent can produce vasodilatation, promote healing of cutaneous ulcerations, delay trophic changes, and provide effective relief of symptoms. Many patients with these conditions benefit from relatively low levels of blockade, phenoxybenzamine sometimes being effective in oral doses as low as 30 or 40 mg daily. Consequently, this highly effective agent often may be used without the complications of palpitation, postural hypotension, etc. inevitably associated with extensive blockade in ambulatory patients. Tolazoline and azapetine are also frequently employed with varying degrees of relief (93, 267). However, they must be administered much more frequently than phenoxybenzamine, and maximal tolerated doses are often required. It must be recognized that progressive organic changes can become flow-limiting even in conditions which were initially primarily "vasospastic." At this stage α-adrenergic blockade would not be expected to be beneficial. The presence of such changes may explain a number of apparently conflicting reports regarding the effects of α-adrenergic blockade in conditions such as Raynaud's syndrome.

A special case of pure adrenergic vasospasm is that induced by infusion of sympathomimetic agents such as noradrenaline. Local infiltration with 2.5–5.0 mg of phentolamine or addition of this agent to the solution of the sympathomimetic substance may prevent the ischemic skin necrosis which can result from this severe iatrogenic vasoconstriction.

The other extreme among types of peripheral vascular insufficiency is the ischemia of skeletal muscle due to organic vascular changes, which presents most frequently as intermittent claudication. Many agents can increase muscle blood flow in normal subjects at rest, but careful studies have shown that "vasodilators" are as likely to decrease as to increase muscle flow in limbs compromised by occlusive vascular disease (82). Even in those patients in whom drugs can increase skeletal muscle blood flow at rest (261), it is unlikely that they can produce a useful increase when most needed, i.e., when flow is sufficiently below the requirements of an active muscle to produce pain. No drug has been shown to raise muscle blood flow above the level induced by exercise to tolerance in either normal or atherosclerotic subjects, and the extensive evidence that local metabolic factors can readily produce maximal vasodilatation in this vascular bed argues strongly against the possibility of such an effect.

Many reports of favorable responses to therapy with α-adrenergic blocking agents and other vasodilators in intermittent claudication have appeared. However, this is a highly subjective condition, and several carefully controlled studies have demonstrated that the commonly employed vasodilators do not alter work capacity or the course of the disease more than does placebo medication (109, 261). It is of interest to note that there is a widespread tendency to treat intermittent claudication with ineffectual oral doses of relatively weak agents, a practice which at least minimizes side effects.

The reported responses to therapy with α-adrenergic blocking agents, not always attributable to α-adrenergic blockade, in vascular insufficiencies of other types are highly variable, probably owing to variations in the relative importance of occlusive and "vasospastic" components, as well as to obvious differences in the adequacy and objectivity of the observations. Few reports include a full complement of the information required for definitive conclusions. However, good therapeutic responses to adrenergic blocking agents have been reported in at least some cases of circulatory insufficiency associated with atherosclerosis, phlebitis and phlebothrombosis, thromboangiitis obliterans, trauma, peripheral emboli, causalgia, and frostbite sequelae (22, 170, 242, 264). Some benefit may be obtained even in conditions involving a major component of organic occlusion, presumably by dilatation of collateral vessels (59, 76). The major effect is on skin blood flow, and the poor healing of skin lesions associated with these conditions has been reported to be particularly favorably influenced. Vasodilatation due to α-adrenergic blockade is usually somewhat more marked in the lower than in the upper limbs. However, the response to drug therapy compares more favorably with that to sympathectomy in the latter because surgical denervation is often less satisfactory in this area.

Extensive blockade of sympathetic vasoconstriction is not practicable in ambulatory patients, both because this can be achieved only with phenoxybenzamine given intravenously and because it inevitably produces postural hypotension. In hospitalized patients with acute peripheral vascular insufficiency not amenable to surgery, maximal inhibition of sympathetic vasoconstrictor tone with intravenous phenoxybenzamine may be beneficial, even when a considerable component of mechanical obstruction is involved. However, the possibility that unequal vasodilatation in parallel beds beyond a rigid, flow-limiting obstruction may actually decrease the perfusion of some jeopardized tissues must be kept in mind. The coronary and cerebral vascular beds are not under significant sympathetic control, and α-adrenergic blocking agents appear to have no place in the therapy of coronary insufficiency or of cerebral vascular accidents.

D. Shock

Vasoconstriction, mediated by the sympathetic nervous system, is a cardinal feature of the classical shock syndrome, and can play an important etiological role in the progressive hemodynamic decompensation characteristic of this condition. Its contribution is apparent in the observations that cerebral decortication (72) or buffer nerve section (208), which increase sympathetic vasoconstrictor activity, and infusion of adrenaline (63), noradrenaline (118, 272), or other sympathomimetic amines (145) can potentiate shock due to hemorrhage, trauma, or bacterial endotoxin. Infused sympathomimetic agents can themselves induce lethal shock with hemodynamic characteristics and pathological findings comparable to those of shock due to the other factors mentioned. Conversely, many different workers have demonstrated that procedures or drugs which limit adrenergic vasoconstriction, including sympathectomy, spinal anesthesia, α-adrenergic and ganglionic blocking agents, and direct vasodilators, can significantly increase the survival rate or survival time of animals subjected to shock-inducing procedures involving trauma, hemorrhage, or bacterial endotoxin. [See Lillehei *et al.* (144), Nickerson (183), and Nickerson and Gourzis (191) for references.] The haloalkylamine adrenergic blocking agents have been most thoroughly investigated for ability to protect against various types of shock and, where direct comparison is possible, appear to be the most effective (186). Protection can be attributed to three specific effects of the α-adrenergic blockade: (*a*) increased total blood flow, particularly in the abdominal viscera, (*b*) reversal of the vasoconstriction-induced shift of fluid from the vascular to the interstitial compartment, and (*c*) local redistribution of blood flow such that a larger percentage passes through channels which readily exchange metabolites with tissue cells, presumably true capillaries.

Phenoxybenzamine is currently under investigation in the treatment of clinical shock due to hemorrhage, trauma, infection, or a combination of these factors, and the results have been very encouraging. The specific "antishock" effects mentioned above can be clearly seen in patients who have not responded to fully adequate intravascular fluid volume replacement. The most common pattern of response in an initial small fall in blood pressure, followed by gradual widening of the pulse pressure, due predominantly to an increasing systolic pressure, an increase in the mean arterial pressure, warming and increased rates of capillary filling in the extremities, and correction of oliguria. Two additional effects of α-adrenergic blockade also contribute to the practical clinical management of shock. (*a*) The sharp fall in blood pressure induced when phenoxybenzamine is administered intravenously in the presence of hypovolemia provides a quick and reliable indication of the adequacy of intravascular fluid volume replacement, a point often difficult to establish clinically or by indicator dilution techniques. (*b*) The shift of blood from the pulmonary to the systemic vascular bed associated with blockade of sympathetic vasomotor tone allows administration of larger volumes of intravenous fluids more rapidly than would otherwise be possible, particularly in patients with some myocardial inadequacy.

Any drug therapy of shock is secondary to fully adequate circulating volume replacement with blood or other appropriate fluids. Adequate volume replacement therapy is particularly important before the administration of a blocking agent such as phenoxybenzamine, because the inhibition of compensatory vasoconstriction removes much of the ability of the vasculature to adapt to hypovolemia. Because the adequacy of fluid replacement may be difficult to determine accurately prior to phenoxybenzamine administration, the blocking agent should be given slowly and suitable fluids must be immediately available for use if a sharp drop in blood pressure indicates that replacement has in fact been inadequate.

E. Other Conditions

Dibenamine has been shown to decrease right atrial and pulmonary artery pressures in patients with congestive heart failure (107, 108), and cases of pulmonary congestion and frank pulmonary edema refractory to conventional therapy have been reported to respond dramatically to the administration of adrenergic or ganglionic blocking agents (60, 265). Presumably, the therapeutic response involves a greater reduction in systemic than in pulmonary vascular tone, a consequent shift of blood to the systemic vascular bed, and a lowering of pulmonary capillary pressure. The response is quite rapid and predictable after parenteral administration of an agent such as phenoxybenzamine, and appears to warrant more extensive use, particularly in acute left heart failure.

The haloalkylamine α-adrenergic blocking agents very effectively prevent the cardiac arrhythmias which occur frequently in the deeper planes of cyclopropane anesthesia (185). However, cyclopropane is now usually given in combination with supplemental anesthetic or analgesic agents, muscle relaxants, etc., and is rarely administered in high concentration. Consequently, serious cardiac irregularities are now encountered much less frequently than previously and the prophylactic administration of an adrenergic blocking agent is rarely justified. If arrhythmias develop, the accepted practice is to replace the cyclopropane with another anesthetic agent.

The elevated intraocular pressure in some cases of glaucoma is effectively lowered by α-adrenergic blockade. The haloalkylamines appear to be considerably more effective than other blocking agents for this purpose, probably because they can produce a much more complete blockade in tolerated doses. The effect appears not to depend on the miosis produced and can occur in patients refractory to other therapy and in the presence of persistent mydriasis induced by a belladonna alkaloid (34, 35, 204). The effect of a haloalkylamine on intraocular pressure has been found useful particularly in acute glaucoma, to improve conditions for surgery or to tide a patient over a critical period. The response to more prolonged therapy has not been adequately investigated.

Phenoxybenzamine and phentolamine have been reported to reduce or abolish attacks of flushing and diarrhea in patients with the carcinoid syndrome (142). This effect may be due to blockade of 5-hydroxytryptamine (serotonin) receptors, since both agents have this ability. However, the observation that the spontaneous flushes characteristic of this condition can be mimicked more faithfully by adrenaline than by 5-hydroxytryptamine suggests that the symptoms may involve some interaction of these two amines and, consequently, that α-adrenergic blockade per se may be involved in their relief. In the limited number of cases reported, phenoxybenzamine appeared to produce more benefit and fewer severe side effects than did phentolamine.

References

1. Abel, F. L., and Murphy, Q. R., Mesenteric, renal, and iliac vascular resistance in dogs after hemorrhage. *Am. J. Physiol.* **202**, 978 (1962).
2. Acheson, G. H., Farah, A., and French, G. N., Some effects of dibenzyl-β-chlorethylamine (Dibenamine) on the mammalian heart. *J. Pharmacol. Exptl. Therap.* **97**, 455 (1949).
3. Agarwal, S. L., and Harvey, S. C., Mechanism of long duration of action of Dibenzyline. *J. Pharmacol. Exptl. Therap.* **117**, 106 (1956).
4. Ahlquist, R. P., A study of adrenotropic receptors. *Am. J. Physiol.* **153**, 586 (1948).
5. Ahlquist, R. P., Huggins, R. A., and Woodbury, R. A., Pharmacology of benzylimidazoline (Priscol). *J. Pharmacol. Exptl. Therap.* **89**, 271 (1947).
6. Ahlquist, R. P., and Levy, B., Adrenergic receptive mechanisms of canine ileum *J. Pharmacol. Exptl. Therap.* **127**, 146 (1959).

7. Aviado, D. M., The pharmacology of the pulmonary circulation. *Pharmacol. Rev.* **12,** 159 (1960).
8. Barcroft, H., Konzett, H., and Swan, H. J. C., Observations on the action of the dihydrogenated alkaloids of the ergotoxine group on the circulation in man. *J. Physiol.* (*London*) **112,** 273 (1951).
9. Barger, G., and Dale, H. H., Chemical structure and sympathomimetic action of amines. *J. Physiol.* (*London*) **41,** 19 (1910).
10. Bauereisen, E., Die Kreislaufwirkung des Benzylimidazolins (Priscol). *Arch. Exptl. Pathol. Pharmakol.* **199,** 161 (1942).
11. Bean, J. W., and Sidky, M. M., Effect of low O_2 on intestinal blood flow, tonus and motility. *Am. J. Physiol.* **189,** 541 (1957).
12. Belleau, B., Relationships between agonists, antagonists and receptor sites. *In* "Adrenergic Mechanisms" (J. R. Vane, G. E. W. Wolstenholme, and M. O'Connor, eds.), p. 223. Churchill, London; Little, Brown, Boston, Massachusetts, 1960.
13. Belleau, B., and Triggle, D. J., Blockade of adrenergic α-receptors by a carbonium ion. *J. Med. Pharm. Chem.* **5,** 636 (1962).
14. Benfey, B. G., Effect of phenoxybenzamine on vagal inhibition of the heart. *Can. J. Biochem. Physiol.* **40,** 1457 (1962).
15. Benfey, B. G., and Grillo, S. A., Antagonism of acetylcholine by adrenaline antagonists. *Brit. J. Pharmacol.* **20,** 528 (1963).
16. Bernthal, T., and Schwind, F. J., A comparison in intestine and leg of the reflex vascular response to carotid-aortic chemoreceptor stimulation. *Am. J. Physiol.* **143,** 361 (1945).
17. Bloom, F. E., Costa, E., and Salmoiraghi, G. C., Analysis of individual rabbit olfactory bulb neuron responses to the microelectrophoresis of acetylcholine, norepinephrine and serotonin synergists and antagonists. *J. Pharmacol. Exptl. Therap.* **146,** 16 (1964).
18. Bluntschli, H. J., and Goetz, R. H., The effect of ergot derivatives on the circulation in man with special reference to two new hydrogenated compounds (dihydroergotamine and dihydroergocornine). *Am. Heart J.* **35,** 873 (1948).
19. Bovet, D., and Bovet-Nitti, F., "Médicaments du Système Nerveaux Végétatif." Karger, Basel, 1948.
20. Bovet, D., and Simon, A., Recherches sur l'activité sympatholytique des dérivés de l'aminométhylbenzodioxan. *Arch. Intern. Pharmacodyn.* **55,** 15 (1937).
21. Bovet, D., Simon, A., and Depierre, F., Action centrale analgésique et sédative des aminométhylbenzodioxanes, des aminocoumaranes et des phénoxyéthylamines sympathicolytiques. *Compt. Rend. Soc. Biol.* **117,** 961 (1934).
22. Boyd, A. M., Oral Dibenyline in distal senile obliterative arteritis. *Lancet* **II,** 869 (1956).
23. Boyd, H., Burnstock, G., Campbell, G., Lowett, A., O'Shea, J., and Wood, M., The cholinergic blocking action of adrenergic blocking agents in the pharmacological analysis of autonomic innervation. *Brit. J. Pharmacol.* **20,** 418 (1963).
24. Brodie, B. B., Aronow, L., and Axelrod, J., The fate of Dibenzyline in the body and the role of fat in its duration of action. *J. Pharmacol. Exptl. Therap.* **111,** 21 (1954).
25. Brodie, B. B., Butler, W. M., Jr., Horning, M. G., Maickel, R. P., and Maling, H. M., Alcohol-induced triglyceride deposition in liver through derangement of fat transport. *Am. J. Clin. Nutr.* **9,** 432 (1961).

26. Brody, T. M., Calvert, D. N., and Schneider, A. F., Alteration of carbon tetrachloride-induced pathologic changes in the rat by spinal transection, adrenalectomy and adrenergic blocking agents. *J. Pharmacol. Exptl. Therap.* **131,** 341 (1961).

27. Brown, G. L., and Gillespie, J. S., The output of sympathetic transmitter from the spleen of the cat. *J. Physiol. (London)* **138,** 81 (1957).

28. Brunjes, S., Johns, V. J., Jr., and Crane, M. G., Postoperative shock and blood volume. *New Engl. J. Med.* **262,** 393 (1960).

29. Bucherl, E., and Schwab, M., Der Sauerstoffverbrauch des ruhenden Skeletmuskels bei reflektorisch-nervoser vasokonstriktion. *Arch. Ges. Physiol. Pfluegers* **254,** 337 (1952).

30. Burgen, A. S. V., and Emmelin, N. G., "Physiology of the Salivary Glands," p. 86. Arnold, London, 1961.

31. Calvert, D. N., and Brody, T. M., Role of the sympathetic nervous system in CCl_4 hepatotoxicity. *Am. J. Physiol.* **198,** 669 (1960).

32. Celander, O., The range of control exercised by the sympathico-adrenal system. *Acta Physiol. Scand.* **32,** Suppl. 116 (1954).

33. Chess, D., and Yonkman, F. F., Adrenolytic and sympatholytic actions of Priscol (benzyl-imidazoline). *Proc. Soc. Exptl. Biol. Med.* **61,** 127 (1946).

34. Christensen, L., and Swan, K. C., Adrenergic blocking agents in treatment of glaucoma. *Trans. Am. Acad. Ophthalmol. Otolaryngol.* **53,** 489 (1949).

35. Clark, W. B., and Duggan, J. W., The use of Dibenamine in the treatment of acute congestive glaucoma. *Am. J. Ophthalmol.* **34,** 535 (1951).

36. Cobbold, A., Folkow, B., Kjellmer, I., and Mellander, S., Nervous and local chemical control of pre-capillary sphincters in skeletal muscle as measured by changes in filtration coefficient. *Acta Physiol. Scand.* **57,** 180 (1963).

37. Cotten, M. de V., Moran, N. C., and Stopp, P. E., A comparison of the effectiveness of adrenergic blocking drugs in inhibiting the cardiac actions of sympathomimetic amines. *J. Pharmacol. Exptl. Therap.* **121,** 183 (1957).

38. Cranmer, J. I., Brann, A. W., and Bach, L. M. N., An adrenergic basis for bulbar inhibition. *Am. J. Physiol.* **197,** 835 (1959).

39. Dale, H. H., On some physiological actions of ergot. *J. Physiol. (London)* **34,** 163 (1906).

40. Daly, M. de Burgh, and Scott, M. J., An analysis of the primary cardiovascular reflex effects of stimulation of the carotid body chemoreceptors in the dog. *J. Physiol. (London)* **162,** 555 (1962).

41. Danielopolu, D., and Marcou, I., Action de l'adrénaline sur les coronaires et la circulation générale après les diéthylaminométhylbenzodioxan (883F). *Compt. Rend.* **206,** 692 (1938).

42. Davies, R. O., Cameron, W., Hollenberg, N. K., Thomson, A. E., and Nickerson, M., Hemodynamic effects of phenoxybenzamine (Dibenzyline) adrenergic blockade. *Federation Proc.* **23,** 125 (1964).

43. Dawes, G. S., Synthetic substitutes for quinidine. *Brit. J. Pharmacol.* **1,** 90 (1946).

44. Dawes, G. S., Experimental cardiac arrhythmias and quinidine-like drugs. *Pharmacol. Rev.* **4,** 43 (1952).

45. Deal, C. P., Jr., and Green, H. D., Comparison of changes in mesenteric resistance following splanchnic nerve stimulation with responses to epinephrine and norepinephrine. *Circulation Res.* **4,** 38 (1956).

46. DeLong, S. L., and Scheie, H. G., Dibenamine: an experimental and clinical study. *A.M.A. Arch. Ophthalmol.* **50**, 289 (1953).
47. Denison, A. B., Jr., Bardhanabaedye, S., and Green, H. D., Adrenergic drugs and blockade on coronary arterioles and myocardial contraction. *Circulation Res.* **4**, 653 (1956).
48. Dongen, K. van, The action of F-933 (piperidomethyl-3-benzodioxane) on fibrillation of the heart. *Arch. Intern. Pharmacodyn.* **63**, 88 (1939).
49. Dontas, A. S., and Nickerson, M., Central and peripheral components of the action of "ganglionic" blocking agents. *J. Pharmacol. Exptl. Therap.* **120**, 147 (1957).
50. Dresel, P. E., Blockade of some cardiac actions of adrenaline by dichloro-isoproterenol. *Can. J. Biochem. Physiol.* **38**, 375 (1960).
51. Dresel, P. E., MacCannell, K. L., and Nickerson, M., Cardiac arrhythmias induced by minimal doses of epinephrine in cyclopropane-anesthetized dogs. *Circulation Res.* **8**, 948 (1960).
52. Dresel, P. E., and Nickerson, M., The role of potassium in epinephrine-induced cardiac arrhythmias. *J. Pharmacol. Exptl. Therap.* **125**, 142 (1959).
53. Dresel, P. E., and Sutter, M. C., Factors modifying cyclopropane-epinephrine cardiac arrhythmias. *Circulation Res.* **9**, 1284 (1961).
54. Duff, R. S., and Ginsburg, J., Some peripheral vascular effects of intra-arterial Dibenyline in man. *Clin. Sci.* **16**, 188 (1957).
55. Eccles, R. M., and Libet, B., Origin and blockade of the synaptic responses of curarized sympathetic ganglia. *J. Physiol.* (*London*) **157**, 484 (1961).
56. Eckenhoff, J. E., Enderby, G. E., Larson, A., Davies, R., and Indevine, D. E., Human cerebral circulation during deliberate hypotension and head-up tilt. *J. Appl. Physiol.* **18**, 1130 (1963).
57. Eckstein, J. W., and Hamilton, W. K., The pressure-volume responses of human forearm veins during epinephrine and norepinephrine infusions. *J. Clin. Invest.* **36**, 1163 (1957).
58. Eckstein, R. W., Liebow, I. M., and Wiggers, C. J., Limb blood flow and vascular resistance changes in dogs during hemorrhagic hypotension and shock. *Am. J. Physiol.* **147**, 685 (1946).
59. Edwards, E. A., Varieties of digital ischemia and their management. *New Engl. J. Med.* **250**, 709 (1954).
60. Ellestad, M. H., and Olson, W. H., Use of intravenously given ganglionic blocking agents for acute pulmonary edema. *J. Am. Med. Assoc.* **161**, 49 (1956).
61. Ellis, S., Beckett, S. B., and Boutwell, J. H., Dibenamine blockade of epinephrine and glucagon hyperkalemias. *Proc. Soc. Exptl. Biol. Med.* **94**, 343 (1957).
62. Emerson, G. A., Effect of sympathicolytic and other agents on toxicity of digitalis in cats. *Proc. Soc. Exptl. Biol. Med.* **53**, 12 (1943).
63. Erlanger, J., and Gasser, H. S., Studies in secondary traumatic shock. III. Circulatory failure due to adrenalin. *Am. J. Physiol.* **49**, 345 (1919).
64. Euler, U. S. von, and Schmiterlow, G. G., The action of ergotamine on the chemical and mechanical reflexes from the carotid sinus region. *Acta Physiol. Scand.* **8**, 122 (1944).
65. Evans, C. L., and Smith, D. F. G., Sweating responses in the horse. *Proc. Roy. Soc.* (*London*) **B145**, 61 (1956).
66. Finnerty, F. A., Jr., Witkin, L., and Fazekas, J. F., Cerebral hemodynamics during cerebral ischemia induced by acute hypotension. *J. Clin. Invest.* **33**, 1227 (1954).

67. Folkow, B., Role of the nervous system in the control of vascular tone. *Circulation* **21**, 760 (1960).

68. Folkow, B., Haeger, K., and Uvnäs, B., Cholinergic vasodilator nerves in the sympathetic outflow to the muscles of the hind limbs of the cat. *Acta Physiol. Scand.* **15**, 401 (1948).

69. Ford, R. V., Moyer, J. H., and Spurr, C. L., The effect of posture and adrenergic blockade with Dibenzyline on renal hemodynamics and excretion of water and electrolytes in patients with hypertension with and without renal damage. *Am. Heart J.* **46**, 268 (1953).

70. Fourneau, E., and Bovet, D., Recherches sur l'action sympathicolytique d'un nouveau dérivé du dioxane. *Arch. Intern. Pharmacodyn.* **46**, 178 (1933).

71. Freedman, D. X., and Giarman, N. J., Apomorphine test for tranquilizing drugs: effect of Dibenamine. *Science* **124**, 264 (1956).

72. Freeman, N. E., Decrease in blood volume after prolonged hyperactivity of the sympathetic nervous system. *Am. J. Physiol.* **103**, 185 (1933).

73. Freis, E. D., Stanton, J. R., Litter, J., Culbertson, J. W., Halperin, M. H., Moister, F. C., and Wilkins, R. W., The hemodynamic effects of hypotensive drugs in man. II. Dihydroergocornine. *J. Clin. Invest.* **28**, 1387 (1949).

74. Friedberg, L., Katz, L. N., and Steinitz, F. S., The effect of drugs on the pulmonary and systemic arterial pressures in the trained unanesthetized dog. *J. Pharmacol. Exptl. Therap.* **77**, 80 (1943).

75. Friedenwald, J. S., and Buschke, W., The role of epinephrine in the formation of the intraocular fluid. *Am. J. Ophthalmol.* **24**, 1105 (1941).

76. Friend, D. G., and Edwards, E. A., Use of "Dibenzyline" as a vasodilator in patients with severe digital ischemia. *A.M.A. Arch. Internal Med.* **93**, 928 (1954).

77. Froberg, S., and Oro, L., The effects of nicotinic acid, phentolamine and nethalide on the plasma free fatty acids and the blood pressure in the dog. *Acta. Med. Scand.* **174**, 635 (1963).

78. Furchgott, R. F., Dibenamine blockade in strips of rabbit aorta and its use in differentiating receptors. *J. Pharmacol. Exptl. Therap.* **111**, 265 (1954).

79. Furchgott, R. F., The receptors for epinephrine and norepinephrine (adrenergic receptors). *Pharmacol. Rev.* **11**, 429 (1959).

80. Furchgott, R. F., Receptors for sympathomimetic amines. *In* "Adrenergic Mechanisms" (J. R. Vane, G. E. W. Wolstenholme, and M. O'Connor, eds.), p. 246. Churchill, London; Little, Brown, Boston, Massachusetts, 1960.

81. Garb, S., and Chenoweth, M. B., Studies on hydrocarbon-epinephrine induced ventricular fibrillation. *J. Pharmacol. Exptl. Therap.* **94**, 12 (1948).

82. Gillespie, J. A., The case against vasodilator drugs in occlusive vascular disease of the legs. *Lancet* **II**, 995 (1959).

83. Goldenberg, M., Snyder, C. H., and Aranow, H., Jr., New test for hypertension due to circulating epinephrine. *J. Am. Med. Assoc.* **135**, 971 (1947).

84. Goldfischer, J. D., Acute myocardial infarction secondary to ergot therapy. *New Engl. J. Med.* **262**, 860 (1960).

85. Goldstein, L., and Muñoz, C., Influence of adrenergic stimulant and blocking drugs on cerebral electrical activity in curarized animals. *J. Pharmacol. Exptl. Therap.* **132**, 345 (1961).

86. Gowdey, C. W., The change in pharmacological action produced by the introduction of a methyl group into Priscol. *Brit. J. Pharmacol.* **3**, 254 (1948).

87. Graham, J. D. P., The effect of reserpine on the pressor response to injection of 2-halogenoethylamines. *Brit. J. Pharmacol.* **16,** 77 (1961).
88. Graham, J. D. P., 2-Halogenoalkylamines. *Progr. Med. Chem.* **2,** 132 (1962).
89. Grant, W. M., Physiological and pharmacological influences upon intraocular pressure. *Pharmacol. Rev.* **7,** 143 (1955).
90. Green, H. D., Comparison in man of adrenergic blockade produced by Dibenzyline, Ilidar, Priscoline and Regitine. *Circulation* **15,** 47 (1957).
91. Green, H. D., and Denison, A. B., Jr., Absence of vasomotor responses to epinephrine and anterenol in an isolated intracranial circulation. *Circulation Res.* **4,** 565 (1956).
92. Green, H. D., Denison, A. B., Jr., Williams, W. O., Jr., Garvey, A. H., and Tabor, C. G., Comparison of the potency of Dibenzyline, Ilidar, phentolamine (Regitine) and tolazoline (Priscoline) in blocking the vasoconstrictor responses in canine muscle to lumbar sympathetic stimulation and to intra-arterial injections of *l*-epinephrine and *l*-norepinephrine. *J. Pharmacol. Exptl. Therap.* **112,** 462 (1954).
93. Green, H. D., and DuBose, H. H., Clinical trial of Ilidar, a new dibenzazepine adrenergic blocking drug, in the treatment of peripheral vascular diseases and miscellaneous complaints. *Circulation* **10,** 374 (1954).
94. Green, H. D., Hall, L. S., Sexton, J., and Deal, C. P., Autonomic vasomotor responses in the canine hepatic arterial and venous beds. *Am. J. Physiol.* **196,** 196 (1959).
95. Green, H. D., Howard, W. B., and Kenan, L. F., Autonomic control of blood flow in hind paw of dog. *Am. J. Physiol.* **187,** 469 (1956).
96. Green, H. D., and Kepchar, J. H., Control of peripheral resistance in major systemic vascular beds. *Physiol. Rev.* **39,** 617 (1959).
97. Green, H. D., MacLeod, J. A., Anderson, D. A., and Denison, A. B., Jr., Comparison of the blockade produced by Dibenzyline, Ilidar, tolazoline and phentolamine of the vasomotor responses in skin induced by sympathetic nerve stimulation with the blockade of its responses to *l*-epinephrine and *l*-norepinephrine. *J. Pharmacol. Exptl. Therap.* **112,** 218 (1954).
98. Green, H. D., Ottis, K., and Kitchen, T., Autonomic stimulation and blockade on canine splenic inflow, outflow and weight. *Am. J. Physiol.* **198,** 424 (1960).
99. Grimson, K. S., Reardon, M. J., Marzoni, F. A., and Hendrix, J. P., The effects of Priscol (2-benzyl-4,5-imidazoline HCl) on peripheral vascular diseases, hypertension and circulation in patients. *Ann. Surg.* **127,** 968 (1948).
100. Gross, F., Tripod, J., and Meier, R., Regitin (Praparat C 7227), ein neues Imidazolinderivat mit spezifischer sympathikolytischer Wirkung. *Schweiz. Med. Wochschr.* **81,** 352 (1951).
101. Grossman, S. P., Effects of adrenergic and cholinergic blocking agents on hypothalamic mechanisms. *Am. J. Physiol.* **202,** 1230 (1962).
102. Grossman, S. P., Behavioral effects of chemical stimulation of the ventral amygdala. *J. Comp. Physiol. Psychol.* **57,** 29 (1964).
103. Grover, R. F., Reeves, J. T., and Blount, S. G., Jr., Tolazoline hydrochloride (Priscoline). An effective pulmonary vasodilator. *Am. Heart J.* **61,** 5 (1961).
104. Guillemin, R., A re-evaluation of acetylcholine, adrenaline, nor-adrenaline and histamine as possible mediators of the pituitary adrenocorticotrophic activation by stress. *Endocrinology* **56,** 248 (1955).

105. Haddy, F. J., Fleishman, M., and Emanuel, D. A., Effect of epinephrine, norepinephrine and serotonin upon systemic small and large vessel resistance. *Circulation Res.* **5,** 247 (1957).

106. Haimovici, H., Evidence for adrenergic sweating in man. *J. Appl. Physiol.* **2,** 512 (1950).

107. Halmágyi, D., Felkai, B., Iványi, J., and Hetényi, G., Jr., The role of the nervous system in the maintenance of venous hypertension in heart failure. *Brit. Heart J.* **14,** 101 (1952).

108. Halmágyi, D., Felkai, B., Iványi, J., Zsótér, T., Tényi, M., and Szücs, Z., The role of the nervous system in the maintenance of pulmonary arterial hypertension in heart failure. *Brit. Heart J.* **15,** 15 (1953).

109. Hamilton, M., and Wilson, G. M., The treatment of intermittent claudication. *Quart. J. Med.* **21,** 169 (1952).

110. Handley, C. A., and Moyer, J. H., The effect of a dibenzazepine derivative (Ilidar) on renal function. *J. Pharmacol. Exptl. Therap.* **110,** 277 (1954).

111. Handley, C. A., and Moyer, J. H., Unilateral renal adrenergic blockade and the renal response to vasopressor agents and to hemorrhage. *J. Pharmacol. Exptl. Therap.* **112,** 1 (1954).

112. Handovsky, H., Sur l'effect central du diéthylaminométhyl-3-benzo-dioxane (F 883). *Compt. Rend. Soc. Biol.* **118,** 1245 (1935).

113. Harvey, S. C., and Nickerson, M., Reactions of Dibenamine and some congeners with substances of biological interest in relation to the mechanism of adrenergic blockade. *J. Pharmacol. Exptl. Therap.* **112,** 274 (1954).

114. Harvey, S. C., Wang, C.-Y., and Nickerson, M., Blockade of epinephrine-induced hyperglycemia. *J. Pharmacol. Exptl. Therap.* **104,** 363 (1952).

115. Hawkins, R. D., and Haist, R. E., The effect of adrenalectomy, dihydroergotamine, and Dibenzyline on the sensitivity of rats to tolbutamide. *Can. J. Biochem. Physiol.* **41,** 2189 (1963).

116. Hecht, H. H., and Anderson, R. B., The influence of Dibenamine (*N,N*-dibenzyl-β-chloroethyl-amine) on certain functions of the sympathetic nervous system in man. *Am. J. Med.* **3,** 3 (1947).

117. Hermann, H., and Vial, J., Sur quelques actions pharmacodynamiques du 2-benzyl-imidazoline (C. 3259). *Compt. Rend. Soc. Biol.* **136,** 803 (1942).

118. Hollenberg, N. K., The role of the sympathetic nervous system in the development of decompensation during hemorrhagic shock. Ph.D. Thesis, Univ. of Manitoba, Winnipeg, Canada, 1965.

119. Hollenberg, N. K., and Boréus, L. O., The influence of filling rate on apparent venous distensibility in man. To be published, 1967.

120. Hollenberg, N. K., and Uvnäs, B., The role of the cardiovascular response in the resistance to asphyxia of avian divers. *Acta Physiol. Scand.* **58,** 150 (1963).

121. Holmes, F., Induced hypotension in orthopaedic surgery. *J. Bone Joint Surg.* **38B,** 846 (1956).

122. Huggins, R. A., Breckenridge, C. G., and Hoff, H. E., Volume of distribution of potassium and its alteration by sympatholytic and antihistaminic drugs. *Am. J. Physiol.* **163,** 153 (1950).

123. Huggins, R. A., Morse, R. A., Handley, C. A., and La Forge, M., The protective action of various agents against chloroform-epinephrine ventricular fibrillation. *J. Pharmacol. Exptl. Therap.* **95,** 312 (1949).

124. Innes, I. R., Identification of the smooth muscle excitatory receptors for ergot alkaloids. *Brit. J. Pharmacol.* **19**, 120 (1962).

125. Innes, I. R., An action of 5-hydroxytryptamine on adrenaline receptors. *Brit. J. Pharmacol.* **19**, 427 (1962).

126. Innes, I. R., Action of dexamphetamine on 5-hydroxytryptamine receptors. *Brit. J. Pharmacol.* **21**, 427 (1963).

127. Jeffcoate, T. N. A., and Wilson, J. K., The effect of Hydergine on uterine action. *Lancet* **I**, 1187 (1955).

128. Johns, V. J., Jr., and Brunjes, S., Pheochromocytoma. *Am. J. Cardiol.* **9**, 121 (1962).

129. Johnson, H. D., Green, H. D., and Lanier, J. T., Comparison of adrenergic blocking action of Ilidar (Ro 2–3248), Regitine (C-7337) and Priscoline in the innervated saphenous arterial bed (skin exclusive of muscle) and femoral arterial bed (muscle exclusive of skin) of the anesthetized dog. *J. Pharmacol. Exptl. Therap.* **108**, 144 (1953).

130. Johnson, P. C., and Bean, J. W., Effect of sympathetic blocking agents on the toxic action of O_2 at high pressure. *Am. J. Physiol.* **188**, 593 (1957).

131. Jordan, F., and Guillet, P., Mécanisme de l'action des benzodioxanes chez le chien chloralosé. *Compt. Rend. Soc. Biol.* **136**, 807 (1942).

132. Kaplan, S. A., West, C. D., and Fomon, S. J., Effects of unilateral division of splanchnic nerve on the renal excretion of electrolytes in unanesthetized and anesthetized dogs: The mechanism of "crossed stimulation." *Am. J. Physiol.* **175**, 363 (1953).

133. Katz, L. N., and Friedberg, L., The hemodynamic effect of the dioxane derivative 933 F on trained unanesthetized normal and renal hypertensive dogs and its effect on the pressor action of renin. *Am. J. Physiol.* **127**, 29 (1939).

134. Katz, L. N., and Lindner, E., The reaction of the coronary vessels to drugs and other substances. *J. Am. Med. Assoc.* **113**, 2116 (1939).

135. Konzett, H., and Rothlin, E., Investigations on the hypotensive effect of the hydrogenated ergot alkaloids. *Brit. J. Pharmacol.* **8**, 201 (1953).

136. Korner, P. I., Renal blood flow, glomerular filtration rate, renal PAH extraction ratio, and the role of the renal vasomotor nerves in the unanesthetized rabbit. *Circulation Res.* **12**, 353 (1963).

137. Kosman, M. E., and Gerard, R. W., The effect of adrenaline on a conditioned avoidance response. *J. Comp. Physiol. Psychol.* **48**, 506 (1955).

138. Kramer, K., Renal failure in shock. *In* "Shock. Pathogenesis and Therapy" (K. D. Bock, ed.), p. 134. Springer, Berlin, 1962.

139. Lands, A. M., Luduena, F. P., Grant, J. I., Ananenko, E., and Tainter, M. L., Reversal of the depressor action of *N*-isopropylarterenol (Isuprel) by ergotamine and ergotoxine. *J. Pharmacol. Exptl. Therap.* **100**, 284 (1950).

140. Leonard, F., and Huttrer, C. P., Histamine antagonists. *Natl. Res. Council Natl. Acad. Sci. (U.S.), Chem. Biol. Coord. Center, Rev.* No. 3 (1950).

141. Leroy, G. V., Nalefski, L. A., and Christy, H. W., The effect of certain sympatholytic agents on the coronary blood flow of the dog. *J. Lab. Clin. Med.* **33**, 1496 (1948).

142. Levine, R. J., and Sjoerdsma, A., Pressor amines and the carcinoid flush. *Ann. Internal Med.* **58**, 818 (1963).

143. Liljestrand, A., Interaction of ergotamine and carbon dioxide on blood pressure and respiration. *Acta Physiol. Scand.* **15**, 198 (1948).

144. Lillehei, R. C., Longerbeam, J. K., and Rosenberg, J. C., The nature of irreversible shock: its relationship to intestinal changes. *In* "Shock. Pathogenesis and Therapy" (K. D. Bock, ed.), p. 106. Springer, Berlin, 1962.
145. Lillehie, R. C., and MacLean, L. D., Physiological approach to successful treatment of endotoxin shock in the experimental animal. *A.M.A. Arch. Surg.* **78,** 464 (1959).
146. Lum, B. K. B., and Nickerson, M., Cardiac arrhythmias induced by tolazoline (Priscoline). *J. Pharmacol. Exptl. Therap.* **116,** 156 (1956).
147. Lundberg, A., Adrenaline and transmission in the sympathetic ganglion of the cat. *Acta Physiol. Scand.* **26,** 252 (1952).
148. Maddock, W. O., Rankin, V. M., and Youmans, W. B., Prevention of the anti-curare action of epinephrine by Dibenamine. *Proc. Soc. Exptl. Biol. Med.* **67,** 151 (1948).
149. Manning, G. W., and Caudwell, G. C., The effect of Demerol, ergotamine and dihydro-ergotamine on mortality after coronary occlusion in dogs. *Brit. Heart J.* **9,** 85 (1947).
150. Markee, J. E., Everett, J. W., and Sawyer, C. H., The relationship of the nervous system to the release of gonadotrophin and the regulation of the sex cycle. *Recent Progr. Hormone Res.* **7,** 139 (1952).
151. Marrazzi, A. S., The effects of certain drugs on cerebral synapses. *Ann. N.Y. Acad. Sci.* **66,** 496 (1957).
152. Martin, W. R., Riehl, J. L., and Unna, K. R., Chlorpromazine III. The effects of chlorpromazine and chlorpromazine sulfoxide on vascular responses to *l*-epinephrine and levarterenol. *J. Pharmacol. Exptl. Therap.* **130,** 37 (1960).
153. Maxwell, M. H., Breed, E. S., and Smith, H. W., Significance of the renal juxtamedullary circulation in man. *Am. J. Med.* **9,** 216 (1950).
154. Maxwell, M. H., Gomez, D. M., Fishman, A. P., and Smith, H. W., Effects of epinephrine and typhoid vaccine on segmental vascular resistances in the human kidney. *J. Pharmacol. Exptl. Therap.* **109,** 274 (1953).
155. Mayer, S. E., Moran, N. C., and Fain, J., The effect of adrenergic blocking agents on some metabolic actions of catecholamines. *J. Pharmacol. Exptl. Therap.* **134,** 18 (1961).
156. McDougal, M. D., and West, G. B., The inhibition of the peristaltic reflex by sympathomimetic amines. *Brit. J. Pharmacol.* **9,** 131 (1954).
157. McLean, R. A., Kerwin, J. F., and Fellows, E. J., Reaction rate and oral effectiveness of certain adrenergic blocking compounds. *J. Pharmacol. Exptl. Therap.* **119,** 566 (1957).
158. McNay, J., Renal vasodilatation produced by norepinephrine after phenoxybenzamine. *Federation Proc.* **23,** 125 (1964).
159. Medinets, H. E., Kline, N. S., and Mettler, F. A., Effect of *N,N*-dibenzyl-β-chloroethylamine hydrochloride (Dibenamine) on autonomic functions and catatonia in schizophrenic subjects. *Proc. Soc. Exptl. Biol. Med.* **69,** 238 (1948).
160. Mellander, S., Comparative studies on the adrenergic neuro-hormonal control of resistance and capacitance blood vessels in the cat. *Acta Physiol. Scand.* **50,** Suppl. 176 (1960).
161. Moe, G. K., Malton, S. D., Rennick, B. R., and Freyburger, W. A., The role of arterial pressure in the induction of idioventricular rhythms under cyclopropane anesthesia. *J. Pharmacol. Exptl. Therap.* **94,** 319 (1948).

162. Mohme-Lundholm, E., The mechanism of the relaxing effect of adrenaline on smooth muscle. *Acta Physiol. Scand.* **29**, Suppl. 108 (1953).
163. Møller, E., Forgiftning med Vasodil (Priscol). Kasuistisk Meddelelse. *Nord. Med.* **33**, 610 (1947).
164. Moore, P. E., Richardson, A. W., and Green, H. D., Effects of a new dibenzazepine derivative, Ro 2–3248, 6-allyl-6,7-dihydro-5H-dibenz(c,e) azepine phosphate, upon the blood flow, the peripheral resistance and the response to injections of epinephrine of the innervated hind limb of the dog. *J. Pharmacol. Exptl. Therap.* **106**, 14 (1952).
165. Moore, R. M., and Cannon, W. B., The heart rate of unanesthetized normal, vagotomized, and sympathectomized cats as affected by atropine and ergotoxine. *Am. J. Physiol.* **94**, 201 (1930).
166. Moore, W. W., Failure of adrenergic and cholinergic blocking agents to block ovulation in the rat. *Am. J. Physiol.* **200**, 1293 (1961).
167. Moran, N. C., and Perkins, M. E., Adrenergic blockade of the mammalian heart by a dichloro analogue of isoproterenol. *J. Pharmacol. Exptl. Therap.* **124**, 223 (1958).
168. Moran, N. C., and Perkins, M. E., An evaluation of adrenergic blockade of the mammalian heart. *J. Pharmacol. Exptl. Therap.* **133**, 192 (1961).
169. Morris, L. E., Yein, C. S., Haid, B., and White, J. M., Jr., Laboratory and clinical observations on the effect of Regitine (C-7337) on cardiac irregularities during cyclopropane anesthesia. *J. Pharmacol. Exptl. Therap.* **106**, 49 (1952).
170. Moser, M., Prandoni, A. G., Orbison, J. A., and Mattingly, T. W., Clinical experience with sympathetic blocking agents in peripheral vascular disease. *Ann. Internal Med.* **38**, 1245 (1953).
171. Moser, M., Walters, M., Master, A. M., Taymor, R. C., and Metraux, J., Chemical blockade of the sympathetic nervous system in essential hypertension. *A.M.A. Arch. Internal Med.* **89**, 708 (1952).
172. Moyer, J. H., Handley, C. A., and Huggins, R. A., Cardiovascular and renal hemodynamic response to 2-(*N′p*-tolyl-*N′*-*m*-hydroxyphenylaminomethyl) imidazoline hydrochloride (Regitine). *J. Pharmacol. Exptl. Therap.* **108**, 240 (1953).
173. Moyer, J. H., Huggins, R. A., and Handley, C. A., Further cardiovascular and renal hemodynamic studies following the administration of hydrallazine (1-hydrazinophthalazine) and the effect of ganglionic blockade with hexamethonium on these responses. *J. Pharmacol. Exptl. Therap.* **109**, 175 (1953).
174. Muñoz, C., and Goldstein, L., Influence of adrenergic blocking drugs upon the EEG analeptic effect of *dl*-amphetamine in conscious unrestrained rabbits. *J. Pharmacol. Exptl. Therap.* **132**, 354 (1961).
175. Nelson, R. A., May, L. G., Bennett, A., Kobayashi, M., and Gregory, R., Comparison of the effects of pressor and depressor agents and influences on pulmonary and systemic pressures of normotensive and hypertensive subjects. *Am. Heart J.* **50**, 172 (1955).
176. Nickel, J. F., Smythe, C. McC., Papper, E. M., and Bradley, S. E., A study of the mode of action of the adrenal medullary hormones on sodium, potassium and water excretion in man. *J. Clin. Invest.* **33**, 1687 (1954).
177. Nickerson, M., The pharmacology of adrenergic blockade. *Pharmacol. Rev.* **1**, 27 (1949).

178. Nickerson, M., Interpretation of experimental results obtained with Dibenamine. *Endocrinology* **44**, 287 (1949).
179. Nickerson, M., Receptor occupancy and tissue response. *Nature* **178**, 697 (1956).
180. Nickerson, M., Nonequilibrium drug antagonism. *Pharmacol. Rev.* **9**, 246 (1957).
181. Nickerson, M., Blockade of the actions of adrenaline and noradrenaline. *Pharmacol. Rev.* **11**, 443 (1959).
182. Nickerson, M., Mechanism of the prolonged adrenergic blockade produced by haloalkylamines. *Arch. Intern. Pharmacodyn.* **140**, 237 (1962).
183. Nickerson, M., Drug therapy of shock. *In* "Shock. Pathogenesis and Therapy" (K. D. Bock, ed.), p. 356. Springer, Berlin, 1962.
184. Nickerson, M., Berghout, J., and Hammerstrom, R. N., Mechanism of acute lethal effect of epinephrine in rats. *Am. J. Physiol.* **160**, 479 (1950).
185. Nickerson, M., and Brown, H. O., Protection by Dibenamine against "spontaneous" arrhythmias occurring during cyclopropane anesthesia. *Anesthesiology*, **12**, 216 (1951).
186. Nickerson, M., and Carter, S. A., Protection against acute trauma and traumatic shock by vasodilators. *Can. J. Biochem. Physiol.* **37**, 1161 (1959).
187. Nickerson, M., and Chan, G. C.-M., Blockade of responses of isolated myocardium to epinephrine. *J. Pharmacol. Exptl. Therap.* **133**, 186 (1961).
188. Nickerson, M., and Goodman, L. S., The pharmacology of a series of new sympatholytic agents. *Proc. Am. Federation Clin. Res.* **2**, 109 (1945).
189. Nickerson, M., and Goodman, L. S., Pharmacological properties of a new adrenergic blocking agent: *N,N*-dibenzyl-β-chloroethylamine (Dibenamine). *J. Pharmacol. Exptl. Therap.* **89**, 167 (1947).
190. Nickerson, M., and Goodman, L. S., Pharmacological and physiological aspects of adrenergic blockade, with special reference to Dibenamine. *Federation Proc.* **7**, 397 (1948).
191. Nickerson, M., and Gourzis, J. T., Blockade of sympathetic vasoconstriction in the treatment of shock. *J. Trauma* **2**, 399 (1962).
192. Nickerson, M., and Gump, W. S., The chemical basis for adrenergic blocking activity in compounds related to Dibenamine. *J. Pharmacol. Exptl. Therap.* **97**, 25 (1949).
193. Nickerson, M., Henry, J. W., and Nomaguchi, G. M., Blockade of responses to epinephrine and norepinephrine by Dibenamine congeners. *J. Pharmacol. Exptl. Therap.* **107**, 300 (1953).
194. Nickerson, M., and Nomaguchi, G. M., Mechanism of Dibenamine protection against cyclopropane-epinephrine cardiac arrhythmias. *J. Pharmacol. Exptl. Therap.* **95**, 1 (1949).
195. Nickerson, M., and Nomaguchi, G. M., Adrenergic blocking action of phenoxyethyl analogues of Dibenamine. *J. Pharmacol. Exptl. Therap.* **101**, 379 (1951).
196. Nickerson, M., and Smith, S. M., Protection against cyclopropane-epinephrine arrhythmias by Dibenamine and other agents. *Anesthesiology* **10**, 562 (1949).
197. Nissell, O. I., The action of oxygen and carbon dioxide on the bronchioles and vessels of the isolated perfused lungs. *Acta Physiol. Scand.* **21**, Suppl. 73 (1950).
198. O'Brien, G. S., Eid, C. H., Murphy, Q. R., Jr., and Meek, W. J., Effect of elimination of hepatic circulation on cyclopropane-epinephrine ventricular

tachycardia and arterial plasma potassium in dogs. *J. Pharmacol. Exptl. Therap.* **112**, 374 (1954).

199. Ohler, E. A., and Sevy, R. W., Inhibition of stress induced adrenal ascorbic acid depletion by morphine, Dibenzyline and adrenal cortex extract. *Endocrinology* **59**, 347 (1956).
200. Orth, O. S., and Ritchie, G., A pharmacological evaluation of dihydroergotamine methanesulfonate (D.H.E. 45). *J. Pharmacol. Exptl. Therap.* **90**, 166 (1947).
201. Pappenheimer, J. R., and Soto-Rivera, A., Effective osmotic pressure of the plasma proteins and other quantities associated with the capillary circulation in the hind limbs of cats and dogs. *Am. J. Physiol.* **152**, 471 (1948).
202. Phillips, R. A., Dole, V. P., Hamilton, P. B., Emerson, K., Jr., Archibald, K. M., and Van Slyke, D. D., Effects of acute hemorrhagic and traumatic shock on renal function of dogs. *Am. J. Physiol.* **145**, 314 (1946).
203. Powell, C. E., and Slater, I. H., Blocking of inhibitory adrenergic receptors by a dichloro analog of isoproterenol. *J. Pharmacol. Exptl. Therap.* **122**, 480 (1958).
204. Primrose, J., Dibenzyline in glaucoma. *Brit. J. Ophthalmol.* **39**, 307 (1955).
205. Randall, L. O., and Smith, T. H. F., Adrenergic blocking action of some debenzazepine derivatives. *J. Pharmacol. Exptl. Therap.* **103**, 10 (1951).
206. Raymond-Hamet, Sur un nouveau cas d'inversion des effets adrénaliniques. *Compt. Rend.* **180**, 2074 (1925).
207. Redisch, W., Texter, E. C., Jr., Howard, R. M., Stillman, P. H., and Steele, J. M., The action of SKF 688A (phenoxyethyl derivative of Dibenamine) upon certain functions of the sympathetic nervous system in man. *Circulation* **6**, 352 (1952).
208. Remington, J. W., Hamilton, W. F., Boyd, G. H., Jr., Hamilton, W. F., Jr., and Caddell, H. M., Role of vasoconstriction in the response of the dog to hemorrhage. *Am. J. Physiol.* **161**, 116 (1950).
209. Renkin, E. M., and Rosell, S., The influence of sympathetic adrenergic vasoconstrictor nerves on transport of diffusible solutes from blood to tissues in skeletal muscle. *Acta Physiol. Scand.* **54**, 223 (1962).
210. Renkin, E. M., and Rosell, S., Effects of different types of vasodilator mechanisms on vascular tonus and on transcapillary exchange of diffusible material in skeletal muscle. *Acta Physiol. Scand.* **54**, 241 (1962).
211. Roberts, G., Richardson, A. W., and Green, H. D., Effects of Regitine (C-7337) upon the blood flow responses to epinephrine in the innervated hind limb of the dog. *J. Pharmacol. Exptl. Therap.* **105**, 466 (1952).
212. Rockwell, F. V., Dibenamine therapy in certain psychopathologic syndromes. *Psychosomat. Med.* **10**, 230 (1948).
213. Rose, J. C., and Freis, E. D., Alterations in systemic vascular volume of the dog in response to hexamethonium and norepinephrine. *Am. J. Physiol.* **191**, 383 (1957).
214. Roth, G. M., Flock, E. V., Kvale, W. F., Waugh, J. M., and Ogg, J., Pharmacologic and chemical tests as an aid in the diagnosis of pheochromocytoma. *Circulation* **21**, 769 (1960).
215. Rothballer, A. B., The effects of catecholamines on the central nervous system. *Pharmacol. Rev.* **11**, 494 (1959).

216. Rothe, C. F., Schwendenmann, F. C., and Selkurt, E. E., Neurogenic control of skeletal muscle vascular resistance in hemorrhagic shock. *Am. J. Physiol.* **204**, 925 (1963).
217. Rothlin, E., The pharmacology of the natural and dihydrogenated alkaloids of ergot. *Bull. Schweiz. Akad. Med. Wiss.* **2**, 249 (1947).
218. Rothlin, E., and Cerletti, A., Beitrag zum Problem sog. kompetitiver pharmakodynamischer Effekte. *Arch. Intern. Pharmacodyn.* **82**, 118 (1950).
219. Rothlin, E., Konzett, H., and Cerletti, A., The antagonism of ergot alkaloids towards the inhibitory response of the isolated rabbit intestine to epinephrine and norepinephrine. *J. Pharmacol. Exptl. Therap.* **112**, 185 (1954).
220. Rous, P., and Gilding, H. P., Studies of tissue maintenance. I. The changes with diminished blood bulk. *J. Exptl. Med.* **50**, 189 (1929).
221. Rudolph, A. M., Paul, M. H., Sommer, L. S., and Nadas, A. S., Effects of tolazoline hydrochloride (Priscoline) on circulatory dynamics of patients with pulmonary hypertension. *Am. Heart J.* **55**, 424 (1958).
222. Salmoiraghi, G. C., Bloom, F. E., and Costa, E., Adrenergic mechanisms in rabbit olfactory bulb. *Am. J. Physiol.* **207**, 1417 (1964).
223. Sawyer, C. H., Markee, J. E., and Everett, J. W., The mechanism by which Dibenamine blocks pituitary activation in the rabbit and rat. *Proc. Soc. Exptl. Biol. Med.* **71**, 670 (1949).
224. Sawyer, C. H., and Parkerson, G. H., Jr., Mechanisms of partial blockade of the stress response in rats by Dibenamine analogues. *Endocrinology* **52**, 346 (1953).
225. Schotz, M. C., and Page, I. H., Effect of adrenergic blocking agents on the release of free fatty acids from rat adipose tissue. *J. Lipid Res.* **1**, 466 (1960).
226. Schwartz, N. B., Effect of Dibenzyline on the metabolic actions of epinephrine and thyroxine. *Am. J. Physiol.* **203**, 525 (1962).
227. Seed, J. C., and McKay, E. A., Inhibition by piperidinomethyl-3-benzodioxane (933F) of epinephrine vasopressor blockade produced by dibenzyl-β-chlorethylamine. *Proc. Soc. Exptl. Biol. Med.* **70**, 724 (1949).
228. Selkurt, E. E., Renal blood flow and renal clearance during hemorrhagic shock. *Am. J. Physiol.* **145**, 699 (1946).
229. Selkurt, E. E., Renal blood flow and renal clearances during hemorrhage and hemorrhagic shock. *In* "Shock. Pathogenesis and Therapy" (K. D. Bock, ed.), p. 145. Springer, Berlin, 1962.
230. Seward, E. H., Death from phaeochromocytoma. *Lancet* **II**, 903 (1961).
231. Shadle, O. W., Moore, J. C., and Billig, D. M., Effect of *l*-arterenol infusion on "central blood volume" in the dog. *Circulation Res.* **3**, 385 (1955).
232. Sharpey-Schafer, E. P., Venous tone effects of reflex changes, humoral agents and exercise. *Brit. Med. Bull.* **19**, 145 (1963).
233. Sharpey-Schafer, E. P., and Ginsburg, J., Humoral agents and venous tone. Effects of catecholamines, 5-hydroxytryptamine, histamine, and nitrites. *Lancet* **II**, 1337 (1962).
234. Shemano, I., and Nickerson, M., Effect of ambient temperature on thermal responses to drugs. *Can. J. Biochem. Physiol.* **36**, 1243 (1958).
235. Siebens, A. A., Hoffman, B. F., Enson, Y., Farrel, J. E., and Brooks, C. McC., Effects of *l*-epinephrine and *l*-norepinephrine on cardiac excitability. *Am. J. Physiol.* **175**, 1 (1953).

236. Slater, I. H., and Jones, G. T., Pharmacologic properties of ethoxybutamoxane and related compounds. *J. Pharmacol. Exptl. Therap.* **122**, 69A (1958).
237. Soffer, A., Regitine and Benodaine in the diagnosis of pheochromocytoma. *Med. Clin. N. Am.* **38**, 375 (1954).
238. Sokoloff, L., The action of drugs on the cerebral circulation. *Pharmacol. Rev.* **11**, 1 (1959).
239. Sonnenschein, R. R., Local sweating in man induced by intradermal epinephrine. *Proc. Soc. Exptl. Biol. Med.* **71**, 654 (1949).
240. Spencer, M. P., Denison, A. B., Jr., and Green, H. D., The direct renal vascular effects of epinephrine and norepinephrine before and after adrenergic blockade. *Circulation Res.* **2**, 537 (1954).
241. Sréter, F. A., and Friedman, S. M., Effect of adrenergic blocking agents on running ability in the rat. *Am. J. Physiol.* **197**, 478 (1959).
242. Stallworth, J. M., Lee, W. H., Belisle, C., and Nunn, D. B., A clinical and laboratory comparison of the effects of commonly used vasodilator drugs on arterial diseases. *Am. Surgeon* **24**, 700 (1958).
243. Stephenson, R. P., A modification of receptor theory. *Brit. J. Pharmacol.* **11**, 379 (1956).
244. Stern, P. A., and Brody, T. M., Catecholamine excretion following carbon tetrachloride administration. *J. Pharmacol. Exptl. Therap.* **141**, 65 (1963).
245. Stoll, A., and Hofmann, A., Die Alkaloide der Ergotoxingruppe: Ergocristin, Ergokryptin und Ergocornin. *Helv. Chim. Acta* **26**, 1570 (1943).
246. Stoll, A., and Hofmann, A., Die Dihydroderivate der natürlichen linksdrehenden Mutterkornalkaloids. *Helv. Chim. Acta* **26**, 2070 (1943).
247. Study, R. S., and Shipley, R. E., Comparison of direct with indirect renal blood flow, extraction of inulin and diodrast, before and during acute renal nerve stimulation. *Am. J. Physiol.* **163**, 442 (1950).
248. Sutherland, E. W., Øye, I., and Butcher, R. W., The action of epinephrine and the role of the adenyl cyclase system in hormone action. *Recent Progr. Hormone Res.* **21**, 623 (1965).
249. Sutter, M. C., Noradrenaline—Its role in producing and protecting against shock. Ph.D. Thesis, Univ. of Manitoba, Winnipeg, Canada, 1963.
250. Sutton, G. C., Cerletti, A., and Taeschler, M., Comparative analysis of the effect of hydrogenated ergot alkaloids upon presso- and chemo-receptive reflexes in the cat. *Arch. Intern. Pharmacodyn.* **84**, 393 (1950).
251. Szentiványi, M., and Juhász Nagy, A., A new aspect of the nervous control of the coronary blood vessels. *Quart. J. Exptl. Physiol.* **44**, 67 (1959).
252. Taneja, G. C., Adrenergic sweating in cattle. *Nature* **177**, 482 (1956).
253. Thiele, W., Priscol, ein neues Mittel für die Magendiagnostik. *Klin. Wochschr.* **19**, 620 (1940).
254. Tillgren, N., Treatment of headache with dihydroergotamine tartrate. *Acta Med. Scand.* **128**, Suppl. 196, 222 (1947).
255. Tripod, J., Beeinflussung der zentral-erregenden Wirkung von Weckaminen durch Pharmaka mit spezifischer Wirkung auf das autonome Nervensystem. *Helv. Physiol. Pharmacol. Acta* **10**, 403 (1952).
256. Trueta, J., Barclay, A. E., Daniel, P. M., Franklin, K. J., and Prichard, M. M. L., "Studies of the Renal Circulation." Thomas, Springfield, Illinois, 1947.
257. Ullman, T. D., and Stein, J. A., The effect of benzazoline (2-benzyl-4,5-imidazoline hydrochloride) (Priscoline) on renal function in hypertensive man. *Angiology* **6**, 37 (1955).

258. Ullyot, G. E., and Kerwin, J. F., β-Haloethylamine adrenergic blocking agents. *In* "Medicinal Chemistry" (F. F. Blicke and C. M. Sutter, eds.), Vol. 2, p. 234. Wiley, New York, 1956.
259. Uvnäs, B., Action of *n,n*-dibenzyl-chloroethylamine (Dibenamine) on the effect of sympathetic secretory impulses to the submaxillary gland of the cat. *Acta Physiol. Scand.* **15,** 362 (1948).
260. Vleeschhouwer, G. de, Au sujet de l'action du diéthylaminométhyl-3-benzodioxane (F. 883) et du pipéridométhyl-3-benzodioxane (F. 933) sur le système circulatoire. *Arch. Intern. Pharmacodyn.* **50,** 251 (1935).
261. Walder, D. N., Dilatal in the treatment of intermittent claudication in the calf muscles. *Lancet* **I,** 257 (1956).
262. Walters, P. A., Jr., Cooper, T. W., Denison, A. B., Jr., and Green, H. D., Dilator responses to isoproterenol in cutaneous and skeletal muscle vascular beds; effects of adrenergic blocking drugs. *J. Pharmacol. Exptl. Therap.* **115,** 323 (1955).
263. Waltz, D. T., Koppanyi, T., and Maengwyn-Davies, G. D., Isoproterenol vasomotor reversal by sympathomimetic amines. *J. Pharmacol. Exptl. Therap.* **129,** 200 (1960).
264. Wertheimer, L., Redisch, W., and Steele, J. M., Effects of an adrenergic blocking agent (Dibenzyline) upon clinical manifestations of arterial insufficiency in the extremities. *Circulation* **10,** 366 (1954).
265. Wheatley, D., Relief of acute left ventricular failure by "Priscol." *Brit. Med. J.* **I,** 1174 (1952).
266. Williams, F. L., and Rodbard, S., Increased circulating plasma volume following phenoxybenzamine (Dibenzyline). *Am. J. Physiol.* **198,** 169 (1960).
267. Winsor, T., and Hyman, C., Clinical pharmacology of vasodilating drugs. *Clin. Pharmacol. Therap.* **2,** 636 (1961).
268. Witham, A. C., and Fleming, J. W., The effect of epinephrine on the pulmonary circulation in man. *J. Clin. Invest.* **30,** 707 (1951).
269. Woodward, D. J., Hoobler, S. W., and Nickerson, M., Effect of Dibenzyline (SKF 688A) on peripheral blood flow in man. *Federation Proc.* **11,** 404 (1952).
270. Wright, S., Studies of reflex activity in involuntary nervous system. II. Action of ergotamine on vasomotor reflexes. *J. Physiol. (London)* **69,** 331 (1930).
271. Wunsch, R. E., Warnke, R. D., and Myers, G. B., The effects of Dibenamine on severe hypertension. *Ann. Internal Med.* **33,** 613 (1950).
272. Yard, A. C., and Nickerson, M., Shock produced in dogs by infusions of norepinephrine. *Federation Proc.* **15,** 502 (1956).

B. Blockade of β-Adrenergic Receptors

Hsueh-hwa Wang

Department of Pharmacology, College of Physicians and Surgeons, Columbia University, New York, New York

I. Introduction 307
II. Direct Effects of β-Receptor Blocking Compounds 310
III. Specificity of β-Receptor Blockade 311
IV. Effects of Catecholamines on Physiological Systems after β-Receptor Blockade 312
A. The Cardiovascular System 312
B. The Lung 314
C. The Kidney 315
D. The Intestine 315
E. The Uterus 316
F. Metabolic Effects 316
V. The Antiarrhythmic Action of β-Receptor Blocking Compounds 319
VI. Application of β-Receptor Blocking Compounds 322
A. Pharmacological Studies 322
B. Clinical Findings 323
References 324

I. INTRODUCTION

The concept of dual adrenergic receptor mechanisms was originated by Ahlquist in 1948 (3). Ahlquist postulated that there are two fundamental types of adrenergic receptors which he termed α and β. The α-receptors are concerned with most of the excitatory functions of the adrenergic system and one important inhibitory function, that of intestinal relaxation. The β-receptors, on the other hand, are concerned with most of the inhibitory functions of the adrenergic system plus one important excitatory one, that of myocardial stimulation. "Classical" adrenergic blocking drugs such as Dibenamine® block only the responses of α-receptors. A drug which selectively blocked the response of β-receptors was not available until dichloroisoproterenol (DCI) was described by Powell and Slater in 1958 (79); Ahlquist's concept received strong support from the observations of the pharmacological effects of this agent.

Since the introduction of DCI, a number of analogs of isoproterenol, as well as several other compounds with entirely different chemical structures, were also reported to have β-receptor blocking action. In order to ascertain the β-receptor blocking activity of a compound, Levy and Ahlquist (53) proposed a few criteria for a simple screening test. These criteria call for the ability of the drug (*a*) to convert the effect of ethylnorepinephrine (ENE) from a depressor to a pressor response; and (*b*) to reduce, but not reverse, the depressor response of isoproterenol.

The rationale for the first criterion is based on the fact that ENE can activate both α- and β-receptors. Unlike epinephrine, ENE usually produces a depressor response only because its β-receptor stimulating action predominates. Blocking of the β-receptor effect would unmask the action of ENE on α-receptors and a pressor response, or "ENE reversal," would ensue. "ENE reversal" alone is considered conclusive evidence of β-receptor blockade if the drug in question is not itself a vasoconstricting agent. According to the authors, vasoconstricting agents, such as phenylephrine, can induce ENE reversal by causing a sustained state of vasoconstriction in the peripheral vascular beds, thus masking the β-receptor response to ENE.

The rationale for the second criterion is self-evident. A β-receptor blocking compound is expected to inhibit both the cardiac and the vascular effects of isoproterenol, thereby reducing or abolishing the latter's depressor action. A vasoconstricting agent may mask the depressor effect of isoproterenol but will not modify its cardiac effects; consequently isoproterenol administration results in a paradoxical pressor response.

Thus, it can be seen that, although the two prominent manifestations of β-receptor activation, i.e., the positive inotropic and chronotropic effects, are not used by Ahlquist and Levy to evaluate β-receptor blockade, a β-receptor blocking compound must nevertheless inhibit these two actions in order to satisfy their second criterion. Antagonism of the positive inotropic and/or chronotropic action of isoproterenol is adequate evidence of β-receptor blockade without resorting to the use of Ahlquist and Levy's criteria.

In a subsequent communication, Levy and Ahlquist (54) used a few additional criteria to determine whether a drug has α-, β-, or both α- and β-receptor blocking action. A compound which has both α- and β-receptor blocking actions should modify the pressor and femoral vasoconstrictor responses to phenylephrine and epinephrine (α), the positive chronotropic response to isoproterenol (β), and the intestinal inhibitory response to epinephrine (α and β). By these criteria it was shown that several α-receptor blocking compounds also possess weak β-receptor blocking activity. These included dihydroergotamine, dihydroergocornine, and methoxyphenamine. When the same criteria were employed, isoprophenamine HCl (1-*o*-chlorophenyl-2-isopropylaminoethanol HCl hydrate), the dichloro-analogs of epinephrine and of norepinephrine and a number of chloro- and fluoro-analogs of isoproterenol were also shown to have β-receptor blocking activity, but none of these agents was as potent as dichloroisoproterenol (DCI) (54).

In 1962, pronethalol,[1] another isoproterenol analog with potent β-receptor blocking activity, was introduced by Black and Stephenson in England (10). In early 1964 a number of additional β-receptor blocking compounds came upon the scene. These included two derivatives of methane sulfonanilide (23) and four methyl-substituted *N*-isopropylphenylethanolamines (98). Upon preliminary evaluation, these compounds seem to satisfy the criteria for β-receptor blockade, but detailed studies have yet to be made. The present discussion is therefore limited to two potent β-receptor blocking compounds, DCI and pronethalol, both of which have been studied extensively.

Dichloroisoproterenol [1-(3,4,dichlorophenyl)-2-isopropylaminoethanol], and pronethalol [nethalide, Alderlin®, 2-isopropylamino-1-(2-naphthyl)ethanol] are, respectively, the dichloro- and naphthyl-analogs of isoproterenol.

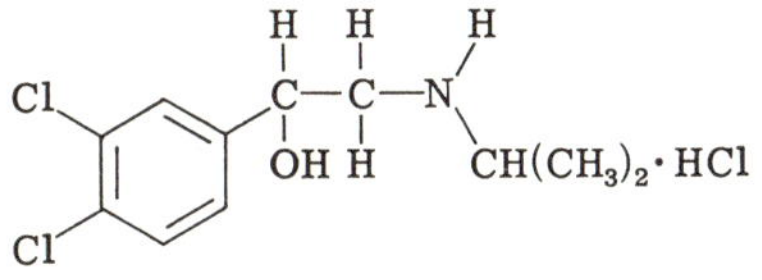

Dichloroisoproterenol
(DCI)

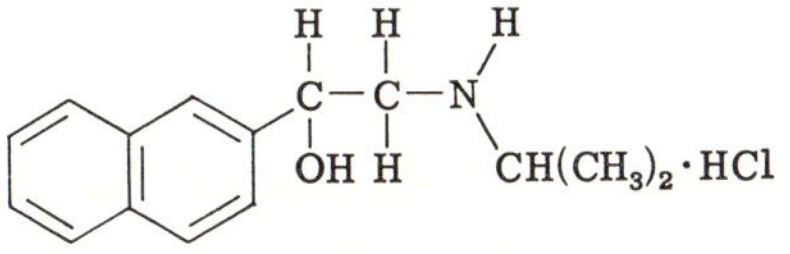

Pronethalol

When the alcoholic hydroxyl group on the β carbon is substituted by a chlorine atom, the resulting compound produces only α-receptor blockade (54). The isopropyl moiety on the N-atom appears to enhance the potency and duration of action of the compound, since the di-

[1] Pronethalol formerly possessed the generic name of nethalide.

chloro-analogs of both epinephrine and norepinephrine are much weaker β-receptor blocking compounds than DCI.

Chronic toxicity tests have been carried out extensively with pronethalol because of its projected clinical use. Although pronethalol, like DCI, when administered intravenously can cause cardiac depression and hypertension, oral administration of a full blocking dose for β-receptors results in no appreciable hemodynamic alterations and remarkably few adverse physiological consequences. However, despite its apparent low toxicity and wide margin of safety, the clinical trial of pronethalol was interrupted because of the discovery that chronic administration of this drug to mice can result in the development of malignant tumors (76). Chronic usage of β-receptor blocking drugs must await the results of studies of the toxicity of newly introduced compounds.

II. DIRECT EFFECTS OF β-RECEPTOR BLOCKING COMPOUNDS

Discussion of the direct effects of these compounds will be limited to their cardiovascular actions since, after the administration of DCI or pronethalol, important changes have been noted almost exclusively in the cardiovascular system.

DCI has intrinsic sympathomimetic properties. Small intravenous doses (0.25–2 mg/kg) given to an anesthetized dog produce tachycardia, a positive inotropic effect, and a slight to moderate decrease in arterial pressure (68). These effects are qualitatively very similar to those of isoproterenol, but the effect of DCI is much weaker and lasts longer. The depressor response after a single intravenous injection of DCI lasts for about 15 minutes, while the cardiac effect persists for more than 1 hour. The dosage of DCI which produces cardiac stimulation overlaps with the dose range which produces partial β-receptor blockade. The persistent change in heart rate and myocardial contractile force caused by DCI often makes the evaluation of blockade difficult. On the other hand, pronethalol has no appreciable intrinsic sympathomimetic activity (10) and is therefore a more desirable compound for either pharmacologic evaluation or possible therapeutic applications.

Higher doses of DCI (2 mg/kg or more), as well as blocking doses of pronethalol (2.5 mg/kg or more), decrease heart rate, myocardial contractile force, and arterial pressure (10, 19, 68). These effects are dose related and are not influenced by vagotomy or atropine. They can be very pronounced following rapid intravenous injection, but are less apparent when a similar dose is given as a slow intravenous infusion. Bradycardia after pronethalol had been attributed to blockade of tonic sympathetic impulses to the heart (10). However, these depressant effects must be partly due to an inherent depressant action of both DCI and pronethalol because similar effects can be demonstrated with isolated, perfused atria and papillary muscles (10, 29), with dog heart-lung preparations (29), and upon direct perfusion of the sinus node (45, 46).

Interestingly, DCI and pronethalol have also been shown to block cardiac inhibition resulting from vagal stimulation (45, 46). This atropine-like effect can be demonstrated with doses of pronethalol which produce adrenergic blockade, but higher concentrations of DCI are required to produce it than are necessary to block the effects of adrenergic stimuli. In the balance, the negative chronotropic effect appears to be predominant and bradycardia usually results despite demonstrable cholinergic blockade.

Hypotension following DCI or pronethalol administration is most probably due to the direct relaxant effect of these compounds on vascular smooth muscle. In anesthetized animals a progressive decline of arterial blood pressure, associated with a decrease in peripheral resistance, can occur even with slow intravenous infusions, indicating peripheral vasodilation (10, 17, 68). A direct vasodilating effect was also shown when these compounds were given intra-arterially (19, 79). In unanesthetized human subjects, arterial blood pressure changes very little following slow intravenous infusion or oral administration of pronethalol (19, 38); the direct vasodilating action of pronethalol is apparently counterbalanced by the presence of high sympathetic tone in the conscious state.

Cardiac output decreases, often markedly, after rapid intravenous injections of DCI or pronethalol. However, when pronethalol is administered slowly by vein, cardiac output remains essentially unchanged (10, 19, 38), or may even be increased (17). With rapid intravenous injection, the decrease in myocardial contractile force and venous pooling resulting from the concomitant decrease in arterial blood pressure can account for the fall in cardiac output. With slow intravenous infusion, the myocardial depressant effect of pronethalol is minimal (10) and an increase in stroke volume compensates for the bradycardia, maintaining cardiac output in the face of slight peripheral vasodilation. It is not known, however, whether pronethalol exerts any action on the venules to affect venous return to the heart.

III. SPECIFICITY OF β-RECEPTOR BLOCKADE

The blockade by DCI and pronethalol of the effect of adrenergic stimuli on β-receptors is generally assumed to be the result of competitive inhibition at the receptor level. Recent studies using tritium-labeled compounds have furnished evidence to substantiate this belief. Graded doses of norepinephrine were shown to cause the release of bound DCI, also in a graded fashion, from isolated perfused rat heart (103). In addition, DCI and pronethalol did not affect either the release of norepinephrine from sympathetic nerve endings upon cardiac sympathetic nerve stimulation or the uptake and metabolism of norepinephrine by myocardial cells (37, 43).

The blockade of β-receptor responses appears to be a specific phenomenon. This is best demonstrated in the heart. The positive inotropic and chronotropic responses elicited by adrenergic stimuli can no longer be demonstrated after DCI or pronethalol administration (10, 68) but are not modified by "classical" α-receptor blocking compounds (69, 73). In addition, DCI and pronethalol do not block either the positive inotropic effects of digitalis glycosides, calcium chloride, and theophylline, or the positive chronotropic effect of theophylline (66, 68).

Sutherland and Rall (80, 94) have demonstrated that an increase in phosphorylase activation is caused by catecholamines, thus providing some insights into the cellular effects of catecholamines. Later, Mayer and Moran (60) showed that the positive inotropic effects produced by epinephrine, norepinephrine, and cardiac sympathetic stimulation was accompanied by an augmentation of the activity of myocardial glycogen phosphorylase. This increase in phosphorylase activity, as well as the positive inotropic effects of catecholamines, are blocked by DCI. On the other hand, no significant increase in phosphorylase activity was found to accompany the positive inotropic effects of digitalis glycosides, calcium chloride, or theophylline. These data further strengthen the belief that β-adrenergic blockade is specific for the effects of adrenergic stimuli. This specificity has led to the increasing use of β-receptor blocking compounds as pharmacological tools.

IV. EFFECTS OF CATECHOLAMINES ON PHYSIOLOGICAL SYSTEMS AFTER β-RECEPTOR BLOCKADE

A. The Cardiovascular System

1. *Hemodynamics*

After a full blocking dose of DCI or pronethalol, the usual cardiac acceleration and increase in myocardial contractile force resulting from either catecholamine administration or cardiac sympathetic nerve stimulation are largely or completely abolished (10, 17, 68). The depressor response of isoproterenol can no longer be elicited. The pressor response to epinephrine is potentiated because the depressor component is eliminated, whereas the pressor response to norepinephrine and carotid occlusion is essentially unaffected. Venodilation ordinarily produced by isoproterenol is also blocked (1).

After β-receptor blockade, it would be of interest to know whether the heart could increase or maintain its output in the face of a rising arterial pressure produced by an increase in circulating catecholamines. Unfortunately, there are few data regarding cardiac output during catecholamine infusions and after β-receptor blockade, and the results of different studies are not in complete accord. Using continuous recording techniques in the dog, Black and Stephenson (10) and Wang and Blumenthal (unpublished data) found cardiac output after β-receptor blockade and during infusions of epinephrine or norepinephrine to be increased, but Hegglin *et al.* (42) found it to be essentially unchanged. Using the dye-dilution technique Donald *et al.* (17) reported a decrease of both stroke and minute volumes under similar conditions. Difference in experimental method may, in part, explain the discrepancies in these results. In man, measurements of cardiac output in response to an increase in circulating catecholamines after β-receptor blockade are not yet available.

2. *Coronary Blood Vessels*

Coronary blood flow invariably increases after cardiac sympathetic nerve stimulation or intracoronary injections of norepinephrine, epinephrine, or isoproterenol. However, the increase in flow is always associated with a simultaneous increase in myocardial contractile force and metabolism. It is therefore difficult to ascertain whether adrenergic stimuli primarily cause coronary dilation, have no effect on the coronary vessels *per se*, or cause coronary constriction which is masked by the potent simultaneous metabolic vasodilator effect. The bulk of the evidence reported recently seems to favor the last possibility. Hashimoto *et al.* (40) correlated myocardial oxygen consumption and coronary blood flow changes in isolated, fibrillating dog hearts and found that norepinephrine and epinephrine increased myocardial oxygen consumption to a greater extent than coronary blood flow, whereas isoproterenol increased both proportionally. Using continuous blood flow recording techniques, an initial, transient decrease in coronary blood flow preceding the prolonged and marked increase had been demonstrated after epinephrine or norepinephrine administration or cardiac sympathetic nerve stimulation in the dog (9, 34). Definitive evidence was finally obtained with the introduction of β-receptor blocking compounds. After DCI administration, intra-arterial injections of epinephrine or norepinephrine

(40), and sympathetic nerve stimulation (6, 89) elicited coronary vasoconstriction, while intra-arterial injection of isoproterenol caused no change in coronary blood flow (40). Thus blockade of the positive inotropic effect of adrenergic compounds eliminates the secondary metabolic factor leading to coronary vasodilation and unmasks the vasoconstricting action of these compounds. It should be emphasized, however, that after β-receptor blockade the coronary vasoconstriction induced by norepinephrine, epinephrine (Wang and Blumenthal, unpublished data), or cardiac sympathetic nerve stimulation (89) is of very small magnitude. Therefore it is doubtful that tonic sympathetic impulses exert any significant influence on the vasomotor control of coronary vessels because the simultaneous metabolic dilator effect of adrenergic stimuli appears to be potent and overwhelming.

On the other hand, the result of intravenous epinephrine or norepinephrine administration after β-receptor blockade is an increase in coronary blood flow (Wang and Blumenthal, unpublished data). The rise in arterial blood pressure accounts for this increase through an increase both in perfusion pressure and in the work of the heart. It is interesting to note that, with the increase in coronary blood flow, the coronary oxygen A-V difference remains essentially unchanged (Wang and Blumenthal, unpublished data). The increase in coronary blood flow is apparently adequate to meet the metabolic needs of the heart without the need for an increase in oxygen extraction. The minor role of the direct vasoconstrictor action of adrenergic stimuli on coronary vessels is again not demonstrated.

B. The Lung

1. *Bronchial Smooth Muscle*

The inhibitory, or relaxant, effects of epinephrine and isoproterenol on bronchial smooth muscle can be completely blocked by DCI or pronethalol in the isolated guinea pig tracheal chain (10, 79). In the dog, isoproterenol had no effect on bronchomotor tone after DCI administration, whereas administration of epinephrine or norepinephrine and postganglionic sympathetic nerve stimulation all resulted in bronchoconstriction. This bronchoconstriction was probably the result of α-receptor activation, since it could be blocked by tolazoline (14). It appears that, although bronchial smooth muscle is primarily innervated by adrenergic β-receptors as Ahlquist (3) originally proposed, the presence of α-receptors can be unmasked in the dog by the use of β-receptor blocking compounds.

2. *Pulmonary Blood Vessels*

An increase in pulmonary vascular resistance, or vasoconstriction, is always seen after intra-arterial administration of epinephrine or norepinephrine, or postganglionic sympathetic nerve stimulation. This response was shown by Castro de la Mata *et al.* (14) to be unaffected by DCI while the pulmonary vasodilation induced by isoproterenol was blocked. These authors concluded therefore that the pulmonary vessels contain both α- and β-receptors, predominantly the former. However, since the decrease in pulmonary vascular resistance to isoproterenol may be secondary to its potent bronchodilator action, these data have not provided evidence conclusively demonstrating the presence of β-receptors in the pulmonary vessels.

C. The Kidney

The effects of catecholamines on renal functions have been extensively studied, but to date there is no agreement as to whether the observed changes are (*a*) the direct effects of catecholamines on renal tubules; (*b*) secondary to vascular changes, or (*c*) reflexly mediated. The following brief account is limited to those renal effects of epinephrine and isoproterenol which can be modified by β-receptor blocking compounds. In the rat, Botting *et al.* (12) demonstrated that doses of isoproterenol and epinephrine, too small to affect glomerular filtration rate or renal plasma flow, do cause antidiuresis and sodium retention, and that isoproterenol is approximately 5–10 times more potent than epinephrine in this respect, thus suggesting the presence of β-receptors in the renal tubules. However, a report from the same laboratory (51) showed that DCI does not inhibit either renal effect of isoproterenol, whereas pronethalol does block the sodium retention but not the antidiuretic effect. The interpretation of these data is complicated by the fact that both DCI and pronethalol themselves cause changes in water and electrolyte excretion similar to those of isoproterenol (51). It should also be pointed out that these studies were carried out in rats and may not pertain to dogs or human beings, since aspects of renal function are known to vary not only quantitatively, but also directionally in different species.

D. The Intestine

The response of the smooth muscle of the gastrointestinal tract to sympathomimetic amines is unique, in that relaxation is induced by both α- and β-receptor activating amines in all species. With the introduction of DCI, Ahlquist and Levy (5) confirmed the earlier concept (3) that the intestine contains α- and β-adrenergic receptors, both subserving relaxation, or inhibition. The inhibitory action of isoproterenol, but not that of norepinephrine or phenylephrine, is blocked by DCI or pronethalol; that of epinephrine is not blocked by α- or β-receptor blocking drugs alone, but only by a combination of the two (5, 52, 58).

E. The Uterus

The response of uterine muscle to sympathomimetic amines is notably variable. Ahlquist (3) originally classified the uterus as containing both α- and β-adrenergic receptors, subserving contraction and relaxation, respectively. However, an inhibitor response was found to be produced by both phenylephrine and isoproterenol in the rat uterus, and Rudzik and Miller (83) proposed that the α- and β-receptors in this species both subserve relaxation, as in the case of the smooth muscle of the intestine. This concept was tested by Tozzi and Levy (96), using perfused rat uterine segments. The inhibitory action of epinephrine, phenylephrine, isoproterenol, or ENE was shown to be blocked by DCI or pronethalol but was not affected by α-receptor blocking compounds. It therefore appears that, unlike relaxation of the smooth muscle of the intestine, the relaxation of uterine muscle is brought about only through the activation of β-receptors.

F. Metabolic Effects

Epinephrine is by far the most potent catecholamine in eliciting metabolic changes. Three of the major metabolic effects of epinephrine, i.e., the effect on K^+ release from liver cells, the effect on carbohydrate metabolism or glycogenolysis, and the effect on lipid metabolism or free fatty acid release, have been studied extensively before and after the administration of various adrenergic blocking drugs. The epinephrine-induced hyperkalemia is essentially an α-receptor response, since it is also induced by norepinephrine but not by isoproterenol and can be effectively inhibited by α-receptor blocking compounds (22, 25, 75). The use of β-receptor blocking compounds, unfortunately, has not yet clarified the role of β-receptors in epinephrine-induced hyperglycemia and hyperlipemia. Pertinent studies will be discussed below.

1. *Hyperglycemia*

The attempt to produce blockade of epinephrine-induced glycogenolysis of liver and skeletal muscle with α-receptor blocking compounds has largely been unsuccessful. α-Receptor blocking compounds, except the ergot alkaloids, are relatively ineffective in antagonizing epinephrine-induced hyperglycemia. All α-receptor blocking compounds, including the ergot alkaloids, have no effect on epinephrine-induced increase in plasma lactic acid (72). The dose of ergotamine which can suppress hyperglycemia induced by epinephrine has no effect on the pressor response of epinephrine. In addition, ergonovine, which possesses no adrenergic blocking activity, can also antagonize epinephrine-induced hyperglycemia (39). In other words, this action of ergot alkaloids cannot be readily explained on the basis of α-receptor blockade. The ergot alkaloids are known to have also a weak β-receptor blocking action.

Epinephrine-induced hyperglycemia can be more effectively inhibited by β-receptor blocking drugs, but the available data are again equivocal. Significant species variability may partially explain the divergence of these results. Epinephrine-induced hyperglycemia was completely abolished by DCI in the rat (15) and the dog (61), but not in mice (61); epinephrine-induced increase in blood lactic acid was partially blocked by DCI in the dog (61). In man, pronethalol had no effect on epinephrine-induced hyperglycemia (77). Norepinephrine-induced hyperglycemia was inhibited by DCI in the dog (61), but not in the rat (15).

Although inhibition of epinephrine-induced glycogenolysis by β-receptor blocking compounds can be definitely demonstrated, it cannot be assumed that β-receptor activation is solely responsible for this effect. Several facts support this view: (*a*) Both DCI and pronethalol can raise blood sugar and lactic acid by their own action. These effects of DCI are quite marked (61), and thereby may obscure the metabolic effects of catecholamines. The metabolic effects of pronethalol are relatively mild (77). In the only species studied (man), it had no effect on epinephrine-induced hyperglycemia. (*b*) The relative potencies of various catecholamines in inducing hyperglycemia are quite different from their potencies in activating β-receptors of other tissues. For example, isoproterenol is much more potent (approximately 10 times) than epinephrine in activating β-receptors in all species. However, with respect to their hyperglycemic actions, isoproterenol is only as potent as epinephrine in the dog (61), and is only one-fifth to one-tenth as potent in the rabbit (24). (*c*) The hyperglycemic, but not the hyperlacticacidemic, effect is susceptible to β-receptor blockade (61). (*d*) Several compounds without β-receptor blocking activity have also been shown to be capable of inhibiting epinephrine-induced hyperglycemia, e.g., the antihistaminics (48, 93) and ergonovine (39). (*e*) The cellular mechanism of the glycogenolytic effect of epinephrine is complex and not completely understood. This involves at least the activation of phosphorylase and interference with glucose utilization by peripheral tissues (24). Results from studies of β-receptor blocking compounds provide no clue as to the site of blockade in these complex reactions. It is quite possible that inhibition can be effected at more than one place.

2. *Hyperlipemia*

Increases in plasma free fatty acid (FFA) levels following mobilization of lipid from adipose tissues as a consequence of epinephrine or norepinephrine infusions have been demonstrated (16, 33). Epinephrine and norepinephrine are equally potent in this respect. The lipid mobilization process is quite susceptible to blockade by various adrenergic blocking compounds. Results obtained from the use of α-receptor blocking compounds are not in complete accord. Although effective blockade has been observed in most studies with ergotamine, Dibenamine, phenoxybenzamine, or phentolamine in rat, dog, and man (32, 41, 85, 102), other investigators have reported a lack of blockade with phenoxybenzamine and Dibenamine (32, 63, 77). On the other hand, studies using β-receptor blocking compounds have uniformly demonstrated effective inhibition of the epinephrine-induced rise in circulating FFA. The *in vivo* studies include the use of DCI in the dog (8, 61) and pronethalol in man (77). The *in vitro* study of Love *et al.* (56) showed inhibition by DCI of FFA production from rat adipose tissue exposed to catecholamines.

Nevertheless, one cannot definitively correlate the adrenergic β-receptors with the lipid-mobilizing action of catecholamines primarily because β-receptor blockade in this respect is not a specific phenomenon. Effective blockade can be produced by a number of α-receptor blocking compounds as was described above, as well as by methoxamine and its derivative, *N*-isopropyl methoxamine (IMA) (13, 84), both of which have no adrenergic blocking activity. Moreover, fat mobilization is known to be influenced by agents other than catecholamines. Certain other neurohumoral substances, e.g., adrenocorticotropic hormone (ACTH), thyrotropic hormone (TSH), and antidiuretic hormone (ADH), also play a role, although their relative effects differ in various species (26). It is perhaps the interplay of all the above-mentioned factors which characterizes the homeostatic control of lipid mobilization. Interruption of this process by drugs can conceivably occur at more than one step.

It can be seen from the above data that, although β-receptor blocking compounds can effectively inhibit the glycogenolytic and fat-mobilizing effects of catecholamines, it is difficult to correlate these metabolic effects quantitatively with β-receptor activation. Furchgott (30) proposed that the adrenergic receptors for glycogenolysis be termed "γ" receptors. Such a classification is purely empirical and would seem to shed no light on the basic mechanisms underlying these effects. Further understanding of the role of adrenergic receptors in the observed metabolic effects of catecholamines may be gained when additional biochemical evidence regarding the site and nature of the blockade becomes available.

V. THE ANTIARRHYTHMIC ACTION OF β-RECEPTOR BLOCKING COMPOUNDS

It is well established that both DCI and pronethalol possess an antiarrhythmic action. It is not definitely established, however, that this action is a consequence of specific β-receptor blockade. The discussion here will be devoted to a critical appraisal of the mechanism of this antagonism. By way of introduction, a brief review of the role of adrenergic β-receptors in catecholamine-induced arrhythmias seems appropriate.

Catecholamines produce ventricular arrhythmias through an action on the pacemaker system of the heart. Electrophysiologically, the most obvious effects of epinephrine on the Purkinje fibers are an increase in the slope of diastolic (phase 4) depolarization and a lowering of membrane potential (44). These actions can lead to two types of arrhythmias: (*a*) ventricular extrasystoles due to enhancement of the automaticity of dormant ventricular pacemakers; and (*b*) reentry-type arrhythmias due to conduction disturbances engendered by the decreased level of membrane potential.

In intact animals, an increase in automaticity of ventricular ectopic foci caused by catecholamines, after suppression of the activity of superventricular pacemakers, was demonstrated by Nathanson and Miller (71) during induced cardiac standstill and complete heart block in man, and by Roberts *et al.* (82) during vagal stimulation of dogs and cats. Isoproterenol was found to be about 10 times more potent than epinephrine or norepinephrine in enhancing the automaticity of the ventricular pacemakers (82), suggesting that this effect is caused by the activation of adrenergic β-receptors.

The effectiveness of DCI and pronethalol in inhibiting the catecholamine-induced arrhythmias has been well documented. In dogs epinephrine-induced ventricular arrhythmias in hydrocarbon-"sensitized" hearts could be prevented by previous administration of DCI (20, 86) or pronethalol (70). After the administration of DCI or pronethalol, the threshold dose of epinephrine or norepinephrine for the induction of arrhythmias was markedly increased (4–5 times). Multifocal ventricular ectopic beats or ventricular tachycardias also could be abolished by DCI (86). A similar antagonism has also been demonstrated in dogs whose hearts were rendered more vulnerable to catecholamines by means other than the use of hydrocarbon anesthetics. Gilbert *et al.* (31) applied successive stimuli to both right and left ventricles in varying time relationships. A norepinephrine infusion under such circumstances produced ventricular arrhythmias ranging from extrasystoles to ventricular fibrillation. DCI in sufficiently high doses prevented the occurrence of this arrhythmia. Moore and Swain (65) and Moran *et al.* (67) observed that ventricular fibrillation produced by the combined use of the substituted propiophenone, U-0882, and catecholamines was antagonized by DCI. Moran *et al.* (67) also demonstrated effective inhibition by DCI of epinephrine- and norepinephrine-induced ventricular arrhythmias in conscious dogs following coronary artery ligation.

Despite the unequivocal effectiveness of DCI and pronethalol in controlling ventricular arrhythmias induced by catecholamines under a variety of conditions, this antagonism is not attributed solely to β-receptor blockade. Important questions concerning the correlation between the antiarrhythmic and β-receptor blocking effects of DCI and pronethalol include the following: (*a*) Since α-receptor blocking compounds are reportedly effective in antagonizing catecholamine-induced arrhythmias (see below), are β-receptor blocking compounds specific for the same action? (*b*) Since β-receptor blocking compounds are reportedly effective in antagonizing arrhythmias induced by digitalis glycosides, do these compounds have an antiarrhythmic action distinct from their β-receptor blocking property? (*c*) Does the reported direct, quinidine-like myocardial depressant action of β-receptor compounds account for the antiarrhythmic effect of these compounds? Each of these questions will be considered below.

a. Specificity of the antiarrhythmic action: effect of α- vs. β-receptor blocking compounds. Before the introduction of β-receptor blocking compounds, Ahlquist (4) classified the receptors in the heart responsible for "myocardial ectopic excitation" as α. This classification was based on the fact that Dibenamine effectively protects the dog heart from epinephrine-cyclopropane arrhythmias (2, 64, 74). Although some direct myocardial action could not be ruled out, the mechanism of this protection was attributed primarily to the prevention of a catecholamine-induced pressor response. The level of arterial pressure and the threshold dose of epinephrine for ventricular ectopic rhythm could be quantitated (64). Prevention of the arterial pressure rise by mechanical means could effectively decrease the incidence of arrhythmia (64). Furthermore, mechanical elevation of arterial pressure could induce arrhythmia in a "Dibenamine-protected" heart (64, 74). More recently, several investigators have compared the effectiveness of α- and β-receptor blocking compounds in antagonizing catecholamine-induced arrhythmias (31, 65, 67). It was again demonstrated that the protection afforded by α-receptor blocking compounds is pressure dependent. The effectiveness of α-receptor blocking compounds was also less than that of the β-receptor blocking compounds. In addition, Dresel and Duncan (21) observed that threshold doses of epinephrine or isoproterenol which enhance automaticity in the cat papillary muscle preparation were increased by DCI, but decreased by phenoxybenzamine. The above evidence indicates that the α-receptor blocking compounds are only partially effective in antagonizing the catecholamine-induced arrhythmias and that this antagonism can be accounted for primarily by their extracardiac actions. On the other hand, the β-receptor blocking compounds are much more effective, and the antagonism here can conceivably be the result of specific β-receptor blockade.

b. Antagonism of arrhythmias induced by digitalis glycosides. It has been demonstrated clearly that, in addition to their effectiveness in antagonizing catecholamine-induced arrhythmias, DCI and pronethalol are also very effective in inhibiting or converting arrhythmias induced by digitalis glycosides (57, 67, 87, 101). In analyzing the mechanism of digitalis-induced arrhythmias, evidence indicating the participation of catecholamines in the production of digitalis arrhythmias has been accumulating. The threshold dose of acetylstrophanthidin required for inducing ventricular arrhythmias was increased after reserpinization (27, 81), cardiac sympathectomy (27), DCI (67), or pronethalol administration (27); but arrhythmias induced by larger doses of acetylstrophanthidin were not affected (67, 81). Vassalle and co-workers demonstrated from both *in vitro* (100) and *in vivo* (99) studies of dog heart that toxic effects of ouabain develop much earlier in the specialized conduction fibers of the heart than in the ventricular muscle fibers. The characteristics of these signs in the Purkinje fibers consisted of a marked decrease in transmembrane potential and frequent development of rapid, spontaneous rhythm, identical to the epinephrine-induced changes. It was suggested by Roberts *et al.* (81) that the early but not the late arrhythmias due to digitalis are mediated through the action of catecholamines. The fact that the former but not the latter can be antagonized by β-receptor blocking drugs (67) provides additional evidence to implicate catecholamines in the development of early digitalis arrhythmias.

c. Electrophysiological findings: Direct myocardial depressant action vs. action on the specialized conduction tissue. Pronethalol was shown to possess a direct depressant action on atrial and ventricular musculature (88, 90, 91). These actions (increase in refractoriness, decrease in excitability and conduction) are both qualitatively and quantitatively comparable to those of quinidine. The atria were shown to be much more susceptible to the depressant effect of pronethalol than the ventricles. However, pronethalol was also shown to affect the pacemaker system of the heart. Microelectrode recordings from isolated canine Purkinje fibers showed a progressive decrease in resting potential and in rate of rise and amplitude of action potential, and a marked decrease in automaticity, when pronethalol was added to the perfusing medium (91). In the intact dog, pronethalol produced sinus slowing and decreased ventricular automaticity and A-V conduction, similar to the effects of reserpine but opposite to those of epinephrine.

The "direct depressant" effects and the effects on the specialized conducting fibers are two separate actions of pronethalol. This was shown by Singer *et al.* (91), who observed that the latter effects can be partially reversed by large doses of epinephrine, whereas the former remain unaltered. Moreover, the effects of epinephrine on the sinus node, ventricular automaticity, and A-V transmission in the intact dog are found to be diminished by small doses and abolished by larger doses of pronethalol (90). These electrophysiological findings suggest that there is a direct antagonism between the effects of pronethalol and epinephrine in the conduction system of the heart and may well explain the action of β-receptor blocking compounds in antagonizing epinephrine-induced arrhythmias on the basis of β-receptor blockade.

The majority of the data presented above are in favor of the hypothesis that the antiarrhythmic action of DCI or pronethalol is the result of specific β-receptor blockade. The evidence is circumstantial but persuasive. Unless contrary evidence, such as the discovery of a β-receptor blocking compound *without* antiarrhythmic action, becomes available, this hypothesis will remain the most likely explanation.

VI. APPLICATION OF β-RECEPTOR BLOCKING COMPOUNDS

A. Pharmacological Studies

β-Receptor blocking compounds are used extensively as pharmacological tools. They can be of value in either of the following two ways:

1. To ascertain the type of receptors present in certain physiological systems. For example, with the use of β-receptor blocking compounds, the presence of β-receptors in the intestinal smooth muscle and the uterine muscle is demonstrated (see Section IV,D and E), and the presence of α-receptors in coronary blood vessels and the bronchial smooth

muscle is unmasked (see Section IV,A and B). It should be pointed out that the presence of β-receptors cannot always be conclusively determined with the production of effective β-receptor blockade. A notable example is the attempted demonstration of β-receptors subserving the metabolic actions of catecholamines (see Section IV,F).

2. To modify the effects of various compounds which are not catecholamines. These effects are usually qualitatively the same as those produced by catecholamines when they involve β-receptor activation of the target organ. Such modification indicates either that the compound can activate the β-receptors or that it can cause catecholamine release. Numerous investigations have been carried out in this regard, and the heart has been the organ of study in the majority of instances. For instance, the positive inotropic actions of glucagon (28), 5-hydroxytryptamine (97), and high doses of cortisone (95), but not of histamine (59), have been shown to be abolished by β-receptor blocking compounds. The positive inotropic response of certain ganglionic stimulants (acetylcholine, nicotine, or tetraethylammonium) can be similarly abolished. This was demonstrated in isolated papillary muscles (50), in the intact dog heart after atropinization (11), and in chick embryos prior to the development of sympathetic innervation (49). These findings have led to many interesting speculations; i.e., that the heart has a catecholamine store even before it is innervated, that the heart may contain certain elements which do not have the morphological characteristics of ganglia but which behave pharmacologically as if they were.

Studies using β-receptor blocking compounds in organs other than the heart have also been carried out. For example, the antidiuretic effect of vasopressin (78) and the intestinal relaxant effect of isoxsuprine (55) were both inhibited by pronethalol. These actions were thus felt to involve β-receptor activation.

B. Clinical Findings

A number of clinical trials using pronethalol have been carried out by British investigators. Preliminary results have not established that pronethalol has a definite place in therapeutics. However, the rationale for administering β-receptor blocking drugs is an interesting one and merits discussion here. Pronethalol is used clinically for two purposes: first, to "protect" the heart from catecholamine stimulation under a variety of circumstances, and, second, to treat cardiac arrhythmias.

The use of pronethalol to protect the heart from sympathetic stimulation is primarily reserved for patients with coronary heart disease. It has generally been assumed that the heart with coronary artery disease responds unfavorably to catecholamine stimulation. After coronary artery ligation in the dog, both the incidence of arrhythmias (36) and the mortality rate (62) were lower if sympathetic innervation of the heart had been previously extirpated. It is also well known that emotional stress can precipitate an anginal attack. Blocking the inotropic and chronotropic responses to catecholamines can conceivably decrease the myocardial oxygen demand. Theoretically this can be quite beneficial in hearts with limited coronary reserve. However, the application of "cardiac sympathetic blockade" is justified only if it can be demonstrated that, in the absence of direct sympathetic stimulation, the heart can still maintain an adequate output and coronary blood flow in the face of a rise in arterial blood pressure. Preliminary studies in dogs have shown that these requirements can be met (see Section IV,A,2). A similar situation probably obtains in patients with coronary heart disease, since such patients demonstrate an increase in exercise tolerance after using pronethalol (19). However, data regarding the effectiveness of pronethalol in severe anginal disease are inadequate for evaluation (7). Cardiac "protection" by pronethalol was also shown to be effective during operation in patients with pheochromocytoma (18). One serious drawback to the clinical use of pronethalol is its myocardial depressant property. In a patient with frank or incipient congestive heart failure, this undesirable effect may outweigh all the benefits which can result from cardiac sympathetic blockade.

The use of pronethalol in the treatment of cardiac arrhythmias has received only very limited clinical investigation. Pronethalol has been shown to be effective in suppressing a variety of arrhythmias, including those induced by digitalis intoxication, and the ventricular arrhythmias seen during the administration of hydrocarbon anesthetics (35, 47, 92). Again, the data are too scanty to permit firm conclusions to be drawn.

References

1. Abboud, F. M., Eckstein, J. W., and Zimmerman, B. G., Effect of "beta-receptor blocking drugs" on venous and arterial responses to isoproterenol. *Clin. Res.* **11,** 162 (1963).
2. Acheson, G. H., Farah, A., and French, G. N., Some effects of Dibenamine on the mammalian heart. *Federation Proc.* **6,** 305 (1947).
3. Ahlquist, R. P., A study of the adrenotropic receptors. *Am. J. Physiol.* **153,** 586 (1948).
4. Ahlquist, R. P., Adrenergic drugs. *In* "Pharmacology in Medicine" (V. A. Drill, ed.), 2nd Ed., Chapt. 27, p. 380. McGraw-Hill, New York, 1958.
5. Ahlquist, R. P., and Levy, B., Adrenergic receptive mechanism of canine ileum. *J. Pharmacol. Exptl. Therap.* **127,** 146 (1959).

6. Alanis, J., Lopez, E., and Rosas, O., Changes in dog's coronary circulation by hypothalamic stimulation. *Arch. Inst. Cardiol. Mex.* **32,** 743 (1962).
7. Alleyne, G. A. O., Dickinson, C. J., Dornhorst, A. C., Fulton, R. M., Green, K. G., Hill, I. D., Hurst, P., Laurence, D. R., Pilkington, T., Prichard, B. N. C., Robinson, B., and Rosenheim, M. L., Effect of pronethalol in angina pectoris. *Brit. Med. J.* **2,** 1226 (1963).
8. Ashmore, J., Preston, J. E., and Love, W. C., Effects of dicholoroisoproterenol on blood sugar and plasma free fatty acids. *Proc. Soc. Exptl. Biol. Med.* **109,** 291 (1962).
9. Berne, R. M., Effect of epinephrine and norepinephrine on coronary circulation. *Circulation Res.* **6,** 644 (1958).
10. Black, J. W., and Stephenson, J. S., Pharmacology of a new adrenergic beta-receptor blocking compound (nethalide). *Lancet* **2,** 311 (1962).
11. Blumenthal, M. R., Effects of acetylcholine on the heart. *Federation Proc.* **23,** 123 (1964).
12. Botting, R., Farmer, J. B., and Lockett, M. F., The effect of subcutaneous adrenaline and isoprenaline on the excretion of electrolytes by rats. *Arch. Intern. Physiol. Biochim.* **69,** 203 (1961).
13. Burns, J. J., Colville, K. I., Lindsay, L. A., and Salvador, R. A., Blockade of some metabolic effects of catecholamines by *N*-isopropyl methoxamine (B.W. 61–43). *J. Pharmacol. Exptl. Therap.* **144,** 163 (1964).
14. Castro de la Mata, R., Penna, M., and Aviado, D. M., Reversal of sympathomimetic bronchodilation by dichloroisoproterenol. *J. Pharmacol. Exptl. Therap.* **135,** 197 (1962).
15. Claassen, V., and Noach, E. L., Dichloro-Isuprel inhibition of sympathomimetic hyperglycemia. *Arch. Intern. Pharmacodyn.* **126,** 332 (1960).
16. Dole, V. P., A relation between non-esterified fatty acids in plasma and the metabolism of glucose. *J. Clin. Invest.* **35,** 150 (1956).
17. Donald, D. E., Kvale, J., and Shepherd, J. T., The effect of an adrenergic beta-receptor antagonist on the cardiovascular system of the dog. *J. Pharmacol. Exptl. Therap.* **143,** 344 (1964).
18. Dornhorst, A. C., and Laurence, D. R., Use of pronethalol in phaeochrome tumors. *Brit. Med. J.* **2,** 1250 (1963).
19. Dornhorst, A. C., and Robinson, B. F., Clinical pharmacology of a beta-adrenergic blocking agent (nethalide). *Lancet* **2,** 314 (1962).
20. Dresel, P. E., Blockade of some cardiac actions of adrenaline by dichloroisoproterenol. *Can. J. Biochem. Physiol.* **38,** 375 (1960).
21. Dresel, P. E., and Duncan, D. G., Induction of automaticity in cat papillary muscles by sympathomimetic amines. *J. Pharmacol. Exptl. Therap.* **133,** 70 (1961).
22. D'Silva, J. L., The action of adrenaline on serum potassium. *J. Physiol.* (*London*) **82,** 393 (1934).
23. Dungan, K. W., and Lish, P. M., Potency and specificity of new adrenergic beta-receptor blocking agents. *Federation Proc.* **23,** 124 (1964).
24. Ellis, S., The metabolic effects of epinephrine and related amines. *Pharmacol. Rev.* **8,** 485 (1956).
25. Ellis, S., Beckett, S. B., and Boutwell, J. H., Dibenamine blockade of epinephrine and glucagon hyperkalemias. *Proc. Soc. Exptl. Biol. Med.* **94,** 343 (1957).
26. Engel, F. L., and White, J. E., Jr., Some hormonal influences on fat mobilization from adipose tissue. *Am. J. Clin. Nutr.* **8,** 691 (1960).

27. Erlij, D., and Mendez, R., Modification of digitoxin intoxication by exclusion of the sympathetic system. *Federation Proc.* **22,** 184 (1963).
28. Farah, A., and Tuttle, R., Studies on the pharmacology of glucagon. *J. Pharmacol. Exptl. Therap.* **129,** 49 (1960).
29. Fleming, W. W., and Hawkins, D. F., The actions of dichloroisoproterenol in the dog heart-lung preparation and the isolated guinea-pig atrium. *J. Pharmacol. Exptl. Therap.* **129,** 1 (1960).
30. Furchgott, R. F., The receptors for epinephrine and norepinephrine (adrenergic receptors). *Pharmacol. Rev.* **11,** 429 (1959).
31. Gilbert, J. L., Lang, G., and Brooks, C. McC., Influence of sympathomimetic pressor drugs on arrhythmias caused by multiple stimuli. *Circulation Res.* **4,** 417 (1959).
32. Goodman, H. M., and Knobil, E., Effect of adrenergic blocking agents on fatty acid mobilization during fasting. *Proc. Soc. Exptl. Biol. Med.* **102,** 493 (1959).
33. Gordon, R. S., Jr., and Cherkes, A., Unesterified fatty acid in human blood plasma. *J. Clin. Invest.* **35,** 206 (1956).
34. Granata, L., Huvos, A., and Gregg, D. E., Hemodynamic changes in coronary and mesenteric arterial beds following sympathetic nerve stimulation. *Physiologist* **4,** 42 (1961).
35. Grandjean, T., and Rivier, J-L., Utilisation d'un antagoniste des catecholamines (ICI 38174, "Alderline") dans le traitement de quelques cas de troubles du rythme cardiaque. *Schweiz. Med. Wochschr.* **93,** 1101 (1963).
36. Harris, A. S., Estandia, A., and Tillotson, R. F., Ventricular ectopic rhythms and ventricular fibrillation following cardiac sympathectomy and coronary occlusion. *Am. J. Physiol.* **165,** 505 (1951).
37. Harrison, D. C., and Chidsey, C. A., The effects of cardioaccelerator nerve stimulation and beta-receptor blockade on the cardiac metabolism of norepinephrine. *Federation Proc.* **22,** 448 (1963).
38. Harrison, D. C., Braunwald, E., Glick, G., Mason, D. T., Chidsey, C. A., and Ross, J., Jr., Effects of beta adrenergic blockade on the circulation, with particular reference to observations in patients with hypertrophic subaortic stenosis. *Circulation* **29,** 84 (1964).
39. Harvey, S. C., Wang, C. Y., and Nickerson, M., Blockade of epinephrine-induced hyperglycemia. *J. Pharmacol. Exptl. Therap.* **104,** 363 (1952).
40. Hashimoto, K., Shigei, T., Imai, S., Saito, Y., Yago, N., Uei, I., and Clark, R. E., Oxygen consumption and coronary vascular tone in the isolated fibrillating dog heart. *Am. J. Physiol.* **198,** 965 (1960).
41. Havel, R. J., and Goldfien, A., The role of the sympathetic nervous system in the metabolism of free fatty acids. *J. Lipid Res.* **1,** 102 (1959).
42. Hegglin, R., Krayenbuhl, H. P., and Luthy, E., Der Einfluss eines beta-Receptoren-blockers (nethalide) auf einige Parameter der Kreislaufdynamik. *Z. Ges. Exptl. Med.* **138,** 141 (1964).
43. Hertting, G., Axelrod, J., and Whitby, L. G., Effect of drugs on the uptake and metabolism of H^3-norepinephrine. *J. Pharmacol. Exptl. Therap.* **134,** 146 (1961).
44. Hoffman, B. F., and Cranefield, P. F., "Electrophysiology of the Heart," p. 183. McGraw-Hill, New York, 1960.
45. James, T. N., and Nadeau, R. A., Chronotropic and vagal-blocking effects of DCI studied by direct perfusion of the sinus node. *J. Pharmacol. Exptl. Therap.* **140,** 73 (1963).

46. James, T. N., and Nadeau, R. A., The chronotropic and vagal-blocking actions of naphthylisoproterenol studied by direct perfusion of the sinus node. *J. Pharmacol. Exptl. Therap.* **143,** 350 (1964).

47. Johnstone, M., Beta-adrenergic blockade with pronethalol during anesthesia. *Brit. J. Anaesthesia* **36,** 224 (1964).

48. Komrad, E. L., and Loew, E. R., Effect of certain antihistaminics on epinephrine-induced hyperglycemia and lacticacidemia. *J. Pharmacol. Exptl. Therap.* **103,** 115 (1951).

49. Lee, W. C., McCarty, L. P., Zodrow, W. W., and Shideman, F. E., The cardiostimulant action of certain ganglionic stimulants on the embryonic chick heart. *J. Pharmacol. Exptl. Therap.* **130,** 30 (1960).

50. Lee, W. C., and Shideman, F. E., Mechanism of the positive inotropic response to certain ganglionic stimulants. *J. Pharmacol. Exptl. Therap.* **126,** 239 (1959).

51. Lees, P., and Lockett, M. F., A study of the beta-adrenergic receptors in rat kidneys. *Brit. J. Pharmacol.* **20,** 135 (1963).

52. Levy, B., Adrenergic blockade produced by the dichloro analogs of epinephrine, arterenol and isoproterenol. *J. Pharmacol. Exptl. Therap.* **127,** 150 (1959).

53. Levy, B., and Ahlquist, R. P., Blockade of the beta-adrenergic receptors. *J. Pharmacol. Exptl. Therap.* **130,** 334 (1960).

54. Levy, B., and Ahlquist, R. P., An analysis of adrenergic blocking activity. *J. Pharmacol. Exptl. Therap.* **133,** 202 (1961).

55. Lish, P. M., Hillyard, I. W., and Dungan, K. W., The uterine relaxant properties of isoxsuprine. *J. Pharmacol. Exptl. Therap.* **129,** 438 (1960).

56. Love, W. C., Carr, L., and Ashmore, J., Lipolysis in adipose tissue: effects of *dl*-3,4-dichloroisoproterenol and related compounds. *J. Pharmacol. Exptl. Therap.* **140,** 287 (1963).

57. Lucchesi, B. R., and Hardman, H. F., The influence of dichloroisoproterenol (DCI) and related compounds upon ouabain and acetylstrophanthidin induced cardiac arrhythmias. *J. Pharmacol. Exptl. Therap.* **132,** 372 (1961).

58. Lum, B. K. B., and Kermani, M. H., Selective loss of response to alpha adrenergic agents following cold storage of the rabbit jejunum. *Federation Proc.* **22,** 449 (1963).

59. Mannaioni, P. F., Interaction between histamine and dichloroisoproterenol, hexamethonium, pempidine and diphenhydramine, in normal and reserpine-treated heart preparations. *Brit. J. Pharmacol.* **15,** 500 (1960).

60. Mayer, S. E., and Moran, N. C., Relation between pharmacologic augmentation of cardiac contractile force and the activation of myocardial glycogen phosphorylase. *J. Pharmacol. Exptl. Therap.* **129,** 271 (1960).

61. Mayer, S., Moran, N. C., and Fain, J., The effect of adrenergic blocking agents on some metabolic actions of catecholamines. *J. Pharmacol. Exptl. Therap.* **134,** 18 (1961).

62. McEachern, C. G., Manning, G. W., and Hall, G. E., Sudden occlusion of coronary arteries following removal of cardio-sensory pathways. *A.M.A. Arch. Internal Med.* **65,** 661 (1940).

63. McElroy, W. T., Jr., and Spitzer, J. J., Effects of adrenergic blocking agents on plasma free fatty acid concentrations. *Am. J. Physiol.* **200,** 318 (1961).

64. Moe, G. K., Malton, S. D., Rennick, B. R., and Freyburger, W. A., The role of arterial pressure in the induction of idioventricular rhythms under cyclopropane anesthesia. *J. Pharmacol. Exptl. Therap.* **94,** 319 (1948).

65. Moore, J. I., and Swain, H. H., Sensitization to ventricular fibrillation. I. Sensitization by a substituted propiophenone, U-0882. *J. Pharmacol. Exptl. Therap.* **128,** 243 (1960).
66. Moran, N. C., Adrenergic receptors within the cardiovascular system. *Circulation* **28,** 987 (1963).
67. Moran, N. C., Moore, J. I., Holcomb, A. K., and Mushet, G., Antagonism of adrenergically-induced cardiac arrhythmias by dichloroisoproterenol. *J. Pharmacol. Exptl. Therap.* **136,** 327 (1962).
68. Moran, N. C., and Perkins, M. E., Adrenergic blockade of the mammalian heart by a dichloro analogue of isoproterenol. *J. Pharmacol. Exptl. Therap.* **124,** 223 (1958).
69. Moran, N. C., and Perkins, M. E., An evaluation of adrenergic blockade of the mammalian heart. *J. Pharmacol. Exptl. Therap.* **133,** 192 (1961).
70. Murray, W. J., McKnight, R. L., and Davis, D. A., Antagonism of hydrocarbon anesthetic-epinephrine arrhythmias in dogs by nethalide, a dichloroisoproterenol analogue. *Proc. Soc. Exptl. Biol. Med.* **113,** 439 (1963).
71. Nathanson, M. H., and Miller, H., The action of norepinephrine, epinephrine and isopropyl norepinephrine on the rhythmic function of the heart. *Circulation* **6,** 238 (1952).
72. Nickerson, M., Blockade of the actions of adrenaline and noradrenaline. *Pharmacol. Rev.* **11,** 443 (1959).
73. Nickerson, M., and Chan, G. C. M., Blockade of responses of isolated myocardium to epinephrine. *J. Pharmacol. Exptl. Therap.* **133,** 186 (1961).
74. Nickerson, M., and Nomaguchi, G. M., Mechanism of Dibenamine protection against cyclopropane-epinephrine cardiac arrhythmias. *J. Pharmacol. Exptl. Therap.* **95,** 1 (1949).
75. O'Brien, G. S., Murphy, Q. R., Jr., and Meek, W. J., The effect of sympathomimetic amines on arterial plasma potassium and cardiac rhythm in anesthetized dogs. *J. Pharmacol. Exptl. Therap.* **109,** 453 (1953).
76. Paget, G. E.., Carcinogenic action of pronethalol. *Brit. Med. J.* **2,** 1267 (1963).
77. Pilkington, T. R. E., Lowe, R. D., Robinson, B. F., and Titterington, E., Effect of adrenergic blockade on glucose and fatty-acid mobilization in man. *Lancet* **2,** 316 (1962).
78. Poisner, A. M., Interaction of oxytocin and vasopressin with beta-adrenergic receptors in the kidney. *Nature* **201,** 199 (1964).
79. Powell, C. E., and Slater, I. H., Blocking of inhibitory adrenergic receptors by a dichloro analog of isoproterenol. *J. Pharmacol. Exptl. Therap.* **122,** 480 (1958).
80. Rall, T. W., and Sutherland, E. W., Formation of a cyclic adenine ribonucleotide by tissue particles. *J. Biol. Chem.* **232,** 1065 (1958).
81. Roberts, J., Ito, R., Reilly, J., and Cairoli, V. J., Influence of reserpine and *beta* TM_{10} on digitalis-induced ventricular arrhythmia. *Circulation Res.* **13,** 149 (1963).
82. Roberts, J., Standaert, F., Kim, Y. I., and Riker, W. F., Jr., The initiation and pharmacologic reactivity of a ventricular pacemaker in the intact animal. *J. Pharmacol. Exptl. Therap.* **117,** 374 (1956).
83. Rudzik, A. D., and Miller, J. W., The mechanism of uterine inhibitory action of relaxin-containing ovarian extracts. *J. Pharmacol. Exptl.. Therap.* **138,** 82 (1962).

84. Salvador, R. A., Colville, K. I., April, S. A., and Burns, J. J., Inhibition of lipid mobilization by *N*-isopropyl methoxamine (B.W. 61–43). *J. Pharmacol. Exptl. Therap.* **144,** 172 (1964).
85. Schotz, M. C., and Page, I. H., Effect of adrenergic blocking agents on the release of free fatty acids from rat adipose tissue. *J. Lipid Res.* **1,** 466 (1960).
86. Schull, L. G., Berry, G., and Villarreal, R., Prevention and correction of ventricular arrhythmias by dichloroisoproterenol in dogs anesthetized with cyclopropane. *Anesthesiology* **22,** 444 (1961).
87. Sekiya, A., and Vaughan Williams, E. M., The effects of pronethalol, dichlorisoprenaline and disopyramide on the toxicity to the heart of ouabain and anesthetics. *Brit. J. Pharmacol.* **21,** 462 (1963).
88. Sekiya, A., and Vaughan Williams, E. M., A comparison of the antifibrillatory actions and effects on intracellular cardiac potentials of pronethalol, disopyramide and quinidine. *Brit. J. Pharmacol.* **21,** 473 (1963).
89. Siegel, J. H., Gilmore, J. P., and Sarnoff, S. J., Myocardial extraction and production of catechol amines. *Circulation Res.* **9,** 1336 (1961).
90. Singer, D. H., and Hoffman, B. F., The adrenergic nervous system and the specialized conducting fibers. *Physiologist* **7, 257** (1964).
91. Singer, D. H., Yeh, B. K., Scherlag, B. J., and Hoffman, B. F., Beta blockade and the specialized conduction system of the heart. *Circulation, Supplement* III 30, 160 (1964).
92. Stock, J. P. P., and Dale, N., Beta-adrenergic receptor blockade in cardiac arrhythmias. *Brit. Med. J.* **2,** 1230 (1963).
93. Susina, S. V., and Unna, K. R., Effects of antihistamine agents on epinephrine-induced hyperglycemia in the dog. *J. Pharmacol. Exptl. Therap.* **101,** 34 (1951).
94. Sutherland, E. W., and Rall, T. W., Fractionation and characterization of a cyclic adenine ribonucleotide formed by tissue particles. *J. Biol. Chem.* **232,** 1077 (1958).
95. Tanz, R. D., Studies on the action of cortisone acetate on isolated cardiac tissue. *J. Pharmacol. Exptl. Therap.* **128,** 168 (1960).
96. Tozzi, S., and Levy, B., The adrenergic receptive mechanism of the rat uterus. *Federation Proc.* **22,** 449 (1963).
97. Trendelenburg, U., The action of histamine and 5-hydroxytryptamine on isolated mammalian atria. *J. Pharmacol. Exptl. Therap.* **130,** 450 (1960).
98. VanDeripe, D. R., Ablad, B., and Moran, N. C., Beta-adrenergic receptor blockade by four methyl substituted *N*-isopropylphenylethanolamines. *Federation Proc.* **23,** 124 (1964).
99. Vassalle, M., Greenspan, K., and Hoffman, B. F., An analysis of arrhythmias induced by ouabain in intact dogs. *Circulation Res.* **13,** 132 (1963).
100. Vassalle, M., Karis, J., Hoffman, B. F., Toxic effects of ouabain on Purkinje fibers and ventricular muscle fibers. *Am. J. Physiol.* **203,** 433 (1962).
101. Vaughan Williams, E. M., and Sekiya, A., Prevention of arrhythmias due to cardiac glycosides by block of sympathetic beta receptors. *Lancet* **1,** 420 (1963).
102. Wertheimer, E., Hamosh, M., and Shafrir, E., Factors affecting fat mobilizaation from adipose tissue. *Am. J. Clin. Nutr.* **8,** 705 (1960).
103. Williams, B. J., Relation between norepinephrine and DCI during cardiac adrenergic blockade. *Federation Proc.* **22,** 448 (1963).

V. The Veratrum Alkaloids

Joseph M. Benforado

Department of Pharmacology, School of Medicine, State University of New York at Buffalo, Buffalo, New York

I. Introduction ... 331
A. Botanical Sources ... 332
B. Previous Reviews ... 333
II. The Chemistry of Veratrum Alkaloids ... 333
A. Native Alkaloids ... 333
B. Semisynthetic Alkaloids ... 338
III. Pharmacological Actions ... 339
A. Cardiovascular Effects ... 340
B. Respiratory Effects ... 361
C. Emetic Action ... 363
D. Central Nervous System Effects ... 365
E. Effects on Nerve and Muscle ... 366
F. Metabolic Effects in Tissues ... 382
IV. Therapeutic Use ... 383
A. Hypertension ... 383
B. Toxicity ... 385
References ... 386

I. INTRODUCTION

The empirical medicinal use of the *Veratrum* plant for a wide variety of purposes dates back to the middle ages, but in the United States, it was about 100 years ago that crude extracts were employed against hypertension (225), which, in selected cases, is the only well-defined therapeutic indication for veratrum alkaloids today. The reflex nature of the cardiovascular effects of small intravenous doses of veratrine was noted in 1867, when von Bezold and Hirt (33) observed that the hypotension and bradycardia produced were abolished by vagotomy. Since that time it has become apparent that the effects of the veratrum alkaloids are protean, and in recent years, following significant advances in the isolation, purification, and chemical characterization of many of the alkaloids, there has been a surge of interest in the use of these substances as tools for pharmacologically dissecting out physiological mechanisms at subcellular, cellular, and higher integrative levels. As the pure alkaloids have become available, qualitative as well as quantitative differences between even closely related chemical species have become apparent (26, 68, 201). This makes it imperative that future investigators rely on the use of pure substances instead of alkaloidal mixtures when this is feasible.

As is often the situation in science, new knowledge in the area of the veratrum alkaloids has in part followed advances in diverse, often unrelated fields. Some examples here are fields such as synthetic chemistry, countercurrent distribution, and electrophysiology.

A. Botanical Sources

The veratrum alkaloids take their name from the genus *Veratrum*. However, many alkaloids in this group are derived from genera other than *Veratrum*, and it has recently been proposed (143) that the term veratrum alkaloids encompass those alkaloids isolated from the tribe Veratreae (family Liliaceae). Only a small proportion of plants which belong to the Veratreae have been studied phytochemically. The majority of important alkaloids which have been detected derive from three genera, *Veratrum*, *Zygadenus*, and *Schoenocaulon* (Table I). Some common names for species within these respective genera are false hellebore, death camas, and sabadilla. On the basis of botanical structure *Schoenocaulon* is a distinct, homogeneous group while the other two genera share some common attributes. *Veratrum* and *Schoenocaulon* elaborate entirely different alkaloids, the former yielding both jerveratrum and ceveratrum alkaloids while the latter yields only ceveratrum alkaloids of a type not seen in *Veratrum*. The genus *Zygadenus* also elaborates only ceveratrum alkaloids, some of which are identical with those found in *Veratrum*. The most important species from which alkaloids have been isolated are *V. album*, *V. viride*, *Z. venenosus*, and *S. officinale*. Although the alkaloids probably occur in all parts of the first three species, the roots and rhizomes are usual sources for isolation. In the fourth species, the alkaloids probably occur only in the seeds.

Alkaloids related chemically and pharmacologically to the veratrum alkaloids have been found in the genus *Fritillaria* (Liliaceous plants) (167) and in the genus *Solanum* (Solanaceae, potato family) (128). Tomatine, isolated from the genus *Lycopersicon* (Solanaceae) has cardiovascular actions related in part to those of the veratrum alkaloids (229). Its aglycone, tomatidine, is a steroidal alkaloid chemically similar to jervine.

Little is known of the pathways of alkaloid synthesis in plants. This and the question of the function of alkaloids in plant economy are fruitful areas for research that have intriguing potential. These are discussed by Robinson (187). The taxonomy and phytochemistry of

Veratrum and related genera has been reviewed by Kupchan and coworkers (143).

B. Previous Reviews

The first major review on the veratrum alkaloids was that of Boehm (36) published in 1920. In 1946, Krayer and Acheson (126) published a comprehensive review on the veratrum alkaloids. Included was reference to other earlier reviews dating back to 1919. Since 1946, the only reviews dealing exclusively with the veratrum alkaloids have been chemically oriented (143, 167), but there have been important reviews in which, among other items, the veratrum alkaloids are discussed from physiological (21, 51, 197) and pharmacological (202, 203, 204, 219) points of view. An excellent textbook chapter by Krayer (124) appeared in 1958.

II. THE CHEMISTRY OF VERATRUM ALKALOIDS

A. Native Alkaloids

Table I lists a selected group of naturally occurring veratrum alkaloids of pharmacological interest together with their empirical formulas and important species in which they are found. Chemically these substances are polycyclic compounds with steroid structure containing a secondary or tertiary nitrogen atom within a ring. Elucidation of the complete chemical structure of the C_{27} alkamines listed, and their derivaties, has been accomplished. Advances are also being made in the determination of configuration (22). These C_{27} alkamines fall into two chemical groups, the jerveratrum group (Fig. 1 and 2), with a skeleton very similar to cholesterol and with a secondary nitrogen in the two examples given, and the ceveratrum alkaloids (Fig. 3, 4, 5, 6, 7), which are tertiary amines, more complex in structure, and highly hydroxylic. The jerveratrum alkaloids occur as free alkamines or as glycoalkaloids combined with one molecule of D-glucose. The ceveratrum alkaloids occur in the plant as esters of various alicyclic or aromatic organic acids. They do not occur as glycosides. The alkamines of the ceveratrum group which have been isolated may not be present in the plant as such but may represent hydrolytic products of cleavage of the ester bonds during isolation. All the zygadenine (Fig. 4) and veracevine (Fig. 5) esters isolated to date are monoesters, while the germine (Fig. 6) and protoverine (Fig. 7) esters are polyesters with, in the case of protoverine, up to four acid radicals esterified at various hydroxyl groups. Protoveratridine (Fig. 6, XXIII), which contrary to its name is a derivative of germine, is also a monoester but probably arises as such

TABLE I

NATURALLY OCCURRING VERATRUM ALKALOIDS[a]

Alkaloid	Formula	Species from which isolated[b]
Alkamines of known structure		
Jerveratrum alkaloids		
veratramine (I)	$C_{27}H_{39}O_2N$	VA, VV
jervine (II)	$C_{27}H_{39}O_3N$	VA, VV
Ceveratrum alkaloids		
zygadenine (III)	$C_{27}H_{43}O_7N$	ZV
veracevine (IV)	$C_{27}H_{43}O_8N$	SO
cevine (V)	$C_{27}H_{43}O_8N$	SO
germine (VI)	$C_{27}H_{43}O_8N$	VV, ZV
protoverine (VII)	$C_{27}H_{43}O_9N$	V[c]
Glycosidic alkaloids of the jerveratrum group		
veratrosine (VIII)	$C_{33}H_{49}O_7N$	VV
pseudojervine (IX)	$C_{33}H_{49}O_8N$	VA, VV
Ester alkaloids of the ceveratrum group		
Esters of zygadenine		
zyacine (X)	$C_{29}H_{45}O_8N$	VA, ZV
angeloylzygadenine (XI)	$C_{32}H_{49}O_8N$	VA
vanilloylzygadenine (XII)	$C_{35}H_{49}O_{10}N$	ZV
veratroylzygadenine (XIII)	$C_{36}H_{51}O_{10}N$	VA, VV, ZV
Esters of veracevine		
cevacine (XIV)	$C_{29}H_{45}O_9N$	SO
cevadine (XV)	$C_{32}H_{49}O_9N$	SO
vanilloylveracevine (XVI)	$C_{35}H_{49}O_{11}N$	SO
veratridine (XVII)	$C_{36}H_{51}O_{11}N$	SO
Esters of germine		
germitetrine (XVIII)	$C_{41}H_{63}O_{14}N$	VA
germitrine (XIX)	$C_{39}H_{61}O_{12}N$	VA, VV
neogermitrine (XX)	$C_{36}H_{55}O_{11}N$	VA, VV, ZV
germerine (XXI)	$C_{37}H_{59}O_{11}N$	VA, VV
germidine (XXII)	$C_{34}H_{53}O_{10}N$	VV, ZV
protoveratridine (XXIII)	$C_{32}H_{51}O_9N$	VV, ZV
Esters of protoverine		
protoveratrine A (XXIV)	$C_{41}H_{63}O_{14}N$	VA, VV
protoveratrine B (XXV)	$C_{41}H_{63}O_{15}N$	VA, VV

[a] A limited list adapted from Kupchan *et al.* (143).

[b] VA (*Veratrum album*), VV (*Veratrum viride*), ZV (*Zygadenus venenosus*), SO (*Schoenocaulon officinale*). Less well known species have been omitted.

[c] This alkamine apparently not isolated; see esters of protoverine in *V.* spp.

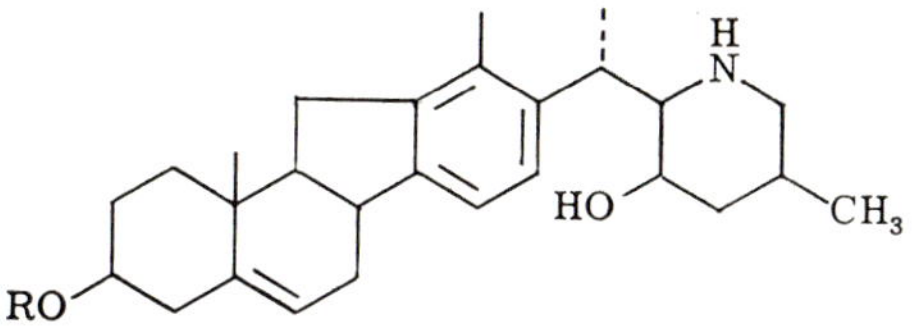

FIG. 1. Alkaloidal structure (Table I) based on veratramine. I: R = H; VIII: R = $C_6H_{11}O_5$ (D-glucosyl). From Kupchan *et al.* (143), with kind permission from the authors and The Lloyd Library and Museum, Cincinnati, Ohio.

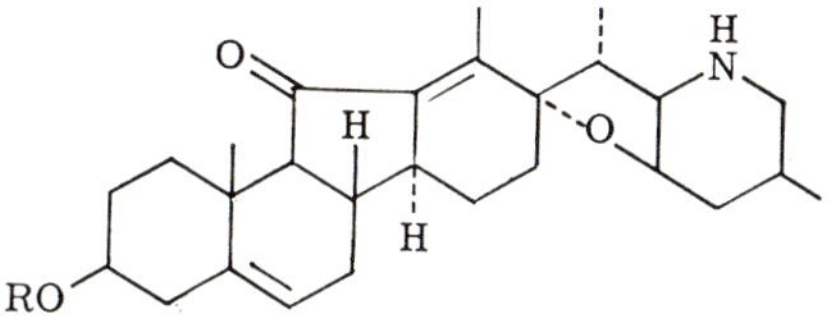

FIG. 2. Alkaloidal structure (Table I) based on jervine. II: R = H; IX: R = $C_6H_{11}O_5$ (D-glucosyl). From Kupchan *et al.* (143), with kind permission from the authors and The Lloyd Library and Museum, Cincinnati, Ohio.

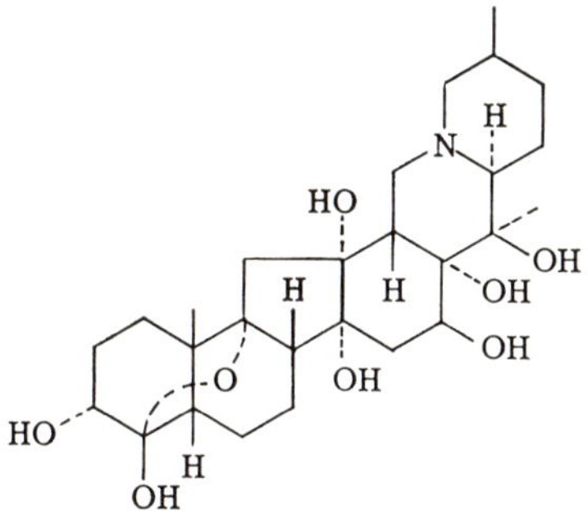

FIG. 3. Alkaloidal structure (Table I) of cevine. V: cevine. From Kupchan *et al.* (143), with kind permission from the authors and The Lloyd Library and Museum, Cincinnati, Ohio.

from polyesters by hydrolysis during extraction. The same may be true (167) for some diesters of germine (Fig. 6). Veratrine, a commercial extract of S. *officinale,* is a mixture containing principally two ester alkaloids, cevadine (Fig. 5, XV) and veratridine (Fig. 5, XVII). Cevine (Fig. 3, V), once thought to be the alkamine of these two esters, is now known to be the result of isomerization during isolation of veracevine (Fig. 5, IV), the true alkamine. Veratrine also contains cevacine

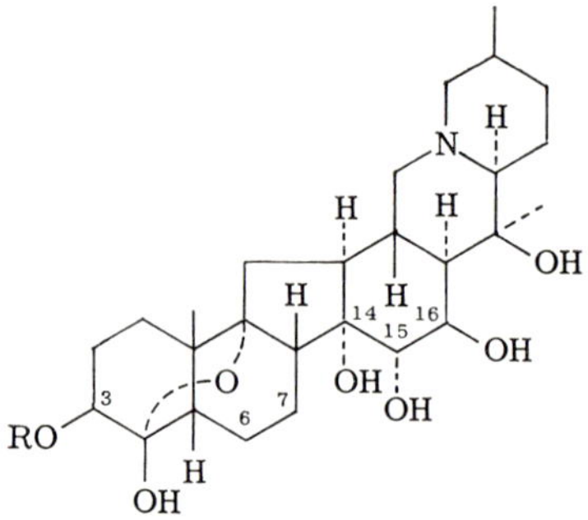

FIG. 4. Alkaloidal structure (Table I) based on zygadenine. III: R = H; X: R = acetyl; XI: R = angeloyl; XII: R = vanilloyl; XIII: R = veratroyl. From Kupchan *et al.* (143), with kind permission from the authors and The Lloyd Library and Museum, Cincinnati, Ohio.

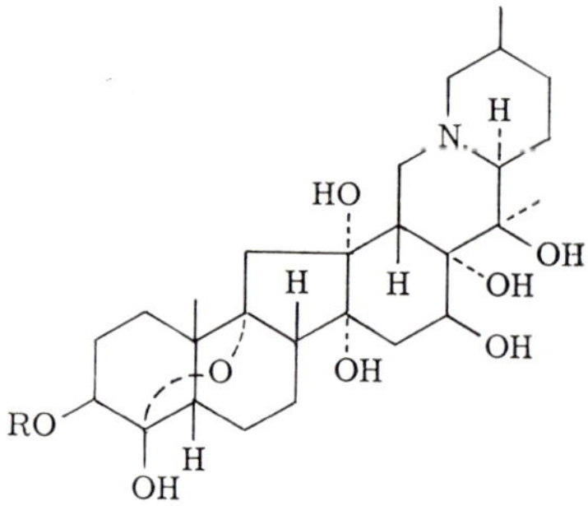

FIG. 5. Alkaloidal structure (Table I) based on veracevine. IV: R = H; XIV: R = acetyl; XV: R = angeloyl; XVI: R = vanilloyl; XVII: R = veratroyl. From Kupchan *et al.* (143), with kind permission from the authors and The Lloyd Library and Museum, Cincinnati, Ohio.

(Fig. 5, XIV), veracevine (Fig. 5, IV) and vanilloylveracevine (Fig. 5, XVI) (142). Germitetrine (Fig. 6, XVIII), a triester, was originally named "germitetrine-B" and was at that time considered a tetraester. Its true structure was resolved when it was shown that one of the acetyl radicals thought to be esterified in the ring structure was in fact present in the *erythro*-2-hydroxy-2-methyl-3-acetyoxybutyryl residue (140).

Chemically, in terms of the structure of its alkaloids, as well as botanically, *Zygadenus* may be considered as an intermediate lying between *Veratrum* and *Schoenocaulon*. The ring structure of the zygadenine alkaloids (Fig. 4) shows resemblance both to the veracevine (Fig. 5) alkaloids and to the germine (Fig. 6) and protoverine (Fig. 7) alkaloids.

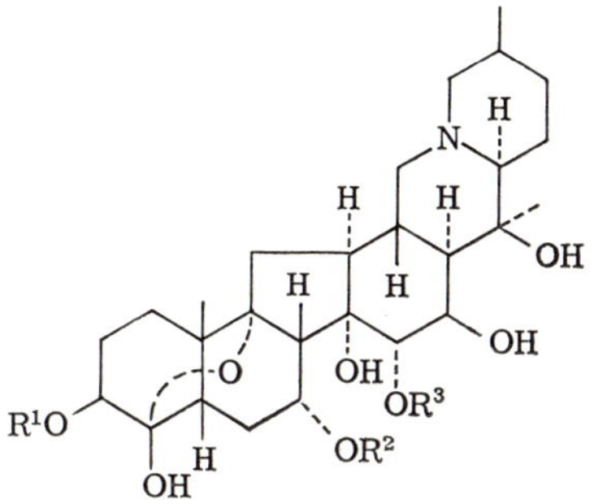

FIG. 6. Alkaloidal structure (Table I) based on germine with substitutions as follows:

	R[1]	R[2]	R[3]
VI:	H	H	H
XVIII:	HMAB[a]	acetyl	MB
XIX:	MB	acetyl	HMB
XX:	acetyl	acetyl	MB
XXI:	angeloyl	acetyl	MB
XXII:	acetyl	H	MB
XXIII:	MB	H	H

[a] HMAB = *erythro*-2-hydroxy-2-methyl-3-acetoxybutyryl; MB = (*l*)2-methylbutyryl; HMB = (*d*)-2-hydroxy-2-methylbutyryl. From Kupchan *et al.* (143), with kind permission from the authors and The Lloyd Library and Museum, Cincinnati, Ohio.

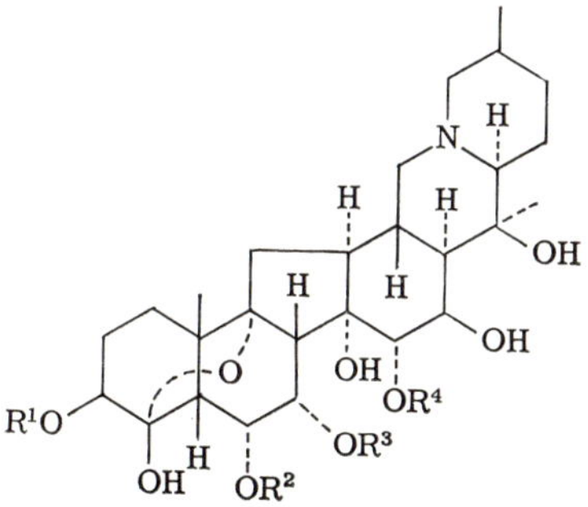

FIG. 7. Alkaloidal structure (Table I) based on protoverine with substitutions as follows:

	R[1]	R[2]	R[3]	R[4]
VII:	H	H	H	H
XXIV:	HMB[a]	acetyl	acetyl	MB
XXV:	t-DMB	acetyl	acetyl	MB

[a] HMB = (*d*)-2-hydroxy-2-methylbutyryl; t-DMB = (*d*)-threo,2,3,-dihydroxy-2-methylbutyryl; MB = (*l*)2-methylbutyryl. From Kupchan *et al.* (143), with kind permission from the authors and The Lloyd Library and Museum, Cincinnati, Ohio.

Further, the monoesters of zygadenine and veracevine contain similar acids (Fig. 4, 5).

B. Semisynthetic Alkaloids

Although none of the naturally occurring veratrum alkaloids have been synthesized, there has been recently much activity in the area of semisynthetic ester alkaloids. In particular, pharmacological actions of semisynthetic esters of germine and protoverine have been studied (68, 69, 70, 88, 89). The polyhydroxyl nature of the alkamines has allowed esterification at various portions of the ring structure with diverse acid radicals as well as selective oxidation of specific hydroxyl functions. The structure-activity relationships which have emerged thus far have shown the importance of structure for potency in hypotensive action (141). For analogs of protoveratrine, alterations in the nature of the ester group at position 15 greatly affect the potency, decreasing it moderately to markedly with the variants tested. In contrast, altered structure of the ester moiety at position 3 does not greatly alter potency. Such studies have also raised the possibility that a semisynthetic molecule may ultimately be found with a higher and more favorable (emetic dose)/(hypotensive dose) ratio than is found for the naturally occurring esters (225). Semisynthetic acetic acid mono- and diesters of germine (Fig. 6) show pharmacological properties which are qualitatively different from similarly synthesized tetra- and pentaesters of the same acid. The former cause a rise in blood pressure in cats while the latter resemble the naturally occurring germine esters in causing the classical fall in blood pressure and heart rate. Some differences in the effect on amphibian muscle are also apparent (68). Similar differences have been noted among the semisynthetic acetic acid esters (up to hexa-acetate) of protoverine (Fig. 7) (88). It is of interest that, of all the monoacetate esters studied, only sabadine (alkamine-sabine), a relatively minor alkaloid found in S. *officinale,* showed the classical effects on the cardiovascular system and amphibian skeletal muscle. The other naturally occurring monoacetate esters, cevacine (Fig. 5, XIV; alkamine-veracevine) and zygacine (Fig. 4, X; alkamine-zygadenine) showed effects similar to germine monoacetate (142).

A semisynthetic steroid secondary amine, using pregnenolone as a starting material, showed chemical and pharmacological similarity to the jerveratrum group of alkaloids (Fig. 1, 2), as did a substance prepared from naturally occurring sapogenins found in *Trillium erectus* (134). A synthetic substance, having an indanone structure found in some of the jerveratrum alkaloids, was found to possess hypotensive activity characteristic of ceveratrum ester alkaloids (194). This may represent a nonspecific action since the pharmacological properties of the two groups of alkaloids are distinctive and not mutually shared (Section III, A,4,*c*; III,E).

III. PHARMACOLOGICAL ACTIONS

The veratrum alkaloids, when administered in μg/kg doses, exert widespread actions which affect most of the organ systems in the body. The tertiary amine ester alkaloids (ceveratrum group) differ somewhat pharmacologically from the secondary amines and their glycosides found in the jerveratrum group, and the ester bond is important for some of the effects produced. The basic action of all of these substances probably resides in their effects on the membranes of excitable cells, although for some (jerveratrum group), *in vitro* activity in homogenate systems has been observed. Pharmacologic activity has been demonstrated in central and peripheral portions of the nervous system and in the various types of muscle tissue. Minor differences in structure are occasionally associated with quantitatively and/or qualitatively different actions. For the alkaloids in the ceveratrum group, stimulation of reflex activity forms an important part of their over-all effects which are sometimes complicated by the appearance of tachyphylaxis (16, 126, 223). Differences in onset and duration of action have been observed (126). They appear to be related to the degree of esterification, the higher polyesters particularly having long durations of action (72).

The absorption, distribution, metabolism, and excretion of these substances have not been studied extensively (126), although there has been recent interest in differences noted in humans between protoveratrines A and B (230, 231). Pircio and Geiling (182) have studied in the rat, following intraperitoneal injection, the excretion and metabolism of radioactive germidine and veratrosine which had been obtained biosynthetically from *V. viride*. Less than 3% of the materials was excreted unchanged and more than 85% of the radioactivity appeared in the feces within 24 hours, chiefly as water-soluble metabolites. The liver, and possibly the intestinal mucosa, were suggested as excretory pathways. However, Matallana *et al.* (151), on the basis of evisceration in the cat, reported that the transient heart rate effect of a single intravenous dose of veratramine (the alkamine of veratrosine) and the rate of elimination during continuous infusion, were not primarily dependent upon the presence of the liver or other abdominal organs. Differences in species, chemical structure and route of administration may have been important variables in these different experiments.

A. Cardiovascular Effects

The cardiovascular effects of the veratrum alkaloids which have been noted in experimental animals and in humans are diverse. These have included, among others, both increases and decreases in heart rate, blood pressure, and cardiac output, as well as effects on cardiac contractility, rhythmicity, excitability, and conduction. In experimental animals, the effects have often varied with the species, the type and depth of anesthesia, the particular alkaloid studied, the dose range employed, the route of administration, and the anatomical and physiological intactness of the preparation. Afferent nervous pathways loom importantly in the cardiovascular effects of these drugs, and investigators, motivated by particular biases, have been prone to highlight the importance of specific mechanisms. Clearly, our present state of knowledge of the functioning of the circulatory system, though still far from complete, must be the base on which an understanding of the circulatory actions of the veratrum alkaloids stands. Even so, the mosaic of effects reported is difficult to fit into a picture which clearly depicts the relative contributions of specific mechanisms as they may be operating in the intact animal or human under the influence of these drugs. The uniqueness of some of the mechanisms involved has spurred continued interest in the veratrum alkaloids, in spite of the fact that for use in human hypertension these agents have been eclipsed by newer drugs.

1. *The Bezold-Jarisch Effect and Other Reflexes*

In 1939, Jarisch (109), motivated by his own experiments and by the early observations of von Bezold (33), designated as the Bezold effect the reflex decrease in blood pressure and heart rate caused by veratrine and by the active principles of the mistletoe, *Viscum album,* acting on the heart. Later, Jarisch and his co-workers characterized a series of other, unrelated chemical agents, which also evoked these reflex effects. The term "detector substances" was applied to the entire group of chemical agents acting in this manner. In 1953, Krayer, in a historical review later published (125), formally suggested the use of the term "Bezold-Jarisch effect" as recognition of the work of Jarisch.

In his definition of the Bezold effect, Jarisch outlined the role of peripheral receptors in the heart (predominantly in ventricular muscle), the afferent path via the vagus nerves and the efferent paths involving the cardiac vagus and the vasomotor outflow to peripheral vessels. Reflex respiratory (Section III,B) effects, also noted by von Bezold, do not originate in the heart and were not included within the meaning of the term. This is the view taken by Dawes and Comroe (51) in their review on chemoreflexes. However, departing from eponymic devices, they suggested a synonomous term, coronary chemoreflex. Although their excellent review left no doubt that the term did not signify the presence of physiological chemoreceptors, the term as since interpreted by others, has led to misunderstanding. It is now generally accepted that the receptors involved are mechano- or stretch receptors (173). Later authors such as Aviado and Schmidt (21) have continued to include apnea (reflexly arising from the lung) within the meaning of the Bezold-Jarisch effect. The former view will be adopted here.

The Bezold-Jarisch effect is not the only reflex involved in the cardiovascular actions of the veratrum alkaloids. The lungs, the carotid sinus, and the carotid body contain important receptor areas which may respond to these drugs. There are observations which have implicated other areas that have not been as adequately documented. Beyond eliciting peripheral reflex activity, the veratrum alkaloids may produce cardiovascular effects by an action on the central nervous system itself. Some of the possible sites where these drugs may act are shown in Fig. 8.

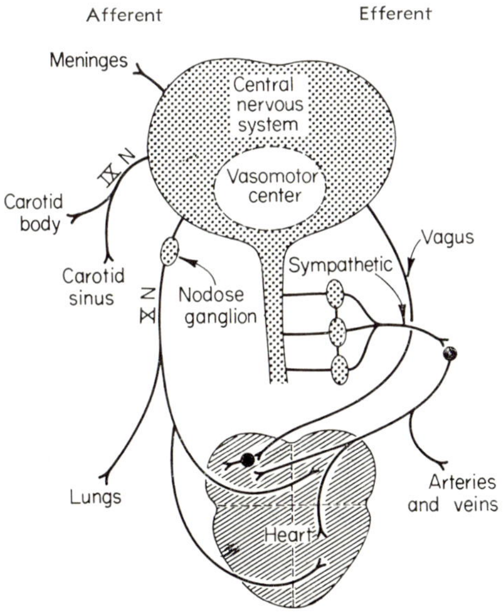

FIG. 8. A schematic diagram showing some of the possible sites of action of the veratrum alkaloids when they act to produce effects on the cardiovascular and other systems. Afferent pathways for reflex action are on the left. The pathways of the Bezold-Jarisch effect, via the cardiac vagus (X N), take origin from all chambers of the heart. The efferent pathways which subserve the cardiovascular effects are noted on the right.

a. Peripheral Receptor Areas. In 1947, Dawes (50) showed that injections of veratridine, cevadine, and protoveratrine directly into selected coronary arteries (via ingenious glass cannulae in dogs and cats) produced falls in blood pressure and heart rate which were abolished by vagotomy. Effective doses were $\frac{1}{10}$ to $\frac{1}{20}$ those required by intravenous injection. Studies in 1949 by Aviado *et al.* (20), who employed cardiac catheterization, showed similar effects with veratridine in dogs. Veriloid®, a mixture of alkaloids obtained from *V. viride,* injected into the coronary arteries of the dog (52) also produced these effects. These observations confirmed the idea of von Bezold that there were receptor areas in the heart which could be excited to produce the reflex effects, although the identity of the sensory elements was not known. These receptor areas are accessible to drugs administered via the coronary circulation, but usually not by topical application to endocardial or pericardial surfaces (21). However, epicardial veratrine has recently been reported to excite vagal endings (139). Receptors are present in both atria and ventricles on both sides of the heart (174). The reflex is abolished by a local anesthetic applied within the pericardial cavity (51), but interference with central mechanisms following systemic absorption could not be excluded. However, a thiopyranoindole derivative has been shown to suppress the reflex at the heart (236) since it did not affect the reflex induced by stimulation of the central end of the severed vagus.

Action potential recordings from single-fiber vagal preparations have shown that the frequency of discharges arising in the atria and ventricles in phase with various portions of the cardiac cycle is accentuated by veratrine (174), and similar effects have been noted for veratridine, germerine, and neogermitrine in atrial, nerve-fiber preparations (180), and for veratridine and Veriloid in ventricular nerve-fiber preparations (179). These observations are the basis for presuming a mechano- or stretch nature (173) for the sensory elements involved. Perfused heart studies have indicated that reflex vasodepression and bradycardia can be observed with elevation of perfusion pressure in the right heart (or with veratridine) (18), and studies on myocardial ischemia have shown that similar effects can be noted during a fall in intraventricular pressure accompanied by cardiac dilatation (55). Stretch and not pressure is thus the adequate stimulus, and the receptors have been termed deformation receptors (174).

Besides the Bezold-Jarisch reflex, with the heart as a peripheral receptor site for veratrum-induced hypotension (18, 50, 150) and with the vagus as the afferent pathway, there are other sites within the thorax (Fig. 8) which may be similarly affected. Reflex decreases in heart rate and blood pressure originating in the lung have been noted with various veratrum alkaloids (18, 190, 214), the vagus being the afferent path. The receptors for these have been thought to be baroreceptors since similar effects were noted with increases in perfusion pressure in the pulmonary circuit but were not seen with changes in carbon dioxide or oxygen tension in the perfusing blood (18). However, Takasaki (214) has since noted such changes (abolished by vagotomy) with Veriloid or veratrine when pulmonary pressures were kept constant. The receptors may be therefore vagal chemoreceptors. An important nonvagal pathway for reflex vasodepression and bradycardia seen with some veratrum alkaloids is that originating in the receptors of the carotid sinus (86, 150). Local injection of protoveratrine or germine esters into the adventitia of the carotid sinus is sufficient to produce the effect (152, 166). Veratridine by this route seems to have little of this action (223) and may indeed block the effect of others of the alkaloids. Moran *et al.* (166) noted that such advential injection, into the carotid sinus, of veratridine reversed the depressor action of other veratrum alkaloids previously applied and resulted in an increase in blood pressure like that seen after section of the carotid sinus nerve. This blocking effect may be due to paralysis of pressoreceptors which had been excited to continuous firing by the first drug application. Such a paralysis would indeed simulate severing of the nerve since tonic activity in the depressor afferents would be gone and the blood pressure would rise. The repetitive firing in the baroreceptors, induced by local or intravenous administration of the veratrum alkaloids, accounts for the now well-known blockade of the carotid sinus pressoreflex (185); the usual decrease in firing occasioned by a local fall in sinus pressure does not occur and the blood pressure does not rise.

Other possible peripheral receptor sites at which the veratrum alkaloids may act to produce depressor responses have been studied only initially. Gruhzit *et al.* (87) have shown that the inotropic action of epinephrine may elicit a reflex vasodilatation in the leg from thoracic receptors whose central connections are made via dorsal roots. These were thought to be mechanoreceptors, and there were preliminary suggestions (86) that veratridine might also activate them. Whether this reflex contributes to blood pressure regulation is not certain. Riker (186) noted that receptors in the abdomen accessible to local intra-arterial injection of veratridine can elicit blood pressure changes of variable direction and magnitude as well as apnea. Small (14 mm Hg) decreases were occasionally noted, but the vasomotor responses were not considered a significant component of the reflex. The afferent path was the splanchnic nerve. Aviado *et al.* (16) detected an intracranial area, possibly meningeal (Fig. 8), which was accessible to occipital arterial or extradural injection of veratridine, from which decreases in blood pressure, heart rate, and respiration could be elicited. These effects were not attributable to recirculation of the drug to other areas. The nodose ganglion of the vagus nerve (Fig. 8) is another possible peripheral site. It has been primarily implicated in veratrum-induced emesis (Section III,C). Borison *et al.* (38) showed that in cervically vagotomized animals, in which the carotid sinus mechanism is hypoactive, nodose ganglionectomy will return the blood pressure to normal during Veriloid-induced hypotension. This observation was partially confirmed by Tanaka and Kanno (216), who observed that the vasodepressor component of a biphasic blood pressure response to protoveratrine in cervically vagotomized animals is abolished by nodose ganglionectomy. However, Wang *et al.* (223), using germine esters and veratridine, could not ascribe any role of circulatory importance to the nodose ganglion.

b. Afferent Pathways. Dawes and Comroe (51) have outlined the difficulties involved in elucidating the particular cardiac vagal branches which carry the afferent nerves for the Bezold-Jarisch effect, and these are discussed further by Aviado and Schmidt (21). Work in the cat (111) and the dog (54) has permitted partial localization. In the cat, the right vagal branches are widely distributed, and in the dog, cardiac vagal fibers were noted to join the left recurrent laryngeal branch of the vagus near the aortic arch. The types of fibers in the vagus which subserve the afferent portion of the reflex have been studied as to conduction velocities (179) and susceptibility to reversible block by cooling (52). Fibers originating in the ventricles are probably very small B and C fibers which are blocked at 8 to 10°C. These temperature requirements distinguish this reflex from other cardiovascular reflexes arising in the lung which also travel in the vagus (51).

Aortic receptors, with the vagus as the afferent pathway, are difficult to study. This pathway is not activated by doses of veratridine sufficient to elicit the Bezold-Jarisch effect (51). The glossopharyngeal innervation of the carotid area is the pathway from the carotid sinus and carotid body, and ingenious techniques (not always successful) have been employed to separate the particular afferents from the two sites (20, 44, 86, 166, 223). Such separation is important since activation of these pathways individually leads to opposite effects on the blood pressure.

Electrophysiological recording of action potentials in the carotid sinus nerve by Jarisch *et al.* (108) suggested that increased firing of the baroreceptors after intravenous injection of veratrine in the cat does not occur and that these receptors do not contribute to the hypotensive response. Similar recording by Dontas (56) indicated that the action of protoveratrine was different. The initial phase of the hypotension, which was attributed to the Bezold-Jarisch reflex, was actually associated with a decrease in pressor spike activity (the usual response to systemic hypotension), but later in time increased firing of the baroreceptors was noted. This elegant work showed the importance of the two areas (heart and baroreceptors) for protoveratrine hypotension and correlated these actions with efferent traffic in the splanchnic nerve. Splanchnic inhibition was never complete but evidenced itself as low-grade continuous activity quite different from the normal, highly synchronized pattern.

c. Central Connections. There are no definitive studies distinguishing the central pathways for the Bezold-Jarisch effect from other reflexes induced by the veratrum alkaloids or by other substances. The task is a formidable one. In studies which have been reported, drugs have been administered intravenously with the possibility of effects originating from multiple reflexogenic areas. However, it does appear that veratrum-induced reflexes may be distinguished from similar reflexes due to other substances. The response to veratridine is not particularly sensitive to small doses of pentobarbital, although similar reflex responses to other substances such as lobeline are (32). Deep barbiturate anesthesia, however, does reduce reflex responses to the veratrum alkaloids (78). Hexobarbital or urethane, administered intracisternally, do not affect the reflex response to protoveratrine, although morphine augments the reflex while procaine inhibits it when these are given by this route (98). A rise in cerebrospinal fluid pressure evokes an increase in blood pressure during Veriloid-induced hypotension (38), indicating that the medullary vasomotor center is still capable of discharging.

d. Efferent Pathways. The efferent paths of the Bezold-Jarisch and other reflexes are undoubtedly the vagal (136) and sympathetic outflows (223). The bradycardia, classically ascribed to the efferent vagus, is not always abolished by atropine (30, 126) and may in part be the result of inhibition of cardiac sympathetic tone. Cardiac slowing may contribute to the hypotension (17, 30), but the fall in blood pressure is mediated in large part by inhibition of sympathetic arteriolar vasomotor tone which can be demonstrated by vasodilatation in the isolated perfused hind limb with nervous connections to the body intact (30, 126). Vasodilatation thus accounts for the increases in regional blood flow which have been noted (126). Dawes *et al.* (53) have elegantly demonstrated a connection between peripheral vasodilatation and the afferent pathway by showing that this effect, noted in the hind limb and in the vascular area of the coeliac axis in the cat (intravenous injection of veratridine), was reversibly abolished by cooling the cervical vagi to 8°C. The vasodilator response (as measured in the dog hind leg) is not influenced by atropine and is not therefore mediated by cholinergic, dilator nerves (30). The possibility of the involvement of a noncholinergic sympathetic vasodilator mechanism is suggested by observations that the sympathetic blocking agent bretylium does not affect the reflex hypotension due to veratridine (17). Beyond effects on heart rate and vasomotor tone, effects on cardiac output also influence the blood pressure (24). The fall in cardiac output noted with veratridine and various germine esters (72) has been attributed to inhibition of sympathetic cardiac inotropic tone and venomotor tone. The importance of neurogenic influence on myocardial contractility has been stressed by Rushmer *et al.* (192). Strain gauge recording of myocardial contraction has detected generalized effects on the myocardium following injections of veratridine into the coronary arteries (228). Although interruption of afferent or efferent paths was not attempted, these reflex effects were easily differentiated from localized effects of acetylcholine and other injections. Reflex effects on venomotor tone have not been studied directly. Thus the inhibition of sympathetic tone seen with the veratrum alkaloids may be general and may contribute to the hypotension by effects on the heart, arterioles and veins.

e. A Role for the Bezold-Jarisch Effect? The possible physiological role of the Bezold-Jarisch effect is still questionable. Investigators have been exceedingly cautious in the interpretation of relevant data and rightly so. Jarisch and Zotterman (110) have suggested a kind of nocioceptive reflex subserved by pain fibers and possibly protecting the heart against undue distension of the wall. Schaefer (198) takes exception to this concept and has summarized the difficulties involved. He presents a general picture which envisages diverse information of varying stimulus intensities as originating in the heart and as being interpreted by central mechanisms which are distributed "at random." This idea, which moves away from the concept of specific fibers with specific actions, is supported by the observations of Neil and Joels (174) who found that, even with single fiber recording, the categorization of atrial receptors into types A and B was too rigid since a type A receptor can show a type B pattern of discharge under the influence of changes in venous filling or following veratrine. It may be that, under drug influence, multiple peripheral receptors are activated maximally, a situation which does not occur physiologically, and that the usual random information feeding into the central nervous system becomes relatively synchronized and capable of being interpreted in a manner which leads to selective inhibition or excitation of specific efferent pathways. The Bezold-Jarisch effect may be involved in some of the manifestations of myocardial infarction (156), and an inconstant tonic vagal depressor reflex in the rabbit has been observed which may be an expression of this reflex (155).

A definitive experimental attack on the problem of afferent, central, and efferent connections of the Bezold-Jarisch effect (and other reflexes like it) will require the coordinated use of highly refined techniques such as single unit recording, differential nerve block, localization of drugs to specific sites, and the production of discrete neuroanatomical lesions. A recently developed multibarreled micropipette electrode technique (193) may also be of value.

2. *The Hypotensive and Cardiodecelerator Actions*

The hypotensive and cardiodecelerator actions of the tertiary amine ester alkaloids, when they are administered intravenously, as is usual in experimental animals, are complex. The effects are not due to direct actions on the heart or blood vessels; the substances, in the concentrations attained with usual doses, do not block ganglia nor are they cholinergic or adrenergic blocking drugs. The importance of their actions on nervous pathways is highlighted by their influence on the response to vasoactive drugs in general. Goth and Harrison (82) have shown that protoveratrine enhanced the blood pressure effects of both hypotensive and hypertensive agents such as histamine and norepinephrine, and that the action was noted only when the carotid sinus and vagus nerves were intact.

Early studies (126) already showed that not only alkaloidal extracts and mixtures elicited decreases in blood pressure and heart rate, but that these effects were also produced by the pure ester alkaloids, the ester bond being important for the action. The alkamine cevine, for example, did not elicit the effects in doses up to 2000 times that of the smallest effective dose of veratridine (162). Similar negative results were noted for germine (75). Early studies also pointed to the possibilities for reflex action from receptor areas in the thorax and in the carotid area, and for central action as well. The role of the vagus as one afferent path for reflex action and as an efferent path for cardiodeceleration had been clarified and the importance of efferent sympathetic pathways for the vasodilatation accompanying the hypotension were known. More recent studies have looked to the relative importance of afferent and central sites for the cardiovascular actions and have also attempted to sort out efferent mechanisms.

Dose-response relations in the dog for the hypotensive and bradycardic effects of rapid intravenous injections of germerine were reported by Benforado *et al.* (30). The curves are steep, as is shown in Fig. 9. Atropine reduced the fall in heart rate but did not completely abolish it and attenuated the blood pressure fall. Such observations have been qualitatively noted in the past (126). Following vagotomy, which interrupts not only cardiac efferents but also afferent pathways from the chest (heart and lungs), cardiac slowing could still be observed, although only at the higher doses, and even then it was much reduced; the procedure also markedly diminished the slope of the blood pressure dose-response curve. Not shown in the figure are hypotensive and bradycardic responses in the presence of intact vagi, but following carotid sinus denervation, and the reversal of these responses (to usually effective doses) after complete debuffering. The experiments indicate that, for the dose levels employed, either the afferent vagus or the carotid sinus

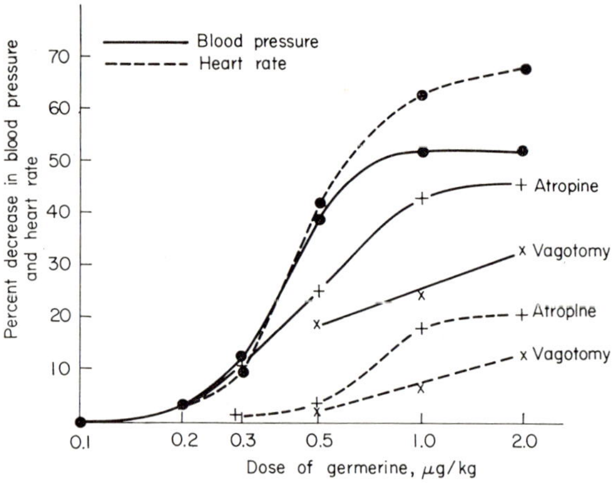

FIG. 9. Dose-response relationship for the hypotensive and bradycardic effect of germerine. Dog, male, 15.4 kg; anesthesia: sodium pentobarbital, 35 mg/kg i.p. Single rapid, intravenous injections of germerine were given—intervals ranging from 20–60 minutes. The unlabeled curves were obtained before administration of atropine, the curves labeled "atropine" after 2 mg/kg of atropine sulfate, and the curves labeled "vagotomy" after both vagi had been cut in the neck. From Benforado *et al.* (30), with kind permission of the publisher, Williams & Wilkins, Baltimore, Maryland.

pathways must be intact for obtaining depressor responses on intravenous injection and that the cardiodecelerator response may contribute in part to the hypotension. Further, it would appear that the decelerator action may have a small extravagal component, probably inhibition of cardiac sympathetic tone. In these same experiments, germerine and other germine esters and veratridine were shown to cause increases in flow in the perfused hind leg on intravenous injection. These observations extended in a quantitative fashion earlier observations on reflex vasodilation (53, 162). Discrepancies between the time course of the vasodilation and the hypotension induced, as well as the fact that maximal dilator responses were observed at only moderate hypotensive doses, suggested that vasodilatation was not the only factor involved in the hypotensive response.

Such has been suggested previously by observations of falls in cardiac output in humans (74, 104, 172) and in experimental animals (24) and by the reported absence of hypotension in dogs given Veriloid when the cardiac output was mechanically held constant (224). This last observation, suggesting that the fall in blood pressure with Veriloid was entirely due to cardiac depression, was examined again by Rose and Lazaro (189). They were able to show that a mechanical pump system with constant output, replacing the left ventricle, will not abolish the blood pressure response to Veriloid if the drug has access to the pulmonary and coronary circulations (the afferent sites for reflex action). Such an experimental technique, which in effect perfused the body at constant flow, confirms the idea that loss of vascular tone must contribute to the blood pressure change.

The problem of the relative contributions of inhibition of neurogenic arteriolar vasomotor tone and decreases in cardiac output to veratrum alkaloid–induced hypotension was approached by Flacke *et al.* (72) by the use of a technique which measured aortic flow directly in the open-chest animal. The procedure (71) permits an evaluation of arteriolar vasomotor tone by the construction of pressure-flow curves. Such curves are based on transient, graded interruptions of flow which induce graded decreases in pressure. Shifts of such pressure-flow curves occur when vasomotor tone is increased by carotid sinus nerve section (shift to the right), or decreased by the use of an adrenergic blocking drug such as Dibenamine® (shift to the left).

Fig. 10 shows such curves in a dog before and after Dibenamine. Also plotted in the diagram is the time course of pressure and flow following the intravenous injection of desacetylgermitetrine. It can be noted that drug injection results first in a decrease in tone (point 2). This is followed by a rapid decline in tone and flow (point 3) with subsequent points showing partial recovery from the response followed by a second more prolonged hypotensive phase in which tone changes and flow changes are generally dissociated in time. Thus the contributions of cardiac output and changes in vasomotor tone to the hypotension are variable in magnitude as well as in time, and it is not possible to characterize in any cogent manner their relative importances. The observations of Dontas (56), (Section III,A,1,*b*) on impulse frequency in the carotid sinus nerve may be pertinent here as a possible explanation for the varied pattern of response. Measurement of right atrial pressures in various experiments showed that the decreases in flow could be accompanied by either decreases, no change, or increases in atrial pressure. The question therefore arises as to the mechanism of the changes in output. Of the possibilities that may be considered, some can be ruled out: cardiac depression due to a direct negative inotropic action (26), bradycardia (72), and constriction of the pulmonary vascular bed (24). However, there is a recent report (15) suggesting reflex pulmonary vasoconstriction dependent on vagal afferents and sympathetic outflow through thoracic 1 to 4. It seems likely that the decrease in cardiac output may be due to generalized reflex inhibition of sympathetic tone which may involve a decreased contractility of the

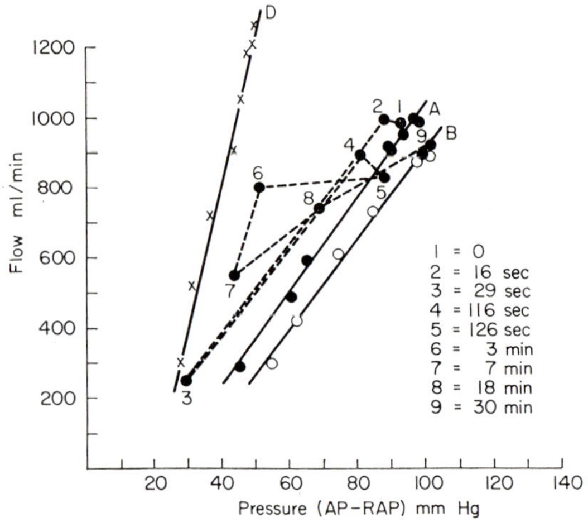

FIG. 10. Effect of an injection of desacetylgermitetrine plotted in a pressure-flow diagram. Changes of systemic cardiac output (flow) and pressures across the systemic circulation (arterial pressure–right atrial pressure). The dotted line connects points obtained at the times indicated at the right. At 0 time (point 1) 2 μg/kg desacetylgermitetrine was injected i.v. The curve marked "A" was obtained immediately before drug injection and curve "B" after drug effects had terminated. The curve on the left was obtained at the end of the experiment after Dibenamine (20 mg/kg) had been given and represents the pressure-flow relationships in this animal after elimination of vasoconstrictor tone. From Flacke *et al.* (72), with kind permission of the authors and the publishers, Williams & Wilkins, Baltimore, Maryland.

heart and an increased capacity of the venous circulation. Each of these factors would affect cardiac filling pressure, but in opposite directions. With both factors operating, the filling pressure at the reduced output might increase, decrease, or not change. The idea of a drug-induced decrease in positive inotropic sympathetic tone and venous tone is worthy of further investigation. For example, the loss of venous tone following ganglionic blockade accounts for decreases in cardiac output which contribute to the fall in blood pressure observed (218), and peripheral reflexes have been shown to influence ventricular function curves by inhibiting sympathetic tone (57). Further, reflex decreases in cardiac contractility have been observed following veratridine administration (17).

A central action accounting for the hypotensive response following intravenous use of the veratrum alkaloids has been suggested by many investigators (185, 208, 209, 213). Some of the suggestions were based on lack of quantitative alteration of the blood pressure change following vagotomy and carotid sinus nerve section. Subsequent investigations have usually disclosed reversal of effect (hypertension) after such procedures (30, 56, 65, 86), and it is difficult to account for all the original observations. However, there are differences among veratrum alkaloids, and anesthesia may have been a contributing factor as well. The observations which most forcibly suggest a central action are those of Taylor and Page (217) based on studies involving crossed circulation in isolated, perfused heads. Localization of Veriloid within the head circulation was noted to lead to vasodepression in the body. The effect was long lasting and could be overcome by cerebral ischemia, which produced its usual rise in blood pressure. Swiss and Maison (213) saw vasodepression in a similar experimental series with various other veratrum alkaloids. Rodbard and Saiki (188) made observations on the pressor response to increased intracranial pressure which suggest that intracranial baroreceptors exist. These might be a locus of central action for the veratrum alkaloids.

Wang *et al.* (223) have suggested a central action for veratridine based on observations that it, but not Veriloid, germine esters, or protoveratrine, decreased the electrical excitability of the vasomotor center. However, such an observation may have little significance for the physiological functioning of the vasomotor center. Observations on reactivity of the center to pressor stimuli such as increased intracranial pressure or carotid body stimulation might be more pertinent. Lim *et al.* (144) injected Veriloid into the vasopressor center and noted a depressed response to electrical stimulation. However, on intravenous administration hypotension was present at a time when no central depression to electrical stimulation was noted.

Krayer *et al.* (136) early demonstrated reflex bradycardia due to veratridine. This was accomplished using the innervated heart-lung-head preparation where the head and heart circulations were distinct, and only nervous connections existed between the two circuits. Localization of the drug within the heart-lung circuit produced a bradycardia which was abolished by severing the vagi. The heart and the carotid sinus were peripheral sites of action for the reflex. Larger doses injected into the head circulation also produced a bradycardia. Such central action was also demonstrated by Heymans and DeVleeschhouwer (97).

3. *The Hypertensive and Cardioaccelerator Actions*

Early investigators, usually using impure preparations, noted conditions under which the decreases in heart rate and blood pressure elicited with the veratrum alkaloids were reversed and explored the possible roles of a direct vasoconstrictor action of high concentrations, a humoral action based on the release of epinephrine from the adrenal medulla, and a central action (126). More recent work has taken advantage of the use of pure alkaloids. Benforado *et al.* (30) studied germine esters and veratridine and observed pressor and cardioaccelerator responses after intravenous injection of usually depressor doses in dogs after vagal section and blockade of the carotid sinus nerves, indicating that large doses are not necessary for the reversed response. Calliauw (44) noted similar effects with protoveratrine A and showed, in addition, reflex hypertension due to carotid body stimulation. A previous report of veratridine-induced reflex hypotension from the carotid body (20) was not later confirmed (86, 166, 223) and may have been due to access of the drug to the carotid sinus or to the central nervous system. Veriloid may produce hypertension by an action on the carotid body (86).

The possibility of a central action is suggested by reports of hypertension following injections into the fourth ventricle (147) or into the cisterna magna (44, 45). However, adequate access of drugs to these areas following intravenous injection is open to question. This objection was overcome by Aviado *et al.* (16), who showed that there was an intracranial site, possibly the medulla, which was accessible to intracisternal or intravertebral arterial injection of veratridine. Such injections led to increases in heart rate and blood pressure. Similar effects of intravertebral arterial injection of protoveratrine have been reported (65). In addition to stimulation of vasomotor centers in the brain, there may also be stimulation of secondary vasomotor centers in the cord (44), although Goth and Harrison (82) failed to note a pressor response to protoveratrine A in completely debuffered dogs after spinal section at cervical 6.

Direct vasoconstriction cannot explain the pressor action of the various veratrum alkaloids. Although early reports suggested the possibility of such an action (126), these have not been substantiated with the pure alkaloids, veratridine being a possible exception. No effects on local blood flow following intra-arterial injection have been observed with the germine esters (30, 223) or with protoveratrine A (44). With veratridine (30) a slight transient decrease was noted in femoral bed blood flow in the dog, but a previous study (162) had failed to detect this under similar experimental circumstances. The transient nature of the response (30 seconds to 2 minutes), and the fact that the dose needed for local effect was about the same as the usual intravenous hypotensive dose, make it seem unlikely that the effect is of any importance for the hypertensive action.

Certain characteristics of the hypertensive action of the veratrum alkaloids suggest a role for the adrenal medulla (126). Moe *et al.* (162), in experiments on the hind limb of the dog perfused from a donor, showed that a hypertensive response to a large (1 mg) dose of veratridine in the donor led to an initial increase in flow in the perfused limb, but that this was followed by a rapid decrease in flow as the donor blood pressure reached its maximum. Since the drug itself failed to cause vasoconstriction on intra-arterial injection, the response was ascribed to a humoral agent, presumably epinephrine, reaching the perfused leg from the donor. The adrenal medulla was suggested as the site of origin. Aronow (5) has studied quantitatively the release of catecholamines from the adrenal medulla caused by the veratrum alkaloids. In vagotomized, atropinized dogs, the control mean values for resting secretion were about 20 mμg/kg/minute (81% epinephrine). Following intravenous administration of veratridine or protoveratrine A, secretions as high as 1 μg/kg/minute of epinephrine were observed and the effects were also noted following acute denervation of the glands. The responses required large doses (100 μg/kg of veratridine) and were accompanied by increases in blood pressure and heart rate. None of the effects were noted after acute adrenalectomy. Thus a direct action at the adrenal medulla may contribute to the hypertensive effect of large doses. Calliauw (44) noted that the hypertensive effect of a small dose of protoveratrine A (3 μg/kg) in a vagotomized spinal dog was abolished by destruction of the cord. This dose level was therefore too low to exert any direct action on the adrenal medulla. Goth and Harrison (82) found no response at all to protoveratrine (4 μg/kg) in the spinal dog. It is possible that the adrenal medulla may be involved also in the hypertensive responses mediated by efferent sympathetic pathways following effects of the veratrum alkaloids at the carotid body, the medulla, or spinal centers.

Hypertensive responses to the veratrum alkaloids have been noted in man (13). Among the semisynthetic esters of germine, the mono- and diacetate elicit a hypertension (but not a tachycardia) in cats on intravenous injection. Flacke (68) found that the rise was occasionally preceded by a transient fall and that it was not dose-related. Its magnitude was considerably increased by section of the vagus and carotid sinus nerves; cord section at cervical 2 did not abolish it, but the response was absent after pithing. Although the mechanism was not explored, on the basis of similar responses to painful stimuli and signs of peripheral sensory stimulation in the animals the suggestion was made that the response might be due to stimulation of sensory receptors. The response, which does not include tachycardia, seems unlike the usual hypertensive responses. The higher polyacetate esters of germine do not have this action, although those of protoverine do (89).

4. *Direct Cardiac Effects*

Although the heart participates in the dramatic cardiovascular effects noted following administration of small doses of the veratrum alkaloids to the intact animal, the cardiac effects noted are the result of an indirect action mediated via the nervous system (Section III,A,2). Direct effects on the heart have been demonstrated also (126), but these have been studied predominantly in isolated preparations. The drug concentrations required for demonstration of these direct effects exceed those usually employed in the intact animal, and it seems likely that the direct cardiac actions play little role in the *in vivo* effects of the veratrum alkaloids except when given in high dosage. However, the effects have been of continuing interest to investigators because they have served to motivate inquiry into cardiac mechanisms. The interest has been further served by the chemical similarities between the aglycones found in the cardiac glycosides and the alkamines of the veratrum alkaloids, both having basic steroid structures. Certain pharmacological similarities as well as dissimilarities between these two groups of plant substances have become apparent.

a. Inotropic Action. A positive inotropic action of various of the ceveratrum alkaloids has been demonstrated in the hearts of lower forms as well as in mammalian hearts (126). The effect has been studied mostly with the ester alkaloids but has also been demonstrated with at least one of the alkamines, cevine (163). The ester bond is therefore not a prerequisite for the inotropic action, although its presence markedly enhances potency, veratridine being 300 times more potent in this regard than cevine. The inotropic action is best seen in hypodynamic preparations following a reduction of calcium in the medium, the use of various cardiac depressants, or spontaneous failure. Veratridine has been shown to increase the efficiency of the failing mammalian heart in a manner similar to that of the cardiac glycosides (126). A negative inotropic action in the Langendorff rabbit heart has been reported for Veriloid (207), but this was noted only with very high concentrations following an early positive inotropic effect. The jerveratrum alkaloids probably do not exert a positive inotropic action, and veratramine in high concentrations can cause heart failure in the isolated dog heart (29). This effect may be related to its depression of respiration demonstrated in heart tissue and in homogenates (183). It has been noted to decrease the amplitude of contraction in rabbit atria at low concentrations (184).

In a comparative study in the dog heart-lung preparation (26), it was shown that various veracevine, zygadenine, germine, and protoverine ester alkaloids, when administered by continuous infusion, produced effects similar to the cardiac glycosides. An increase in cardiac contractility was first noted and this was followed by cardiac irregularities terminating in ventricular fibrillation. The potency range was of the same order as that reported for the cardiac glycosides, highest molar potency being present in the tri- and tetraesters. The therapeutic ratios (the ratio between the dose producing irregularities and the dose producing a positive inotropic action) for some of the veratrum ester alkaloids studied were three to four times those reported for various cardiac glycosides. The failure to note negative inotropic effects at concentrations short of those producing irregularities made it unlikely that any direct cardiac depression (224) was involved in cardiac output decreases associated with the hypotensive response in the intact animal (Section III,A,2).

The mechanism by which the veratrum alkaloids exert their positive inotropic action on the heart is not known, but it seems likely that the effect is unrelated to the veratrine response reported in cardiac muscle (Section III,E,1,*c*). The aftercontraction in cardiac muscle has not been observed to merge with the initial twitch as it does in skeletal muscle; and, as is also observed in skeletal muscle, it is prominent only when the interval between driving stimuli is long such as occurs at driving rates of 1 to 6 per minute in the isolated ventricle strip preparation.

Morales and Acheson (164) have investigated the relation of potassium balance to the inotropic action of veratridine in the dog heart-lung preparation. The positive inotropic action could not be correlated with changes in potassium balance since the effect was shown to occur with either potassium loss or gain. At low concentrations, too low to elicit cardiac irregularities, there was usually a gain in potassium, while at higher concentrations in the presence of irregularities, but with the inotropic effect still evident (strain gauge arch recording), there was always a loss. Experiments in the same laboratory with dihydro-ouabain indicated that its inotropic action occurs concommitantly with potassium loss. Vick and Kahn (20) studied potassium movement in the isolated, hypodynamic guinea pig heart under the influence of veratridine or ouabain. They were able to show that the early inotropic actions and later contractures were accompanied by a net loss of potassium although effects on both influx and efflux were noted. They suggested the possibility that potassium loss, governed by drug action and the cardiac frequency, may be the basis for the inverse dependence of the lethal dose of veratridine on the heart rate in the isolated dog heart which was demonstrated by Benforado and Witt (31). The relation of potassium loss to the inotropic action is not clear, and the variable results noted with veratridine indicate that no certain generalization, suggested by experiences with the cardiac glycosides, can be made (164).

b. Arrhythmic Effects and Effects on Conduction. The veratrum ester alkaloids can produce digitalis-like effects leading to ventricular fibrillation (Fig. 11,A,B). However, in the stages leading to the terminal event, qualitative differences in the character of the cardiac abnormalities produced exist among the alkaloids derived from different alkamines (26). When studied in the dog heart-lung preparation cevadine characteristically produced a sinus tachycardia (Fig. 12E), which was not noted with the other alkaloids studied. For these the abnormalities fell into two groups. Veratridine, as well as the closely related zygadenine ester alkaloids, veratroylzygadenine and vanilloylzygadenine, evoked electrical alternans and 2 : 1 heart block (Fig. 11C,D,E). The other alkaloids, neogermitrine, germitetrine B, and protoveratrines A and B, evoked ventricular premature contraction (bigeminal rhythm) and ventricular tachycardia (Fig. 11B; Fig. 12A,B,D). The protoveratrines also led to atrioventricular nodal pacemaker discharge concurrent with discharge from the sinoatrial node (Fig. 12C). Germidine produced early electrical alternans followed later by bigeminal rhythm, thus appearing to share characteristics of the two groups. These observations with pure alkaloids suggest that, of the arrhythmias noted with veratrine in the intact dog (199), the electrical alternans can be ascribed to veratridine while the sinus tachycardia was probably due to cevadine.

A basis for the above observations is suggested by the work of Swain and McCarthy (210), who employed electrophysiological techniques which permitted quantitative analysis of effects on conduction in the dog heart-lung preparation. Arrhythmias leading to fibrillation were also studied. They worked with veratrine (and its component alkaloids), protoveratrine, and also andromedotoxin which is not a veratrum alkaloid (Section III,E,3). Like the cardiac glycosides, all of the substances depressed Purkinje conduction without depressing myocardial conduction. Nonfibrillatory concentrations of the veratrine alkaloids had little effect on automaticity but increased the refractory periods of both atria and ventricles and the atrioventricular conducting system. This latter observation, coupled with the possibility of two pathways (with different conduction velocities) in the system, suggested an explanation for the electrical alternans which they also observed. Protoveratrine and andromedotoxin, in nonfibrillatory concentrations, increased the spontaneous atrioventricular nodal rate (after the sinoatrial node had been crushed) and led to bigeminal rhythm and ventricular tachycardia but left intracardiac conduction relatively unimpaired. The effect on refractory period was not as prominent as that of veratrine.

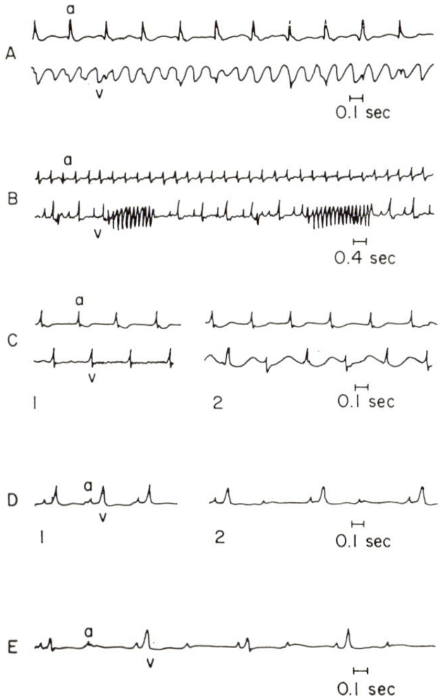

FIG. 11. Cardiac irregularities caused by veratrum ester alkaloids on dog heart-lung preparations. EKG tracings taken with Grass inkwriting oscillograph. The veratrum alkaloids were administered by continuous infusion until the lethal effect was reached. In A, B, and C the upper tracings were taken with direct atrial leads while the lower tracings represent pericardial leads. In D and E pericardial leads alone were used. *a* signifies an atrial complex; *v* signifies a ventricular complex. A, veratridine; atrial P waves recorded simultaneously with fibrillatory complexes from the ventricles. B, germitetrine B: transient flutter-fibrillation complexes from the ventricles. C, veratroylzygadenine: (1) sinus rhythm; (2) sinus rhythm with electrical alternation of the QRS. D, veratridine: (1) sinus rhythm; (2) 2 : 1 heart block. E, veratridine: electrical alternation of the QRS in the presence of 2 : 1 heart block. From Benforado (26), with kind permission from the publisher, Williams & Wilkins, Baltimore, Maryland.

The authors suggested that the ability of all the drugs tested to produce ventricular fibrillation lay in the ultimate differential depression of Purkinje conduction and that the tendency to produce automaticity, a factor not noted with the veratrine alkaloids, was not crucial.

Unexplained is the absence of effects of the veratrine alkaloids on spontaneity in the dog heart noted above (26, 199, 210) such as have been observed in excised tissue of the dog and rat heart (41a, 99). In

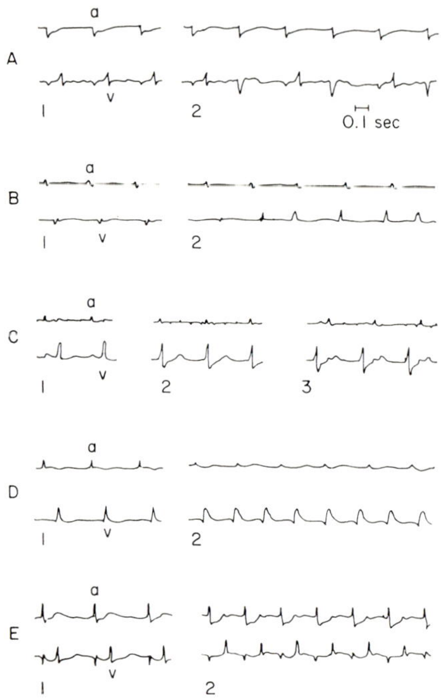

FIG. 12. Cardiac irregularities caused by veratrum ester alkaloids. Dogs. Heart-lung preparations. EKG tracings taken with Grass inkwriting oscillograph. The veratrum alkaloids were administered by continuous infusion until the lethal effect was reached. Upper tracings were taken with direct atrial leads while the lower tracings represent pericardial leads. *a* signifies an atrial complex; *v* signifies a ventricular complex. A, germitetrine B: (1) sinus rhythm; (2) ventricular bigeminal rhythm. B, neogermitrine: (1) sinus rhythm; (2) ventricular ectopic beats. C, protoveratrine A: Form of the P wave remains unchanged throughout (thin vertical lines are time lines). (1) sinus rhythm; (2) A-V nodal pacemaker discharging at the same rate as the S-A node; P wave written simultaneously with nodal complex; (3) shift of the P wave to 0.1 second after nodal complex; the S-A node and the A-V node discharging independently at the same rate with only a shift in phase. D, protoveratrine A: (1) sinus rhythm; (2) ventricular tachycardia. E, cevadine: (1) sinus rhythm; (2) sinus tachycardia. From Benforado (26), with kind permission from the publisher, Williams & Wilkins, Baltimore, Maryland.

these situations, transmembrane recording has indicated high-frequency repetitive discharge such as is associated with the veratrine response in nerve and skeletal muscle. The ectopic pacemaker induced in ventricular Purkinje fibers by veratrine is like that produced by epinephrine or norepinephrine, and the mechanism is probably different from that of discharge in normal pacemakers (99). During high-frequency firing, the upstroke of one action potential follows closely after the repolarization phase of the previous action potential, and the maximum resting potential is almost identical with the threshold potential.

Studies on the relation of K^+ to veratrum alkaloid cardiotoxicity have indicated that, as for the cardiac glycosides, irregularities are accompanied by K^+ loss from the heart (Section III,A,4,*a*). However, although K^+ administration will decrease the toxic effects of digitalis on the guinea pig heart, the toxicity due to veratrine is increased (95). Nonetheless, there appears to be a relationship between veratridine cardiotoxicity and potassium loss which may be frequency-related (31, 220). A further observation suggesting such a relationship was noted in driven rat ventricle strips exposed to veratridine (27). In these experiments, the usual "all or none" contraction due to a driving stimulus is converted to a voltage-sensitive alternation of the height of contraction following the drug. The phenomenon was attributed to increases in refractory period produced by the drug, and the time required for the phenomenon to appear was inversely related to the driving frequency. A decrease in the K^+ concentration of the medium significantly hastened the time of onset of alternation at high driving frequencies.

The relation of Ca^{++} to veratrum alkaloid cardiotoxicity has yet to be studied. The general antagonistic action of Ca^{++} to the veratrine response in nerve and skeletal muscle (Section III,E,2) suggests that cardiotoxicity may be similarly affected. There have been clinical reports of veratrum alkaloid–induced abnormalities of conduction and spontaneity which are resistant to atropine (35, 41) and presumably due to direct cardiac effects of overdosage.

c. Antiaccelerator Action. In 1949, Krayer (120) reported that veratramine, a secondary amine of the jerveratrum group of veratrum alkaloids, was able to decrease the positive chronotropic effect of epinephrine in various mammalian preparations. This was of particular interest since at that time the then known adrenergic blocking agents had no such effect in mammalian hearts and the action was not affected by atropine as would be expected if a cholinergic mechanism were involved. Of further interest was the observation that the antagonistic action was limited to the chronotropic effect and did not extend to the inotropic action or vasopressor action of epinephrine. A similar antagonism was subsequently noted against the chronotropic action of other sympathomimetic amines (132, 170) and against accelerans nerve stimulation (135). Further selectivity regarding the site of action was shown by the inability of veratramine to antagonize the action of epinephrine on the conducting tissue of the heart (131). The same type of antagonism was demonstrated also for jervine, a related alkamine, and the glycosidic alkaloids, veratrosine and pseudojervine (120, 121, 133), for sparteine (77), as well as for some of the *Solanum* alkaloids structurally related to veratramine (128), and for quinine and quinidine (123). With quinine alkaloids the action was not selective since severe irregularities of rate and rhythm were also noted. The term antiaccelerator was introduced to denote this type of specific and selective antagonistic action to the positive chronotropic effect of epinephrine and related substances acting upon pacemaker tissue of the heart, and the possibility was suggested that the antagonism might be competitive (122).

The demonstration that veratramine had a negative chronotropic action in the heart not under the influence of sympathomimetic amines (127) made the idea of competetive antagonism as the basis for the antiaccelerator effect seem unlikely. However, there remained the possibility that the negative chronotropic or cardiodecelerator action, which was not atropine-sensitive, might be due to an antiaccelerator action exerted against catecholamines endogenously produced within the heart itself, possibly in cardiac nerves. This was shown not to be the case by observations that veratramine exerts a cardiodecelerator action in the denervated heart (106, 223) as well as in the heart depleted of catecholamines by reserpine (107). That the antiaccelerator action might be independent of the cardiodecelerator action was suggested by observations on occasional differences in time course of the two effects in spinal cats (106). However, the most likely explanation of the antiaccelerator action is the cardiodecelerator effect, the antagonism to sympathomimetic amines thus being of the physiological type. This is suggested by the observation that increases in rate due to other drugs such as histamine (171) are counteracted by veratramine. Hawkins has supported the idea of a physiological type of antagonism in guinea pig atria (93, 94). The concentrations of veratramine required for antiaccelerator action and cardiodecelerator action are the same, and the rise in rate produced by a 5°C rise in temperature is antagonized in a similar manner to the rise in rate produced by epinephrine.

One observation which speaks against the dependence of the antiaccelerator effect of veratramine on the cardiodecelerator action is the discrepancy between the doses required for these two actions in the dog heart-lung preparation under atrioventricular nodal rhythm (29). At doses of less than 1 mg (about 1 liter of blood), cardiodeceleration and "periodic rhythm" (see below) were evident, but antiaccelerator action against ephedrine required 40 mg for 40% inhibition of acceleration. The observations could not be extended to higher doses because of failure of the heart.

The atropine-resistant negative chronotropic action of veratramine merits further investigation since, in guinea pig atria, unlike the action of acetylcholine, the effect (0.1–0.8 μg/ml) is not accompanied by decreases in amplitude of contraction (93). In rabbit atria, however, similar concentrations have negative inotropic effects which are antagonized by acetylcholine or epinephrine (184).

A peculiar type of periodicity of pacemaker discharge produced by veratramine and characterized by phasic periods of asystole has been noted for both the sinoatrial (93, 118) and atrioventricular (29, 127) nodes. It has been termed "periodic rhythm." Sympathomimetic amines or accelerans nerve stimulation appear to terminate the periodicity when it is present and to cause it to return when it has spontaneously disappeared (29, 118). This action of veratramine on pacemaker tissue has not been adequately studied and may be based in part on an effect of veratramine on metabolism which decreases the oxygen consumption of heart muscle (183). At high concentration in the dog heart-lung preparation veratramine has been shown to have antiarrhythmic, quinidine-like effects against auricular flutter (29). However, the concentrations required cannot be attained *in vivo* because of central nervous system effects leading to seizures seen at even lower concentrations (120). The cardiac effects of the jerveratrum group of the veratrum alkaloids have no therapeutic significance. Further research in the area may, however, significantly advance an understanding of the heart itself.

B. Respiratory Effects

Actions on respiration are prominent effects of the veratrum alkaloids in experimental animals, the most usual being apnea, or slowing, with reduction in depth. However, stimulation is also encountered and the response is sometimes biphasic with inhibition followed by stimulation. There are numerous possibilities for sites of action; peripheral reflex, central, and peripheral motor (bronchial muscle or skeletal respiratory muscle). Early observations (126) indicated that the inhibitory effects of the veratrum ester alkaloids on respiration were at least dual in nature, reflex and central, and that these effects became evident at doses somewhat higher than those required to elicit reflex cardiovascular effects. The importance of the vagus nerve for the induced reflex depression of respiration was known, but specific receptor sites within the thorax had not been clearly elucidated even by the early 1940's.

In 1947, Dawes (50) showed that the decreased rate and depth of respiration elicited with small doses of veratridine originated in the lungs (Fig. 8), since these effects were not seen when the drug was given into the coronary arteries in doses required to produce reflex cardiovascular actions. Vagotomy abolished the respiratory depression, but on increasing the dose, depression was again evident. This was ascribed to a central nervous system action. It now appears that there are at least two types of vagal receptors in the lungs which may be excited by the veratrum alkaloids to cause apnea (21, 51). The first of these are the Hering-Breuer stretch receptors which are stimulated to fire continuously, and the other receptors appear to be in the pulmonary veins and are accessible to veratridine given into the perfused lung or via inhalation. These latter ones are probably different from receptors stimulated by antihistamines since the antihistamines produce apnea only when administered intravascularly and the reflex is still active after tachphylaxis to veratridine has occurred (19). The relative contribution of these two receptor sites to the reflex respiratory effects seen in the intact animal is problematical, and the situation is complicated by the multiple possibilities for additional sites and reflexes. Differential cooling of the vagi (51) and single fiber recording of afferent impulse activity (157, 178) may aid in ultimate differentiation.

A series of germine esters (mostly germitrine) were studied for their effects on pulmonary stretch receptors by Paintal (180). He employed single-unit recording and introduced the drug into the pulmonary circulation via a catheter in the right atrium. Small and large doses, up to 400 μg, were employed. Stimulation, desensitization, and paralysis (large doses) were noted. Desensitization began from the moment the receptors were stimulated by the drug, and, although the stimulation usually resulted in large increases in firing frequency, there was a reduced response to lung inflation, the natural stimulus. In this regard, the veratrum alkaloids differed from trichlorethylene, which sensitized but did not stimulate.

The possibility of reflex apnea from sites outside the thorax is suggested by the report of Riker (186) that injection of microgram doses of veratridine into the superior mesenteric artery of the dog produces an immediate but transient apnea which is not affected by vagotomy, although it is abolished by splanchnic nerve section. The receptors were considered to be not pressor receptors but probably pain receptors of the type stimulated by traction on the mesentery.

Injection of protoveratrine into the cisterna magna (44) produces respiratory depression, and a central action has also been suggested as the basis for the decrease in respiration noted with the drug (intravenous in rabbits after vagotomy or nodose ganglionectomy (216). This latter peripheral site, important for emetic action (III,C), is not involved in the respiratory response. There is a possibility that peripheral motor sites may be affected and contribute to respiratory depression (23, 168). Mosey and Kaplan (168) studied veracevine, germine, and protoverine esters in the dog and observed respiratory depression (after vagotomy) which could not be completely central since it was still evident during electrophrenic control of breathing. They attributed this to nonvagal, noncholinergic factors resulting in bronchoconstriction, but could not differentiate between direct and reflex action on bronchial muscle. The possibility of respiratory skeletal muscle as a peripheral motor site for respiratory failure seen with lethal effects of the veratrum alkaloids in animals has not been explored (126).

Stimulation of respiration may result from the action of the veratrum alkaloids at various sites (Fig. 8). This has been reported for veratrine acting on the carotid body (4, 108). Stimulation following veratridine has also been reported after denervation of the carotid mechanism when the drug is injected into the fourth ventricle (147) or into the cisterna magna (16). An intracranial area, possibly medullary, may be involved. Effects on this area (accessible to cisternal or vertebral arterial injection) lead to respiratory stimulation although effects at another intracranial area, possibly meningeal, lead to respiratory depression (16). Circulatory effects accompany the respiratory effects. The doses required to activate these intracranial receptors are much larger than those needed for effects on cardiopulmonary areas.

Hapke (90) has shown that the reflex respiratory depression produced by protoveratrine A is additive with that produced by barbiturates, but could be antagonized by centrally acting analeptics or by intravenous procaine. He also suggested (91) that the reflex respiratory action is mainly on phylogenetically younger structures, since diaphragmatic respiration is affected more than is the thoracic.

C. Emetic Action

The clinical usefulness of the veratrum alkaloids is limited by the narrow range between the hypotensive and emetic doses. The emetic effect in animals (181, 216, 225) and in man (75, 231) is not due to contaminants present in extracts, since it is seen with the pure alkaloids. The emesis occurs on parenteral administration and after denervation of the gastrointestinal tract in the cat (37) and the dog (211); the effect is therefore not due to irritation of the gut and was early attributed to a central action. Borison and Fairbanks (37), in a study on the cat, showed that midcervical vagotomy and carotid sinus nerve section, procedures which affect the cardiovascular response, did not affect the emesis due to Veriloid. Neither did ablation of the chemoreceptor trigger zone in the medulla, an area important for the emetic effects of apomorphine and of the cardiac glycosides. However, interruption of the vagus above the nodose ganglion prevented the emetic response to Veriloid, but not to other substances for which the site of action is elsewhere. Table II

TABLE II

EFFECT OF CHRONIC BILATERAL EXCISION OF NODOSE GANGLION ON EMETIC RESPONSE TO VERILIOD[a]

Cat no.	Days post-operative	Emetic drug and route	Dose (mg/kg)	Response and latency (minutes)
109[b]	1	Veriloid, i.v.	0.025	no vomiting
	2	Lanatoside C, i.v.	0.16	vomited, 79
	4	Veriloid, i.v.	0.025	no vomiting
47	2	Lobeline sulfate, i.m.	3.0	vomited, 1
	3	Veriloid, i.v.	0.025	no vomiting
5[c]	3	Veriloid, i.v.	0.04	no vomiting
43[d]	4	Veriloid, i.v.	0.025	no vomiting
52	1	Veriloid, i.v.	0.025	no vomiting
	3	Veriloid, i.v.	0.050	no vomiting
	3	Apomorphine hydrochloride, s.c.	25.0	vomited, 5

[a] From Borison and Fairbanks (37), with kind permission from the authors and the publishers, Williams & Wilkins, Baltimore, Maryland.

[b] Only vagotomy, *above* the nodose ganglia, was performed in this cat.

[c] Vomited preoperatively in response to 0.025 mg/kg intravenous Veriloid.

[d] Vomited preoperatively in response to 0.015 mg/kg intravenous Veriloid.

shows a portion of the data supporting this finding. The importance of the nodose ganglion for the emesis producd in the cat and for the retching produced in the rabbit by protoveratrine was shown by Tanaka and Kanno (216). Thus it appears that the emesis is not necessarily central in origin, but may result from stimulation of a peripheral receptor close to the central nervous system. Recently, Borison and Sampson (39) have related Veriloid emesis in cats to the vagal body, which has been identified in close relation to the nodose ganglion. It has been shown in the monkey that cardiac denervation, with or without chemoreceptor trigger zone ablation, did not alter the emetic response to protoveratrine (181).

An early report that some veratrum alkaloid preparations tested in animals may have a higher therapeutic range than others in regard to emetic and hypotensive effects (176) was not substantiated in a study which compared various preparations at equihypotensive levels (1), thus corroborating a previous study (211) of ED_{50} values for emesis and hypotension in which a good correlation was apparent. It thus appeared that the emetic action was a dose-related concomitant of the hypotensive action. However, Borison *et al.* (38) showed that the emetic response to Veriloid in cats is mediated by a mechanism independent of the hypotensive effect, since surgical procedures which resulted in a reversal of the hypotensive action did not affect the emesis. The possibility of a dissociation between hypotensive and emetic action was furthered by the observation, in man, that protoveratrine B may be better tolerated than protoveratrine A in doses required to produce normotension in hypertensives (231). This work led to a study of hypotensive-emetic relationships among a large series of semisynthetic esters of protoverine in unanesthetized dogs (225). Although the results indicated that dissociation is possible (some compounds evoked emesis without hypotension), only three compounds out of 37 screened were shown to have hypotensive-emetic ratios suggestively superior to those found for protoveratrine A or B. Further work has not been reported.

The emetic response to the veratrum alkaloids in animals is not antagonized by atropine (211), dimenhydrinate (Dramamine®) (112, 211), or various phenothiazine derivatives (40, 226). However, the ED_{50} for emesis due to Veriloid in unanesthetized dogs was slightly, though significantly, elevated by treatment with sedative doses of Rauwiloid®, an extract of *Rauwolfia serpentina,* but not by treatment with sedative doses of phenobarbital (83). This suggestion of antiemetic specificity has not been reported on further. In man, the use of chlorpromazine has not changed the margin of safety for protoveratrine (47).

D. Central Nervous System Effects

Krayer (120), in experiments on the antiaccelerator action of veratramine (Section III,A,4,*c*), showed that it evoked seizures in the intact animal, but not in the spinal preparation. These observations led to a study in mice by Tanaka (215) of the central nervous system effects of veratramine, jervine, and veratrosine as well as of the tertiary amine alkamines and certain of their esters. Qualitative differences were apparent. Of the tertiary amine alkamines, cevine, veracevine, and germine produced an increase in reflex excitability and a peculiar motor phenomenon described as "jumping fits." Protoverine had no such actions even at lethal doses. With the esters of these alkamines, however, the effects produced were different. Retching movements (not noted with the alkamines) occurred but there was no motor excitation. The LD_{50} values for the esters were much lower than those for the alkamines; for protoveratrines A and B they were 1000 times lower. The presence of the ester bond therefore was quantitatively as well as qualitatively important. The secondary amines such as veratramine produced tremors and a unique convulsive pattern which was clearly antagonized by ether and by mephenesin but only irregularly affected by a wide variety of other central depressants. These observations were furthered by Schoetensack and Hallmann (200), who used a wide range of doses of various possible antagonists and related the doses employed to the LD_{50} values of the antagonists. They were able to distinguish selective antagonism to the tremor and the convulsive pattern by various agents. Their study suggests that veratramine, the effect of which can be pharmacologically distinguished by antagonists from the effects of other convulsants, may be a valuable tool for defining the sites of action of various central nervous system depressants. The specificity of drugs against veratramine has also been studied by Melson (160). Two dioxolane derivatives showed marked antagonistic action, and one of them (2,2-methyl, *p*-chlorphenyl-4-hydroxymethyl-1,3-dioxolane), at 50% of its LD_{50}, provided protection against the lethal effects of veratramine.

Veratramine has been noted to produce reversible mental derangement in man at a dose of 250 μg/kg, but seizures were not noted (149). Veratrine, when applied to the cortex of cats and rabbits, changes the steady potential, the evoked response, and the EEG of the somatic receiving area (81).

Flacke (68) reported that semisynthetic acetate esters of germine produce central nervous system effects in mice which are mixtures of the effects noted by Tanaka (215) for the alkamines and naturally occurring esters. Thus, by sharing properties of both, the germine semisynthetic esters fall midway between germine itself and its natural esters in producing effects on the central nervous system.

E. Effects on Nerve and Muscle

1. *The Veratrine Response*

The veratrum alkaloids are known to cause repetetive firing in nerve and muscle, and this characteristic action has been termed the veratrine response since it was originally observed with veratrine. There seems no doubt that the ease with which contraction can be measured in muscle was responsible for the fact that much of the earlier work on the pharmacological effects of the veratrum alkaloids was done on this tissue. The basic similarity of effect on the excitable membrane of nerve and muscle was observed later (126). The characteristic veratrine response in muscle can be explained as a phenomenon which, as in nerve, originates in the membrane and is reflected in the contraction through a poorly understood excitation-coupling mechanism which is the transducer between the membrane and the contractile protein.

a. Skeletal Muscle. The classical mechanical response of frog muscle which develops in the presence of veratrine and related drugs in response to direct single shocks is usually characterized by an initial increase in the size of the twitch accompanied by a delay in relaxation. As the effect of the drug becomes more pronounced, a secondary aftercontraction appears during the relaxation phase. Its time course of rise and fall is much slower than the twitch itself. Finally, in subsequent contractions under the full effect of appropriate drug concentrations, the aftercontraction arises earlier and earlier during relaxation, may exceed the twitch in height, and ultimately fuses with the twitch, resulting in a smooth contraction to levels many times the control twitch height. This is followed by a prolonged relaxation. The upper left portion of Fig. 13 shows some characteristics of the phenomenon in a directly stimulated frog sartorius muscle exposed to veratridine.

The veratrine response in muscle can also be demonstrated when the muscle is stimulated indirectly via its nerve, but the response is still present when the muscle is directly stimulated after curarization (68, 70, 126, 232) or after denervation and degeneration of the nerve supply (69, 70, 126). The muscle alone therefore is capable of exhibiting the veratrine response. Much early work delved into the problem of whether the veratrine response in muscle was a tetanus involving propagated electrical activity or a contracture in which conducted disturbances are absent (126). This work was hampered by the lack of cathode ray oscillographic recording equipment which is conventionally used today to record rapidly changing electrical potentials. However, in 1912 Hoffman (100), using a string galvanometer, found electrical oscillations accompanying the veratrine response in frog muscle. There is no question at present that high-frequency repetitive discharge accompanies the early phase of the veratrine response in skeletal muscle. This has been demonstrated (Fig. 14) in entire amphibian muscle (43, 69, 114, 232) as well as in single-fiber preparations (137) and in mammalian muscle (70). However, contracture may contribute to the later portion of the veratrine response, particularly following cessation of high-frequency discharge (105). The relation of the large negative afterpotential evoked during the veratrine response to the tetanic and contracture phases is discussed in Section III,E,1,*e*. Burns *et al.* (43) have noted repetitive firing in veratrinized muscle only after local application and not when the entire muscle was exposed to the drug. They suggested that differences in the repolarization rates (negative after-potential) of treated and untreated fibers was the immediate cause of current flow leading to repetitive firing. The observations should be repeated, since uniform drug application to muscle, in the hands of other investigators (69, 232), has not prevented the observation of repetitive firing.

When muscles are exposed to those alkaloids which elicit a veratrine response, they characteristically do not show any activity in the absence of a stimulus. Thus, as is usually the situation in nerve, at least one stimulus is required to evoke the response. However, the situation in nerve may be different; sensory receptors have been noted to discharge after germitrine in the absence of any apparent normal stimulus (180). The reported spontaneous activity in muscle induced by the veratrum alkaloids (126) may therefore represent an indirect effect evoked via nerve endings. Spontaneous twitches have been reported in the frog rectus

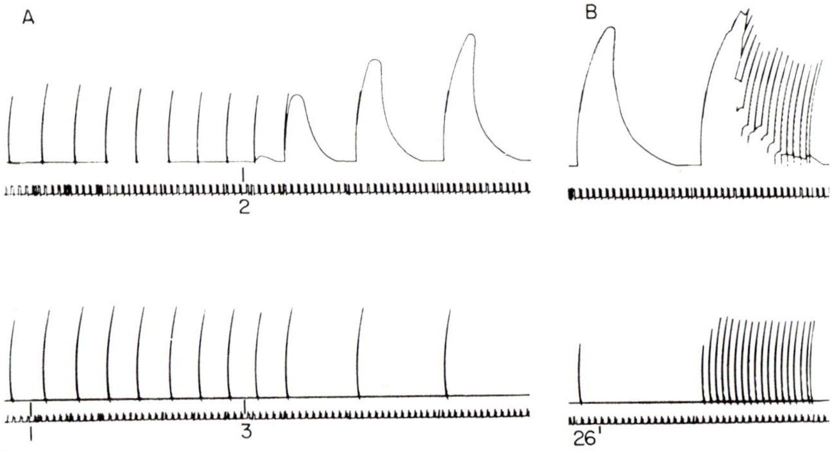

FIG. 13. The prevention of the "veratrine response" by veratramine. *Rana pipiens*, male. Both sartorius muscles suspended in bicarbonate buffer solution in twin chambers and attached to tension levers. Stimulation (40 V, 0.5 msec, square waves) at 2-minute intervals, except at the end when stimulation was at the rate of one per second. The segment B begins 26 minutes after the end of segment A. Time is recorded in seconds but the drum was arrested for most of the 2-minute intervals between successive stimuli. At the signal 1 in A, the "lower" muscle was exposed to veratramine 1 : 100,000. At 2 in A, the "upper" muscle was exposed to veratridine 1 : 5 million. Immediately after this at the signal 3, the veratramine solution 1 : 100,000 was removed from the bath of the "lower" muscle and a solution was substituted containing veratramine 1 : 100,000 and veratridine 1 : 5 million. From Krayer and George (129), with kind permission of the authors and the publisher, Williams & Wilkins, Baltimore, Maryland.

abdominis muscle following veratridine (119). These synchronized contractions were superimposed on a slow contracture and probably represent activity of the twitch fibers in this "slow" muscle. The twitches were abolished by tubocurarine, which suggests that they were of nervous origin. Of interest here is the observation that veratrine causes increases in the frequency and amplitude of miniature end plate potentials in rat diaphragm with the occurrence of occasional propagated responses (102). Further, in isolated right ventricle strips of the rat which are ordinarily quiescent, veratridine often evokes spontaneous activity (25), and this has also been noted in rat atria following veratrine (41a). However, for both skeletal and cardiac muscle, parallel studies before and

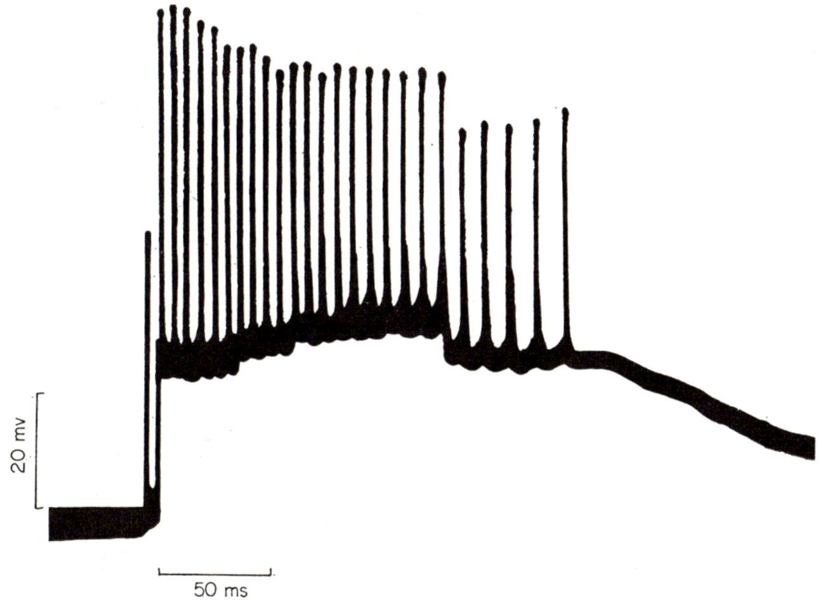

FIG. 14. Repetitive electrical activity following a single stimulation in the presence of germine monoacetate (GMA). Microelectrode recording from frog sartorius muscle. Temperature 23°C. Direct supramaximal stimulation (stimulation artifact visible before the first action potential). GMA (0.5×10^{-5} gm/ml) had been added 32 minutes before the exposure. From Flacke (69), with kind permission of the author and the publisher, Williams & Wilkins, Baltimore, Maryland.

after denervation would be ideally suited for deciding the importance of the presence of nerves for "spontaneous" activity.

The capacity to elicit an aftercontraction is a property of many of the ester alkaloids. The alkamines such as germine (68) and zygadenine (130) do not have this action, although twitch height may be increased.

The classical type of response noted with the veratrine ester alkaloids (described above) is seen also with the naturally occurring germine and protoverine esters but with some differences. Boehm (36) noted that the veratrine response seen with protoveratrine is transient. The phenomenon regresses, even on continued stimulation at regular intervals, and ultimately disappears; the twitch height then decreases and the muscle usually becomes inexcitable. Krayer *et al.* (130) noted similar effects for neogermitrine. However, the diacyl esters of germine, germidine, and neogermidine, and the monoacyl ester, protoveratridine, elicited the classical type of response as did the vanilloyl and veratroyl esters of zygadenine. The reasons for the marked differences observed and for the importance of the type and degree of esterification among the naturally occurring alkaloids has not been studied. For the germine esters the nature of the alkamine cannot account for the difference. Sabadine (142), a minor alkaloid found in veratrine, elicits a veratridine-like response. It is a monoacetate ester of the alkamine sabine which shows structural similarities to veracevine and zygadenine. Cevacine and zygacine, monoacetate esters of these latter two alkamines, evoke a type of response in which the aftercontraction is absent. There is usually only an increase in twitch height with a moderate prolongation of contraction associated with delayed relaxation.

Recently synthesized semisynthetic esters of germine and protoverine have been tested for their capacity to elicit the veratrine response in frog muscle. Flacke (68) noted that tetra- and pentaacetic acid esters of germine produced a veratrine response like that of veratridine while with the mono- and diesters a difference was noted. With these latter esters the response resembled that seen with cevacine and zygacine; no aftercontraction was apparent. This type of response was also noted with acetonide di- and triacetate esters of protoverine (88). On the other hand, tri-, penta-, and hexaacetate esters resembled the higher acetate germine esters in their effects. Germine mono- and diacetate produce effects in cat muscle similar to those noted in amphibian muscle (70).

b. Smooth Muscle. Although the veratrine response occurs in vertebrate striated muscle and in certain invertebrate muscle, definition of the phenomenon in smooth muscle has been difficult because of the usual presence of spontaneous myogenic activity and more importantly the presence of nerves which change the activity of smooth muscle and upon which drugs may act. Although smooth muscle has not been adequately studied, there have been reports suggestive of the presence of the response (126). Spasmogenic activity in isolated rabbit intestine has been noted with esters of various veratrum alkamines (84).

c. Cardiac Muscle. The situation in cardiac muscle has only been explored initially. The early literature indicated a prolongation of systole. Following the elucidation of the importance of tetanus for the response in skeletal muscle, the presence of veratrine response in the heart was discounted on theoretical considerations because of the peculiar properties of heart muscle which prevent tetanic contraction (126). However, recent work has suggested that heart muscle may exhibit a veratrine response, which in its time course is strikingly similar to the early phases of the response in skeletal muscle (28). In the rat right ventricle strip preparation exposed to veratridine (3×10^{-7}–10^{-5} mg/ml), driven or spontaneous (Fig. 15) beats may show delayed relaxation and aftercontractions which can reach 40% of the initial twitch height, although a complete merging of the aftercontraction with the initial twitch is not observed. This veratrine response in heart muscle is sensitive to the interval between beats as is the case in skeletal muscle (232), and when the strips are driven at rates of 70 to 100/minute,

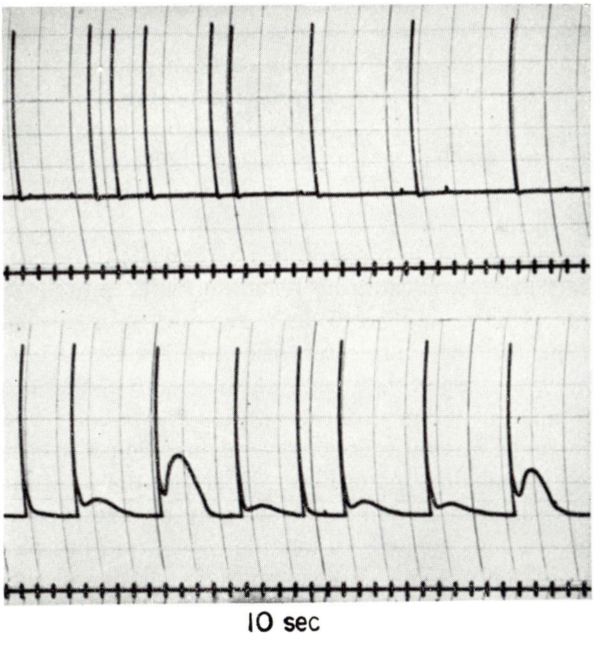

FIG. 15. Isometric tension recordings of a rat right ventricle strip preparation at 28°C. Upper: Control tracing before drug, electrical stimulation at 1/minute (3 spontaneous beats early in the record). Lower: After veratridine (10 μg/ml) all beats spontaneous (no electrical stimulation). Note the delayed relaxation and the varying aftercontractions.

the delayed relaxation disappears. Another similarity with skeletal muscle is the sensitivity to potassium; reduction in the external K^+ to half normal or to zero enhances the effect while doubling the external K^+ antagonizes it. A dissimilarity with skeletal muscle is the absence of antagonism to the effect by a wide variety of antiveratrinic substances, including quinidine and ouabain (Section III,E,2).

Although repetitive discharge need not accompany the veratrine response in cardiac muscle, such activity is sometimes noted in the myogram as rapid contractions superimposed on the aftercontraction (25). Repetitive firing in rat atria due to veratrine has been observed during transmembrane recording (41a). The repetitive spikes appear during the prolonged repolarization phase (normal, 50–100 milliseconds; after veratrine, 5–10 seconds). Based on preliminary experiments employing transmembrane recording (25) it seems likely that repetitive discharge is not a prerequisite for the aftercontraction in cardiac muscle and that the prolonged repolarization phase (negative afterpotential) may be sufficient to explain the phenomenon. However, Wallon *et al.* (222), employing the isolated rabbit heart, noted a dissociation between the action potential duration and the duration of contraction. No aftercontraction was evident, but there was early an increase in the amplitude of contraction and a slowed relaxation associated with delayed repolarization. At a later time, when the delayed repolarization was quite marked, the mechanogram more closely resembled the control tracing. Other factors, possibly fatigue of the contractile mechanism, may have been involved.

d. Nerve. In nerve-muscle preparations, where the muscle is indirectly stimulated via its nerve, a veratrine response in the muscle may be observed when veratrine is applied to the nerve during single shocks (126). That the response in the muscle was due to discharge from the nerve was shown by its absence following local blockade of nerve conduction distal to the point of drug application. Repetitive discharge in nerve in response to single stimuli following veratrinization has been noted in amphibian and mammalian motor fibers. Effects of the veratrum alkaloids on visceral and somatic afferent pathways may be interpreted as arising from the same phenomenon. These include the Bezold-Jarisch effect and other circulatory reflexes, respiratory reflexes, and increased reflex excitability such as may be noted in the lid reflex and knee jerk (68). It is also probable that these alkaloids can stimulate receptors involved in afferent pathways in the absence of normal stimuli. This has been demonstrated for pulmonary stretch receptors (180) and may be the basis for sensory phenomena noted in humans during the use of veratrum alkaloids in therapy (104). Flacke (68) has reported the presence of prickling and tingling sensations in the palms and soles of human volunteers who received germine diacetate intravenously.

e. Mechanism. The basis for the veratrine response is intimately associated with effects of the veratrum alkaloids on excitable membranes (126). Concentration-related effects in various tissues have been noted in the magnitude of the action potential, negative and positive afterpotentials, excitability, refractory period, maximum conduction frequency, and repetitive discharge. At high concentrations a decreased excitability and depolarization type block of conduction is usually observed. This may be a partial explanation for the tachyphylaxis which is often noted when the substances are studied for their reflex effects.

A prominent feature of the electrophysiological actions of the veratrum alkaloids is the large negative afterpotential which follows the passage of an action potential through a region of tissue which has been exposed to the drugs. This local (nonpropagated) response usually has a larger amplitude and more extended time course than the normal negative afterpotential. It may extend in time to seconds or minutes. Kuffler (137) has shown in nerve-muscle preparations that the veratrine afterpotential is a process distinct from the normal short negative afterpotential in that it may show a rising phase during recovery from the spike. If it attains a critical height, the threshold of the membrane, a second action potential ensues. This process may be repetitive and the afterpotentials can summate, giving rise to long bursts of firing. This oscillatory phenomenon in the membrane, although at first self-generating, is also ultimately self-limiting since the induced train of impulses eventually ceases, often abruptly. Transmembrane potential recordings (61, 232) have shown that the repetitive action potentials superimposed on the negative afterpotential decrease in magnitude as they die away. The mechanism for this self-limiting action is unknown, but it is presumed to be related to ion movements. Considering that the ion fluxes related to the normal action potential in various tissues are still being worked out, it may be some time before we arrive at a clear understanding of the veratrum action. Although repetitive discharge does not occur in the absence of an augmented negative afterpotential, various discordant relations between the two phenomena and the changes in excitability of tissues have still to be worked out (126). In the case of muscle, the repetitive firing accounts for the tetanic aspect of the contractile response, but, as suggested by Kuffler (138) in experiments on single fibers, local, nonpropagated membrane responses (the negative afterpotential without repetitive firing) may be associated with contracture. Such contractures were noted in fibers following cessation of tetanic discharge and were correlated with the negative afterpotential.

In some fibers, repeatedly studied, failure of propagation of induced repetitive firing for any appreciable distance from the stimulus site was observed. In these, contractures were noted at threshold levels of the negative afterpotential which had previously initiated repetitive firing. Contractures which were not preceded by a tetanus, or those which were, could be suppressed by anodal currents. Thus, the contractile mechanism was able to respond to membrane activity in a manner correlated with some threshold of depolarization during the negative afterpotential. This concept of excitation-coupling, and the importance for potentiation of contraction and duration of the active state of both a threshold for mechanical activation and the state of membrane depolarization, is discussed by Sandow *et al.* (196). Its specific application to the effects of veratrine in skeletal muscle are outlined by Etzensperger (61).

The ionic basis for the negative afterpotential seen with the veratrum alkaloids is not understood, and conflicting data have appeared. The situation in muscle and nerve and even in various nerve preparations may be different. Potassium loss alone cannot account for the size of the negative afterpotential in nerve (203). For muscle (73) and nerve (203) a high Na^+ conductance has been suggested, and for muscle the possibility of an action which decreases chloride permeability has been entertained (63). Falk and Landa (64) have shown certain similarities in skeletal muscle between the effects of the veratrum alkaloids and those of replacing chloride in the medium with impermeant ions. Ahmad and Lewis (3) noted that protoveratrines A and B depress Ca^{47} uptake in frog muscle. They support the view of Shanes (203) that such drugs produce ion leaks in membranes by displacing Ca^{++} and that Ca^{++} may link the contractile events in muscle with the preceding electrical phenomena in the membrane.

The idea that the local release of K^+ may be the mechanism by which the veratrum alkaloids produce their effects on some tissues was partially based on observations of an increase in K^+ in perfusates of tissues exposed to veratrine (126). Lister and Lewis (146) have detected such increases following protoveratrine in coronary blood but not in blood perfusing skeletal muscle. They suggested that the high efflux of K^+ noted in the coronary bed may act on nerve endings in the heart to elicit the Bezold-Jarisch effect. Such an indirect action may explain the latent period observed after administration of certain veratrum alkaloids (179). Dawes (50), however, has shown that local injection of K^+ into the coronary arteries does not elicit the characteristic reflex seen with similar injection of veratridine, although the decrease in heart rate and blood pressure occasioned by administration of K^+ intra-arterially into the central nervous system was greatly enhanced by prior veratridine administration. Similar sensitization to the effects of K^+ on muscle (85) and the carotid sinus (16) have also been reported.

Flacke (69) has related the muscle contraction during the veratrine response to tetanic tension in the same preparation and has shown that, for various of the veratrum alkaloids, the ratio of the augmented contraction produced to maximum tetanic tension may vary widely. In frog muscle, at concentrations which produced optimal effects, the mean ratio for veratridine was 0.35 while for germine mono- and diacetate, it closely approached 1.0. More highly acetylated semisynthetic germine esters gave intermediate values. Fig. 16 shows the relation of twitch tension to tetanic tension before and after germine diacetate. Since the amplitude of the active state in muscle is the same in the twitch and during a tetanus, it would appear that these drugs increase the duration of the active state by their ability to produce repetitive firing. Flacke noted in some but not all experiments that the duration of the re-

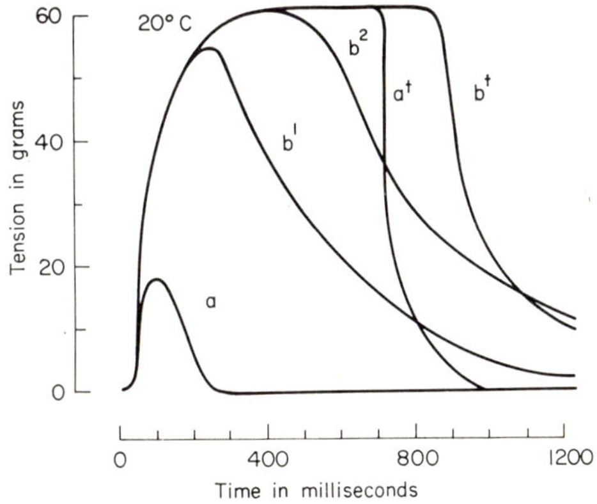

FIG. 16. The effect of germine diacetate (GDA) on tension development in frog sartorious muscle. Frog sartorius muscle in bicarbonate buffer solution. Tension recorded isometrically with a force-displacement transducer on a direct-writing oscillograph at high paper speed. Direct electrical stimulation, supramaximal voltage. Curve a is the tension curve of a normal twitch, curve a^t is the tension curve of the untreated muscle during tetanic stimulation (80 stimuli/second). Curve b^1 was obtained 6 minutes after addition of GDA (10^{-5} gm/ml) to the bath, curve b^2 10 minutes later (single shocks). Curve b^t is the tetanic tension curve in the presence of GDA (obtained 2 minutes after curve b^2). Note that the rising part and the peak tension of curve b^2 and the tetanic curves are identical; note also the delayed relaxation after tetanic stimulation under the influence of the drug (curve b^t). The curves have been redrawn from the original, because different amplifications had been used for twitch and tetanic tension curves. From Flacke (69), with kind permission of the author and the publisher, Williams & Wilkins, Baltimore, Maryland.

petitive firing after the drug was sufficient to explain the fact that the augmented contraction closely approached maximum tetanic tension. The additional observation that these drugs do not alter tetanic tension when tested in concentrations which produce an optimal veratrine response indicates that contractile protein function is not directly affected. The failure of many of the veratrum alkaloids to produce ratios near 1.0 may be related to variations of individual muscle fibers in their sensitivities to the drugs and to factors which cause fatigue of the response. Incomplete conduction as a basis for the different ratios noted was excluded by "massive" stimulation techniques employing multiple electrodes.

The presence of only an increase in twitch height and the absence of an aftercontraction noted with many of the alkaloids and the quite different development of the classical type of response involving an aftercontraction is probably related to the time course of the repetitive firing. On this basis, the two types of veratrine responses have been termed brief and prolonged (68, 69, 142). Fig. 14 shows the repetitive activity of the brief type in which an aftercontraction is absent. Witt and Swaine (232) have observed prolonged firing associated with an aftercontraction following veratridine. The question of the possible relation of the sustained negative afterpotential to the contraction following cessation of repetitive firing is still conjectural, and the possibility remains that the later portions of the prolonged type of veratrine response in skeletal muscle (delayed relaxation during the aftercontraction) may be due to a contracture dependent on the negative afterpotential. This may also be true for late phases during the brief type of veratrine response. In heart muscle, in the absence of repetitive discharge (Section III,E,1,*c*), the entire veratrine response may be a consequence of the prolonged negative afterpotential.

f. Observations in Man. The veratrine response has been observed in human skeletal muscle. Hofmann (101) has studied the effects of intra-arterial injections of veratrine, veratridine, and cevadine on muscle responses in normal and myasthenic patients. In both groups there was an increase in the force of contraction on indirect stimulation of muscle (nerve electrodes), but a tetanic phase was not always seen and the inotropic effect was ascribed chiefly to a contracture. Veratridine did not affect the action of acetylcholine, but when used alone it led to a greater increase in the force of contraction than did neostigmine in normal individuals or in myasthenics. No decurarizing effect in normal individuals receiving curare was noted. This stands in contrast to the decurarizing effect of various veratrum alkaloids reported in indirectly stimulated amphibian muscle (85).

During the use of protoveratrine in hypertension, effects on skeletal muscle are occasionally seen (116, 230). The effects are similar to the muscle spasms observed in human myotonias (126, 177). Patients complain of tightness in various muscle groups, and tetanic flexion has been noted. These effects are reversible after the drug is withdrawn.

2. *Antagonism of the Veratrine Response*

The veratrine response in nerve and muscle has long been known to be affected by drugs and other factors such as the frequency of stimulation (126). Figure 13 (upper right, control muscle) shows the fatigue of the veratrine response when the frequency of electrical stimulation of the muscle is changed from 1 every 2 minutes to 1 per second. Within a few twitches, the aftercontraction and delayed relaxation disappear and only the twitch remains. Paradoxically, this procedure of rapid stimulation will often bring out a latent veratrine response in a muscle under appropriate drug treatment at a time when a veratrine response to a single stimulus is not yet apparent (68). The basis for this dual effect remains to be explored. Fig. 13 (lower left) also shows the antagonistic effect of veratramine on the development of the veratrine response due to veratridine in frog muscle. Veratramine can also abolish the response once it has developed (129). This latter effect of veratramine has been studied in relation to the repetitive discharge which accompanies the mechanical response. Witt and Swaine (232) have shown that, with the decrease of the aftercontraction, there is a concomitant decrease in the frequency of the repetitive firing. The antagonism therefore appears to be correlated with effects taking place at the muscle membrane. Although a wide variety of drugs and procedures can affect the response of nerve and muscle to an effective stimulus, the antagonism of the veratrine response is of particular interest because the initial response to the stimulus remains unaffected. As is shown in Fig. 13, the aftercontraction is prevented, but the initial twitch is not affected. This is also true when drugs or procedures abolish the response after it has been allowed to develop. The basis for this selective type of antagonism is unknown, but it is presumed to be related to those changes in ion permeability of the membrane subsequent to, and consequent on, the effects produced by the initial stimulus in the presence of drugs such as veratridine.

In muscle, a wide variety of unrelated drugs possess antiveratrinic activity. Although within certain groups of drugs there may be some particular structure-activity relationships which lead to inactivity (6, 7, 9, 227), it seems probable that physical characteristics, and not specific drug-receptor interactions, determine the antagonistic effect. The array of antagonistic drugs is bewildering, and the experimental work involved has for the most part been descriptive. The observations have raced ahead of any adequate theory of the veratrine response. Antagonistic drugs fall into two general categories, although many antagonists have not been adequately studied in this regard.

In the first category are those drugs which, like veratramine (129), can prevent the development of the response or abolish it once it has been established. In this category fall such drugs as the cinchona alkaloids and cupreines (9), local anesthetics (206), some unsaturated lactones and peroxides (227), coumarin and its derivatives (11), sparteine (76), andromedotoxin (165), various rauwolfia alkaloids (7), and certain tranquilizers (8). Although there is a general parallel between antiveratrinic activity and antiarrhythmic cardiac action (8, 10) as well as with antiaccelerator action (76, 77, 123), adequate comparisons have not been made for all the groups listed. Veratramine, the prototype of this category of drugs, may itself have a veratrine response–like action at high concentrations (129). There is an increase in the height of the initial twitch and evidence of delayed relaxation, but the effect is inconstant, and high concentrations lead to ultimate inexcitability of the muscle. Sparteine (76) also increases twitch height.

The second category of drugs which affect the veratrine response has the cardiac glycosides as a prototype (6). Although the various types of glycosides tested were able to abolish the veratrine response they could not prevent it. The antagonistic effect was also seen with an aglycone, strophanthidin. Structural changes which caused loss of cardiac activity similarly affected the antiveratrinic activity. The erythrophleum alkaloids, which have cardiac activity, fall into this second category (66). Other groups of antagonistic drugs, not adequately categorized, include certain substituted indoles (92) and some cholinesterase inhibitors (114, 195).

A theoretical basis for the two-fold categorization of antiveratrinic drugs is lacking. The cardiac glycosides are known to inhibit active transport of ions. The relation of this property to the inability of these drugs to prevent the veratrine response is speculative. The wide divergence of chemical structure associated with the ability of drugs to prevent or abolish the veratrine response is much like the nonspecific action of general anesthetics. Some common physical property should be looked for, perhaps surface activity, as suggested by studies in model systems (Section III,E,4). Important here would be a study of the effect of changes in chemical structure of a molecule on surface activity since among related drugs an occasional exception to antiveratrinic action is noted.

In muscle, and in nerve, the concentrations of various ions in the medium affect the veratrine response following veratrine or veratridine. Decreases in Na^+ (67, 114) and increases in Ca^{++} (67, 117) or K^+ (67) have been shown to exert antagonistic effects. An increase in Ca^{++} has also been shown to antagonize the veratrine response seen with semisynthetic esters of germine (68) and protoverine (88) as well as with the naturally occurring ester, sabadine (142). Dawes (50) has shown that the Bezold-Jarisch effect, elicited by the intracoronary injection of veratridine, is antagonized by Ca^{++} and enhanced by citrate (a Ca^{++} chelator). Paintal (180) noted similar relationships in experiments employing single-unit recording of impulse frequency in various stretch receptors stimulated by veratrum alkaloids.

Interference with metabolic processes by anoxia, cyanide, iodoacetic acid, and dinitrophenol will reduce the aftercontraction in muscle but will also depress the initial twitch (232). The antagonistic drugs and ions mentioned above are of interest because of their specificity against effects subsequent to the initial response. In this regard Ca^{++} may have the most selective antagonistic action on muscle. Flacke (67) has reported that, while veratramine, quinine, ouabain, erythrophleine, increased Ca^{++} or K^+, and decreased Na^+ all have specific antiveratrinic action (without effects on the twitch), only with Ca^{++} can the muscle still attain full tetanic tension after the veratrine response has been abolished. Thus Ca^{++}, which is thought to be involved in excitation coupling in muscle, may play a central role in the veratrine response. Lister and Lewis (145) have shown that protoveratrine A, acting on electrically stimulated frog muscle, causes an increased release of Ca^{++} and suggested this as a possible explanation for permeability increases to other ions. The veratrum alkaloids may compete with Ca^{++} for loci in the membrane and antagonistic drugs may reverse this. Such an interpretation was made for protoveratrine effects on brain slices and for the antagonistic action of cocaine (115). The interpretation is supported by observations made in model systems (Section III,E,4) and in nerve (96).

3. *Veratrinic Responses*

Responses in nerve and muscle similar to the veratrine response, but evoked by agents other than the veratrum alkaloids, have been termed veratrinic (126). Scorpion venom (2), andromedotoxin, a nonnitrogenous principle of *Rhododendron maximum* (165), and 2,4-dichlorophenoxyacetate (62), among others (126), have been reported to evoke veratrinic responses in muscle. Often the responses have been antagonized by procedures which have been shown to antagonize the veratrine response, but systematic comparisons have not been made. The response to 2,4-dichlorophenoxyacetate, like the veratrine response, is obliterated by quinine, Ca^{++}, and activity; α-tocopherol phosphate also antagonizes the response, but this substance has not been tested on the veratrine response. Veratrine and veratrinic responses may be shown ultimately to be based, in part at least, on a common mechanism. However, differences are apparent since there is an accentuation of the 2,4-dichlorophenoxyacetate response in muscle by K^+ but quite the reverse for the veratrine response (68).

The myotonias of the human and the goat, being of unknown origin, are classed as veratrinic responses (126). In dystrophia myotonica, a heredofamilial form in man, there is K^+ loss and Na^+ gain in muscle cells, and membrane stabilizers, such as quinidine or procaineamide, are effective in decreasing spontaneous muscle activity and in reducing relaxation times toward normal (177). The defect in this disease is in the muscle, since it is still present after nerve block or curare (in myotonia of the goat it is present after nerve section) (126).

4. *Studies in Model Systems*

A molecular approach to an understanding of the action of drugs on excitable membranes is that based on the use of lipoidal monolayers. Such models only approximate the structure of the plasma membrane, but their simplicity makes for heuristic delight.

Shanes (203) has characterized the veratrum alkaloids of the ceveratrum group as labilizers because of their ability to produce ion leaks in membranes. Local anesthetics are classed as stabilizers since they prevent the increase in sodium permeability required for excitation. Changes in ion permeability due to effects of stabilizers or labilizers may be envisaged as being due to interactions of these molecules with areas of the membrane where ion passage occurs. For stabilizers, any interactions which interfered with the opening of channels during excitation would have little effect on ion movement in the resting state, while interactions which led to compression of these channels might be expected to interfere with ion passage in the absence of excitation. In the case of labilizers, ion passage could be enhanced during rest as well as during activity by interactions which enlarged these channels. However, the effects of such ion leaks could be partially counterbalanced by increased ion pumping using energy sources derived from metabolism.

In going to a model system, the plasma membrane has been approximated by the use of films of lipoidal substances (such as stearic acid monolayers) on Ringer's solution. Measurement of the surface pressure by means of a Langmuir-type balance gives an estimate of the intermolecular forces acting within the layer. For stabilizers it has been shown that their potencies parallel their ability to enter the monolayer as indicated by an increase in the surface pressure. Labilizers, on the other hand, decrease the surface pressure of these monolayers apparently by removal of monolayer molecules. In such a system, antagonisms between stabilizers, such as procaine and Ca^{++}, and labilizers, such as veratrine and veratridine, have been shown (80, 205).

Gershfeld (79) has examined the behavior of veracevine, veratridine and cevadine, and veratramine at air-water interfaces. Veracevine had very little interfacial activity, while the other molecules did but with some differences. Although veratridine and cevadine showed both vertical and horizontal orientation at the interface, veratramine showed only horizontal orientation. These latter findings were related to the different positioning of various hydroxyl groups in the molecules. It may be that interfacial activity (lacking for veracevine) is required to concentrate drugs at their sites of action and that the physical properties underlying surface orientation may in part determine drug action. Veratramine is known to antagonize the veratrine response in muscle. However, broad generalizations based on physical models can be tested, and it would be of interest to see if other antiveratrinic substances (Section III,E,2) behave similarly to veratramine.

Beyond the importance of interfacial activity, there is the effect of ionic forces on the interactions of drugs with monolayers (205). This is brought out by the reduced interaction of veratridine with stearate layers in the presence of Ca^{++} or H^{+}, which neutralize the charge on the stearate carboxyl group, thus antagonizing the veratridine effect. The concentration of veratridine which produces effects in monolayer systems (2×10^{-6} *M*) is about the same as that needed in living systems.

In nerve and muscle, the veratrum ester alkaloids can produce a block of conduction at concentrations higher than those required for repetitive activity. The mechanism of the block is different from that produced by stabilizers. It involves membrane depolarization consequent to ion leakage which is so large that it cannot be compensated for by metabolic pumps which operate to maintain ionic balances at rest. The decrease in the resting potential thus produced prevents the large transitory increase in Na^{+} permeability which is required for excitation, and block ensues. The mechanism by which the resting membrane potential governs Na^{+} permeability is speculative (203). Of interest from the point of view of model-system studies is the observation that local anesthetics can be shown to overcome a veratrine block. Herr and Akcasu (96) studied desheathed frog nerves and noted that low concentrations of dibucaine, which in themselves did not block conduction, delayed the onset of a veratrine block. Further, similar concentrations temporarily restored conduction during a veratrine block. The antagonistic actions of Ca^{++} and Mg^{++} were similar to those of the local anesthetics.

The interrelations with Ca^{++} are of particular interest since in living systems the effects of reduced Ca^{++} and of the veratrum alkaloids are in many respects similar, and it is possible that one effect of the veratrum alkaloids is to compete with Ca^{++} and to displace it from its binding site on the membrane, thus leading to passive leakage of other ions in response to concentration gradients. A decrease in the Ca^{47} uptake by frog sartorius has been demonstrated for protoveratrines A and B (3). Ca^{++} has been reported to antagonize the effects of veratrine which increase postganglionic discharge in ganglia (117), the effects of various veratrum alkaloids on amphibian skeletal muscle (68, 88), the depolarizing effects of veratrine or veratridine in frog nerve (96), and veratrum alkaloid effects on stretch receptors in lung (180) and on those receptors involved in the Bezold-Jarisch reflex (50). In the frog heart, on the other hand Ca^{++} lack prevents veratrine from exerting its full inotropic effect (154).

F. Metabolic Effects in Tissues

The effects of the veratrum alkaloids on tissue respiration have not been extensively investigated. Reiter (183) studied the metabolic actions of veratridine, veratramine, and the glycosides veratrosine and pseudojervine on heart muscle. Using intact atria and homogenates of ventricle, he found no effects on anaerobic glycolysis. However, a striking difference was noted between the tertiary and secondary amines on aerobic metabolism. Veratridine produced increases in oxygen consumption only in intact tissue, and at high concentrations led to a depression of respiration. Veratramine and the other secondary amines caused a decrease in respiration in homogenates as well as in intact tissue, and the effect was concentration related. The inhibition occurred at an early phase in the Krebs cycle, the cytochromes not being affected. These studies on heart muscle are of interest since they indicate that the tertiary amines exert their effects on oxygen consumption by acting in relation to the intact cell, probably by affecting the permeability of the membrane. The data on the secondary amines suggest that at low concentrations (10^{-6} M) some direct cardiac effects of veratramine (Section III,A,4,*c*) are probably associated with only minimal effects on oxygen consumption while with other effects, at higher concentrations (10^{-4} M), oxygen consumption may be inhibited by 50% (29).

Studies of the effects of protoveratrine on brain slices by Wollenberger (233) have also shown the importance of the intact cell for stimulation of respiration. Potassium in the medium was necessary for the respiratory action, and concentrations which stimulated respiration inhibited the net uptake of potassium. During electrical stimulation of brain slices (234) the protoveratrine stimulation of respiration was quite sensitive to the interval between stimuli. At high frequencies (100/second) no respiratory stimulation ascribable to the drug was noted, but at low rates of stimulation (less than 1/second) an effect was seen. A similar frequency sensitivity is seen in skeletal and heart muscle during the veratrine response (Section III,E,2).

Kini and Quastel (115) noted that the stimulating effect of protoveratrine on oxygen consumption of brain slices and on the transformation of labeled glucose into aminoacids was similar to that seen when the K^+/Ca^{++} ratio is increased. The effects of both of these procedures were antagonized by cocaine. They suggested an antagonism of Ca^{++} as a mechanism for the protoveratrine effect. Interrelations between the veratrum alkaloids, Ca^{++}, and local anesthetics are well known in physiological and model systems (Section III,E,2 and 4). It is probable that metabolic effects in brain have a basis in common with the effects on nerve and muscle and that stimulation of respiration is secondary to changes in ion permeability at the cell membrane.

IV. THERAPEUTIC USE

A. Hypertension

With the availability of pure alkaloids and standardized galenical preparations about 1950, there was a resurgence of clinical interest in the use of the veratrum alkaloids for the treatment of hypertension. The singular nature of the mechanism of the hypotensive response, an action on afferent pathways involved in control of the cardiovascular system, raised the possibility of specific control of hypertension which lacked the undesirable effects of drugs such as ganglionic blocking agents, which act more peripherally. The veratrum alkaloids, when properly employed in hypertensives, lead to decreases in blood pressure which are the result of an inhibition of sympathetic outflow to the cardiovascular system. The bradycardia due to stimulation of vagal outflow to the heart contributes slightly to the decrease in blood pressure, which is attributable to decreases in vasomotor tone (172) and cardiac output (74, 104, 172). These alterations in cardiovascular dynamics usually occur with minimal orthostatic hypotension (161) and with preservation of adaptive sympathetic vasomotor reflexes (74, 153, 159).

The great limitation which has prevented the general use of the veratrum alkaloids in the treatment of hypertension has been the narrow therapeutic range (58). These substances evoke a hypotensive response in doses which are very close to those which lead to side effects, the most prominent of which are nausea and vomiting. Their use requires close supervision of an intelligent patient (112, 235) and delicate control of dose (49); they are not satisfactory for ambulatory therapy (46). There have been reports of the use of veratrum alkaloids in conjunction with other antihypertensive agents such as the rauwolfia alkaloids (221) and diuretics (113). When used with rauwolfia alkaloids, the incidence of side effects may be decreased because of the smaller doses which can be employed. When used in maximum tolerated doses, protoveratrine A did not enhance the hypotensive effect of benzothiadiazine diuretics, which by themselves produced a greater blood pressure fall than did protoveratrine A alone.

Although the veratrum alkaloids have no place in the routine treatment of hypertension, they do have a role in the treatment of eclampsia and toxemias of pregnancy (12, 42, 60, 158, 235), in hypertensive crisis with encephalopathy (48, 103, 235), and in acute left ventricular failure associated with hypertension (48, 103, 172, 191). The rapidity of onset of action, within minutes after intravenous administration of protoveratrines A and B, makes for favorable use in emergencies (231). Studies on effects in toxemia of pregnancy have indicated that the blood pressure can be reduced even after spinal blockade to the level of cervical 4, a procedure which only slightly affects the blood pressure by itself (14). This, coupled with the observation that, in toxemia, blood pressure is reduced by veratrum alkaloids but not by ganglionic blockade with tetraethylammonium (13), suggests a peculiar desirability for their use in toxemia. When employed in hypertensive crises, convulsions are controlled (42, 60, 158), as is the retinopathy (103, 158), and a decrease in elevated pulmonary arterial pressure is noted during left ventricular failure (172) where the cardiac output may increase (74).

The preparations available for clinical use are listed in Table III. Winer (230), in a comparison of protoveratrine A and protoveratrine B on oral administration in humans, showed that protoveratrine B was relatively inactive in oral doses several times those of effective doses of protoveratrine A. In a later study (231) he showed that, on intravenous administration, protoveratrine B was only slightly less potent than protoveratrine A, suggesting that the difference with oral use was due to poor gastrointestinal absorption or inactivation of protoveratrine B. The importance of the proportion of the two substances when they are present as mixtures for oral administration (Table III) is therefore apparent. Winer also noted that protoveratrine B was significantly better tolerated than protoveratrine A as regards the nausea provoked on intravenous

TABLE III

PURIFIED ALKALOIDS AND ALKALOIDAL MIXTURES AVAILABLE FOR USE IN HUMANS[a]

Alkavervir (Veriloid)	A mixture of alkaloids obtained from *Veratrum viride*.
Cryptenamine acetates (Unitensin Acetates) and Cryptenamine tannates (Unitensin Tannates)	Mixtures containing acetic acid or tannic acid salts, respectively, of alkaloids obtained from *Veratrum viride*.
Protoveratrine A (Protalba, Puroverine[b])	Derived from *Veratrum album*.
Protoveratrines A and B (Veralba)	A mixture of the two alkaloids chemically standardized to contain 55% protoveratrine A and 45% protoveratrine B. Derived from *Veratrum album*.
Protoveratrine A and B maleates (Provell Maleate)	A mixture of the maleic acid salts of the two alkaloids. Derived from *Veratrum album*.

[a] Many of these preparations have been employed in experimental animal work.

[b] Puroverine was originally two alkaloids (124) in which the proportion of protoveratrine A to protoveratrine B was 2 : 1. It now contains only protoveratrine A.

administration. However, no preparation of protoveratrine B is commercially available for human use.

B. TOXICITY

In clinical use, other than severe falls in blood pressure and heart rate due to overdosage, the toxicity due to the veratrum alkaloids is associated with nausea and vomiting (49, 75, 161, 235), salivation and rhinorrhea (49), paresthesias of the face, throat, and thorax (104), cardiac arrhythmias (35, 41, 148, 231), and tightness in various muscle groups which resembles that seen in human myotonia (116, 230). Severe falls in blood pressure may be counteracted by pressor agents (42, 235), while the bradycardia, being mainly of vagal origin, responds to atropine (49, 104, 175, 235). The nausea and vomiting are not controlled with specific antiemetic therapy, although the barbiturates have been employed (112). In animal studies, however, barbiturates were shown not to change the ED_{50} for emesis (83). The importance of route of administration on toxicity is brought out by the observation in animal studies that oral administration of the veratrum alkaloids did not lead to lethality in species capable of emesis (212). Cardiac arrhythmias or EKG changes of vagal origin, such as sinus arrest, wandering pacemaker, various degrees of heart block, atrioventricular nodal rhythm, and T wave inversion can be controlled by atropine (59, 148, 231). However, certain abnormalities of conduction or rhythm are atropine resistant (35, 41) and may represent direct effects on the heart, such as have been studied in experimental animals (26). Quinidine has been employed against veratrum-induced ventricular arrhythmias (41). The possibility of exaggeration of digitalis arrhythmias in man by the veratrum alkaloids has been suggested (159), but the phenomenon has been studied only in experimental animals where additive effects were noted (169).

In grazing animals, congenital anomalies have been attributed to the ingestion of *V. californicum*, but the studies have not clearly attributed these to the alkaloidal content of the plant (34).

References

1. Abreu, B. E., Richards, A. B., Alexander, W. M., and Weaver, L. C., Cardiovascular, emetic and pharmacodynamic properties of certain veratrum alkaloids. *J. Pharmacol. Exptl. Therap.* **112,** 73 (1954).
2. Adam, K. R., and Weiss, C., Actions of scorpion venom on skeletal muscle. *Brit. J. Pharmacol.* **14,** 334 (1959).
3. Ahmad, K., and Lewis, J. J., The influence of drugs which stimulate skeletal muscle and of their antagonists on flux of calcium, potassium and sodium ions. *J. Pharmacol. Exptl. Therap.* **136,** 298 (1962).
4. Anichkov, S. V., and Belen'kii, M. L., "Pharmacology of the Carotid Body Chemoreceptors," p. 131. Macmillan, New York, 1963.
5. Aronow, L., The effect of the veratrum alkaloids on adrenal medullary secretion. Ph.D. Thesis, Harvard Univ., Cambridge, Massachusetts, 1956.
6. Arora, R. B., Studies on veratrum alkaloids. XVII. The antiveratrinic action of the cardiac glycosides and of bufotoxin. *J. Pharmacol. Exptl. Therap.* **108,** 26 (1953).
7. Arora, R. B., Antiveratrinic action of *Rauwolfia serpentina* alkaloids. *Arch. Intern. Pharmacodyn.* **106,** 28 (1956).
8. Arora, R. B., Antiarrhythmics. Quinidine-like activity of some ataraxic agents. *J. Pharmacol. Exptl. Therap.* **124,** 53 (1958).
9. Arora, R. B., and Dandiya, P. C., A study of the chemical configuration responsible for the antiveratrinic activity of cinchona alkaloids and cupreines. *J. Pharmacol. Exptl. Therap.* **118,** 230 (1956).
10. Arora, R. B., and Das, P. K., Antiveratrinic activity of antiarrhythmic drugs. *Arch. Intern. Pharmacodyn.* **107,** 202 (1956).
11. Arora, R. B., Seshadri, T. R., and Krishnaswamy, N. R., Antiveratrinic activity of coumarin and its derivative compounds. *Arch. Intern. Pharmacodyn.* **124,** 150 (1960).
12. Assali, N. S., Hemodynamic effects of hypotensive drugs used in obstetrics. *Obstet. Gynecol. Survey* **9,** 776 (1954).
13. Assali, N. S., Brust, A. A., Garber, S. T., and Ferris, E. B., Comparative study of the effects of tetraethylammonium chloride and *Veratrum viride* on blood pressure in normal and toxemic pregnancy. *J. Clin. Invest.* **29,** 290 (1950).
14. Assali, N. S., and Prystowsky, H., Studies on autonomic blockade. III. Effect of high spinal anesthesia on the vasodepressor action of *Veratrum* in human subjects. *J. Pharmacol. Exptl. Therap.* **100,** 251 (1950).

15. Aviado, D. M., Nervous influences on the pulmonary circulation: increased intracranial pressure, veratridine and bretylium. *Arch. Exptl. Pathol. Pharmakol.* **240**, 446 (1961).
16. Aviado, D. M., Cerletti, A., Li, T. H., and Schmidt, C. F., The activation of carotid sinus pressoreceptors and intracranial receptors by veratridine and potassium. *J. Pharmacol. Exptl. Therap.* **115**, 329 (1955).
17. Aviado, D. M., and Dil, A. H., The effects of a new sympathetic blocking drug (bretylium) on cardiovascular control. *J. Pharmacol. Exptl. Therap.* **129**, 328 (1960).
18. Aviado, D. M., Li, T. H., Kalow, W., Schmidt, C. F., Turnbull, G. L., Peskin, G. W., Hess, M. E., and Weiss, A. J., Respiratory and circulatory reflexes from the perfused heart and pulmonary circulation of the dog. *Am. J. Physiol.* **165**, 261 (1951).
19. Aviado, D. M., Pontius, R. G., and Li, T. H., The mechanism of apnea following intravenous injection of various antihistaminic compounds; its relation to their chemical structure. *J. Pharmacol. Exptl. Therap.* **99**, 425 (1950).
20. Aviado, D. M., Pontius, R. G., and Schmidt, C. F., The reflex respiratory and circulatory actions of veratridine on pulmonary, cardiac and carotid receptors. *J. Pharmacol. Exptl. Therap.* **97**, 420 (1949).
21. Aviado, D. M., and Schmidt, C. F., Reflexes from stretch receptors in blood vessels, heart and lungs. *Physiol. Rev.* **35**, 247 (1955).
22. Bailey, D. M., Hamon, D. P. G., and Johnson, W. S., On the C-9 configuration of veratramine and jervine. *Tetrahedron Letters* **9**, 555 (1963).
23. Barer, G. R., and Nusser, E., The part played by bronchial muscles in pulmonary reflexes. *Brit. J. Pharmacol.* **8**, 315 (1953).
24. Barer, G. R., and Nusser, E., Cardiac output during excitation of chemoreflexes in the cat. *Brit. J. Pharmacol.* **13**, 372 (1958).
25. Benforado, J. M., and Smith, E., Unpublished observations (1960).
26. Benforado, J. M., Studies on veratrum alkaloids. XXVI. Comparison of the cardiac action of various tertiary amine ester alkaloids. *J. Pharmacol. Exptl. Therap.* **120**, 412 (1957).
27. Benforado, J. M., Frequency-dependent pharmacological and physiological effects on the rat ventricle strip. *J. Pharmacol. Exptl. Therap.* **122**, 86 (1958).
28. Benforado, J. M., Veratrine response in the rat right ventricle strip. *Federation Proc.* **19**, 111 (1960).
29. Benforado, J. M., Dörner, J., and Fuentes, J., The effects of veratramine on atrio-ventricular nodal rhythm and on auricular flutter in the dog heart-lung preparation. *Arch. Exptl. Pathol. Pharmakol.* **240**, 382 (1961).
30. Benforado, J. M., Flacke, W., Swaine, C. R., and Mosimann, W., Studies on veratrum alkaloids. XXIX. The action of some germine esters and of veratridine upon blood pressure, heart rate and femoral blood flow in the dog. *J. Pharmacol. Exptl. Therap.* **130**, 311 (1960).
31. Benforado, J. M., and Witt, P. N., The influence of heart rate upon the lethal dose of veratridine in the heart-lung preparation of the dog. *J. Pharmacol. Exptl. Therap.* **110**, 334 (1954).
32. Bevan, J. A., and Verity, M. A., Action of lobeline on intrathoracic receptors: a comparison with phenyldiguanide, serotonin and veratridine. *J. Pharmacol. Exptl. Therap.* **132**, 42 (1961).
33. Bezold, A. von, and Hirt, L., Über die physiologischen Wirkungen des essigsauren Veratrins. *Untersuch. Physiol. Lab. Wurzburg* **1**, 73 (1867).

34. Binns, W., James, L. F., and Shupe, J. L., Toxicosis of *Veratrum californicum* in ewes and its relationship to congenital deformity in lambs. *Ann. N.Y. Acad. Sci.* **111,** 571 (1964).

35. Black, M. M., and Lyons, R. H., Prolonged depression of atrioventricular conduction caused by large dosages of protoveratine. *Am. Heart J.* **48,** 266 (1954).

36. Boehm, R., Veratrin und Protoveratrin. *Heffter's Handbuch Exptl. Pharmakol.* **2,** Pt. 1, 249 (1920).

37. Borison, H. L., and Fairbanks, V. F., Mechanism of veratrum-induced emesis in the cat. *J. Pharmacol. Exptl. Therap.* **105,** 317 (1952).

38. Borison, H. L., Fairbanks, V. F., and White, C. A., Afferent reflex factors in Veriloid-induced hypotension. *Arch. Intern. Pharmacodyn.* **101,** 189 (1955).

39. Borison, H. L., and Sampson, S. R., The vagal body: receptor site for emetic action of veratrum alkaloids? *Federation Proc.* **20,** 169 (1961).

40. Brand, E. D., Harris, T. D., Borison, H. L., and Goodman, L. S., The antiemetic activity of 10-(γ-dimethylaminopropyl)-2-chlorophenothiazine (chlorpromazine) in dog and cat. *J. Pharmacol. Exptl. Therap.* **110,** 86 (1954).

41. Bronsky, D., Berstein, M., and Chesrow, E. J., Cardiac arrhythmia from *Veratrum viride. Geriatrics* **12,** 389 (1957).

41a. Brooks, C. McC., Hoffman, B. F., Suckling, E. E., and Orias, O., "Excitability of the Heart," p. 261. Grune & Stratton, New York, 1955.

42. Bryant, R. D., Hypotensive drugs in the management of toxemia of pregnancy. *Postgrad. Med.* **22,** 354 (1957).

43. Burns, B. D., Frank, G. B., and Salmoiraghi, G., The mechanism of afterdischarges caused by veratrine in frog's skeletal muscles. *Brit. J. Pharmacol.* **10,** 363 (1955).

44. Calliauw, L., On the hypertensive action of protoveratrine A. *Arch. Intern. Pharmacodyn.* **107,** 75 (1956).

45. Cicardo, V. H., Arterial hypertension by veratrum derivatives injected into the nervous centers. *Arch. Intern. Pharmacodyn.* **94,** 65 (1953).

46. Coe, W. S., Best, M. M., and Kinsman, J. M., *Veratrum viride* in the treatment of hypertensive vascular disease. *J. Am. Med. Assoc.* **143,** 5 (1950).

47. Conner, P. K., McConn, R. G., and Moyer, J. H., An attempt to alleviate the emetic effect of protoveratrine by the concurrent use of chlorpromazine in the treatment of hypertension. *Am. Practitioner Dig. Treat.* **7,** 1127 (1956).

48. Corcoran, A. C., The choice of drugs in the treatment of hypertension. *In* "Drugs of Choice 1964–65" (W. Modell, ed.), Chapt. 24. Mosby, Saint Louis, Missouri, 1964.

49. Currens, J. H., Myers, G. S., and White, P. D., The use of protoveratrine in the treatment of hypertensive vascular disease. *Am. Heart. J.* **46,** 576 (1953).

50. Dawes, G. S., Studies on veratrum alkaloids. VII. Receptor areas in the coronary arteries and elsewhere as revealed by the use of veratridine. *J. Pharmacol. Exptl. Therap.* **89,** 325 (1947).

51. Dawes, G. S., and Comroe, J. H., Chemoreflexes from the heart and lungs. *Physiol. Rev.* **34,** 167 (1954).

52. Dawes, G. S., Mott, J. C., and Widdicombe, J. G., The depressor action of the veratrum alkaloids. *Brit. J. Pharmacol.* **6,** 675 (1951).

53. Dawes, G. S., Mott, J. C., and Widdicombe, J. G., Respiratory and cardiovascular reflexes from the heart and lungs. *J. Physiol. (London)* **115**, 258 (1951).
54. Dawes, G. S., and Widdicombe, J. G., The afferent pathway of the Bezold reflex: the left vagal branches in dogs. *Brit. J. Pharmacol.* **8**, 395 (1953).
55. Dokukin, A. V., Role of stretch receptors of the left ventricle in reflex hemodynamic changes in myocardial ischemia. *Byul. Eksperim. Biol. i Med.* **55**, 29 (1963). English transl. in *Federation Proc.* **23**, T296 (1964).
56. Dontas, A. S., Effects of protoveratrine, serotonin and ATP on afferent and splanchnic nerve activity. *Circulation Res.* **3**, 363 (1955).
57. Downing, S. E., Remensnyder, J. P., and Mitchell, J. H., Cardiovascular responses to hypoxic stimulation of the carotid bodies. *Circulation Res.* **10**, 676 (1962).
58. Doyle, A. E., and Smirk, F. H., The use of the pure veratrum alkaloids neogermitrine and protoveratrine in hypertension. *Brit. Heart J.* **15**, 439 (1953).
59. Elek, S. R., McNair, J. D., and Griffith, G. C., The electrocardiographic effects of intravenous *Veratrum viride*. *Circulation* **7**, 903 (1953).
60. Elliott, P. M., Intravenous protoveratrine in the prevention and management of eclampsia. *J. Obstet. Gynaecol. Brit. Empire* **66**, 610 (1959).
61. Etzensperger, J., Etude des réponses électrique et mécanique de la fibre musculaire striée intoxiquée par la vératrine. Incidences sur le probleme du couplage excitation-contraction. *Compt. Rend. Soc. Biol.* **156**, 1125 (1962).
62. Eyzaguirre, C., Folk, B. P., Zierler, K. L., and Lilienthal, J. L., Jr., Experimental myotonia and repetitive phenomena: the veratrinic effects of 2,4-dichlorphenoxyacetate (2,4-D) in the rat. *Am. J. Physiol.* **155**, 69 (1948).
63. Falk, G., Drugs and muscle contraction. *Proc. Western Pharmacol. Soc.* **1**, 21 (1958).
64. Falk, G., and Landa, J. F., Prolonged response of skeletal muscle in the absence of penetrating ions. *Am. J. Physiol.* **198**, 289 (1960).
65. Fernandez, E., and Cerletti, A., Studies on the hypotensive mechanism of protoveratrine. *Arch. Intern. Pharmacodyn.* **100**, 425 (1955).
66. Flacke, W., The action of the erythrophleum alkaloids on the single twitch and on the "veratrine response" of the sartorius muscle of the frog. *J. Pharmacol. Exptl. Therap.* **113**, 21 (1955).
67. Flacke, W., Veratrine response and antiveratrinic activity. *Pharmacologist* **1**, 72 (1959).
68. Flacke, W., Pharmacological activity of some esters of germine with acetic acid *Arch. Exptl. Pathol. Pharmakol.* **240**, 369 (1961).
69. Flacke, W., Studies on veratrum alkaloids. XXXIII. The action of some esters of germine with acetic acid on the sartorius muscle of the frog. *J. Pharmacol. Exptl. Therap.* **137**, 62 (1962).
70. Flacke, W., Studies on veratrum alkaloids. XXXVI. The action of germine monoacetate and germine diacetate on mammalian skeletal muscle. *J. Pharmacol. Exptl. Therap.* **141**, 230 (1963).
71. Flacke, W., Benforado, J., Mosimann, W., and Swaine, C. R., Vascular tone and the action of vasoactive drugs: a technique for experimental determination of the relationship between pressure and flow in the dog with intact circulatory reflexes. *J. Pharmacol. Exptl. Therap.* **128**, 145 (1960).

72. Flacke, W., Benforado, J. M., Swaine, C. R., and Mosimann, W., Studies on veratrum alkaloids. XXX. The action of some esters of germine on cardiac output and vascular tone with observations on drug-induced decrease of positive inotropic sympathetic tone. *J. Pharmacol. Exptl. Therap.* **130,** 321 (1960).
73. Frank, G. B., Effect of veratine on muscle fibre membrane and on negative after-potential. *J. Neurophysiol.* **21,** 263 (1958).
74. Freis, E. D., Stanton, J. R., Culbertson, J. W., Litter, J., Halperin, M. H., Burnett, C. H., and Wilkins, R. W., The hemodynamic effects of hypotensive drugs in man. I. *Veratrum viride. J. Clin. Invest.* **28,** 353 (1949).
75. Freis, E. D., Stanton, J. R., and Moister, F. C., Assay in man of the chemical fractions of *Veratrum viride,* and identification of the pure alkaloids germitrine and germidine as potent hypotensive principles derived from the drug. *J. Pharmacol. Exptl. Therap.* **98,** 166 (1950).
76. Fuentes, J., The antagonistic action of sparteine upon the veratrine response. *J. Pharmacol. Exptl. Therap.* **119,** 225 (1957).
77. Fuentes, J., The antiaccelerator effect of sparteine on the heart-lung preparation of the dog. *J. Pharmacol. Exptl. Therap.* **119,** 427 (1957).
78. Gellhorn, E., Hypothalamic-cortical system in barbiturate anesthesia. *Arch. Intern. Pharmacodyn.* **93,** 434 (1953).
79. Gershfeld, N. L., The influence of structure on the orientation of the veratrum alkaloids at the air/water interface. *Biochim. Biophys. Acta* **42,** 282 (1960).
80. Gershfeld, N. L., and Shanes, A. M., Antagonism of veratrine by calcium ion in monolayers of stearic acid. *Science* **129,** 1427 (1959).
81. Goldring, S., and O'Leary, J. L., Correlation between steady transcortical potential and evoked response. *Electroencephalog. Clin. Neurophysiol.* **6,** 189 (1954).
82. Goth, A., and Harrison, F., Influence of protoveratrine on effect of vasoactive drugs. *Proc. Soc. Exptl. Biol. Med.* **87,** 437 (1954).
83. Gourzis, J. T., Influence of Rauwiloid, an alkaloidal extract of *Rauwolfia serpentina,* on veratrum-induced emesis in dogs. *J. Pharmacol. Exptl. Therap.* **113,** 24 (1955).
84. Gourzis, J. T., and Bauer, R. O., The effect of veratrum derivatives on the isolated intestine of the rabbit and on the intact intestine of the trained unanesthetized dog. *J. Pharmacol. Exptl. Therap.* **103,** 471 (1951).
85. Goutier, R., Sensitization to potassium ions and decurarization by some veratrum alkaloids. *Brit. J. Pharmacol.* **5,** 33 (1950).
86. Gruhzit, C. C., Freyburger, W. A., and Moe, G. K., The action of Veriloid on carotid pressoreceptors. *J. Pharmacol. Exptl. Therap.* **109,** 261 (1953).
87. Gruhzit, C. C., Freyburger, W. A., and Moe, G. K., The nature of the reflex vasodilation by epinephrine. *J. Pharmacol. Exptl. Therap.* **112,** 138 (1954).
88. Gujral, P. K., Action of the acetic acid esters of protoverine on the isolated frog sartorius muscle. *Pharmacologist* **5,** 275 (1963).
89. Gujral, P. K., Action of the acetic acid esters of protoverine on muscular contraction and blood pressure in the cat. *Federation Proc.* **23,** 543 (1964).
90. Hapke, H. J., Beeinflussung der narkotischen atemhemmung durch protoveratrin. *Arch. Intern. Pharmacodyn.* **134,** 454 (1961).
91. Hapke, H. J., Veranderungen der spontanatmung nach protoveratrin A. *Arch. Intern. Pharmacodyn.* **146,** 192 (1963).

92. Harris, L. S., and Uhle, F. C., 4-substituted indoles as antagonists to 5-hydroxytryptamine and to the veratrine response. *J. Pharmacol. Exptl. Therap.* **128,** 358 (1960).
93. Hawkins, D. F., Studies on veratrum alkaloids. XXXIV. Actions of veratramine on spontaneously beating guinea-pig atrium preparations. *J. Pharmacol. Exptl. Therap.* **137,** 306 (1962).
94. Hawkins, D. F., Studies on veratrum alkaloids. XXXV. The effect of veratramine on responses of spontaneously beating guinea-pig atrium preparations to epinephrine. *J. Pharmacol. Exptl. Therap.* **138,** 292 (1962).
95. Hazard, R., and Mouillé, P., Digitaline, vératrine et potassium. *Compt. Rend. Soc. Biol.* **153,** 1764 (1959).
96. Herr, F., and Akcasu, A., Action of veratrine and membrane stabilizers on nerves. *J. Pharmacol. Exptl. Therap.* **130,** 328 (1960).
97. Heymans, C., and DeVleeschhouwer, G., Mechanisms of bradycardia by veratridine. *Arch. Intern. Pharmacodyn.* **84,** 409 (1950).
98. Hirose, T., Yasukata, M., Yoshioka, T., and Tanaka, K., Inhibitory effects of certain drugs on the central pathway of Bezold reflex. *Yonage Acta Med.* **3,** 171 (1955).
99. Hoffman, B. F., and Cranefield, P. F., "Electrophysiology of the Heart," p. 123. McGraw-Hill, New York, New York, 1960.
100. Hoffmann, P., Über die Aktionsströme des mit Veratrin vergifteten Muskels. *Z. Biol.* **58,** 55 (1912).
101. Hofmann, W. W., Action of veratrine on human skeletal muscle with special reference to myasthenia gravis. *Neurology* **8,** 917 (1958).
102. Hofmann, W. W., Feigen, G. A., and Genther, G. H., Effects of veratrine, nitrate ion and γ-aminobutyric acid on mammalian miniature end-plate potentials. *Nature* **193,** 175 (1962).
103. Hoobler, S. W., Corley, R. W., Kabza, T. G., and Loyke, H. F., Treatment of hypertension with oral protoveratrine. *Ann. Internal. Med.* **37,** 465 (1952).
104. Hoobler, S. W., Kabza, T. G., and Corley, R. W., The effect of protoveratrine on the cardiac output and on some regional circulations in man. *J. Clin. Invest.* **34,** 559 (1955).
105. Hunt, C. C., and Kuffler, S. W., Pharmacology of the neuromuscular junction. *Pharmacol. Rev.* **2,** 96 (1950).
106. Innes, I. R., Kosterlitz, H. W., and Krayer, O., Studies on veratrum alkaloids. XXIV. The inhibition by veratramine and veratrosine of the cardioaccelerator effect of electrical stimulation of the accelerator nerves. *J. Pharmacol. Exptl. Therap.* **117,** 317 (1956).
107. Innes, I. R., and Krayer, O., Studies on veratrum alkaloids. XXVII. The negative chronotropic action of veratramine and reserpine in the heart depleted of catecholamines. *J. Pharmacol. Exptl. Therap.* **124,** 245 (1958).
108. Jarisch, A., Landgren, S., Neil, E., and Zotterman, Y., Impulse activity in the carotid sinus nerve following intra-carotid injection of potassium chloride, veratrine, sodium citrate, adenosinetriphosphate and α-dinitrophenol. *Acta Physiol. Scand.* **25,** 195 (1952).
109. Jarisch, A., and Richter, H., Der Bezold-Effekt, eine vergessene Kreislaufreaktion. *Klin. Wochschr.* **1,** 185 (1939).
110. Jarisch, A., and Zotterman, Y., Depressor reflexes from the heart. *Acta Physiol. Scand.* **16,** 31 (1949).

111. Jones, J. V., The afferent pathway of the Bezold reflex: the right vagal branches in cats. *Brit. J. Pharmacol.* **8,** 352 (1953).
112. Kauntze, R., and Trounce, J., Treatment of arterial hypertension with Veriloid. *Lancet* **2,** 1002 (1951).
113. Kert, M. J., Roth, S. I., Mailman, R. H., Dashe, A. M., and Avedon, M., Clinical evaluation of protoveratrine A used alone and in combination with diuretic agents. *Angiology* **13,** 180 (1962).
114. Kiebel, G., and Sandow, A., Effects of excitation-blocking drugs and sodium deficiency on the veratrine electrical response. *J. Pharmacol. Exptl. Therap.* **121,** 199 (1957).
115. Kini, M. M., and Quastel, J. H., Effects of veratrine and cocaine on cerebral carbohydrate-amino acid interrelations. *Science* **131,** 412 (1960).
116. Kolb, E. J., and Korein, J., Neuromuscular toxicity of veratrum alkaloids. *Neurology* **11,** 159 (1961).
117. Komalahiranya, A., and Volle, R. L., Actions of inorganic ions and veratrine on asynchronous postganglionic discharge in sympathetic ganglia treated with diisopropyl phosphorofluoridate (DFP). *J. Pharmacol. Exptl. Therap.* **138,** 57 (1962).
118. Kosterlitz, H. W., Krayer, O., and Matallana, A., Studies on veratrum alkaloids. XXII. Periodic activity of the sinoauricular node of the denervated cat heart caused by veratramine. *J. Pharmacol. Exptl. Therap.* **113,** 460 (1955).
119. Kraatz, C. P., Cholinesterase inhibition and spontaneous activity of the frog rectus abdominis muscle. *J. Pharmacol. Exptl. Therap.* **130,** 194 (1960).
120. Krayer, O., Studies on veratrum alkaloids. VIII. Veratramine, an antagonist to the cardioaccelerator action of epinephrine. *J. Pharmacol. Exptl. Therap.* **96,** 422 (1949).
121. Krayer, O., Studies on veratrum alkaloids. IX. The inhibition by veratrosine of the cardioaccelerator action of epinephrine and of norepinephrine. *J. Pharmacol. Exptl. Therap.* **97,** 256 (1949).
122. Krayer, O., Studies on veratrum alkaloids. XII. A quantitative comparison of the antiaccelerator cardiac action of veratramine, veratrosine, jervine and pseudojervine. *J. Pharmacol. Exptl. Therap.* **98,** 427 (1950).
123. Krayer, O., The antiaccelerator cardiac action of quinine and quinidine. *J. Pharmacol. Exptl. Therap.* **100,** 146 (1950).
124. Krayer, O., Veratrum alkaloids. *In* "Pharmacology in Medicine" (V. A. Drill, ed.), 2nd Ed., Chapt. 33. McGraw-Hill, New York, 1958.
125. Krayer, O., The history of the Bezold-Jarisch effect. *Arch. Exptl. Pathol. Pharmakol.* **240,** 361 (1961).
126. Krayer, O., and Acheson, G. H., The pharmacology of the veratrum alkaloids. *Physiol. Rev.* **26,** 383 (1946).
127. Krayer, O., Arora, R. B., and Meilman, E., Studies on veratrum alkaloids, XXI. The action of veratramine upon impulse generation in the dog heart. *J. Pharmacol. Exptl. Therap.* **113,** 446 (1955).
128. Krayer, O., and Briggs, L. H., Studies on Solanum alkaloids: I. The antiaccelerator cardiac action of β-dihydrosolasodine and tetrahydrosolasodine. *Brit. J. Pharmacol.* **5,** 118 (1950).
129. Krayer, O., and George, H. W., Studies on veratrum alkaloids. XV. The quinine-like effect of veratramine upon the single twitch and upon the "veratrine response" of the sartorius muscle of the frog. *J. Pharmacol. Exptl. Therap.* **103,** 249 (1951).

130. Krayer, O., Kupchan, S. M., Deliwala, C. V., and Rogers, B. H., Untersuchungen über die Veratrumalkaloide. XVIII. Die chemischen und pharmakologischen Beziehungen zwischen den Zygadenusalkaloiden und den Veratrumalkaloiden. *Arch. Exptl. Pathol. Pharmakol.* **219**, 371 (1953).

131. Krayer, O., Mandoki, J. J., and Mendez, C., Studies on veratrum alkaloids. XVI. The action of epinephrine and of veratramine on the functional refractory period of the auriculo-ventricular transmission in the heart-lung preparation of the dog. *J. Pharmacol. Exptl. Therap.* **103**, 412 (1951).

132. Krayer, O., and Ourisson, P., Studies on veratrum alkaloids. XIX. The action of veratramine upon cardioacceleration caused by ephedrine, tyramine, phenylephrine and isopropylarterenol. *J. Pharmacol. Exptl. Therap.* **112**, 341 (1954).

133. Krayer, O., and Reiter, M., Studies on veratrum alkaloids. XI. Jervine and pseudojervine, antagonists to the cardioaccelerator action of epinephrine and of accelerans stimulation. *Arch. Intern. Pharmacodyn.* **81**, 409 (1950).

134. Krayer, O., Uhle, F. C., and Ourisson, P., Studies on veratrum alkaloids. XIV. The antiaccelerator cardiac action of derivatives of veratramine and jervine and of synthetic steroid secondary alkamines obtained from pregnenolone and from sapogenins. *J. Pharmacol. Exptl. Therap.* **102**, 261 (1951).

135. Krayer, O., and Van Maanen, E. F., Studies on veratrum alkaloids, X. The inhibition by veratramine of the positive chronotropic effect of accelerans stimulation and of norephinephrine. *J. Pharmacol. Exptl. Therap.* **97**, 301 (1949).

136. Krayer, O., Wood, E. H., and Montes, G., Studies on veratrum alkaloids. IV. The sites of the heart rate lowering action of veratridine. *J. Pharmacol. Exptl. Therap.* **79**, 215 (1943).

137. Kuffler, S. W., Action of veratrine on nerve-muscle preparations. *J. Neurophysiol.* **8**, 113 (1945).

138. Kuffler, S. W., The relation of electrical potential changes to contracture in skeletal muscle. *J. Neurophysiol.* **9**, 367 (1946).

139. Kulaev, B. S., Characteristics of afferent impulses evoked in cardiac nerves by chemical stimulation of epicardial receptors. *Fiziol. Zh. SSSR* **48**, 1350 (1962). English transl. in *Federation Proc.* **22**, T749 (1963).

140. Kupchan, S. M., Hypotensive veratrum ester alkaloids. *J. Pharm. Sci.* **50**, 273 (1961).

141. Kupchan, S. M., Fujita, E., Grivas, J. C., and Weaver, L. C., Veratrum alkaloids. L, Structure-activity relationships in a series of synthetic hypotensive analogs of the protoveratrines. *J. Pharm. Sci.* **51**, 1140 (1962).

142. Kupchan, S. M., Gruenfeld, N., and Katsui, N., Veratrum alkaloids. XLIX. The structures and configurations of sabine and sabadine. *J. Med. Pharm. Chem.* **5**, 690 (1962).

143. Kupchan, S. M., Zimmerman, J. H., and Afonso, A., The alkaloids and taxonomy of veratrum and related genera. *Lloydia* **24**, 1 (1961).

144. Lim, R. K. S., Moffitt, R. L., and Glass, H. G., Observations on the mechanism of central hypotension. *J. Pharmacol. Exptl. Therap.* **113**, 33 (1955):

145. Lister, R. E., and Lewis, J. J., The effect of protoveratrine A on potassium and calcium ion movement in muscle and nerve. *J. Pharm. Pharmacol.* **11**, Suppl. 176T (1959).

146. Lister, R. E., and Lewis, J. J., The effects of protoveratrine on plasma potassium levels in the cat and rabbit. *J. Pharm. Pharmacol.* **11**, Suppl. 185T (1959).

147. Loeschcke, H. H., and Koepchen, H. P., Über das Verhalten der Atmung und des arteriellen Drucks bei Einbringen von Veratridin, Lobelin und Cyanid in den Liquor cerebrospinalis. *Arch. Ges. Physiol.* **266**, 586 (1958).

148. Margolin, E. G., Levine, H. D., and Merrill, J. P. Cardiac arrhythmias associated with protoveratrine. *Am. Heart J.* **52**, 257 (1956).

149. Marsh, D. F., Herring, D. A., and Howard, A., Veratramine. *J. Pharmacol. Exptl. Therap.* **103**, 172 (1951).

150. Martini, L., and Calliauw, L., On the pharmacology of protoveratrine in dogs. *Arch. Intern. Pharmacodyn.* **101**, 49 (1955).

151. Matallana, A., Flacke, W. E., and Krayer, O., The action of veratramine upon the heart rate in the cat. *J. Pharmacol. Exptl. Therap.* **113**, 36 (1955).

152. Matton, G., Action de la protoveratrine sur les barorécepteurs du sinus carotidien du chien hypertendu. *Arch. Intern. Pharmacodyn.* **103**, 13 (1955).

153. McCall, M. L., Continuing vasodilator infusion therapy. *Obstet. Gynecol.* **4**, 403 (1954).

154. McCartney, E., and Ransom, F., Sodium citrate and the action of certain drugs upon the frog's heart. *J. Physiol.* (*London*) **51**, 287 (1917).

155. McLain, P. L., and Bryan, J. H., A depressor reflex with vagal afferents in the rabbit. *Pharmacologist* **5**, 249 (1963).

156. Meesmann, W., Untersuchungen zur pathophysiologie und therapie des herzinfarktes. *Arch. Kreislaufforsch.* **36**, 212 (1961).

157. Meier, R., Bein, H. J., and Helmich, H., Zur Wirkung des Veratrins auf die vagale Atemsteuerung des Kaninchens. *Experientia* **5**, 484 (1949).

158. Meilman, E., Clinical studies on veratrum alkaloids. 4. Use of protoveratrine in toxemia of pregnancy. *J. Am. Med. Assoc.* **153**, 540 (1953).

159. Meilman, E., and Krayer, O., Clinical studies on veratrum alkaloids. I. The action of protoveratrine and veratridine in hypertension. *Circulation* **1**, 204 (1950).

160. Melson, F., Wirkungen einiger 1,3-dioxolane gegenüber der veratramin-intoxikation bei der albino-maus. *Arch. Intern. Pharmacodyn.* **133**, 327 (1961).

161. Miller, S. I., Ford, R. V., and Moyer, J. H., Dibenzyline: results of therapy in patients with hypertension and comparison with hexamethonium, 1-hydrazinophthalazine and semipurified extracts of veratrum. *New Engl. J. Med.* **248**, 576 (1953).

162. Moe, G. K., Bassett, D. L., and Krayer, O., Studies on veratrum alkaloids. V. The effect of veratridine and cevine upon the circulation in anesthetized dogs, with particular reference to femoral arterial flow. *J. Pharmacol. Exptl. Therap.* **80**, 272 (1944).

163. Moe, G. K., and Krayer, O., Studies on veratrum alkaloids. II. The action of veratridine and cevine upon the isolated mammalian heart. *J. Pharmacol. Exptl. Therap.* **77**, 220 (1943).

164. Morales, A. G., and Acheson, G. H., Effects of veratridine on the potassium balance of the dog heart-lung preparation. *J. Pharmacol. Exptl. Therap.* **134**, 238 (1961).

165. Moran, N. C., Dresel, P. E., Perkins, M. E., and Richardson, A. P., The pharmacological actions of andromedotoxin, an active principle from *Rhododendron maximum. J. Pharmacol. Exptl. Therap.* **110**, 415 (1954).

166. Moran, N. C., Perkins, M. E., and Richardson, A. P., Veratridine blockade of the carotid sinus pressoreceptors. *J. Pharmacol. Exptl. Therap.* **111**, 459 (1954).
167. Morgan, K. J., and Barltop, J. A., Veratrum alkaloids. *Quart. Rev.* (*London*) **12**, 34 (1958).
168. Mosey, L., and Kaplan, A., Respiratory effects of potent hypotensive derivatives of *Veratrum. J. Pharmacol. Exptl. Therap.* **104**, 67 (1952).
169. Mosey, L., Maison, G. L., and Stutzman, J. W., Cardiac effects of a hypotensive veratrum derivative in dogs premedicated with digitalis or quinidine. *Proc. Exptl. Biol. Med.* **76**, 486 (1951).
170. Murnaghan, M. F., The antiaccelerator effect of veratramine on the isolated perfused heart of the cat. *Can. J. Biochem. Physiol.* **35**, 173 (1957).
171. Murnaghan, M. F., Mechanism of action of histamine on the heart. *Proc. 1st Intern. Pharmacol. Meeting, Stockholm, 1961* **10**, 13 (1963).
172. Myers, G. S., Friedlich, A. L., Scannell, J. G., O'Neil, J. R., McGinty, J. F., and Currens, J. H., The hemodynamic effects of protoveratrine in hypertensive patients with congestive failure. *Proc. New Engl. Cardiovascular Soc.* p. 4 (1951–1952).
173. Neil, E., Afferent impulse activity in cardiovascular receptor fibers. *Physiol. Rev.* **40**, Suppl. 4, 201 (1960).
174. Neil, E., and Joels, N., The impulse activity in cardiac afferent vagal fibers. *Arch. Exptl. Pathol. Pharmakol.* **240**, 453 (1961).
175. Newman, A. J., Intoxication with *Veratrum viride. J. Pediat.* **40**, 233 (1952).
176. O'Dell, T. B., and Napoli, M. D., Biological properties of cryptenamine, a new *Veratrum viride* alkaloid preparation *Proc. Soc. Exptl. Biol. Med.* **85**, 400 (1954).
177. Pachomov, N., and Caughey, J. E., Dystrophia myotonica, a clinical and electromyographical study of the effects of certain drugs on myotonia. *Neurology* **10**, 28 (1960).
178. Paintal, A. S., The response of pulmonary and cardiovascular vagal receptors to certain drugs. *J. Physiol.* (*London*) **121**, 182 (1953).
179. Paintal, A. S., A study of ventricular pressure receptors and their role in the Bezold reflex. *Quart. J. Exptl. Physiol.* **40**, 348 (1955).
180. Paintal, A. S., The influence of certain chemical substances on the initiation of sensory discharges in pulmonary and gastric stretch receptors and atrial receptors. *J. Physiol.* (*London*) **135**, 486 (1957).
181. Peng, M. T., and Wang, S. C., Emetic responses of monkeys to apomorphine, Hydergine, deslanoside and protoveratrine. *Proc. Soc. Exptl. Biol. Med.* **110**, 211 (1962).
182. Pircio, A., and Geiling, E. M. K., Biosynthesis and metabolism of some radioactive *Veratrum viride* alkaloids. *J. Am. Pharm. Assoc.* **41**, 552 (1952).
183. Reiter, M., Studies on veratrum alkaloids. XIII. Metabolic action of veratridine and of the secondary amine bases veratramine, veratrosine, and pseudojervine on cardiac tissue of the rat. *J. Pharmacol. Exptl. Therap.* **99**, 132 (1950).
184. Reuse-Blom, S., L'action de la vératramine sur l'oreillette isolée du coeur de lapin. *Comp. Rend. Soc. Biol.* **153**, 711 (1959).
185. Richardson, A. P., Walker, H. A., Farrar, C. B., Griffith, W., Pound, E., and Davidson, J. R., The mechanism of the hypotensive action of veratrum alkaloids. *Proc. Soc. Exptl. Biol. Med.* **79**, 79 (1952).

186. Riker, W. K., Reflexes from intestinal mesentery elicted by veratridine, acetylcholine and nicotine. *J. Pharmacol. Exptl. Therap.* **124,** 120 (1958).
187. Robinson, T., Alkaloids. *Sci. Am.* **201,** 113 (1959).
188. Rodbard, S., and Saiki, H., Mechanism of the pressor response to increased intracranial pressure. *Am. J. Physiol.* **168,** 234 (1952).
189. Rose, J. C., and Lazaro, E. J., The extracardiac hypotensive effect of *Veratrum. J. Pharmacol. Exptl. Therap.* **117,** 461 (1956).
190. Rose, J. C., and Lazaro, E. J., Veratrum hypotension due to reflexes of pulmonary origin. *J. Pharmacol. Exptl. Therap.* **119,** 324 (1957).
191. Royce, S. W., Hypertensive phase of acute nephritis: specific therapy with a derivative of *Veratrum viride. Pediatrics* **12,** 358 (1953).
192. Rushmer, R. F., Smith, O., and Franklin, D., Mechanisms of cardiac control in exercise. *Circulation Res.* **7,** 602 (1959).
193. Salmoiraghi, G. C., and Bloom, F. E., Pharmacology of individual neurons. *Science* **144,** 493 (1964).
194. Sam, J., and Plampin, J. N., Hypotensive basic ethers in the indan series. *J. Am. Chem. Soc.* **82,** 5205 (1960).
195. Sandow, A., and Kiebel, G., Effects of eserine-veratrine interaction on mechanical responses of muscle. *Am. J. Physiol.* **169,** 649 (1952).
196. Sandow, A., Taylor, S. R., Isaacson, A., and Seguin, J. J. Electrochemical coupling in potentiation of muscular contraction. *Science* **143,** 577 (1964).
197. Schaefer, H., Elektrophysiologie der Herznerven. *Ergeb. Physiol. Biol. Chem. Exptl. Pharmakol.* **46,** 71 (1950).
198. Schaefer, H., Central control of cardiac function. *Physiol. Rev.* **40,** Suppl. 4, 213 (1960).
199. Scherf, D., Blumenfeld, S., Mueller, P., and Terranova, R., Experimental study on ectopic beats following intravenous injection of veratrine. *Proc. Soc. Exptl. Biol. Med.* **81,** 701 (1952).
200. Schoetensack, W., and Hallmann, G., Die Veratramin-Erregung und ihre pharmakologische Beeinflussung. *Arzneimittel-Forsch.* **5,** 428 (1964).
201. Shanes, A. M., The ultraviolet spectra and neurophysiological effects of "veratrine" alkaloids. *J. Pharmacol. Exptl. Therap.* **105,** 216 (1952).
202. Shanes, A. M., Electrochemical aspects of physiological and pharmacological action in excitable cells. Part I. The resting cell and its alteration by extrinsic factors. *Pharmacol. Rev.* **10,** 59 (1958).
203. Shanes, A. M., Electrochemical aspects of physiological and pharmacological action in excitable cells. Part II. The action potential and excitation. *Pharmacol. Rev.* **10,** 165 (1958).
204. Shanes, A. M., Drugs and nerve conduction. *Ann. Rev. Pharmacol.* 3, 185 (1963).
205. Shanes, A. M., and Gershfeld, N. L., Interactions of veratrum alkaloids, procaine, and calcium with monolayers of stearic acid and their implications for pharmacological action. *J. Gen. Physiol.* **44,** 345 (1960).
206. Sharma, V. N., and Arora, R. B., The antiveratrinic action of some local anesthetics. *J. Pharm. Pharmacol.* **14,** 515 (1962).
207. Stearns, N. S., and Maison, G. L., The action of Veriloid upon the isolated mammalian heart. *J. Pharmacol. Exptl. Therap.* **100,** 238 (1950).
208. Stutzman, J. W., Maison, G. L., and Bauer, R. O., The pharmacology of Veriloid, a purified extract of *Veratrum viride. Proc. New Engl. Cardiovascular. Soc.* p. 36 (1949–1950).

209. Stutzman, J. W., Simon, H., and Maison, G. L., Role of vagus nerves in depressor action of veratrum derivatives. *J. Pharmacol. Exptl. Therap.* **101**, 310 (1951).

210. Swain, H. H., and McCarthy, D. A., Veratrine, protoveratrine, and andromedotoxin arrhythmias in the isolated dog heart. *J. Pharmacol. Exptl. Therap.* **121**, 379 (1957).

211. Swiss, E. D., The emetic properties of veratrum derivatives. *J. Pharmacol. Exptl. Therap.* **104**, 76 (1952).

212. Swiss, E. D., and Bauer, R. O., Acute toxicity of veratrum derivatives. *Proc. Soc. Exptl. Biol. Med.* **76**, 847 (1951).

213. Swiss, E. D., and Maison, G. L., The site of cardiovascular action of veratrum derivatives. *J. Pharmacol. Exptl. Therap.* **105**, 87 (1952).

214. Takasaki, K., Arterial pressure changes by drugs injected into isolated pulmonary circulation in dogs. *Am. J. Physiol.* **203**, 947 (1962).

215. Tanaka, K., Studies on veratrum alkaloids. XX. Actions of veratrum alkaloids upon the central nervous system of mice. *J. Pharmacol. Exptl. Therap.* **113**, 89 (1955).

216. Tanaka, K., and Kanno, T., The role of nodose ganglia in the emetic and hypotensive action of protoveratrine. *Yonage Acta Med.* **2**, 8 (1956).

217. Taylor, R. D., and Page, I. H., Further studies of the cerebral chemoreceptor buffers as influenced by vasoconstrictor and vasodilator drugs and *Veratrum viride*. *Circulation* **4**, 184 (1951).

218. Trapold, J. H., Role of venous return in the cardiovascular response following injection of ganglionic-blocking agents. *Circulation Res.* **5**, 444 (1957).

219. Trautwein, W., Generation and conduction of impulses in the heart as affected by drugs. *Pharmacol. Rev.* **15**, 277 (1963).

220. Vick, R. L., and Kahn, J. B., The effects of ouabain and veratridine on potassium movement in the isolated guinea pig heart. *J. Pharmacol. Exptl. Therap.* **121**, 389 (1957).

221. Voskian, J., Assali, N. S., and Noll, L., Hemodynamic effects and clinical application of a mixture of veratrum and rauwolfia alkaloids. *Surg. Gynecol. Obstet.* **102**, 37 (1956).

222. Wallon, G., Coraboeuf, E., and Gargouïl, Y. M., Action de la vératrine sur les phénomènes mécaniques et électriques d'un coeur isolé et pefusé. *Compt. Rend. Soc. Biol.* **153**, 2077 (1959).

223. Wang, S. C., Ngai, S. H., and Grossman, R. G., Mechanism of vasomotor action of veratrum alkaloids: extravagal sites of action of Veriloid, protoveratrine, germitrine, neogermitrine, germerine, veratridine and veratramine. *J. Pharmacol. Exptl. Therap.* **113**, 100 (1955).

224. Waud, R. A., Lansing, A. M., and Lewis, R. A., The effects of veratrum, Dibenzyline and hexamethonium on blood pressure as studied with an artificial heart-lung. *J. Pharmacol. Exptl. Therap.* **114**, 271 (1955).

225. Weaver, L. C., Jones, W. R., and Kupchan, S. M., Veratrum alkaloids. LI. Hypotensive-emetic relationship in unanesthetized dogs among analogs of the protoveratrines. *J. Pharm. Sci.* **51**, 1144 (1962).

226. Weaver, L. C., Rahdert, E., Richards, A. B., and Abreu, B. E., A study of protoveratrine induced emesis in dogs. *Pharmacologist* **5**, 266 (1963).

227. Wenzel, D. G., and Smith, C. M., Antiveratrinic activity of lactones and peroxides. *J. Am. Pharm Assoc.* **47**, 269 (1958).

228. West, J. W., Atrial and ventricular force of contraction influenced by intracoronary injections. *Am. J. Physiol.* **203,** 1145 (1962).
229. Wilson, R. H., Poley, G. W., and DeEds, F., Some pharmacologic and toxicologic properties of tomatine and its derivatives. *Toxicol. Appl. Pharmacol.* **3,** 39 (1961).
230. Winer, B. M., A comparison between protoveratrine A and protoveratrine B orally in arterial hypertension. *New Engl. J. Med.* **255,** 1173 (1956).
231. Winer, B. M., Comparative studies of protoveratrine A and protoveratrine B intravenously in hypertensive man. *Circulation* **22,** 1074 (1960).
232. Witt, P. N., and Swaine, C. R., Studies on veratrum alkaloids. XXV. Veratrine response and antiveratrinic action in frog sartorius muscle. *J. Pharmacol. Exptl. Therap.* **120,** 63 (1957).
233. Wollenberger, A., Action of protoveratrine on the metabolism of cerebral cortex. 1. Unstimulated cerebral-cortex tissue. *Biochem. J.* **61,** 68 (1955).
234. Wollenberger, A., Action of protoveratrine on the metabolism of cerebral cortex. 2. Electrically stimulated cerebral-cortex tissue. *Bichem. J.* **61,** 77 (1955).
235. Wyss, St., and Spuhler, O., Protoveratrin in der Behandlung der Hypertonien. *Acta Med. Scand.* **153,** 221 (1956).
236. Zakusov, V. V., Principles of pharmacological influence on coronary chemoreflexes. *Arch. Intern. Pharmacodyn.* **140,** 646 (1962).

VI. NEUROTOXINS

Bernard C. Whaler

Department of Physiology, Queen Elizabeth College (University of London), Campden Hill Rd., London, England

I. INTRODUCTION

A wide variety of substances is used by animal species for defensive or offensive operation against predators or prey. As mixtures of pharmacologically active materials these go usually under the general name of venoms or stings. Frequently one or more components of the mixture are highly toxic and either relatively selective for species or active over a wider area of the animal kingdom. This review will attempt to cover those where the biological effect of the toxin appears to be exerted mainly and in a fairly direct manner upon nerve cells, nerve fibers, and their transmission processes.

Almost all animal phyla, from the Protozoa to Mammalia, but excluding Aves, contain species able to elaborate a neurotoxin. In some cases, e.g., the protozoa, it seems to be present almost as a biological accident. This is the case, too, with the bacterial toxins of *Clostridium tetani* and *Clostridium botulinum*. The biological advantage, if indeed any exists, is not obvious. More usually the possession of a neurotoxin by a predatory species would seem to have a useful function.

The field which will be covered in this article includes the two major bacterial neurotoxins, those of *Cl. botulinum* and *Cl. tetani*, each in separate main sections; a third major section is devoted to an examination of neurotoxins of animal origin.

II. BOTULISM

A. Introduction

The neurotoxin of *Cl. botulinum* has received intensive study because of its importance in the food-canning industry and its extreme toxicity, in which it exceeds all other known materials. The *Shigella shiga* toxin (326), which for many years was believed to be neurotoxic but which is now thought to act only indirectly on nervous tissue, being primarily effective on blood vessels (76), is slightly less toxic; so too is that of *Cl. tetani*, but these toxicities differ by only about one order of magnitude and may approach even more closely if the appropriate test animals are selected (319).

In 1955 Wright (354) published a searching review on the toxin; since then other articles have appeared by Stevenson (307), Lamanna (205), and van Heyningen and Arseculeratne (325, 182a).

Six types of *Cl. botulinum* exist, designated types A–F, each of which appears to produce its own specific toxin. "Specific" here is used in the immunological sense; the biological action of the toxins appears to be similar although there are large differences in, for example, oral toxicity between species for any one type. Types A–E have been known for many years, whereas type F was isolated recently by Dolman and Murakami (109).

With the increasing development of prepackaging of foods in polythene-type packs there has been a revival of interest by the food industry in *Cl. botulinum,* since it presents, once again, a potential health hazard. The germination of spores (157, 263, 296, 310, 311, 314, 315), irradiation sterilization (21, 85, 97, 183, 189, 270, 295, 330), and the general question of the growth of the organism and toxin development (42, 44, 45, 46, 48, 49, 145, 179, 182, 190, 221, 255, 286, 287, 288, 300) have received considerable study in the last few years.

B. Purification of Toxins: Toxoiding

Methods for separating toxin from bacterial cultures and its purification were developed in both American and Canadian laboratories and first published in 1946 and 1947 (6, 29, 177, 178, 213, 214, 251, 275, 280, 281) in papers detailing the procedures for the production of a safe and effective toxoid. It is clear from the data in Table I that, in 1946–1947, a high degree of purity had been achieved for types A and B, if the later (1957–1961) values are to be accepted as approaching 100% purity. These early isolation methods were somewhat laborious and complex; at this time, too, the toxoid was producing undesirable side effects and a reexamination of purification methods was undertaken. These led to the publication between 1954 and 1961 of a series of papers setting out improved purification methods and toxoiding procedures for types A–E (29, 69, 70, 111, 112, 130, 146, 154, 352). These toxoids, prepared by formalin treatment of pure toxin, have been shown to give powerful protection against specific toxin in mice, guinea pigs, and rabbits, and in some cases stimulate the production of measurable antitoxin levels in man.

The Canadian investigators Barron and Reed (29) utilized the technique of growing the organisms in cellophane sacs suspended in the culture medium. Although the toxin yield and specific activity were inferior to that achieved some years later by Yarinsky, Duff, and their colleagues (130, 154) the alum-precipitated toxoid was claimed to have good antigenic power.

The cellophane sac technique was first used in this connection by Polson and Sterne (267) in studies directed toward the production of type D toxoid. By separating bacterial cells and their products from high-molecular-weight components of the culture medium the technique was believed to allow a simpler and more effective purification and toxoiding of the product.

As Table I makes clear these toxins are of extraordinary potency. Types A and B seem to be very similar in specific toxicity and perhaps also in their molecular properties of weight and shape, since the sedimentation coefficients are similar. Type D, of similar sedimentation coefficient, surpasses A and B in toxicity by a factor of 2–3 (70) or, in one case (337),

TABLE I

SPECIFIC TOXICITIES AND SEDIMENTATION COEFFICIENTS OF *Cl. botulinum* TOXINS

Type	Specific toxicity (LD_{50}/mg N)	Sedimentation data: $S_{20,w}$ "major" component	% protein	Buffer	Molarity	pH	$S_{20,w}$ "minor" components	Date	Ref.
A	240×10^6	—	—	—	—	—	—	1946	(214)
	220×10^6	—	—	—	—	—	—	1946	(6)
	269×10^6	14.5	0.3	Acetate	0.05	3.8	—	1957	(111)
B	262×10^6	14.9	0.5	Phosphate	0.1	6.0	10.9	1957	(112)
	313×10^6	12.7	0.25	Succinate	0.2	5.5	—	1957	(112)
C	$20–60 \times 10^6$	—	—	—	—	—	—	1958	(69)
D	up to 822×10^6	14.3	—	Acetate	0.05	3.8	12.3, 11.1	1960	(70)
	up to 822×10^6	14.6	—	Succinate	0.2	5.5	10.2	1960	(70)
	up to 822×10^6	15.2	—	Phosphate	0.08	6.7	10.9	1960	(70)
E	45×10^6 or more[a]	12.5	—	Phosphate	0.08	5.1	4.75	1961	(130)
	0.6×10^6 [b]	5.1	—	In "physiological saline"	—	—	1.1	1962	(147)
	10×10^6 [a]	no boundary formed	—	In "physiological saline"	—	—	—	1962	(147)

[a] Activated by trypsin.
[b] Not activated.

by a factor of some 10,000. This toxicity, 4×10^{12} mouse m.l.d. mg N, was reported in 1950 by Wentzel *et al.* for a batch of cellophane sac toxin, purified by electrophoretic methods until it was homogeneous, and is probably the most toxic material ever described. If the factor of approximately 1.5 which the work of Lamanna *et al.* (213) suggests is used to convert m.l.d.[1] to LD_{50} the toxicity becomes still more exceptional. Since 1950 a value of this order has never been obtained and the nature of either the "potentiation" or the peculiar properties of these batches of culture is not at all understood. In some respects this report is reminiscent of those by Bronfenbrenner and Schlesinger (52, 53) in which the authors reported occasional toxic broths of exceptional potency. While the assay methods were somewhat crude it seems not impossible that there occurs, occasionally, a chain of circumstances in which both culture and diluent combine to produce an especially high toxicity. The phenomenon resembles to some extent the increases in toxicity which appear to occur after the ingestion of foodstuffs containing the toxin, particularly of type E, and which will be referred to later.

Types C and E have much lower toxicities than the others and, in the case of type E, "activation" by proteolytic enzymes is necessary for the higher values to be achieved (79, 113, 130, 145, 147, 154, 286).

C. Sedimentation Characteristics of Pure Toxin

Studies on the sedimentation characteristics of purified toxins have been made using the analytical ultracentrifuge. Wagman and Bateman (333, 334) and Wagman (331) showed that a single sedimenting toxin boundary can be reversibly altered to give at least two components if the ionic strength, pH, and composition of the solution are suitably manipulated. Cammack (66, 67) has carried out similar studies on type A toxin and has evidence that a dimer molecule ($S_{20,w}$[2] = ca. 32) may be formed. In his studies Cammack often found two components; both gave evidence of change associated with alterations in solvent conditions. Other references to sedimentation coefficients may be given here (70, 111, 112, 130, 147, 172, 175, 186, 332) and will be referred to again later.

The existence of a second sedimenting fraction in what is believed to be pure toxin raises doubts as to the validity of the concept of purity in this connection. One may consider the protein molecule as capable of existing as a series of similar small subunits: the single-component toxin then is perhaps a polymer of these (see Wagman, 331). In support of this view might be cited the activation which seems to be associated

[1] Minimum lethal dose is the smallest quantity of toxin which is capable of killing all of the injected animals in a particular test group.

[2] Sedimentation value, corrected for temperature and solvent.

with exposure to intestinal conditions, particularly with type E (130, 147), in which toxicity is appreciably enhanced. This one may imagine as being due to the uncovering of toxophore groupings or the splitting of a larger molecule into smaller—and still toxic—fragments (147). In cases such as this one might well argue that purity is a term applicable to either the single or the polymeric state.

An alternative view would interpret a second sedimenting component as proper evidence of impurity. If this were so then the references so far made to "pure" toxin would be invalid and "purity" would need qualification. While it may ultimately be shown that both of these interpretations are to some extent correct, evidence for a molecular species or component of the toxin which gives a physical basis for this alternative view has existed for some considerable time. This is the hemagglutinating factor described in 1948 by Lamanna (204).

Types A, B, and E toxins, even when in the so-called pure state, are in fact associated with a separable factor which has the ability to cause agglutination of red cells. This can be separated from the toxic fraction by adsorption using successive exposures to erythrocytes, and the hemagglutinating activity is then reduced to minimal amounts (204, 209, 211, 212, 220, 231). Accurate specific activity toxicity tests have not been made on such toxin, but one would expect an increase in specific toxicity of the adsorbed material. Cammack (66) separated a two-component and relatively pure toxin into fractions with $S_{20,w}$ values of 16.3 and 11.9 and showed that the slower-sedimenting fragment had a very low toxicity (25×10^6 LD_{50}/mg N against a starting pooled toxicity of $170–210 \times 10^6$ LD_{50}/mg N). Unfortunately he ran into difficulty in the hemagglutinin tests and finally suggested that the slow component was not even the hemagglutinin. At present the whole matter of molecular weight, shape, and constitution seems to be very poorly understood.

Only in one case has pure toxin been subjected to exhaustive adsorption by erythrocytes and subsequently examined in the ultracentrifuge. This was done in 1960 by Hildebrand, Lamanna, and Heckly (175); $S_{20,w}$ values in the range 3.7–8.4 were obtained. These compare with $S_{20,w}$ values of 12–21 before treatment and are also distinctly lower than those given in Table I. Unfortunately, it is not at all clear from the data given whether the $S_{20,w}$ values were obtained under comparable solvent conditions. If, as seems distinctly possible, one series was in 0.05 *M* phosphate buffer pH 6.3 and the other (adsorbed) series in isotonic NaCl–phosphate buffer of pH 7.3, these results, although extremely interesting, are less valuable than they would have been if comparable solvents had been used.

One consequence of these results is that the specific toxicity for hemagglutinin-free toxin is, as yet, undetermined. A second is that so far very few experiments have been made using hemagglutinin-free, i.e., pure, toxin. In many cases the distinction may be unnecessary but certain experiments appear worth attempting; in particular, ultracentrifugal analysis of the type carried out by Wagman (331) or by Cammack (66, 67). Similarly the effect of proteolytic enzymes upon adsorbed toxin might be illuminating.

D. Molecular Weights of the Toxins

Values for the molecular weights of the toxins A, B, D, and E have been estimated. Putnam *et al.* (271) gave for type A a value of slightly over 900,000: that of Kegeles (186) was 1,130,000. Cammack (67) found, on the basis of ultracentrifugation and diffusion gradient studies, values of 720,000–781,000 under conditions of $pH = 3.80$ and $I = 0.10$; at pH 4.8 and $I = 0.10$, the dimer of molecular weight $1.36–1.46 \times 10^6$ was obtained. Wagman (331) concluded that the native molecule at pH 3.8 (molecular weight approximately 1×10^6) was composed of about 13 loosely bound components; he also obtained evidence for particles of weight 40,000–100,000 at pH 7.5. Considerable variation depending especially upon solvent conditions clearly exists, and the probable presence of the hemagglutinating fraction cannot have contributed to the reliability of the available results. The sedimentation coefficients lie mainly in the range 10–15 (see Table I): if this is related to the value of about $0.9–1.1 \times 10^6$ for the molecular weight, then the much lower values, 3.7–8.4, for the $S_{20,w}$ of hemagglutinin-free toxin (175) would favor a distinctly smaller molecular weight.

Lamanna and Glassman (210) estimated that for type B toxin the molecular weight was about 60,000. Wagman and Bateman (333) suggested 500,000, whereas Duff *et al.* (112) in 1957 suggested that it was probably similar to type A. The latter suggestion, while tentative, was based on the similarity in $S_{20,w}$ values between the two toxins. A similar suggestion was made later by Cardella *et al.* (70) for type D toxin. Thus types A, B, and D may be alike in this respect, although diffusion-constant values are required for a complete calculation of molecular weights.

Type C toxin does not yet appear to have been investigated in this way. In the case of type E the published $S_{20,w}$ values are at variance. Those of Fiock, Yarinsky, and Duff (130) give values for trypsin-activated toxin of $S_{20,w} = 12.5$ and 4.75 in 0.08 *M* phosphate buffer of pH 5.1, the 12.5 component being the major one. Gerwing, Dolman, and Arnott (147) have $S_{20,w}$ values for unactivated toxin of 5.6 and 1.1 in "physiological saline," of which the 5.6 fraction was toxic; after treatment with trypsin they had no definable peaks in the ultracentrifuge and probably a dialyzable molecule. Although solvent conditions were very different, which itself prevents much useful comparison, these results are so much at variance that considerably more investigation is required.

E. Botulism

Dolman (106) has collected data on botulism in a number of countries. Types A and B have been mainly implicated. Although many untyped cases have occurred, it seems probable from their geographical situation that many of these too would be A or B. In the case of type A, the majority of outbreaks in the United States occurred many years ago mainly as a result of inadequate sterilization during the process of home canning. Europe, excluding France, has not suffered much botulism: in France type B seems to be the predominant organism, with many cases but few human fatalities.

Since the review by Wright (354) the most remarkable series of clinical reports are those of Dolman and his group (8, 102, 103, 104, 105, 106, 107, 108, 110, 114) dealing almost exclusively with type E or fish-borne botulism. This type was first identified by Gunnison, Cummings, and Meyer (161) from samples obtained from sturgeon in the U.S.S.R. It has been shown (see Dolman, 104, 105) that type E spores are heavily distributed in the sea and coastal mud and in the soil of the northern part of the North American continent, perhaps less so in Greenland, much less so in northern Europe, and again rather heavily around the northern Japanese seaboards. Because of this distribution and a variety of other factors, ranging from the food habits of the native populations to specific growth characteristics of the organism itself (Ohye and Scott, 255; Dolman, 103, 104, 105), type E botulism is a serious problem in some of these countries, with a fatality rate for recorded cases of 50% or more. Strangely enough, botulism as a specific disease appears to have been unknown in Japan until 1951, yet by 1957, 23 outbreaks had occurred (104).

Ohye and Scott (255) obtained from marine mud in southern hemisphere waters a strain which shows many cultural resemblances to type E; however, the culture fluids, which were toxic to mice, were neutralized by type B, but not type E, antitoxin. While this latter evidence should be conclusive, the authors appear slightly reluctant to accept it and quote Pederson (258) as having shown that type B antitoxin can partially protect against type E. Even if this were true, it is still rather difficult to understand the failure of the specific type E antitoxin to protect mice in their own experiments. Confirmation of Pederson's findings would be interesting, since it is the first occasion upon which cross reaction except $C\alpha$ and $C\beta$ in toxicity tests has been shown to occur. It is necessary to specify the term "toxicity tests" since cross reaction of types

A and B antisera in Ouchterlony plate analysis suggests that the hemagglutinin fraction is common to the two types (Lamanna and Lowenthal, 212; Björklund and Berengo, 38).

Information on botulism in the U.S.S.R. is limited, for this author, mainly to the years 1957–1961, when English translations of the complete journals of Microbiology, Epidemiology, and Immunobiology were available, although abstracts have appeared regularly. In many respects Russian ideas differ markedly from those of Western Europe and the American continent, particularly on the nature of the disease itself. In these latter countries it is usually regarded as an intoxication from eating food which already contains the toxin. Minervin (234) argues, on the other hand, that it is of a toxicoinfective character and this may result in symptoms appearing some days after the ingestion of contaminated food, or reappearing a few days after an apparently satisfactory recovery. Dolman (106) mentions this view and concedes that it might explain similar occurrences in cases described by him. It is also argued by Minervin that the organism may be invasive in character; pure cultures have been isolated from various tissues, including the brain, removed shortly after death.

Some support for the toxicoinfective hypothesis comes from experiments by Shvedov (298, 299; quoted by Minervin, 234). After oral administration to rabbits and mice of toxin plus organisms, toxin could be recovered from the intestine up to 8 days later; when toxin alone was given orally it could not be recovered after 12 hours had elapsed. Other experiments support the concept that the production of toxin and its absorption from the intestine can continue for considerable periods after oral ingestion of organisms. To help in treatment of suspected botulism it is therefore recommended that apart from its parenteral administration antitoxin should also be introduced into the gut if the best therapeutic effect is to be achieved. Experiments on rabbits appear to have given encouraging results (234).

Two further points of interest arise from the limited Russian material studied. One is the demonstration (196) that cattle are a useful source of antitoxin. For types A, B, and E, antisera of titer as high as that obtained from horses were prepared from immunized cattle destined for slaughter. Apart from possible cheapness, it seems useful to have antisera from species other than the horse because of the dangers of anaphylaxis after any previous treatment with horse antiserum.

The second concerns the more general question of the identification of type at an early stage in the poisoning so as to allow for correct treatment and especially the use of the appropriate antitoxin. A number of Russian authors have investigated this problem. Minervin (quoted by

Kovtunovitch, 195) devised a method based on the inhibition of phagocytosis by botulinum toxin. In the presence of toxin the phagocytic index of neutrophil leukocytes was reduced. The method is claimed to be distinctly more sensitive than the mouse test and, more important, potentially much more rapid. Specific antisera are used and, with all antisera available and given proper controls, this method would appear to give the possibility of a relatively rapid diagnosis. The sensitivity is claimed to be such that serum or plasma from patients may contain enough toxin to make the test possible. Freeman (135), however, has reported that he was unable to obtain any significant reduction in phagocytosis using a similar method. In spite of this negative report there are a number of favorable Russian papers on this method and also on an indirect hemagglutination test for which excellent results are claimed (61, 235, 301, 302).

F. Experimental Studies

1. *The Physiological Basis of the Paralysis*

The early investigations of the 1920's implicated various motor and autonomic nerves in the botulinic paralysis. The concept of cholinergic neuromuscular transmission did not emerge until later, and the distribution of cholinergic and adrenergic fibers was still unknown. Nevertheless, it is clear from the papers of Edmunds and Long (118), Edmunds and Keiper (117), and Dickson and Shevsky (99, 100) that these investigators unwittingly mapped out the distribution of cholinergic fibers before this was done systematically by direct experiments. These authors, as well as Bishop and Bronfenbrenner (37), excluded the nerve trunk and the muscle as susceptible sites.

Subsequent to the growth in the 1930's of our knowledge of humoral transmission at nerve endings, the site of action of botulinum toxin received renewed attention. Three groups working simultaneously in different laboratories studied the physiology of the paralysis, the nature of which was narrowed down to an interference with transmitter release, particularly at cholinergic nerve endings.

Guyton and MacDonald (162) and Ambache (9, 10) examined skeletal and eye muscles poisoned *in vivo* by localized injections of sublethal doses of toxin. Burgen, Dickens, and Zatman (62) carried out their experiments *in vitro* using much larger doses of toxins. All three groups found that the paralyzed muscles could be made to contract as usual by close intravascular injections of acetylcholine, thus distinguishing this type of paralysis from that produced by curare, which blocks the action of acetylcholine at end plates. Confirming also that the toxin did not affect conduction when applied to nerve trunks, these results pinpointed the lesion of type A toxin to the nerve endings. Ambache (11, 12, 14; Ambache and Lessin, 17) extended these experiments to cholinergically innervated smooth muscle systems in which there are no end plates. There, too, the effector cells remained fully sensitive to acetylcholine. The action of the toxin was in no sense atropine-like (as believed by Dickson, 98), but could again be localized to a lesion of the cholinergic endings in the smooth muscles concerned. That acetylcholine output is in fact reduced by type A toxin was shown conclusively on phrenic-diaphragm preparations by Burgen, Dickens, and Zatman (62, rats) and by Brooks (54, guinea pigs), as also later by Harry (169) on electrically stimulated guinea pig ilea.

Using microelectrode techniques Brooks (55) found that as the toxin began to be effective at the end plate region there was a decline in frequency (but not of size) of the spontaneous miniature end plate potentials. These ultimately ceased at a time which coincided approximately with neuromuscular block. At this point a temporary restoration of transmission could be obtained if the nerve was stimulated repetitively.

It might be expected that such a drastic change in nerve-ending function would produce detectable histological changes. This is not so. Guyton and MacDonald (162) reported some swelling of end plates and other minor changes in the poisoned gastrocnemius muscles of guinea pigs. Thesleff (312) has published electron photomicrographs taken by Katz of poisoned frog sartorius and cat tenuissimus muscles; these show that the ultramicroscopic structure of the motor terminals was unchanged by the intoxication. It seems clear from these photographs that the vesicles present in the nerve endings—which are believed to contain acetylcholine—are unaffected by botulinum toxin, confirmation of the inability of the toxin to interfere with the synthesis of acetylcholine (62). Brooks (54) has shown also, by direct assay of the acetylcholine released from a poisoned muscle by strong direct stimulation, that synthesis is not affected.

It has been estimated that 20 million molecules of the toxin are sufficient to kill a mouse; the precise cytological localization of toxic molecules in order that so few (relatively) have such an enormous effect is of more than passing interest. Such localization can be either inferred from pharmacological data or needs to be demonstrated physically. The direct physical demonstration is difficult and, using both the light and the electron microscope, no effects due to the toxin have hitherto been found. However Zacks *et al.* (356) have now successfully carried physical techniques one stage further by labeling the toxin molecule with electron-dense ferritin and subsequently examining ultrathin sections of muscle paralyzed by such toxin. Electron photomicrographs reveal the ferritin—and by implication the toxin—as restricted mainly to the primary and secondary synaptic clefts in the so-called "amorphous surface material" coating the Schwann cell and muscle surface membranes. In addition, a definite pattern in the spatial distribution frequency of the ferritin strengthens the conclusion that this represents more than a random or nonspecific effect.

The long-lasting nature of these lesions was stressed by Guyton and MacDonald (162), who found that fully poisoned muscles in the guinea pig showed only a 50% recovery after about 6 months and even after 12 months recovery was still only 90% complete. With much less severe poisoning, as is evident from many clinical reports, recovery is relatively rapid although even in these cases disturbances may continue for many weeks. In muscles—and salivary gland too—paralyzed by the toxin, a supersensitivity to acetylcholine develops, strictly comparable with the well-known denervation supersensitivity (Thesleff, 312; Emmelin, 119).

The effect of neuromuscular activity on the development of the paralysis of rat diaphragm preparation *in vitro* was described by Hughes and Whaler (180). The intoxication was shown to proceed more rapidly as the frequency of repetitive stimulation was increased. This acceleration of paralysis was not dependent upon the contraction process in the muscle—which might perhaps assist diffusion of the toxin molecule—since it occurred in fully curarized preparations. Thus, nerve ending activity appears to favor the action of the toxin in some way. Since anticholinesterases increased and high doses of atropine decreased the rate at which paralysis occurred, these results suggest that free acetylcholine or the physical state of nerve ending membranes during the release process itself may somehow play an important part in the progress of the intoxication.

The electric organ of *Electrophorus electricus,* which is in some ways analogous with the nerve end plate region of voluntary muscle, is also susceptible to the toxin (16).

Using artificial respiration to keep severely poisoned animals alive, Guyton and MacDonald were able to examine the circulatory collapse which accompanies the intoxication. By the use of vasoconstrictor drugs at an early stage it was possible to prevent the usual fall in blood pressure. Pedersen and Christensen (259) have emphasized the potential value of antishock treatment in human cases of the disease. This circulatory failure is, presumably, a result of interference with acetylcholine transmission in sympathetic ganglia with a resulting failure of vasomotor tone. The heart does not seem to be appreciably affected, although vagal inhibition is blocked by the toxin.

In experiments in which Ambache (9, 10, 12) injected small doses of type A toxin into rabbits' eyes the relative selectivity of the toxin for cholinergic endings was shown by two observations. Firstly, corneal sensation was unimpaired, as indicated by reflex retraction of the eyeball and protraction of the nictitating membrane; even when enough toxin had escaped from the eyeball to paralyze the voluntary muscles of the eyelids and those which move the eyeball, whenever the cornea was touched the animals moved their heads away. Secondly, within the eyeball itself, although the miotic response to oculomotor stimulation was paralyzed, further mydriasis occurred on cervical sympathetic stimulation.

This result, and others on the cat's iris and nictitating membrane, suggested again a relatively greater resistance to type A toxin of adrenergic postganglionic endings. In a subsequent study Ambache (12, 13) examined the susceptibility to type A toxin of a variety of autonomic pre- and postganglionic nerve endings. All those known to be cholinergic could be easily paralyzed, for instance, the sudomotor fibers to the cat's paw, which are postganglionic sympathetic fibers by classification but are in fact cholinergic. Paralysis of the cholinergic preganglionic fibers to the ciliary ganglion was also easily obtained by retrobulbar injections, and localized injections of toxin around or into the tough sheath of the cat's superior cervical ganglion produced complete paralysis of the synapses supplying the dilator pupillae with 48–67% sparing of those supplying the nictitating membrane; control injections of boiled toxin on the contralateral side paralyzed neither. This relative sparing of one set of preganglionic endings (those in the nictitating membrane pathway) may possibly indicate some localization of the two types of synapses in the superior cervical ganglion and a restriction of toxin action to its immediate site of injection; if there is such a lack of diffusion to the other synapses in the superior cervical ganglion, it could perhaps be due to a tight packing of cells in this ganglion.

In further experiments Ambache and Lessin (17) changed over to type D toxin, which was considered slightly safer to handle in the laboratory, since it appears to be innocuous, by mouth, to humans (see Sterne, quoted in 17). However, laboratory workers should be warned that the risk from inhalation or cutaneous absorption of toxin through abrasions, etc., still exists even with type D (208). Using large doses of this toxin Ambache and Lessin showed the relative ease and rapidity with which it is possible to paralyze the motor parasympathetic postganglionic neurons of the intestinal nerve plexuses *in vitro*. They emphasize the value of the toxin for rapid denervation of surgically inaccessible autonomic neurons of this kind. After a 5–20-minute exposure to type D toxin (50–1000 times the dose of type A used by Burgen *et al.*) striking changes in the pharmacological responses of the intestine were observed in the next 1–3 hours. Following such "denervation" of the rabbit and guinea pig gut there was no decrease in the response to drugs such as muscarine, 2268F, and 5-methylfurfuryltrimethylammonium, all of which act directly upon the smooth muscle cells; this again distinguishes the action of botulinum toxin from that of atropine, which blocks all these drugs. However, the response to ganglion-stimulating drugs such as nicotine, dimethylphenylpiperazinium, and *m*-bromophenyl ether of choline rapidly declined and finally disappeared, even when the dose level was raised 10 times. "Darmstöff" behaved likewise (15). Histamine responses were unaltered in the guinea pig but reduced in the rabbit ileum, where they appear to be predominantly neuronal in origin.

These experiments with type D *in vitro* were preceded by an earlier investigation on rabbits *in vivo* (11) in which type A toxin was injected subperitoneally into a space created between the longitudinal muscle of the small intestine and its serosal covering by a forerunning pilot injection of air. When the rabbits died 3.5–7.5 hours later the poisoned intestinal segments were suspended in Tyrode's solution; subsequent pharmacological tests *in vitro* revealed an interesting reversal of nicotine action. The motor response to small doses of nicotine, if present at first, gradually disappeared and was replaced by an inhibitory response; in many experiments this change had already occurred before death, and nicotine was inhibitory from the start of the *in vitro* experiment. The inhibitory response to nicotine, which was obtained in 12 out of 15 preparations, could be blocked reversibly by hexamethonium, by ephedrine, and by large "paralyzing" doses of nicotine. It was therefore mediated by catecholamines and provided, incidentally, yet further evidence for the greater resistance of adrenergic systems to toxin. The probable adrenergic nature of nicotine inhibition was confirmed later by Gillespie and MacKenna (150) who were able to abolish the effect in the rabbit colon by pretreatment of the animal with reserpine. In this preparation, inhibition occurs readily (and without toxin treatment) because the motor response to nicotine is weak and is overshadowed by the inhibitory one.

The possibility that very large doses of toxin may affect adrenergic as well as cholinergic endings was raised by Ambache (12) and again by Rand and Whaler (272a, 339). They studied the effect of type D toxin on the pilomotor response in the cat's tail evoked by stimulation of adrenergic postganglionic fibers of the lumbar sympathetic trunk (65). Some 14–30 hours after the intradermal injection of toxin into the bases of hair tufts the pilomotor response to stimulation was markedly reduced compared with the response of other tufts given an injection of diluent buffer or left uninjected.

In other experiments Rand and Whaler (272a) found that the normal inhibitory effect caused by stimulation of the periarterial nerves of the rabbit ileum *in vitro* was abolished by the toxin. This, like the pilomotor response, is believed to be mediated by adrenergic fibers and contrasts with the persistence of a nicotine-induced adrenergic inhibition obtained by Ambache. This difference could be due to several factors, e.g., dose levels, types of toxin, or the existence of two separate adrenergic mechanisms in the rabbit gut, a possibility also suggested by the results of Gillespie and MacKenna (150).

These experiments of Ambache (12) and of Rand and Whaler (272a) which appear to question the usual belief that botulinum toxin is specific to cholinergic sites may, however, be interpreted differently. If we regard the susceptibility to botulinum toxin as *prima facie* evidence for the participation of acetylcholine in nervous transmission, then these results support the theory of Burn and Rand (64, 65) of a cholinergic link in adrenaline or noradrenaline release.

The action of botulinum toxin upon peripheral structures is therefore clearly established. Injections into the brain stem (91) have usually failed to implicate central neurons in the paralysis (but see 160), and other experiments have shown that admixture of toxin with brain tissue suspensions does not alter toxicity as is the case with tetanus. However, Tyler (316, 317, 318) has recently examined humans suffering from botulism; apart from contributing further evidence for the peripheral action of the toxin in man he has presented evidence for an effect upon the upper motoneuron pathway. Electromyographic records showed the presence of "H" reflexes under certain conditions. Since these reflexes are believed to represent a failure of inhibitory mechanisms, at the spinal cord level, in the lower motor neuron pathway (222), their association with botulism suggests that the toxin may have minor central effects. The Renshaw cells of the spinal cord are known to be cholinergic, and interference by the toxin at these sites may possibly occur.

2. *The Absorption of the Toxin from the Gut*

Considerable progress has been made in the experimental study of the absorption of toxin from the alimentary canal. Lamanna, in particular, has considered this aspect (206, 207, 215). Because of its toxicity, its protein nature, and its associations as a food poisoning agent, botulinum toxin has come to be regarded as something unique. In some respects this is understandable, but there is nothing particularly uncommon in the absorption of minute amounts of protein, and the interest mainly arises because of its extreme toxicity. Lamanna (206) has discussed this at some length and has demonstrated quite clearly that perhaps all highly toxic proteins, and certainly those of bacterial origin, can be lethal. Both tetanus and diphtheria toxins are toxic when administered by mouth in fairly high dosage; that they are not normally so is probably because their production and accumulation does not involve foodstuffs as happens with *Cl. botulinum.* The amounts of toxin required, expressed as a ratio of the orally administered LD_{50} to the intraperitoneal LD_{50}, are not very dissimilar for *Cl. botulinum* type A, tetanus, and diphtheria toxins. Lamanna (206) also discusses the use of trypsin inhibitors in unsuccessful attempts to alter the oral effectiveness of botulinum and tetanus toxins.

Absorption of toxin seems to take place mainly in the small intestine. Wright (354) concluded that the stomach and upper small intestine were the most likely regions, and experiments by May and Whaler (227, 228) on rats favored the upper small intestine. The reasons for this are not altogether clear. However, the detoxication by proteolytic enzymes which can undoubtedly occur makes it seem likely that the earlier the toxin can be absorbed during its passage along the alimentary canal the more effective a given oral dose will be. Absorption from the colonic region is probably slight (Dack and Hoskins, 90), and therefore a rapid passage through the small intestine might, by taking the toxin into an impermeable region, reduce its effectiveness. The length of the small intestine may be important for giving both time as well as sufficient surface area for the absorption of toxin before chyme reaches the relatively impermeable colon (206).

The effectiveness of a given oral dose depends also, in mice, upon the time of ingestion relative to general feeding times. May and Whaler (228) showed that considerable differences in oral potency occurred as a result of altering this factor, but whether these reflected differing degrees of inactivation by proteolytic enzymes, speed of emptying of the stomach and intestine, or differences in the permeability of the intestinal mucosa was not determined.

Although there is no reason in principle why minute quantities of proteins should not be absorbed from the intestine, the possibility of a small toxic unit, split off by the digestive processes and readily diffusible through the gut, clearly exists (10, 331; see also 332). Thus the size of the particle absorbed by the intestine has excited considerable interest. Lymph collected from unanesthetized rats ingesting toxin was itself toxic (228), and dialysis against 0.9% saline produced no evidence that the molecule could diffuse through cellophane tubing. This in itself does not necessarily indicate that a toxic molecule of protein dimension had been absorbed, since adsorption of a small fragment on to lymph protein might occur. Some evidence for the concept that a protein molecule was involved was the fact that the lymphatic route seemed to be the primary one for the absorbed toxin. Since it is often held that protein molecules in the extravascular spaces do not reenter the capillaries directly but return to the circulation via the lymphatic vessels, an appearance principally in lymph would favor the idea that a large molecule was involved. In a few experiments, rats were completely protected from botulism, after ingesting large doses of toxin, by continuous lymphatic drainage. Other rats injected intraperitoneally with the lymph collected from these animals often showed the usual symptoms of botulism and some died (228).

Heckly, Hildebrand, and Lamanna (172) confirmed many of these results and, using ultracentrifugation techniques, demonstrated a toxic material in lymph and plasma which sedimented at speeds consistent with protein dimensions. Using electrophoretic techniques they have also shown that the apparent size of the toxic particle is not due to adsorption on serum albumin. In their experiments they found for the toxin present in lymph an $S_{20,w}$ value of 7.9 (95% confidence limits 4.4–11.4), compared with a starting material of 17.9 (limits 12–21). On the other hand Wagman (332) has shown that dialyzable fragments can be produced when the toxin is subjected to the action of pepsin *in vitro*.

Although neither proteolytic activity nor pH was measured, it was shown also (172) that crystalline toxin held for 2 hours in the duodenum of the rat had unaltered sedimentation characteristics. This suggests that no alteration of the molecule takes place in the duodenum at least. Since the sedimentation value for absorbed toxin is in the same range as that for the hemagglutinin-free material (172, 175) and since this value is also less than that for crystalline toxin, one wonders where the change in size or shape of the molecule takes place. After *intravenous* injection of toxin the ultracentrifugation of lymph and of blood shows that dissociation of the molecule has taken place, giving a particle which sediments at rates midway between "absorbed" and "original" toxin (175). One might, of course, expect some combination of erythrocytes with the hemagglutinin, resulting in an alteration of the equilibrium which probably exists between this factor and the toxic units of the molecule; there could thus be a definite reduction in the $S_{20,w}$ value. The situation is still far from being understood, and further experiments are desirable.

G. Activation Phenomena

There are two separate but related aspects of this. One is the suggestion often made in clinical papers that the small amount of toxin in the ingested food must have been potentiated in some way. This arises from the finding that gastric samples or uneaten food residues often contain amounts of toxin (as measured, for example, by intraperitoneal injection of extracts into mice) too small to be the likely cause of the symptoms. The second observation is that large increases in specific toxicity occur in some cases if the culture or relatively pure toxin is treated with trypsin; this is associated particularly with type E. Spanning, as it were, these two aspects is the study of the development of toxin by the organism itself.

In spite of considerable study no very satisfactory explanation of the phenomenon of clinical potentiation has been given. Often, it seems, there is indeed very little left of the food originally consumed by a person suffering from botulism, either in the food container or in the stomach and its contents. In other cases only part of the foodstuff may have been associated with appreciable bacterial growth, and thus the sampling technique may be responsible for the apparent lack of toxin. In spite of these explanations the idea has persisted that the gut secretions possess some potentiating factor; as will appear later, this does seem to be so in the case of type E. A contributory factor toward the protection or potentiation concept has been the long-held belief that botulinum as an orally toxic protein was virtually unique, although this attitude has now been shown to be incorrect (206). Since botulinum shows no outstanding difference from other proteins it is likely, so the argument runs, that it is (*a*) protected specifically from digestion, (*b*) potentiated by digestive splitting, or (*c*) generally potentiated, perhaps by being preferentially absorbed, by an "oral potentiating factor" (81).

An alternative to activation by digestive juices is thus the idea that certain cultures contain a specific material which contributes to toxicity by its indirect effects on destruction and/or absorption of the toxin. Bronfenbrenner and Schlesinger (51, 53) claimed that partial purification of the toxin by ammonium sulfate fractionation reduced its toxicity by the oral route. Coleman (81), using rats and either fairly pure or relatively crude type A toxin showed that the former had little oral toxicity by comparison with its intraperitoneal effectiveness, whereas crude toxin was much more effective in this respect. From these results he postulated an "oral potentiating factor" which, so far, has not been seriously examined further.

By contrast the activation of type E toxin, particularly by trypsin, is well documented, and some reference has been made already to this phenomenon. Treatment with trypsin of the crude culture or of relatively pure toxin, gives a considerable increase (up to about 50 times) in the specific toxicity (113, 130, 147). Clearly the oral ingestion of a low-toxicity culture of this type could have an effect considerably larger than might be expected from its intraperitoneal assay figures.

Considerable disagreement exists, however, between two groups of investigators on some aspects of the behavior of type E toxin under these conditions. One group (130) treated type E cultures at pH 6.0 for 2 hours with 0.1% trypsin and subsequently purified the toxin to a specific toxicity of at least 45×10^6 LD_{50}/mg N: a further precipitation stage "gave more pure fractions." In the ultracentrifuge this toxin had $S_{20,w}$ values of 12.5 and 4.75, with the faster-sedimenting fraction as the major component. There is no mention of the more highly purified fractions being tested in this way. The second group (147) purified toxin from type E cultures, and this had $S_{20,w}$ values of 5.6 and 1.1, the former being the toxic component. The specific toxicity of this material was about 0.6×10^6 m.l.d./mg N. Treatment with trypsin increased the specific toxicity about 16-fold, and this was accompanied by the loss of a definable peak in the ultracentrifuge. Indeed the authors suggest that the toxic material was dialyzable.

One possible explanation of these differences, apart from the strain of organism used, lies in the time at which trypsin activation was carried out. One group purified activated toxin, the other group activated pure toxin. Clearly certain experiments need repeating and others require to be carried out. There is also the need, referred to earlier, for sedimentation runs to be carried out under standardized conditions. The ionic composition, ionic strength, and pH of the solvent has a profound effect on sedimentation characteristics, and the differences referred to above could represent nothing more than these variables.

The timing and manner of toxin production by the organism has attracted considerable interest. It seems to be clear from the studies of Gendon (145), Bonventre and Kempe (43, 44, 45), Boroff (46), and Boroff, Raynaud, and Prévot (47) that during the phase of active growth there is only a small production of toxin, with probably a larger synthesis of a protoxin molecule; thus the toxin does not seem to be a true exotoxin insofar as its production is concerned, becoming "exo" only as a result of the breakup of the microorganisms. Associated with this and perhaps largely responsible for it is a phase of proteolytic autolysis; during this period the toxic material itself begins to appear in large quantities. Type E cells appear to be somewhat less proteolytic than others, and their behavior with respect to the toxic activity of cultures and the marked intensification of toxicity by treatment with trypsin may be a manifestation of this situation (255, 286, 287, 288).

The experiments of Boroff (46) on type C have shown that autolysis of cells is responsible for a large increase in toxicity and this change occurs naturally following the cessation of active growth or can be induced in young growing cultures by the addition of culture fluid from "old" cultures. Bonventre and Kempe (44, 45) have shown that the toxicity of cultures of type A increases 10–200 times during the autolysis phase. They showed also that young, i.e., 16-hour, cells could be sonically disrupted with some increase in toxicity, and that treatment with trypsin gave a much greater increase in toxicity, approaching the value which would have been obtained had normal growth been allowed to continue. In these experiments one is, to some extent, accelerating the normal processes. Thus it seems that types A and B organisms produce a weakly toxic precursor which, during the proteolytic phase following active growth, results in the development of high toxicities. This toxin, it may be noted, cannot have its toxicity appreciably increased by subsequent proteolysis. With the less proteolytic type E organisms, toxicity can be enhanced by later treatment.

Sakaguchi and Tohyama (287, 288) have demonstrated the effect of a contaminant (tentatively identified as a *Clostridium* species and itself nontoxigenic to mice) upon the production of toxin by type E organisms. There is an increase in toxicity of about 10–100 times as compared with pure type E cultures, and the authors ascribe this activity to a proteolytic enzyme contributed by the contaminant.

Apart from discoveries yet to be made in the fields so far covered, botulinum toxin would appear to present a useful material for protein analysis in relating structure to function. Here we have a protein which can be purified to a fairly high degree, capable of reacting immunologically and possessed of extraordinary toxicity. At certain stages in its production it is much less toxic; it can be toxoided fairly readily and its molecular structure can change in an apparently remarkable fashion if pH or ionic strength is altered. We have therefore in this molecule one which could be of considerable value in relating structure to activity.

III. TETANUS

A. Introduction

In addition to reviews already referred to (307, 325, 354), Laurence and Webster (219) after briefly summarizing the essential features of tetanus have devoted the major part of their work to the pharmacology and therapeutics of the disease. The most comprehensive treatise is that of Pelloja (260), which contains a voluminous bibliography.

Tetanus usually occurs following the entry of spores into wounds which contain anaerobic tissue. The conditions governing the germination and growth of spores under such circumstances are complex and have been summarized elsewhere (348). After germination the organisms grow and produce their extremely potent toxin. This diffuses into the surrounding tissues from which either it is distributed around the body in the blood or it enters local nerve trunks. In both cases the toxin reaches the central nervous system, where it exerts its main effect. In the usual form this frequently shows itself first as a tetanic stiffening of the masseter muscles —from which is derived the common name of lockjaw—followed by the progressive and widespread involvement of other muscles. These later stages may be absent or overshadowed by respiratory paralysis and death. In an alternative form of the disease symptoms are more limited, affecting only muscles of the infected region.

These two forms of the disease are referred to as general, or descending, and local, or ascending, tetanus. The former follows the dissemination of toxin by the vascular system and is the more dangerous in that the brain stem is involved; the latter occurs as a result of the ascent of toxin into the central nervous system along the local nerve trunks. In this form the effects remain segmentally limited if the quantity of toxin is low; otherwise, the whole of the central nervous system may become progressively involved. Experimentally these two forms of the disease can be produced by intravenous or by intramuscular injections, respectively, of toxin. Following intramuscular injection, intravenous antitoxin must also be given in order to prevent general effects due to the entry of toxin from the injection site into the bloodstream.

B. Potency of the Toxin

Tetanus toxin vies with botulinum and *Sh. shiga* toxins as the most toxic substance known. With the mouse as test animal tetanus is slightly less toxic than botulinum type A but by less than a factor of 10 when expressed as LD_{50}/mg N. With the guinea pig as test animal this difference disappears and the two substances are equally toxic on a weight basis. When account is taken of their molecular weights, however, tetanus toxin emerges as about 15 times less active if expressed on a molar basis (319).

Under conditions where tetanus toxin is introduced directly into the medulla oblongata there is a large reduction in the quantity of toxin required to kill (131, 349). Using rabbits, only 0.001 m.l.d. was required to cause death. The explanation is that injections into the medulla rapidly affect the respiratory and pharyngeal muscles and death occurs as a result. Since there is reason to believe that the response in other species would be similar it is clear that when the toxin is introduced close to a critical effector site it is 10–100 times more toxic than botulinum toxin.

C. Site of Action of the Toxin

The extensive and polemical literature has been carefully evaluated by Wright (354). The burden of evidence seems to be that the toxin exerts its effects mainly at central sites. Experimental local tetanus has been of value in that it has made possible investigations which were uncomplicated by the need to circumvent the asphyxiation which is common in the more usual forms of the disease. Both the mechanism of the spasticity and the site from which it is effected have been analyzed.

The importance of the central nervous system is suggested by the following observations: (*a*) Section of the motor nerve root (but not of sensory roots) both abolishes existing tetanus and prevents the development of local tetanus in the muscles innervated by that nerve (7, 31, 181, 199, 202, 273; see also 18). That sensory root section is ineffective serves also to exclude excessive proprioceptive and other afferent stimulation as a cause of the tetanus, although Perdrup (262) argues against this view. (*b*) General anesthesia and centrally acting muscle relaxant drugs abolish the spasticity, although in many cases normal reflex muscle activity will occur in response to a suitable stimulus. Thus the nerve and muscle apparatus do not appear to be rendered peculiarly sensitive to stimulation (335, 351). (*c*) Experiments designed to analyze the mode of spread of the toxin to its active site also implicate central neurons. This aspect will be discussed further in the next section.

That tetanus toxin exerts its effect primarily at peripheral sites has been argued by Harvey (170), by Abel and his colleagues (2, 3, 4, 5), and by others (262). These workers criticized particularly the experimental techniques of those who used intraneural and intramuscular injections. In addition it has been claimed that motor nerve section neither prevents the development of spasticity nor ends one already existing except in cases where there has been time for the nerve endings to become degenerate. Wright (353, 354), in discussing this problem, has in turn criticized some of Abel's experiments and the conclusions derived from them and concludes that the case for tetanus toxin exerting more than a minor effect at peripheral sites has not been made (255a).

Peripheral effects resulting in paralysis do, however, occur both in experimental and in clinical tetanus. Experimentally, the local effects of a partially purified toxin have been studied by Ambache, Morgan, and

Wright (20). Injections of small amounts of toxin into the anterior chamber of rabbits' eyes led to effects which were entirely localized to the eye, i.e., to mydriasis and to a loss of the reaction to light, a reflex which depends upon the integrity, on the efferent side, of the postganglionic cholinergic oculomotor fibers to the iris. Stimulation of the oculomotor nerve itself failed to constrict the iris; on the other hand, cervical sympathetic stimulation dilated the pupil as usual indicating a relative sparing of the adrenergic fibers and endings in the eye. This cholinergic type of paralysis produced by unboiled but not by boiled tetanus toxin bore resemblances to the effect of botulinum toxin but was specifically prevented by tetanus antitoxin and not by botulinum antitoxin. A further resemblance between the two paralyses was that the smooth muscle in the sphincter pupillae still responded to acetylcholine. In a subsequent study (19) a reduction in the acetylcholine content of the iris and aqueous humor was found, as well as a sensitization of the intoxicated sphincter muscle to carbaminoylcholine, as occurs after surgical denervation; there was no change in iris cholinesterase.

Clinically, paralytic symptoms have been reported. In addition to lingual and facial paralysis, and ophthalmoplegia, there are also reports that atony of the bladder and retention of urine, constipation, and tachycardia all occur (86, 115).

With parabiotic animals both central and peripheral effects have been shown (226, 293). Injection of tetanus toxin into one member of the pair resulted in the appearance of classical tetanus and death. This was often associated in the other member with circulatory and respiratory failure, but unaccompanied by the usual signs of tetanus and not prevented by antitoxin. In explanation, the authors suggest a second toxic agent, produced either from the toxin or as a result of its action. Rather similar results have been reported by Fedinec (128), and clarification of the agent involved, the manner of its production, and its precise relationship with the toxin, as well as the way in which it exerts its effect, is now required.

The experiments of Davies and Wright (94) are also of interest in this respect. They showed that tetanus toxoid given before the toxin prevented or delayed death. In those animals in which death was delayed the terminal effects were flaccid muscles, and the effects were generally similar to those of botulinum toxin rather than the usual effects of tetanus toxin. It is tempting to relate all of these results to interference with acetylcholine release at nerve endings throughout the body as shown above for the eye, although much more precise work would be required before such speculation could be verified.

Using partially purified toxin it has recently been shown by van Heyningen and his colleagues (129) that it was possible to adsorb out much of the centrally acting toxic material, leaving a solution which, applied to mouse intercostal muscles *in vitro,* increased the frequency of miniature end plate potential discharge. This represents, in effect, an *increase* in acetylcholine release; suitable tests appear to have eliminated the possibility of this being due to an effect of Ca^{++} or of K^{+}. Further evidence that this is a real effect lies in the fact that it was prevented by antitoxin (255a).

Thus there are distinct resemblances between the two clostridial neurotoxins. Botulinum acts mainly at peripheral sites, but a central effect is not excluded; with tetanus the reverse is true.

D. Entry of Toxin to Its Site of Action

Under conditions producing local tetanus there seems now to be no doubt that toxin makes its way from the site of production (or injection) into the spinal cord by centripetal movement along the nerve trunks; the portal of entry for general tetanus is not so clearly established.

After a period during which Abel's views dominated the field, attention was again directed to the alternative possibility, namely, that toxin reaches the central nervous system as a result of transport along nerve trunks. Ambache and Lippold (18) noticed that, when tetanus toxin was placed subperitoneally in the vicinity of the vagus nerves, either in their esophageal portion or on the anterior wall of the stomach, a bradycardia of central origin occurred which was prevented by antitoxin. Since the bradycardia was abolished by vagotomy, atropine (transiently), and Na pentobarbital, it was due to a local tetanus of the cardioinhibitory center. The bradycardia was also seen after deliberate injections of toxin into the central end of the vagus nerve, and its occurrence after subperitoneal injections indicated a migration of toxin along the vagi to the brain. Clinically, although functional derangements within the autonomic system occur in tetanus they are usually overshadowed by the severe disturbances in the somatic nerves and nerve centers.

Some years prior to this, Acheson, Ratnoff, and Schoenbach (7) had reexamined the question of the action of tetanus toxin. They systematically eliminated the muscle fibers, the neuromuscular junction, and the afferent and efferent nerves, concluding that the toxin acted at the spinal cord. They also demonstrated, yet again, the segmental nature of local tetanus and its prevention, after a local intramuscular injection of the toxin, by section of the regional nerve trunks.

Following intramuscular injection (combined with intravenous antitoxin to prevent general effects), tetanus toxin can be demonstrated in the nerve trunk supplying the region. The greater the lapse of time following the injection the nearer to the spinal cord is the toxin found, and it can be shown that the distance travelled is roughly proportional to the time after the initial injection. Furthermore, the toxin remains in the nerve trunk. Section of the nerve close to the spinal cord or, even more specifically, section of the motor (anterior) root, completely prevents the onset of tetanus, thus further emphasizing the importance of the nerve route (138, 140, 351). The intramuscular or preferably intraneural injection of antitoxin some time before the toxin prevents the onset of tetanus (140, 350). These results all favor the nerve trunk and its motor root as the pathway of entry into the central nervous system from local sources. Kryzhanovskii and his colleagues (200) have excluded the epineuria and lymphatics of the nerve as responsible for the transport of toxin.

Other very convincing experiments (30, 353) were those in which a mild sclerosing agent was used to create, in effect, a physical barrier within the sciatic nerve. Such treatment did not prevent the passage of nerve impulses and had little visible effect upon use and movement of the leg. Tetanus did not follow the local injection of toxin, and furthermore the toxin was shown to have accumulated within the nerve but distal to the sclerosed region. Direct intraneural injection of toxin proximal to the block led to the usual pattern of development of local tetanus. These and similar experiments (92, 350) again emphasize the relative unimportance of peripheral effects of toxin upon muscle and nerve, although it should be remembered that this is not itself proof since vascular antitoxin was always present in these experiments.

The manner of the centripetal spread within nerves has attracted attention. Wright (353, 354) concluded that the toxin could ascend in the small volume of fluid which is normally present in the spaces between individual nerve fibers. The driving force for such movement is believed to be contributed by pressure developed during muscular activity.

He also attributed the failure of local tetanus to develop following toxin injections into structures innervated by purely sensory fibers to the absence of this driving force. It is not inconceivable that other factors might operate, particularly in mixed nerve trunks. If toxin moves centripetally in the fluid-filled spaces between individual nerve fibers and is propelled by the pressure which develops when muscles contract, the question arises as to why these factors do not operate to force toxin equally into both motor and sensory roots. It has been shown that posterior roots do not contain toxin whereas anterior roots do, yet there is no *a priori* reason why this should be so.

One possibility would be that a peripheral distinction operates to allow toxin to enter only into motor fiber regions of the nerve trunk; its subsequent movement only into the anterior root would then be explicable. It would be illuminating to reexamine the movement of radio-iodinated rabbit serum in peripheral nerve to see particularly whether it entered into both the posterior roots and spinal ganglia as well as into those of the anterior division.

Kryzhanovskii *et al.* (201, 202, 203) have used a variety of animal species to study the distribution and movement of toxin in local tetanus. Like others before them, they too conclude that tetanus toxin ascends in the regional nerve and enters the spinal cord through the anterior root. They have also shown that the spinal ganglia on both sides of the spinal cord frequently contain toxin and that the purely sensory portion of nerve on the ipsilateral side (between the junction of the motor and sensory fibers of the trunk and the ganglion itself) may also contain toxin, although the part proximal to the ganglion does not. Thus it is possible that, on the ipsilateral side at least, toxin is forced into sensory fibers but fails to penetrate further because of the hindrance provided by the spinal ganglion. The difficulty here is that the contralateral ganglia also contain the toxin. The source of this toxin is not clear, although the authors suggest that, in spite of the presence of antitoxin, it is blood borne. Clearly this aspect of the spread of tetanus toxin requires further investigation.

When larger doses of toxin are given locally, in addition to the usual segmental effects, toxin ascends in the spinal cord with progressive development of advancing tetanus and eventually affects the innervation of the respiratory muscles. During the early stages of this spread, section of the spinal cord can prevent access to the more cephalad regions of the cord (31, 131, 138), although leaving the distal tetanic symptoms arising from the spinal cord unaffected.

The route by which toxin from the bloodstream enters the nervous system in general tetanus is not yet properly established. Although the capillaries of the central nervous system are generally rather impermeable to large molecules, it has been argued that cranial sites may allow entry of toxin (136, 137). Similarly, spinal ganglia may represent a means of access (139, 201, 202, 203). It should also be remembered that a high degree of capillary permeability is not necessarily required in view of the extraordinary sensitivity of the medulla to the toxin (131, 349).

E. The Physiology of Tetanus Poisoning

The outstanding characteristic of tetanus is the convulsive rigidity of affected muscles. Evidence that this is centrally induced and is not reflexly dependent upon an intense sensory inflow or a local action on nerve, end plate, or muscle fiber has already been referred to. Section of the spinal cord cephalad to a region of local tetanus fails to alleviate in any marked degree the existing symptoms; the effects cannot therefore be attributed to hyperactivity of cranial neurons impinging upon the spinal motoneurons. Thus, by exclusion, the segment of the cord which gives rise to the nerve trunks concerned is therefore the region upon which the toxin is having its effect.

The intense motor discharge is believed to be due to a failure of inhibitory mechanisms in the interneuron pathways associated with the motoneurons of the spinal cord. The precise nature of the action of tetanus toxin—as well as of strychnine and other similar drugs—has been investigated by Brooks, Curtis, and Eccles using cats (56, 89, 116). They recorded both impulse discharge in ventral (motor) roots of spinal nerves and potentials from the dorsal surface of the spinal cord before and during the development of local tetanus. These experiments represent the closest approach yet made to analyzing the site of action of this toxin (see also 75, 92, 198, 309, 347).

Monosynaptic spinal reflexes were not significantly altered, but polysynaptic ones were increased because many, and perhaps all, of the usual forms of motoneuron inhibition were depressed, both by tetanus toxin and by strychnine. The excitatory phenomena which are so prominent in the intoxication are not due to an excitation by toxin of motoneurons. Thus it was found that the inhibition of motoneurons which can, normally, be effected by Renshaw cells was abolished after the onset of local tetanus and there was no parallel conversion to an excitatory effect. The reduction and disappearance of inhibition is believed to be due, therefore, to a progressive diminution in the ability of inhibitory interneurons to effect satisfactory inhibitory postsynaptic potentials at motoneurons. Thus, as the toxin becomes effective there is a progressive decrease in inhibitory influence, and one is left with a motoneuron which, because of the loss of these inhibitory influences, responds the more readily to excitatory impulses. Since inhibition is of fundamental importance in the proper operation of the nervous system, such interference with inhibitory mechanisms produces profound effects.

While it is clear that both tetanus toxin and strychnine operate to prevent inhibition in the central nervous system, it is not known whether this is due to an inability of released inhibitory transmitter substance to combine with its postsynaptic receptor site or to a decrease in the amount of transmitter actually released. Until the substance itself has been isolated it will not be easy to answer this question, although it is tempting to attribute to tetanus toxin an effect akin to that of botulinum, namely, to cause a reduction and eventual cessation of transmitter release at inhibitory synapses. The alternative would be that it had an effect similar to that of curare operating at the neuromuscular junction.

The peripheral actions of tetanus toxin have already been referred to. Clearly they do not seem to be responsible for the lethal effect of the toxin, although their role, if any, in normal clinical tetanus and the functional relationship which these effects bear to the central action is still of interest for a full understanding of the disease.

F. Biochemical Effects

Apart from the effect referred to earlier upon the acetylcholine content in the eye (19, 20) and the effect on inhibitory transmission in the spinal cord, one other line of study requires comment. This relates to the long-standing observation that admixture of tetanus toxin with brain tissue reduces its toxicity. In spite of the newer knowledge concerning the central site of action of toxin the relationship between all of these findings still remains elusive.

Fulthorpe (144) and van Heyningen and his colleagues (320, 328) have isolated and studied the specific substance in neural tissue responsible for the adsorption of toxin. This is a water-soluble ganglioside complexed with water-insoluble cerebrosides and sphingomyelins (321, 328). The combination with toxin is dependent upon the ganglioside containing both hexosamine and sialic acid, although other factors are presumably involved since different gangliosides with the same sialic acid content may vary eight-fold in their toxin-fixing capacity (323, 328). This combination is relatively specific for tetanus toxin and, to a lesser extent, tetanus toxoid. In particular, botulinum and diphtheria toxins are not fixed, although strychnine and other drugs whose activity resembles tetanus toxin are fixed (322, 324; see also 254).

Reference was made earlier to Kryzhanovskii's demonstration of the presence of toxin in spinal ganglia, and it was suggested that the ganglion might act as a barrier to prevent the further centripetal movement of toxin into the posterior horn of the spinal cord. In view of the possible importance of gangliosides as receptors for the toxin it is not unreasonable to suggest that the proposed "filtering" of toxin may be due to its combination with ganglioside present in the ganglion itself. If toxin-combining ganglioside could be demonstrated in spinal ganglia this might provide some explanation for what is otherwise the peculiar difference between toxin movement in motor and sensory roots. Whether it is borne along the nerve and into the ganglion or absorbed from the bloodstream, the appearance of toxin in both ipsi- and contralateral ganglia suggests a fairly high avidity by ganglion substance for the toxin.

van Heyningen's studies have also revealed a possible explanation for the relative lack of sensitivity of frogs to tetanus toxin (284) in that only a low affinity exists between the toxin and frog brain emulsions (329).

One further difference is that the frog brain ganglioside is extractable with water, in contrast to that present in mammalian brain. However, like frogs, pigeons are highly resistant to the toxin. This is not due to an abnormally impermeable blood-brain barrier, but it may reflect a lower avidity of the brain tissue for toxin (93), although other results (329) suggest that suspensions of brain tissue from birds fix toxin to an extent roughly comparable with mammals.

Although ganglioside-toxin combination may prove, ultimately, to be relatively unimportant in our understanding of the action of tetanus toxin, the opposite might well be true (230a). The gangliosides which van Heyningen has isolated show varying affinities for toxin; some are able to combine with up to 20 times their own weight of toxin. If the more avid gangliosides were associated particularly with inhibitory neurons a highly satisfactory correlation would be established for the molecular basis of tetanus activity. While the affinity for ganglioside which strychnine shares with tetanus toxin encourages a belief in the significance of gangliosides in the mechanism of tetanus intoxication, the highly localized action of the toxin in contrast to the diffuse distribution of ganglioside within the central nervous system dictates considerable caution in any speculation.

IV. ANIMAL NEUROTOXINS

A. Introduction

In spite of a copious literature involving almost all animal Orders information as specific as that for the bacterial neurotoxins is not available. Clinical reports and the investigations of field biologists take us some way, but detailed physiological and biochemical investigations are few. In this section we shall examine neurotoxins isolated from or believed to be constituents of predatory animal venoms and stings, or present in the flesh and hence producing toxic symptoms after ingestion.

As we shall see, one of the main difficulties seems to be the small scale of neurotoxin production; feeding ticks, for example, produce only a minute volume of toxic saliva and even these amounts are probably large with reference to that of, say, wasps or spiders. Because of this, conventional physiological techniques are not sensitive enough; however, increased sensitivity can be obtained by using the natural prey as test animal. Beard (32) has done this with exceptional success in studies of a wasp and the technique has enabled him to assess the venom toxicity in terms of its natural effectiveness. Intermittent toxin production is another difficulty. Gregson (158), using a tick secretion, was unable to demonstrate toxic effects on small sensitive animals even with relatively large volumes of saliva, yet at certain times a single tick is able to paralyze a bullock or sheep. To some extent changes in the secretion after collection may be responsible: many secretions have proteolytic components, and not all investigators seem to have appreciated this point.

Considerable information has been obtained in certain instances. Usually this has been due to one or more of the following factors: (*a*) a high proportion of toxic substance in the organism, e.g., 14 mg of Sphaeroides toxin isolated from 3.3 kg crude starting material; (*b*) ready availability of the species concerned; (*c*) commercial interest in the toxic material itself, for example the food industry and mussel and clam poisoning; (*d*) the use of large-scale preparative methods as a result of (*b*) and (*c*) comparable with those used in work on the two Clostridia toxins.

There are a number of review articles, symposia, and textbooks which provide useful information and an extensive bibliography (23, 34, 60, 80, 87, 88, 122a, 125, 173, 185, 252, 336).

B. Protozoa

The possibility that the toxicity to humans of certain fishes is due to their feeding habits and in particular to the direct or, via intermediate prey, indirect ingestion of protozoa has not been adequately demonstrated. However, in the case of poisonous mussels (*Mytilus californianus*) and butter clams (*Saxidomas giganteus*) which occur particularly on the Northwestern American coast the toxicity has been shown to be due to the ingestion of enormous quantities of marine dinoflagellates (290, 291, 292). In this area *Gonyaulex catenella* is the main species but others are known (1, 35); in the absence of these protozoa the molluscs remain nontoxic. Identity of toxin isolated from molluscs and from pure cultures of *G. catenella* has been confirmed (63, 291).

The toxin, sometimes referred to as saxitoxin, has been isolated and purified to a high degree and its chemistry and biological activity investigated (41, 247, 290, 291, 292). It is a basic substance of molecular weight 372, but its structure has not yet been determined and attempts to isolate smaller active groups are still unsuccessful.

Toxicity for mice is 0.18 μg (intraperitoneal, m.l.d., 20-gm animal), i.e., 9 μg/kg, and for the rabbit 3–4 μg/kg, intravenously. References to the biological action of the toxin are given by Schantz (291), but the main study is that of Murtha (247). Cardiovascular, neuromuscular, and central nervous system effects have been demonstrated (41, 247, 290). Some part of the cardiovascular effect—a profound fall in blood pressure—has a central nervous system component, since high cervical cord section and vagotomy prior to the injection of lethal doses prevents much of the blood pressure change.

The respiration rapidly stops after the injection of small doses into the cat, and a more dramatic neurotoxic effect is inhibition of the knee jerk reflex. Since under these conditions the motor fibers themselves were relatively unaffected, the blockade is most likely in central (spinal) neurons, although an effect upon the sensory nerves cannot be excluded at this stage. Low-frequency stimulation of the reflex pathway was affected much more than rapid stimulation, suggesting that in spite of the neurotoxic action facilitation could to some extent alleviate the blockade. Changes in the phrenic nerve spike potentials also followed the injection of toxin, and the response of the diaphragm to indirect stimulation ceased. In some cases the muscle responded less readily to a direct stimulus.

Effects as widespread as these suggest that a general cell membrane change may be the means by which the toxin acts, although the high sensitivity of the nervous system justifies our interest in the toxin.

Less extensive but otherwise similar studies on another dinoflagellate toxin have been reported (1, 36, 355); this was effective against a wide range of animals and possessed neurotoxic and neuromuscular activities. The toxic material is said to be nondialyzable. Mortality of fish due to the toxin of a phytoflagellate is said to involve neuromuscular block and interference with spinal reflexes (35).

C. Coelenterata

This group includes the hydroids, jellyfish, sea anemones, and corals. Species which affect man have attracted some attention: although precise data on the action of the toxins on mammals, still less the natural prey, are not yet available, Lane (217) has described means of concentrating nematocysts of *Physalia* and this should lead to the purification of active molecules. Halstead (166) summarizes much of the available information on marine toxic organisms.

A crude toxic material from Physalia nematocysts (216, 217, 218) can be separated chromatographically into at least three fractions, including one with ten times the toxicity of the original. Crude toxin is thermolabile and destroyed by organic solvents.

A clearly neurotoxic action occurs when crude toxin is injected into mice at a dose level of 2–2.5 mg/kg. There is a decrease in muscle tone, flaccid paralysis of the hind limb, respiratory failure, and death. Injection of 16.2 μg into the ventral lymph sac of the frog gave loss of the postural and righting reflexes, and death. Stimulation of the sciatic nerve was ineffective, but direct stimulation of the muscle remained effective. In fish, the injected side shows motor paralysis (216). Apart from these effects pain, direct action on the heart, skin petechiae, and effects attributable to parasympathetic stimulation have been reported in man. This multiplicity of effects may indicate that a cytotoxin is operative; until more analyses with purified fractions have been made it should be perhaps accepted that a number of separable agents are involved.

Southcott (305) has reviewed the coelenterates of medical importance and attributes to two species of the Class Scyphozoa, Order Cubomedusae, a highly neurotoxic action. These, *Chironex fleckeri* and *Chiropsalmus quadrigatus,* may cause rapid death in humans probably by respiratory arrest. As with *Physalia* the nematocyst toxin is probably complex and severe skin damage as well as excruciating pain is characteristic of the stings (191). Species of other orders are listed as neurotoxic, but in none of these has the action been closely investigated (28, 264, 304).

The sea anemone *Rhodactis howesii,* toxic to man when ingested raw, appears to have a neurotoxic component. Extracts given to mice led to respiratory difficulty and eventual failure. Severe hemorrhages and damage to kidneys and other tissues were also reported (127). Other sea anemones have in their tentacles a complex variety of pharmacologically active molecules (225, 336), probably very similar to those present in jellyfish.

D. Annelida

A marine annelid *Lumbriconereis heteropoda* produces nereistoxin, an organic sulfur-containing toxin of low molecular weight. This has a powerful action on the autonomic nervous system, and in mice doses of 38 mg/kg and in rabbits 1.8 mg/kg are lethal. Fish are more susceptible, 0.6 p.p.m. being lethal at pH 7.6–8.0 for the killifish (*Oryzias latipes*) (171). The specific role of the toxin is unknown.

E. Arthropoda

1. *Insects*

Beard (34) has reviewed present knowledge of insect venoms and toxins.

Bee stings, often uncomfortable to man, may on occasion be highly dangerous. This is believed to be due to an anaphylactic response (232), but the venom is rather complex and contains constituents which, particularly after multiple stings, could have other effects. Apart from acetylcholine and histamine it contains a number of enzymes and other high-molecular-weight substances which have a biological activity but to which enzymic action has not been ascribed (176, 250). The venom can be separated into three major fractions, of which that known as FI or melittin contains the neurotoxin (250). However this fraction has a number of effects upon the blood pressure and upon cardiac, skeletal, and smooth muscle and causes hemolysis of red cells. So far a common denominator for these activities has not been determined, and FI is probably yet a rather complex mixture. Tested upon the rat phrenic nerve-diaphragm preparation or the perfused superior cervical ganglion of the cat it first increases and then subsequently blocks nervous transmission (164, 250). These effects are irreversible and in animals can lead to respiratory paralysis and death.

Wasps too have venom constituents which paralyze their prey (32, 126, 274, 340). This permits suitable larvae to be retained as food for the wasps' young. Whether this is a true neurotoxic effect or one caused by something of a more general cytotoxic nature has not been wholly determined. In the case of one particular species of wasp, *Habrobracon juglandis,* Beard (32) has carried out an extensive investigation. Using as test animal the natural prey *Galleria mellonella* he determined the toxicity of the venom and calculated that one part in 200 million of host blood was sufficient to cause paralysis. The volume injected per sting was calculated as 20–65 micro-microliters (from this and host volume the figure of 1/200,000,000 given above has been determined); this toxin is therefore of extreme potency, allowing the wasp to paralyze prey some 1000 times its own weight.

The toxin was not dialyzable but was heat labile and did not precipitate with most of the other proteins when *Galleria* blood was treated with alcohol. It showed a high degree of species specificity, and its action was restricted to a limited number of larvae. In another species, *Ephestia,* the site of action was localized to the neuromuscular junction, since paralyzed larvae muscles were responsive to direct but not indirect stimulation. Other evidence excluded central nervous system ganglia and transmission in motor nerves.

This study by Beard is particularly interesting and valuable since, apart from the knowledge gained on this particular wasp, the technique of utilizing a natural prey for experimentation serves as a useful pattern for other studies. The biology of many other wasps may not be quite so convenient as for *Habrobracon* but the example is now before us.

In a discussion of other arthropod venoms Beard (33) includes reference to another wasp, *Phytodietis,* which immobilizes its prey while ovipositing using a very short-acting substance; paralysis lasts only about 10 minutes. Clearly such a substance must be extremely potent at its effector sites.

2. *Spiders*

Spiders are claimed (25, 40, 346) to produce a neurotoxic venom, although direct data seem to be scanty. Venom analysis with natural prey is required on the line of Beard's work. The technique of "milking" spiders (as is done with snakes) for their venom is being used and allows the use of reasonable quantities of a homogeneous material. Bücherl (59) used venom of *Phoneutria fera;* 0.34 mg given intravenously to a mouse was lethal, acting on both central and peripheral nervous systems. The specific site(s) has not been determined.

3. *Ticks*

A number of paralyzing ticks are known. Of these major studies have been carried out only on one, *Dermacentor.* Parasitic upon many wild and domesticated animals, the Ixodid ticks seem to be particularly prevalent in the Far East, Africa, and the American continent, where they may be of considerable economic importance. *Dermacentor andersoni* of the Canadian Rocky Mountain region has received intensive study. This species causes ascending flaccid paralysis in man, horse, dog, sheep, cattle, groundhogs, and marmots; cats, rabbits, rats, mice, wild sheep and goats, moose, and deer are unaffected, although the latter two species may die from exsanguination if the infestation is heavy (121, 159). A number of feeding ticks are normally required for paralysis to develop, but cases in which humans and large cattle were paralyzed by a single feeding tick have been recorded (159). It is generally accepted that the amount of neurotoxin secreted by the feeding tick increases appreciably as feeding continues (121), and after the fifth to seventh day paralysis will take place most rapidly. This delay does not appear to be due to a gradual accumulation of toxin in the bloodstream, since in most animals [groundhogs and marmots excepted (120)] removal of the tick leads to rapid recovery; rather it is a change in the toxicity of the secretion itself. In addition paralysis can be produced consistently and fairly rapidly (24–36 hours) in marmots if ticks which have already been feeding for some days on other animals are used for the infestation (121). The toxin does not appear to evoke an immune or anaphylactic reaction.

Rose and Gregson (282) obtained evidence for a neuromuscular effect. They suggested also that the sensory pathways were unaffected although Emmons and McLennan (121) claim that in the marmot at least there is a depressed conduction in sensory fibers.

Attempts to obtain visible effects on lambs, dogs, mice, and frogs by the injection of saliva from female ticks were unsuccessful (158). Other experiments (159) using extracts of tick salivary gland caused death but without any obvious paralysis. Rose and Gregson (282) produced evidence for a neuromuscular block, and more recent experiments (120, 121, 245, 246) have extended these findings. As well as diminished conduction occurring in sensory nerves a similar phenomenon was evident in motor fibers, and Emmons and McLennan (121) believe also that central spinal (and perhaps cranial) neurons may be affected since there is a poorer reflex response to sensory nerve stimulation than the conduction depression of the separate nerve tracts would suggest. The neurons which are implicated may be those involved in the monosynaptic (muscle spindle) reflexes (124).

Although acetylcholine release at nerve endings in paralyzed animals is defective (120), this is not due to a deficiency of synthesis (121) and is presumably a reflection of diminished motor nerve activity (246). Thus both motor and sensory nerve fibers, as well as spinal neurons and the transmitter release mechanism at terminal nerve endings, are all affected by the toxin. A general clinical review of the paralysis has been given by Blattner (39).

4. *Scorpions*

The species of scorpions harmful to man have been mostly studied. These are chiefly, but not entirely, Mexican and Brazilian. Although the venom production per animal is low compared with snakes, scorpions can usually be collected in very large numbers, giving useful amounts of venom for experimental purposes. The venoms are complex (95, 96, 101, 256, 269), but some separation of constituents is possible.

Central and peripheral effects have been demonstrated (95, 256, 297, 306), as well as activity mediated via the autonomic nervous system (297). Injection of venom from Mexican scorpions (95) into cats and other animals gave rise to muscular twitches and fibrillations which increased after destruction of the brain. Destruction of the spinal cord abolished most of the activity, which is therefore due to excessive motoneuron firing. The response to single sensory stimuli was repetitive, tending to summate in tetanic form. As might be anticipated the venom has an anticurare action. It also has two other distinct neurotoxic effects. One is central, upon the respiratory center, which is depressed or blocked. The second is believed to be direct at the neuromuscular junction or the muscle fiber. Topical application or close intra-arterial injection gives a fibrillation which is independent of a connection with the spinal cord and not effective on denervated muscles (95, 256).

Miranda and his colleagues (236, 237, 238, 239) have paid particular attention to the venoms from *Androctonus australis* and *Buthus occitanus*. Venom obtained either by electrical stimulation of, or by manual expression from, the telsons of these species proved much easier to purify than did that extracted from whole telsons. With the latter, essential early purification stages resulted in the loss of most of one neurotoxic component. The use of Sephadex and Amberlite columns has led to the isolation from each species of two highly purified fractions, each of which is believed to be neurotoxic.

The LD_{50} values of these toxins is from 1–4 μg/mouse; amino acid analysis of the *Androctomus* toxins I and II and toxin I of *Buthus* offers no explanation of their toxicity. Each one has a high percentage of aspartic acid and of lysine, with virtually no methionine. Molecular weight determinations, on the basis of either their amino acid analysis or their behavior in the ultracentrifuge, gave 13,000–13,500 and 10,000–11,000 for *Androctonus* I and II, respectively, and 17,000–18,000 for *Buthus* I. The lower molecular weight of one of the *Androctonus* toxins accords with the finding that dialysis of whole venom, particularly in 0.2 *M* phosphate buffer pH 7.07, causes a loss of some 30% of its activity. These toxins are stable in aqueous solution and fairly resistant to heat (64% loss of toxicity after 60 minutes at 80°C) but they are destroyed upon treatment with 0.5% trypsin and chymotrypsin.

The purified substances given to mice in sublethal doses did not lead to the development of immunity. Other workers have shown that anti-scorpion venom sera can be prepared in horses, and the failure in the experiments with mice could be due either to species differences or to a decrease in antigenicity as the venom is purified.

The relative wealth of information obtained by Miranda and his group on the chemistry and composition of these venoms is not yet matched by studies on the biological activity of the venoms. Only general effects following lethal and sublethal injections are recorded, but they include clonic movements, marked ascending paralysis, and respiratory failure.

F. Mollusca

There is some evidence that octopus saliva contains, among other things, a neurotoxin (148). In addition to a number of amines (histamine, taurine, tyramine, *p*-hydroxyphenylethanol amine) and acetylcholine saliva contains a nondiffusible substance which is heat and trypsin sensitive. Injection of this substance, cephalotoxin, into the crab is followed by a reduction in movement and paralysis. Injection of the diffusible components does not lead to these symptoms. This effect is a central one, since nerve muscle pincer and leg preparations from crustacea were not affected by the toxin.

Certain gastropods contain in their salivary glands tetramine and choline; ingestion of these can give rise in man to symptoms of poisoning.

Injection or administration *per os* to animals can give rise to respiratory and neuromuscular disturbances sufficiently severe to cause death. In *Neptunea arthritica,* tetramine is the major component (4–8.4 mg/gm gland), but in other species this amine as well as choline esters (e.g., urocanylcholine) are present (24, 341). In other cases, no identification has yet been made (84).

Marine snails of the genus *Conus* produce a neurotoxin, believed to be used for the immobilization of prey. *In vivo* this snail can cause rapid paralysis of crabs and of other snails (123, 193, 194). Extracts of the venom duct contain a variety of active molecules of which some are non-dialyzable. Intraperitoneal injection into mice leads to the development of flaccid paralysis. Intracerebral injections were followed by a period of hyperexcitability and often convulsions. Respiratory difficulty and ataxia were also observed. These phenomena all suggest a central effect. Although the point was not tested experimentally, the authors (194) suggested that interference with neuromuscular transmission was an important effect of the toxin.

G. Echinodermata

The sea urchin *Toxopneustes pileolus* is believed to produce a neurotoxin. This belief arises from clinical reports of lip and facial paralysis and respiratory difficulty (122).

Holothurin, a crystalline steroid glycoside (142) from the sea cucumber *Actinopyga agassizi,* has a direct action on muscle tissue causing contracture (143, 253). At 1×10^{-4} M it produces irreversible paralysis of the response of the rat diaphragm muscle to indirect stimulation, and eventually the muscle itself fails to respond when directly stimulated. The nerve fiber is also blocked. These effects suggest a membrane action or one upsetting ionic shifts. At very low doses (10^{-9}–10^{-10} M) physostigmine can partially protect against the toxin, it is believed by a charge effect and not by one due to anticholinesterase activities (141).

H. Pisces

As a common foodstuff fishes, if toxic, can produce serious effects. Others have venomous spines, etc., and toxin enters through the wound. Of the former most are tropical and no common pattern can be derived to account for their toxicity. General reviews of phyla containing toxic species have been given by Halstead and Mitchell (166, 168) and Mills (233).

The Moray eel, *Gymnothorax* spp., gives rise to ataxia and other symptoms, including respiratory difficulty, in man and in experimental animals (272). Halstead (167) lists six main groups of fish, which include

Moray eels and also a number of species under the common heading Ciguatera. These latter give rise to a variety of symptoms which might reflect both central and peripheral neuromuscular effects (26, 174). Both have been shown to occur in man and also when tested on experimental animals, but precise details of location and mechanism are unknown. Neurotoxic symptoms were also seen in two people who died after eating the local "trigger fish" on Tonga (224).

The species which have the most potent toxin and about which most is known are the puffer fishes. Purified toxin has an LD_{50} for the mouse of 0.02 μg/gm (247) and can paralyze the rat phrenic nerve–diaphragm preparation if the concentration is 0.06 μg/ml. Given intravenously to anesthetized cats the toxin has marked cardiovascular effects, with a pronounced fall in blood pressure. Central neural effects (e.g., respiratory depression, especially after intracarotid injection) and peripheral block are produced by the toxin. Close intra-arterial injection gave neuromuscular block first to slow and then to fast stimulation rates. With sufficiently high doses the muscle failed to respond even to direct stimulation. Most of these effects were reversible. Intravenous administration caused an ascending paralysis of hind limbs, diaphragm, and fore limbs, in that order and reversible (247, 248).

Other attempts have been made to study the action of the toxin (132, 133). These locate one main action as a reduction in acetylcholine output at the nerve ending. With the rat diaphragm there was a 61% reduction in acetylcholine output: the dose used did not give complete diaphragmatic paralysis even though it was lethal when given intravenously. This suggests that other sites are perhaps more important. Injections of choline into rats did not protect against the toxin.

Another highly toxic substance, tetrodotoxin, has been isolated from the ovary of the Japanese Kugu fish (*Speroides rubripee*) and had an m.l.d. of 0.008 μg in the mouse (249). Tetrodotoxin has now been shown to block the sodium movement in stimulated nerve leaving the potassium movement unaffected (249a). It is also believed to be similar to, or identical with, tarichatoxin (see Amphibia section; 243a).

Venomous fish are those whose spines or other projections give entry for a toxic agent. Those important in the Pacific area have been reviewed (168). The venom of these fishes has not been properly investigated, and strict neurotoxic effects are not yet established in every case. Wiener (343) collected stone-fish venom which gave neurotoxic effects in mice and guinea pigs and possibly in other species. A pronounced necrosis occurs with this venom, and this adds to the difficulty of analysis. However large doses (4 lethal doses) of the venom cause very rapid death, which might imply a central neurotoxic action (see 265, 289, 342, 343).

The dorsal spines of the weever fishes contain a neurotoxin. Two species, *Trachinus vipera* (lesser) and *Trachinus draco* (greater weever fish), have been studied. Russell and Emery (285) have surveyed earlier work and attempted to analyze the mechanism of action of the venom. Carlisle (74) in an elegant and informative paper has shown that venom injected by the fish into a small piece of sponge has a number of components. The component giving the neurotoxic effects is nondialyzable and appears to be a complex of two separable albumins and a mucopolysaccharide. Extensive animal tests have not been made: subepidermal injections in man produced "respiratory distress" and the nondialyzable toxin was lethal to the goby (*Gobius ruthensparri*). Large doses killed within 90 seconds: after brief and violent threshing movements the fish turned on its back, respiration ceased, and it died with fins and operculum fully extended. Respiratory paralysis in cats occurred as an initial brief apnea, with temporary gasping; then even this ceased and death occurred (285). There seems to be a definite central action, although cardiovascular changes (very low blood pressure) could cause secondary "neurotoxic" effects. Peripherally the toxin seems to have a direct effect upon the muscle.

I. Amphibia

Two amphibians have so far been shown to produce a neurotoxin. Tarichatoxin can be isolated from the eggs or the developing embryos of the Californian newt, *Taricha torosa*. Preparations containing 7 m.l.d./μg have been prepared: this toxicity is similar to that of muscle or clam toxin and of puffer fish toxin (57, 184). The chemical structure of the compound is unknown, but a molecular weight of approximately 300, an empirical formula $C_{11}H_{17}N_3O_8$, and the possibility of its being a tertiary amine have been suggested (184).

Injections into mice are followed by hind-limb weakness and clonic convulsions especially of the respiratory muscles; later the limbs show flaccid paralysis. In some cases convulsions were not produced; there was gradual paralysis of the animal until respiration ceased.

In cats, the response to indirect stimulation of the tibialis anticus muscle rapidly failed after injection of the toxin; at this stage the muscle responded to intra-arterial acetylcholine and to direct stimulation. In experiments on isolated nerves Kao and Fuhrman (184) showed that transmission along autonomic and somatic motor nerves was blocked by the toxin; this blockade was reversible if the toxin was washed away. These authors reject the possibility that one part of the neuromuscular block might be due to a reduction in acetylcholine release at the nerve ending; this rejection seems to be somewhat premature, since their published evidence leaves the point open. Sensory nerves are reversibly blocked by the toxin as demonstrated by the induction of corneal anesthesia in the rabbit eye.

Of rather more interest in view of its extreme potency and strange origin is kokoi toxin. This material, which has been purified to a high degree, is, with the exception of botulinus, tetanus, and Kugu fish, the most potent of known toxins. It has an m.l.d. for the mouse of 0.03–0.05 μg and is believed to be an alkaloid, although detailed information on its chemical composition is sparse.

The toxin is present in the skin of the Colombian frog, *Phyllohates bicolor,* and is used as a blow-pipe arrow poison by the Choco Indians of Western Colombia. Märki and Witkop (223) obtained from the skins of 330 of the frogs (which weigh just over 1 gm each) 910 mg of crude extract which, over 3–5 purification stages, reduced to about 3 mg and increased 60-fold in specific toxicity.

Tested *in vitro* on the rat diaphragm kokoi toxin caused a gradual increase in resting tension which continued to increase after neuromuscular transmission ceased. For sometime after the failure of neuromuscular transmission the muscle continued to respond to direct stimulation, but even this rapidly declined and ceased within 10 minutes after toxin was first added to 0.03 μg/ml concentration. These changes were irreversible.

Other experiments using the isolated sciatic nerve–gastrocnemius preparations of *Bufo marinus* showed that the action potential of nerve was unaffected by the toxin and at a time when neuromuscular transmission had ceased. Given intravenously to mice powerful tonic convulsions were produced; at high dose levels death, accompanied by complete muscular rigidity, occurred in a few seconds. It seems to be quite clear that the toxin has both central and peripheral neurotoxic effects combined with, at a certain stage, more generalized effects upon membranes.

J. Reptilia

1. *Snakes*

Knowledge of snake venoms is limited mainly to those species venomous to man and covers therefore only a limited number of animals in the Order Serpentes. A further restriction is that, of these, only some contain a neurotoxic component. The Order can be divided into thirteen families (for classification see 294) of which only five—which do, however, contain the majority of snakes—are of interest. These are the Colubridae, Elapidae (cobras, mambas, kraits), Hydrophidae (sea snakes), Viperidae (vipers and adders), and Crotalidae (pit vipers: moccasins, rattlers). Each of these families has species whose venom contains neurotoxin, but the Elapidae and Hydrophidae are the most important in this respect (294, 338, 229a).

A primary source for the suggestion of neurotoxic activity comes in clinical reports: respiratory difficulty, muscular weakness, and paralysis is commonly mentioned (68, 163, 187, 268). Detailed analysis of these effects and experimental studies using whole or, preferably, fractionated venom are relatively uncommon. This has had the result that in many cases we are still not quite certain that a true neurotoxin is involved and whether the action is central, peripheral, or both. Apart from neurotoxins seven other major types of active molecule may occur in venoms (294). Their activities are (*a*) hemolytic, (*b*) anticoagulant, (*c*) hemorrhagic, (*d*) thrombus forming, (*e*) cytolytic, (*f*) antibacterial, and (*g*) digestive. Mixtures of three or four are common, and these can give rise to tremendous molecular complexity. For example immunological analysis of the venom of *Vipera palestinae* gave evidence for 26 antigens (192), and one cannot assume that all components are necessarily antigenic or even toxic (155, 243, 266, 344).

The venom of Elapid snakes commonly contains neurotoxic, hemolytic, and anticoagulant activity (22, 50, 77, 78, 149, 153, 156, 266, 308). Medullary-pontine respiratory centers are often suggested as the site of action (149, 153). Apart from the question of peripheral and other central sites there is always the possibility that hemorrhage for example can lead to hypoxic or pressure damage of central neurons to give an effect which would be wrongly classified as a neurotoxic damage. These effects can be differentiated: for example, in one case (153) 3–30 LD_{50} doses of venom were given to produce rapid death in experimental animals with manifestations of only neurotoxic activity and before any hemorrhagic or other histological change occurred.

Considerable evidence is accumulating for an effect at the neuromuscular junction (72, 77, 78, 187, 188, 229, 230, 240, 241, 261, 308). Using the rat diaphragm preparation with Formosan cobra venom (*Naja naja atra*) or Krait venom (*Bungarus multicinctus*), Su (308) showed that at a concentration of about 0.3 μg/ml the response to nervous stimulation was blocked, yet much higher doses (10 μg/ml) or long periods of treatment were required to abolish the response to direct stimulation; 500 μg/ml did not block conduction in the phrenic nerve. These and other results (77, 78, 261) demonstrated that what was apparently a curare-like block was not reversed by neostigmine, and KCl tended to increase the blockade. The depolarizing action of acetylcholine in the diaphragm and the frog rectus abdominus is prevented, and in the latter preparation some protection against the venom was given by dimethyltubocurarine. Su claims also that there may be a reduction in acetylcholine output.

A recent paper by Chang and Lee (78a) has clarified a number of contradictory findings. Venom of *B. multicinctus* was separated electrophoretically, and four components separated, all migrating toward the cathode. Fraction I was a cholinesterase and probably nontoxic, while F II, F III, and F IV all had neurotoxic activity. Fraction II had an irreversible postsynaptic, curare-like effect but did not reduce transmitter release. Fractions III and IV however, both acted presynaptically, causing a reduction in the release of acetylcholine. Thus the findings reported above by Su are no longer contradictory, but relate to different, specific components of the venom, with an effect at separate sites and with a distinct time course of action.

Venom from *Walterinnesia aegyptea* has also been investigated; a definite presynaptic effect upon *Bufo* (toad) neuromuscular preparations has been demonstrated, but the authors claim that the motor end plates remain sensitive to transmitter (240, 241). Meldrum (229, 230), using starch-gel fractions of cobra (*N. naja*) venom, has analyzed the peripheral effect of the neurotoxic component using frog sartorius and rat diaphragm preparations. A decline and eventual disappearance of miniature end plate and end plate potentials followed treatment by the toxin; subsequently there was a marked reduction in membrane potential. Such an effect upon the membrane would explain the insensitivity to applied acetylcholine and the ineffectiveness of both anticholinesterase and KCl. The neurotoxic component is not associated specifically with phospholipase A and can be completely separated from it.

Venom from many of the Hydrophidae is neurotoxic (71, 72, 277). Barme (27) has given figures for the toxicity of the venom of several species which suggests that it is in general somewhat greater than that of most land snakes (see also 242, 345). On the isolated rat diaphragm preparation and also by *in vivo* experiments Carey and Wright (72, 73) have shown that the toxin of *Enhydrina schistosa* irreversibly paralyzes the neuromuscular junction, an effect which is not antagonized by anticholinesterase. The response to close injections of acetylcholine disappears and with large doses of toxin the muscle ceases to respond to direct stimulation. These effects seem to be very similar to those mentioned earlier and may suggest a common basis of action of many venoms. Experiments to test for a central neurotoxic effect (72) showed that the medulla was not an important site of action.

Although it has been usually assumed that the toxin has a similar action in man (276, 277), Reid has recently suggested that in humans the venom is mainly myotoxic rather than neurotoxic (278, 279). The respiratory effects are due to skeletal muscle damage or other indirect events (inhaling vomit, infection), and a contributory cause of death may be hyperkalemia and acute renal failure associated with myohemoglobinuria. Such wide differences in activity are not common, although Schmidt and Inger (294, p. 216) mention that the venom of the snakes of genus *Fordonia* is extremely active on crabs but has little effect upon frogs and mammals.

Few viper venoms are neurotoxic. Mole vipers (genus *Atractaspis*), adders (genus *Bitis*), and the genus *Echis* are believed to have a potent neurotoxin (82, 83, 151, 294), although some doubt has been raised in the case of *Echis* species (152), and the sites of action have not been very adequately explored.

Of the Crotalidae, moccasin venoms are believed to be effective at the neuromuscular junction (165, 283) and upon the respiratory centers (58, 165). After large doses which caused rapid death the diaphragm responded to phrenic nerve stimulation, and presumably the venom may act rather more slowly at the peripheral site. In *Bothrops* species the blood effects are predominant and there may not be a neurotoxin present. Rattlesnake venom possesses potent hemorrhagic, cytolytic, and neurotoxic components. Crotoxin, a protein which is separable into at least two fragments, is still incompletely understood. Curare-like and anticonvulsive effects (244) as well as a possible further neurotoxic fraction are probably present, and although this material was one of the first to be isolated in a relatively pure state its activity and constitution is still undetermined (134, 244, 303).

2. *Lizards*

The Gila monster (*Heloderma suspectum*) and the beaded lizard (*Heloderma horridum*) are the only two venomous lizards. Specific evidence of a neurotoxic effect is not available, but Tinkham (313) considers that it is neurotoxic and myelo- or cytotoxic.

K. Mammalia

The salivary glands of the short-tailed shrew, *Blarina brevicauda,* contain pharmacologically active agents, although there has not been unequivocal demonstration that these are neurotoxic. Injection of extracts of the gland causes a cessation of respiration, partial motor paralysis, and convulsions. As little as 30 mg of gland/mouse could be lethal (197, 257).

References

1. Abbott, B. C., and Ballantine, D., The toxin from *Gymnodinium veneficum* Ballantyne. *J. Marine Biol. Assoc. U.K.* **36**, 169 (1957).
2. Abel, J. J., On poisons and disease and some experiments with toxin of *Bacillus tetani*. *Science* **79**, 121 (1934).
3. Abel, J. J., Evans, E. A., Hampil, B., and Lee, F. C., Researches on tetanus. II The toxin of *Bacillus tetani* is not transported to the central nervous system by any component of the peripheral nerve trunks. *Bull. Johns Hopkins Hosp.* **56**, 84 (1935).
4. Abel, J. J., Firor, W. M., and Chalian, W., Researches on tetanus. IX Further evidence to show that the tetanus toxin is not carried to the central neurones by way of the axis cylinders of the motor nerves. *Bull. Johns Hopkins Hosp.* **63**, 373 (1938).
5. Abel, J. J., Hampil, B., and Jonas, A. F. J., Researches on tetanus. III Further experiments to prove that tetanus toxin is not carried in peripheral nerves to the central nervous system. *Bull. Johns Hopkins Hosp.* **56**, 317 (1935).
6. Abrams, A., Kegeles, G., and Hottle, G. A., The purification of toxin from *Clostridium botulinum* type A. *J. Biol. Chem.* **164**, 63 (1946).
7. Acheson, G. H., Ratnoff, O. D., and Schoenbach, E. B., The localized action on the spinal cord of intramuscularly injected tetanus toxin. *J. Exptl. Med.* **75**, 465 (1942).
8. Ager, E. A., and Dolman, C. E., Type E Botulism: Report of an outbreak in Washington. *J. Am. Med. Assoc.* **187**, 538 (1964).
9. Ambache, N., Peripheral action of botulinum toxin. *Nature* **161**, 482 (1948).
10. Ambache, N., The peripheral action of *Cl. botulinum* toxin. *J. Physiol.* (*London*) **108**, 127 (1949).
11. Ambache, N., Unmasking, after cholinergic paralysis by botulinum toxin, of a reversed action of nicotine on the mammalian intestine, revealing the probable presence of local inhibitory ganglion cells in the enteric plexus. *Brit. J. Pharmacol.* **6**, 51 (1951).
12. Ambache, N., A further survey of the action of *Cl. botulinum* toxin upon different types of autonomic nerve fibre. *J. Physiol.* (*London*) **113**, 1 (1951).
13. Ambache, N., Effect of botulinum toxin upon the superior cervical ganglion. *J. Physiol.* (*London*) **116**, 9P (1952).
14. Ambache, N., Autonomic ganglionic stimulants. *Arch. Intern. Pharmacodyn.* **97**, 427 (1954).
15. Ambache, N., The action of "Darmstöff" on the rabbit ileum. *J. Physiol.* (*London*) **125**, 38P (1954).
16. Ambache, N., and Ferreira, H. M., Paralysis of the discharge in *Electrophorus electricus* produced by botulinum toxin. *Dos Anais Acad. Brasil. Cienc.* **24**, 225 (1952).
17. Ambache, N., and Lessin, A. W., Classification of intestinomotor drugs by means of type D botulinum toxin. *J. Physiol.* (*London*) **127**, 449 (1955).
18. Ambache, N., and Lippold, O. C. J., Bradycardia of central origin produced by injections of tetanus toxin into the vagus nerve. *J. Physiol.* (*London*) **108**, 186 (1949).
19. Ambache, N., Morgan, R. S., and Wright, G. P., The action of tetanus toxin on the acetylcholine and cholinesterase contents of the rabbit's iris. *Brit. J. Exptl. Pathol.* **29**, 408 (1948).

20. Ambache, N., Morgan, R. S., and Wright, G. P., The action of tetanus toxin on the rabbit's iris. *J. Physiol.* (*London*) **107**, 45 (1948).
21. Anellis, A., and Koch, R. B., Comparative resistance of strains of *Cl. botulinum* to gamma rays. *Appl. Microbiol.* **10**, 326 (1962).
22. Aravindakshan, I., and Braganca, B. M., Preferential inhibition of phosphorylation in different parts of the respiratory chain in mitochondria obtained from animals injected with cobra venom. *Biochem. J.* **79**, 80 (1961).
23. Arthur, D. R., "Ticks and Disease." Macmillan (Pergamon), New York, 1962.
24. Asano, M., and Itoh, M., Salivary poison of a marine gastropod, *Neptunea arthritica* Bernardi, and the seasonal variation of its toxicity. *Ann. N.Y. Acad. Sci.* **90**, 674 (1960).
25. Atkins, J. A., Wingo, C. W., Sodeman, W. A., and Flynn, J. E., Necrotic arachnidism. *Am. J. Trop. Med. Hyg.* **7**, 165 (1958).
26. Banner, A. H., Scheuer, P. J., Sasaki, S., Helfrich, P., and Alender, C. B., Observations on ciguatera-type toxin in fish. *Ann. N.Y. Acad. Sci.* **90**, 770 (1960).
27. Barme, M., Venomous sea snakes of Viet Nam and their venoms. *In* "Venomous and Poisonous Animals and Noxious Plants of the Pacific Region" (H. L. Keegan and W. V. Macfarlane, eds.), p. 373. Macmillan (Pergamon), New York, 1963.
28. Barnes, J. H., Observations on jellyfish stingings in North Queensland. *Med. J. Australia* **2**, 993 (1960).
29. Barron, A. L., and Reed, G. B., *Clostridium botulinum* type E toxin and toxoid. *Can. J. Microbiol.* **1**, 108 (1954).
30. Baylis, J. H., Mackintosh, J., Morgan, R. S., and Wright, G. P., The effect of sclerosis of the nerve trunk on the ascent of tetanus toxin in the sciatic nerve of rabbits and on the development of local tetanus. *J. Pathol. Bacteriol.* **64**, 33 (1952).
31. Baylis, J. H., Joseph, J., Mackintosh, J., Morgan, R. S., and Wright, G. P., The effect of transection on the ascent of tetanus toxin in the rabbit's spinal cord. *J. Pathol. Bacteriol.* **64**, 47 (1952).
32. Beard, R. L., The toxicology of *Habrobracon* venom: a study of a natural insecticide. *Conn. Univ. Storrs Agr. Exptl. Sta. Bull.* **562** (1952).
33. Beard, R. L., The nature of certain arthropod venoms and their effects on insect physiology. *Verhandl. 11th Intern. Kongr. Entomol., Vienna, 1960* Band III, Symp. 3 (1960).
34. Beard, R. L., Insect toxins and venoms. *Ann. Rev. Entomol.* **8**, 1 (1963).
35. Bergmann, F., Parnas, I., and Reich, K., Pharmacological effects of the Ichthyotoxin of the Phytoflagellate *Prymnesium parvum*. *Biochem. Pharmacol.* **12**, Suppl., 126 (1963).
36. Bergmann, F., Parnas, I., and Reich, K., Observations on the mechanism of action and on the quantitative assay of ichthyotoxin from *Prymnesium parvum* Carter. *Toxicol. Appl. Pharmacol.* **5**, 637 (1963).
37. Bishop, G. H., and Bronfenbrenner, J. J., The site of action of botulinus toxin. *Am. J. Physiol.* **117**, 393 (1936).
38. Björklund, B., and Berengo, A., Studies on the antigenic composition of some *Clostridia* toxins with the aid of gel diffusion. *Acta Pathol. Microbiol. Scand.* **34**, 79 (1954).
39. Blattner, R. J., The mechanism of Tick Paralysis. *J. Pediat.* **56**, 698 (1960).
40. Bogen, E., The treatment of spider bite poisoning. *Publ. Am. Assoc. Advan. Sci.* **44**, 101 (1956).

41. Bolton, B. L., Bergner, A. D., O'Neill, J. J., and Wagley, P. F., Effect of a shellfish poison on end-plate potentials. *Bull. Johns Hopkins Hosp.* **105,** 233 (1959).
42. Bonventre, P. F., and Kempe, L. L., The physiology of toxin production by *Cl. botulinum* types A & B. II Effect of carbohydrate source on growth, autolysis and toxin production. *Appl. Microbiol.* **7,** 372 (1959).
43. Bonventre, P. F., and Kempe, L. L., Toxicity enhancement of *Cl. botulinum* type A and B culture filtrates by proteolytic enzymes. *J. Bacteriol.* **78,** 892 (1959).
44. Bonventre, P. F., and Kempe, L. L., Physiology of toxin production by *Cl. botulinum* types A and B. IV Activation of the toxin. *J. Bacteriol.* **79,** 24 (1960).
45. Bonventre, P. F., and Kempe, L. L., Physiology of toxin production by *Cl. botulinum* types A and B. I Growth, autolysis, and toxin production. *J. Bacteriol.* **79,** 18 (1960).
46. Boroff, D. A., Study of toxins of *Cl. botulinum.* III Relation of autolysis to toxin production. *J. Bacteriol.* **70,** 363 (1955).
47. Boroff, D. A., Raynaud, M., and Prévot, A. R., Studies of toxin of *Cl. botulinum* type D. *J. Immunol.* **68,** 503 (1952).
48. Bouisset, L., Breuillard, J., and Grizou, V., Growth and toxigenesis of *Cl. botulinum* A. *Compt. Rend. Soc. Biol.* **151,** 387 (1957).
49. Bowers, L. E., and Williams, O. B., Effect of arginine on growth and lysis of *Cl. botulinum. J. Bacteriol.* **85,** 1175 (1963).
50. Braganca, B. M., Neurochemical effects of snake venoms. *In* "Neurochemistry" (K. A. C. Elliott, I. H. Page, and J. H. Quastel, eds.), p. 840. Thomas, Springfield, Illinois, 1955.
51. Bronfenbrenner, J., and Schlesinger, M. J., The composite nature of botulinus toxin. *Proc. Soc. Exptl. Biol. Med.* **18,** 254 (1920–1921).
52. Bronfenbrenner, J., and Schlesinger, M. J., Further studies on the nature of botulinus toxin. *Proc. Soc. Exptl. Biol. Med.* **19,** 1 (1921–1922).
53. Bronfenbrenner, J., and Schlesinger, M. J., The state of aggregation of particles of botulinus toxin. *Proc. Soc. Exptl. Biol. Med.* **19,** 297 (1921–1922).
54. Brooks, V. B., The action of botulinum toxin on motor-nerve filaments. *J. Physiol. (London)* **123,** 501 (1954).
55. Brooks, V. B., An intracellular study of the action of repetitive nerve volleys and of botulinum toxin on miniature end-plate potentials. *J. Physiol. (London)* **134,** 264 (1956).
56. Brooks, V. B., Curtis, D. R., and Eccles, J. C., The action of tetanus toxin on the inhibition of motoneurones. *J. Physiol. (London)* **135,** 655 (1957).
57. Brown, M. S., and Mosher, H. S., Tarichatoxin: isolation and purification. *Science* **140,** 295 (1963).
58. Brown, R. V., The effects of water moccasin venom on dogs. *Am. J. Physiol.* **134,** 202 (1941).
59. Bücherl, W., Studies on dried venom of *Phoneutria fera* Perty, 1833. *Publ. Am. Assoc. Advan. Sci.* **44,** 95 (1956).
60. Buckley, E. E., and Porges, N., eds., Venoms. *Publ. Am. Assoc. Advan. Sci.* **44** (1956).
61. Bulatova, T. I., and Kabanova, Ye. A., Identification of the botulism pathogen with luminescent sera. *J. Microbiol. Epidemiol. Immunobiol. (USSR) (Engl. Transl.)* **31,** 403 (1960).

62. Burgen, A. S. V., Dickens, F., and Zatman, L. J., The action of botulinum toxin on the neuromuscular junction. *J. Physiol. (London)* **109,** 10 (1949).
63. Burke, J. M., Marchisotto, J., McLaughlin, J. J. A., and Provasoli, L., Analysis of the toxin produced by *Gonyaulax catenella* in axenic culture. *Ann. N.Y. Acad. Sci.* **90,** 837 (1960).
64. Burn, J. H., and Rand, M. J., Sympathetic post-ganglionic mechanism. *Nature* **184,** 163 (1959).
65. Burn, J. H., and Rand, M. J., Sympathetic post-ganglionic cholinergic fibres. *Brit. J. Pharmacol.* **15,** 56 (1960).
66. Cammack, K. A., The significance of a second macromolecular component observed in preparations of *Cl. botulinum* type A toxin. *Biochem. J.* **67,** 30P (1957).
67. Cammack, K. A., Physico-chemical studies on the toxin from *Cl. botulinum* type A. Ph.D. Thesis, Univ. of London, London, 1960.
68. Campbell, C. H., and Young, L. N., The symptomatology, clinical course and successful treatment of Papuan elapine snake envenomation. *Med. J. Australia* **1,** 478 (1961).
69. Cardella, M. A., Duff, J. T., Gottfried, C., and Begel, J. S., Immunity to toxins of *Cl. botulinum.* IV Production and purification of type C toxin for conversion to toxoid. *J. Bacteriol.* **75,** 360 (1958).
70. Cardella, M. A., Duff, J. T., Wingfield, B. H., and Gottfried, C., Immunity to toxins of *Cl. botulinum.* VI Purification and detoxification of type D toxin and the immunological response to toxoid. *J. Bacteriol.* **79,** 372 (1960).
71. Carey, J. E., and Wright, E. A., The toxicity and immunological properties of some sea-snake venoms with particular reference to that of *Enhydrina schistosa. Trans. Roy. Soc., Trop. Med. Hyg.* **54,** 50 (1960).
72. Carey, J. E., and Wright, E. A., The site of action of the venom of the sea snake *Enhydrina schistosa. Trans. Roy. Soc. Trop. Med. Hyg.* **55,** 153 (1961).
73. Carey, J. E., and Wright, E. A., Studies on the fractions of the venom of the sea snake *Enhydrina schistosa. Australian J. Exptl. Biol. Med. Sci.* **40,** 427 (1962).
74. Carlisle, D. B., On the venom of the lesser weeverfish, *Trachinus vipera. J. Marine Biol. Assoc. U.K.* **42,** 155 (1962).
75. Carrea, R., and Lanari, A., Chronic effect of tetanus toxin applied locally to the cerebral cortex of the dog. *Science* **137,** 342 (1962).
76. Cavanagh, J. B., Howard, J. G., and Whitby, J. L., The neurotoxin of *Shigella shiga.* A comparative study of the effects produced in various laboratory animals. *Brit. J. Exptl. Pathol.* **37,** 272 (1956).
77. Chang, C. C., Studies on the mechanism of curare-like action of *Bungarus multicinctus* venom. I Effect on the phrenic nerve diaphragm preparation of the rat. *T'ai-wan I Hsueh Hui Tsa Chih* **59,** 315 (1960).
78. Chang, C. C., Studies on the mechanism of curare-like action of *Bungarus multicinctus* venom II Effect on response of rectus abdominis muscle of the frog to acetylcholine. *T'ai-wan I Hsueh Hui Tsa* **59,** 416 (1960).
78a. Chang, C. C., and Lee, C. Y., Isolation of neurotoxins from the venom of *Bungarus multicinctus* and their modes of neuromuscular blocking action. *Arch. Intern. Pharmacodyn.* **144,** 241 (1963).
79. Chertkova, F. A., Grodko, N. S., Ushakova, A. A., Denisova, I. A., Kats, F. M., and Dudarenko, G. V., Standard *Cl. botulinum* type E antiserum. *J. Microbiol. Epidemiol. Immunobiol. (USSR) (Engl. Transl.)* **31,** 682 (1960).

80. Clausen, C. P., "Entomophagous Insects," p. 688. McGraw-Hill, New York, 1940.
81. Coleman, I. W., Studies on the oral toxicity of *Cl. botulinum* toxin type A. *Can. J. Biochem. Physiol.* **32,** 27 (1954).
82. Corkill, N. L., Snake poisoning in the Sudan. *Publ. Am. Assoc. Advan. Sci.* **44,** 331 (1956).
83. Corkill, N. L., Ionides, C. J. P., and Pitman, C. R. S., Biting and poisoning by the mole vipers of the genus *Atractaspis. Trans. Roy. Soc. Trop. Med. Hyg.* **53,** 95 (1959).
84. Cornman, I., Toxic properties of the saliva of *Cassis. Nature* **200,** 88 (1963).
85. Costilow, R. N., Fermentative activities of control and radiation-"killed" spores of *Cl. botulinum. J. Bacteriol.* **84,** 1268 (1962).
86. Courtois-Suffit, M., and Giroux, R., "The Abnormal Forms of Tetanus" (transl. by D. Bruce and F. Golla), 249 pp. Oxford Univ. Press (Univ. London), London and New York, 1918.
87. Courville, D. A., Halstead, B. W., and Hessel, D. W., Marine Biotoxins: isolation and properties. *Chem. Rev.* **58,** 235 (1958).
88. Crescitelli, F., and Geissman, T. A., Invertebrate Pharmacology: selected topics. *Ann. Rev. Pharmacol.* **2,** 143 (1962).
89. Curtis, D. R., Pharmacological investigations upon inhibition of spinal neurones. *J. Physiol.* (*London*) **145,** 175 (1959).
90. Dack, G. M., and Hoskins, D., Absorption of botulinum toxin from the colon of *Macaca mulatta. J. Infect. Diseases* **71,** 260 (1942).
91. Davies, J. R., Morgan, R. S., Wright, E. A., and Wright, G. P., The results of direct injections of botulinum toxin into the central nervous system of rabbits. *J. Physiol.* (*London*) **120,** 618 (1953).
92. Davies, J. R., Morgan, R. S., Wright, E. A., and Wright, G. P., The effect of local tetanus intoxication on the hind limb reflexes of the rabbit. *Arch. Intern. Physiol.* **62,** 248 (1954).
93. Davies, J. R., Morgan, R. S., and Wright, E. A., The susceptibility of pigeons to tetanus toxin. *J. Pathol. Bacteriol.* **69,** 295 (1955).
94. Davies, J. R., and Wright, E. A., The specific precocious protective action of tetanus toxoid. *Brit. J. Exptl. Pathol.* **36,** 487 (1955).
95. del Pozo, E. C., Mechanism of Pharmacological Actions of Scorpion Venoms. *Publ. Am. Assoc. Advan. Sci.* **44,** 123 (1956).
96. del Magelhaes, O., Scorpionism. *J. Trop. Med. Hyg.* **41,** 393 (1938).
97. Denny, C. B., Bohrer, C. W., Perkins, W. E., and Townsend, C. T., Destruction of *Cl. botulinum* by ionizing radiation. I. In neutral phosphate at room and freezing temperatures. *Food Res.* **24,** 44 (1959).
98. Dickson, E. C., Botulism. A clinical and experimental study. *Monograph Rockefeller Inst. Med. Res.* **8** (1918).
99. Dickson, E. C., and Shevky, E., Botulism. Studies on the manner in which the toxin of *Cl. botulinum* acts upon the body. I. The effect upon the autonomic nervous system. *J. Exptl. Med.* **38,** 711 (1923).
100. Dickson, E. C., and Shevky, E., Botulism. Studies on the manner in which the toxin of *Cl. botulinum* acts upon the body. II. The effect on the voluntary nervous system. *J. Exptl. Med.* **38,** 327 (1923).
101. Diniz, C. R., and Goncalves, J. M., Some chemical and pharmacological properties of brazilian scorpion venoms. *Publ. Am. Assoc. Advan. Sci.* **44,** 131 (1956).

102. Dolman, C. E., Additional botulism episodes in Canada. *Can. Med. Assoc. J.* **71**, 245 (1954).
103. Dolman, C. E., Recent observations on type E botulism. *Can. J. Public Health* **48**, 187 (1957).
104. Dolman, C. E., Type E (Fish-borne) Botulism: a review. *Jap. J. Med. Sci. Biol.* **10**, 383 (1957).
105. Dolman, C. E., Type E botulism: a hazard of the north. *Arctic* **13**, 230 (1960).
106. Dolman, C. E., Further outbreaks of botulism in Canada. *Can. Med. Assoc. J.* **84**, 191 (1961).
107. Dolman, C. E., Chang, H., Kerr, D. E., and Shearer, A. R., Fish-borne and type E botulism: two cases due to home-pickled herring. *Can. J. Public Health* **41**, 215 (1950).
108. Dolman, C. E., Darby, G. E., and Lane, R. F., Type E botulism due to salmon eggs. *Can. J. Public Health* **46**, 135 (1955).
109. Dolman, C. E., and Murakami, L., *Clostridium botulinum* type F with recent observations of other types. *J. Infect. Diseases* **109**, 107 (1961).
110. Dolman, C. E., Tomsich, M., Campbell, C. C. R., and Laing, W. B., Fish eggs as a cause of human botulism. Two outbreaks in British Columbia due to types E and B botulinus toxins. *J. Infect. Diseases* **106**, 5 (1960).
111. Duff, J. T., Wright, G. G., Klerer, J., Moore, D. E., and Bibler, R. H., Studies on immunity to toxins of *Cl. botulinum.* I A simplified procedure for isolation of type A toxin. *J. Bacteriol.* **73**, 42 (1957).
112. Duff, J. T., Klerer, J., Bibler, R. H., Moore, D. E., Gottfried, C., and Wright, G. G., Studies on immunity to toxins of *Cl. botulinum.* II Production and purification of type B toxin for toxoid. *J. Bacteriol.* **73**, 597 (1957).
113. Duff, J. T., Wright, G. G., and Yarinsky, A., Activation of *Cl. botulinum* Type E toxin by trypsin. *J. Bacteriol.* **72**, 455 (1956).
114. Eadie, G. A., Molner, J. G., Solomon, R. J., and Aach, R. D., Type E botulism: report of an outbreak in Michigan. *J. Am. Med. Assoc.* **187**, 496 (1964).
115. Eastman, P. F., and Nesbit, R. M., Studies of urinary retention during tetanus. *J. Urol.* **48**, 219 (1942).
116. Eccles, J. C., "The Physiology of Synapses." Springer, Berlin, 1964.
117. Edmunds, C. W., and Keiper, G. F., Further studies of the action of botulinus toxin. *J. Am. Med. Assoc.* **83**, 495 (1924).
118. Edmunds, C. W., and Long, P. H., Contribution to the pathologic physiology of Botulism. *J. Am. Med. Assoc.* **81**, 542 (1923).
119. Emmelin, N., Supersensitivity of salivary gland caused by botulinum toxin. *J. Physiol.* (*London*) **156**, 121 (1961).
120. Emmons, P., and McLennan, H., Failure of acetylcholine release in tick paralysis. *Nature* **183**, 474 (1959).
121. Emmons, P., and McLennan, H., Some observations on tick paralysis in marmots. *J. Exptl. Biol.* **37**, 355 (1960).
122. Endean, R., The venomous sea-urchin *Toxopneustes pileolus. Med. J. Australia* **1**, 320 (1961).
122a. Endean, R., Marine toxins. *Sci. J.* **2**, 57–63 (1966).
123. Endean, R., and Rudkin, C., Studies on the venoms of some *Conidae. Toxicon* **1**, 49 (1963).
124. Esplin, D. W., Philip, C. B., and Hughes, L. E., Impairment of muscle stretch reflexes in tick paralysis. *Science* **132**, 958 (1960).

125. Essex, H. E., Certain animal venoms and their physiologic action. *Physiol. Rev.* **25**, 148 (1945).
126. Evans, H. E., Predatory wasps. *Sci. Am.* **208** (4), 145 (1963).
127. Farber, L., and Lerke, P., Studies on the toxicity of *Rhodactis howesii* (mata malu). *In* "Venomous and Poisonous Animals and Noxious Plants of the Pacific Region" (H. L. Keegan and W. V. MacFarlane, eds.), p. 67. Macmillan (Pergamon), New York, 1963.
128. Fedinec, A., Studies on the mode of spread of tetanus toxin in experimental animals. *Biochem. Pharmacol.* **12**, Suppl., 230 (1963).
129. Feigen, G. A., Peterson, N. S., Hofman, W. W., Genther, G. H., and van Heyningen, W. E., The effect of impure tetanus toxin on the frequency of miniature end-plate potentials. *J. Gen. Microbiol.* **33**, 489 (1963).
130. Fiock, M. A., Yarinsky, A., and Duff, J. T., Studies on immunity to toxins of *Cl. botulinum*. VII Purification and detoxification of trypsin-activated Type E toxin. *J. Bacteriol.* **82**, 66 (1961).
131. Firor, W. M., Lamont, A., and Schumacker, H. B., Studies on the cause of death in tetanus. *Ann. Surg.* **111**, 246 (1940).
132. Fleisher, J. H., Killos, P. J., and Harrison, C. S., Effects of Puffer Poison on neuromuscular transmission. *Federation Proc.* **19**, 264 (1960).
133. Fleisher, J. H., Killos, P. J., and Harrison, C. S., Effects of Puffer Poison on neuromuscular transmission. *J. Pharmacol. Exptl. Therap.* **133**, 98 (1961).
134. Fraenkel-Conrat, H., and Singer, B., Fractionation and composition of crotoxin. *Arch. Biochem. Biophys.* **60**, 64 (1956).
135. Freeman, N. L., Phagocytosis of staphylococci by mouse leucocytes in the presence of botulinal toxin. *J. Bacteriol.* **81**, 156 (1961).
136. Friedemann, U., Blood-brain barrier. *Physiol. Rev.* **22**, 125 (1942).
137. Friedemann, U., Dynamics and mechanism of immunity reactions *in vivo*. *Bacteriol. Rev.* **11**, 275 (1947).
138. Friedemann, U., Hollander, A., and Tarlov, I. M., Investigations on the pathogenesis of tetanus. *J. Immunol.* **40**, 325 (1941).
139. Friedemann, U., Zuger, B., and Hollander, A., Investigations on the pathogenesis of tetanus. I The permeability of the C.N.S. barrier to tetanal toxin. Passive immunity against toxin introduced by various routes. *J. Immunol.* **36**, 473 (1939).
140. Friedemann, U., Zuger, B., and Hollander, A., Investigations into the pathogenesis of tetanus. II The influence of section of the nerve on the neutralisation of intramuscularly injected tetanal toxin by circulating antitoxin. *J. Immunol.* **36**, 485 (1939).
141. Friess, S. L., and Durant, R. C., Protective interactions of physostigmine and holothurin A at the mammalian neuromuscular junction. *Biochem. Pharmacol.* **12**, Suppl., 166 (1963).
142. Friess, S. L., Standaert, F. G., Whitcomb, E. R., Nigrelli, R. F., Chanley, J. D., and Sobotka, H., Some pharmacologic properties of holothurin, an active neurotoxin from the sea cucumber. *J. Pharmacol. Exptl. Therap.* **126**, 323 (1959).
143. Friess, S. L., Standaert, F. G., Whitcomb, E. R., Nigrelli, R. F., Chanley, J. D., and Sobotka, H., Some pharmacologic properties of holothurin A, a glycosidic mixture from the sea cucumber. *Ann. N.Y. Acad. Sci.* **90**, 893 (1960).
144. Fulthorpe, A. J., Adsorption of tetanus toxin by brain tissue. *J. Hyg.* **54**, 315 (1956).

145. Gendon, I. Z., Growth and toxin formation of *Cl. botulinum* type A in cellophane sacs. *J. Microbiol. Epidemiol. Immunobiol.* (*USSR*) (*Engl. Transl.*) **28,** 373 (1957).
146. Gerwing, J., Dolman, C. E., and Arnott, D. A., Purification and activation of *Cl. botulinum* type E toxin. *J. Bacteriol.* **81,** 819 (1961).
147. Gerwing, J., Dolman, C. E., and Arnott, D. A., Activation phenomenon of *Cl. botulinum* type E toxin. *J. Bacteriol.* **84,** 302 (1962).
148. Ghiretti, F., Toxicity of octopus saliva against crustacea. *Ann. N.Y. Acad. Sci.* **90,** 726 (1960).
149. Ghosh, B. N., and Sarkar, N. K., Active principles of snake venoms. *Publ. Am. Assoc. Advan. Sci.* **44,** 189 (1956).
150. Gillespie, J. S., and MacKenna, B. R., The inhibitory action of nicotine on the rabbit colon. *J. Physiol.* (*London*) **152,** 191 (1960).
151. Gitter, S., Kochwa, S., de Vries, A., and Leffkowitz, M., Studies on electrophoretic fractions of *Vipera xanthina palestinae* venom. *Am. J. Trop. Med. Hyg.* **6,** 180 (1957).
152. Gitter, S., Levi, G., Kochwa, S., de Vries, A., Rechnic, J., and Casper, J., Studies on the venom of *Echis colorata. Am. J. Trop. Med. Hyg.* **9,** 391 (1960).
153. Gitter, S., Moroz-Perlmutter, C., Boss, J. H., Livni, E., Rechnic, J., Goldblum, N., and de Vries, A., Studies on the snake venoms of the Near East: *Walterinnesia aegyptia* and *Pseudocerastes fieldii. Am. J. Trop. Med. Hyg.* **11,** 861 (1962).
154. Gordon, M., Fiock, M. A., Yarinsky, A., and Duff, J. T., Studies on immunity to toxins of *Cl. botulinum.* III Preparation, purification and detoxification of type E toxin. *J. Bacteriol.* **74,** 533 (1957).
155. Grasset, E., Brechbuhler, T., Schwartz, D. E., and Pongratz, E., Comparative analysis and electrophoretic fractionations of snake venoms with special reference to *Vipera russelli* and *Vipera aspis* venoms. *Publ. Am. Assoc. Advan. Sci.* **44,** 153 (1956).
156. Gray, H. H., Green Mamba envenomation: case report. *Trans. Roy. Soc. Trop. Med. Hyg.* **56,** 390 (1962).
157. Grecz, N., Anellis, A., and Schneider, M. D., Procedure for cleaning of *Cl. botulinum* spores. *J. Bacteriol.* **84,** 552 (1962).
158. Gregson, J. D., Experiments on oral secretion of the Rocky Mountain Wood Tick, *Dermacentor andersoni,* Stiles (Acarina: Ixodidae). *Can. Entomologist* **89,** 1 (1957).
159. Gregson, J. D., Host susceptibility to paralysis by the tick *Dermacentor andersoni* Stiles (Acarina: Ixodidae). *Can. Entomologist* **90,** 421 (1958).
160. Gromakovskaya, M. M., Effect of tetanus and botulinus toxins on the chronaxie of immune and non-immune rabbits. *Bull. Exptl. Biol. Med.* (*USSR*) (*Engl. Transl.*) **43,** 44 (1957).
161. Gunnison, J. B., Cummings, J. R., and Meyer, K. F., *Cl. botulinum* type E. *Proc. Soc. Exptl. Biol. Med.* **35,** 278 (1936).
162. Guyton, A. C., and MacDonald, M. A., Physiology of Botulinus toxin. *A.M.A. Arch. Neurol. Psychiat.* **57,** 578 (1947).
163. Haast, W. E., and Winer, M. L., Complete and spontaneous recovery from the bite of a Blue Krait snake (*Bungarus caeruleus*). *Am. J. Trop. Med. Hyg.* **4,** 1135 (1955).

164. Habermann, E., Zur Pharmakologie des Melitten. *Arch. Exptl. Pathol. Pharmakol.* **222,** 173 (1954).

165. Hadidian, Z., Proteolytic activity and physiologic and pharmacologic actions of *Agkistrodon piscivorus* venom. *Publ. Am. Assoc. Advan. Sci.* **44,** 205 (1956).

166. Halstead, B. W., Animal phyla known to contain poisonous marine animals. *Publ. Am. Assoc. Advan. Sci.* **44,** 9 (1956).

167. Halstead, B. W., Current status of research on Pacific poisonous fishes and Ichthyosarcotoxism. *Publ. Am. Assoc. Advan. Sci.* **44,** 29 (1956).

168. Halstead, B. W., and Mitchell, L. R., A review of the venomous fishes of the Pacific area. *In* "Venomous and Poisonous Animals and Noxious Plants of the Pacific Region" (H. L. Keegan and W. V. MacFarlane, eds.), p. 173. Macmillan (Pergamon), New York, 1963.

169. Harry, J., Effect of cooling, local anaesthetic compounds and botulinum toxin on the responses of and the acetylcholine output from the electrically transmurally stimulated isolated guinea-pig ileum. *Brit. J. Pharmacol.* **19,** 42 (1962).

170. Harvey, A. M., The peripheral action of tetanus toxin. *J. Physiol.* (*London*) **96,** 348 (1939).

171. Hashimoto, Y., and Okaichi, T., Some chemical properties of Nereistoxin. *Ann. N.Y. Acad. Sci.* **90,** 667 (1960).

172. Heckly, R. J., Hildebrand, G. J., and Lamanna, C., Size of toxic particle passing the intestinal barrier in botulism. *J. Exptl. Med.* **111,** 745 (1960).

173. Herms, W. B., "Medical Entomology," 4th Ed. Macmillan, New York, 1950.

174. Hessel, D. W., Halstead, B. W., and Peckham, N. H., Marine Biotoxins. I Ciguatera poison: some biological and chemical aspects. *Ann. N.Y. Acad. Sci.* **90,** 788 (1960).

175. Hildebrand, G. J., Lamanna, C., and Heckly, R. J., Distribution and particle size of type A botulinum toxin in body fluids of intravenously injected rabbits. *Proc. Soc. Exptl. Biol. Med.* **107,** 284 (1961).

176. Hodgeson, N. B., Bee venom. Its components and their properties. *Bee World* **36,** 217 (1955).

177. Hottle, G. A., and Abrams, A., Detoxification of crystalline botulinum type A toxin. *J. Immunol.* **55,** 183 (1947).

178. Hottle, G. A., Nigg, C., and Lichty, J. A., Studies in botulinum toxoid, types A and B. II Methods for determining antigenicity in animals. *J. Immunol.* **55,** 255 (1947).

179. Höyem, T., and Skulberg, A., Trypsin inhibitors produced by *Clostridium botulinum* cultures. *Nature* **195,** 922 (1962).

180. Hughes, R., and Whaler, B. C., Influence of nerve-ending activity and of drugs on the rate of paralysis of rat diaphragm preparations by *Cl. botulinum* type A toxin. *J. Physiol.* (*London*) **160,** 221 (1962).

181. Hutter, O. F., Effect of denervation on development of local tetanus. *J. Physiol.* (*London*) **112,** 1P (1951).

182. Ingram, M., and Handford, P. M., The influence of moisture and temperature on the destruction of *Cl. botulinum* in acid bread. *J. Appl. Bacteriol.* **20,** 442 (1957).

182a. Ingram, M., and Roberts, T. A., eds., "Botulism, 1966." Chapman & Hall, London, 1967.

183. Ingram, M., and Thornley, M. J., The effect of low temperatures on the inactivation by ionizing radiations of *Cl. botulinum* spores in meat. *J. Appl. Bacteriol.* **24,** 94 (1961).

184. Kao, C. Y., and Fuhrman, F. A., Pharmacological studies on tarichatoxin, a potent neurotoxin. *J. Pharmacol. Exptl. Therap.* **140,** 31 (1963).

185. Keegan, H. L., and Macfarlane, W. V., eds., "Venomous and Poisonous Animals and Noxious Plants of the Pacific Region." Macmillan (Pergamon), New York, 1963.

186. Kegeles, G., The molecular size and shape of Botulinus toxin. *J. Am. Chem. Soc.* **68** (2), 1670 (1946).

187. Kellaway, C. H., Animal poisons. *Ann. Rev. Biochem.* **8,** 541 (1939).

188. Kellaway, C. H., Cherry, R. O., and Williams, F. F., The peripheral action of the Australian snake venoms. 2. The curare-like action in mammals. *Australian J. Exptl. Biol. Med. Sci.* **10,** 181 (1932).

189. Kempe, L. L., and Graikoski, J. T., Gamma-ray sterilization and residual toxicity studies of ground beef inoculated with spores of *Cl. botulinum. Appl. Microbiol.* **10,** 31 (1962).

190. Kindler, S. H., and Mager, J., Nutritional studies with the *Cl. botulinum* group. *J. Gen. Microbiol.* **15,** 386 (1956).

191. Kingston, C. W., and Southcott, R. V., Skin histopathology in fatal jelly fish stinging. *Trans. Roy. Soc. Trop. Med. Hyg.* **54,** 373 (1960).

192. Kochwa, S., Perlmutter, C., Gitter, S., Rechnic, J., and de Vries, A., Studies on *V. palestinae* venom. Fractionation by ion exchange chromatography. *Am. J. Trop. Med. Hyg.* **9,** 374 (1960).

193. Kohn, A. J., Venomous marine snails of the genus *Conus. In* "Venomous and Poisonous Animals and Noxious Plants of the Pacific Region" (H. L. Keegan and W. V. Macfarlane, eds.), p. 83. Macmillan (Pergamon), New York, 1963.

194. Kohn, A. J., Saunders, P. R., and Wiener, S., Preliminary studies on the venom of the marine snail *Conus. Ann. N.Y. Acad. Sci.* **90,** 706 (1960).

195. Kovtunovitch, L. G., A new method of detecting *Cl. botulinum* toxin. *J. Microbiol. Epidemiol. Immunobiol.* (*USSR*) (*Engl. Transl.*) **28,** 1157 (1957).

196. Kravchenko, A. T., and Rezepov, F. F., Preparation of *Cl. botulinum* antisera in cattle. *J. Microbiol. Epidemiol. Immunobiol.* (*USSR*) (*Engl. Transl.*) **30** (4), 79 (1959).

197. Krayer, O., Properties of a toxin from the salivary gland of the shrew, *Blarina brevicauda. J. Pharmacol. Exptl. Therap.* **114,** 127 (1955).

198. Kryzhanovskii, G. N., Central nervous changes in experimental tetanus and the mode of action of tetanus toxin. I Irradiation of the excitation on stimulating the tetanized limb. *Bull. Exptl. Biol. Med.* (*USSR*) (*Engl. Transl.*) **44,** 1456 (1957).

199. Kryzhanovskii, G. N., Functional changes in the central nervous system in tetanus and the mode of action of the tetanus toxin. III The central and peripheral action of the tetanus toxin. *Bull. Exptl. Biol. Med.* (*USSR*) (*Engl. Transl.*) **49,** 34 (1960).

200. Kryzhanovskii, G. N., Pevnitskii, L. A., Grafova, V. N., and Polgar, A. A., Routes of tetanus toxin entrance into the central nervous system and some

problems in the pathogenesis of experimental tetanus. I Experiments on albino rats. *Bull. Exptl. Biol. Med.* (*USSR*) (*Engl. Transl.*) **51,** 298 (1961).

201. Kryzhanovskii, G. N., Pevnitskii, L. A., Grafova, V. N., and Polgar, A. A., Routes of entrance of tetanus toxin into the central nervous system and some problems connected with the pathogenesis of experimental tetanus. II Experiments on mice, guinea pigs, rabbits and cats. *Bull. Exptl. Biol. Med.* (*USSR*) (*Engl. Transl.*) **52,** 894 (1961).

202. Kryzhanovskii, G. N., Pevnitskii, L. A., Grafova, V. N., and Polgar, A. A., Routes of entrance of tetanus toxin into the central nervous system and certain questions in the pathogenesis of experimental tetanus. IV On the pathogenesis of ascending and descending tetanus. *Bull. Exptl. Biol. Med.* (*USSR*) (*Engl. Transl.*) **52,** 1370 (1961).

203. Kryzhanovskii, G. N., Pevnitskii, L. A., Grafova, V. N., and Polgar, A. A., Routes of tetanus toxin entrance into the central nervous system and some problems in the pathogenesis of experimental tetanus. Communication III Experiments on monkeys and dogs. *Bull. Exptl. Biol. Med.* (*USSR*) (*Engl. Transl.*) **52,** 1256 (1962).

204. Lamanna, C., Haemagglutination by Botulinal toxin. *Proc. Soc. Exptl. Biol. Med.* **69,** 332 (1948).

205. Lamanna, C., The most poisonous poison. *Science* **130,** 763 (1959).

206. Lamanna, C., Oral poisoning by bacterial exotoxins exemplified in botulism. *Ann. N.Y. Acad. Sci.* **88,** 1109 (1960).

207. Lamanna, C., Toxicity of bacterial exotoxins by the oral route. *Science* **131,** 1100 (1960).

208. Lamanna, C., Immunological aspects of airborne infection: some general considerations of response to inhalation of toxins. *Bacteriol. Rev.* **25,** 323 (1961).

209. Lamanna, C., and Aragon, P. R., On the nature of the receptors of erythrocytes involved in botulinal haemagglutination. *Bacteriol. Proc.* (*Soc. Am. Bacteriologists*) **56,** 94 (1956).

210. Lamanna, C., and Glassman, H. N., The isolation of type B botulinum toxin. *J. Bacteriol.* **54,** 575 (1947).

211. Lamanna, C., and Lowenthal, J. P., Factors affecting the botulinus haemagglutinating reactions and the relationship between haemagglutinating activity and toxicity of toxin preparations. *Am. J. Hyg.* **54,** 342 (1951).

212. Lamanna, C., and Lowenthal, J. P., The lack of identity between haemagglutinin and the toxin of type A botulinal organism. *J. Bacteriol.* **61,** 751 (1951).

213. Lamanna, C., McElroy, O. E., and Eklund, H. W., Botulinum toxin (type A); including a study of shaking with chloroform as a step in the isolation procedure. *J. Bacteriol.* **52,** 1 (1946).

214. Lamanna, C., McElroy, O. E., and Eklund, H. W., The purification and crystallisation of *Cl. botulinum* type A toxin. *Science* **103,** 613 (1946).

215. Lamanna, C., and Meyers, C. E., Influence of ingested foods on the oral toxicity in mice of crystalline botulinal type A toxin. *J. Bacteriol.* **79,** 406 (1960).

216. Lane, C. E., The toxin of *Physalia* nematocysts. *Ann. N.Y. Acad. Sci.* **90,** 742 (1960).

217. Lane, C. E., *Physalia* Nematocysts and their toxin. *In* "The Biology of Hydra." Univ. of Miami Press, Coral Gables, Florida, 1961.

218. Lane, C. E., and Dodge, E., The toxicity of *Physalia* nematocysts. *Biol. Bull.* **115**, 219 (1958).
219. Laurence, D. R., and Webster, R. A., Pathologic physiology, pharmacology and therapeutics of tetanus. *Clin. Pharmacol. Therap.* **4**, 36 (1963).
220. Lowenthal, J. P., and Lamanna, C., Characterisation of botulinal haemagglutination. *Am. J. Hyg.* **57**, 46 (1953).
221. McKee, M. T., Bell, J. F., and Hoyer, B. H., Culture of *Cl. botulinum* type C with controlled pH. *J. Bacteriol.* **75**, 135 (1958).
222. Magladery, J. W., Teasdall, R. D., Park, A. M., and Languth, H. W., Electrophysiological studies of reflex activity in patients with lesions of the nervous system. I A comparison of spinal motoneurone excitability following afferent nerve volleys in normal persons and patients with upper motor neurone lesions. *Bull. Johns Hopkins Hosp.* **91**, 219 (1952).
223. Märki, F., and Witkop, B., The venom of the Colombian Arrow Poison Frog, *Phyllohates bicolor. Experientia* **19**, 329 (1963).
224. Matheson, F., and Puloka, T., Two fatal cases of poisoning by noxious fish. *J. Trop. Med. Hyg.* **64**, 163 (1961).
225. Mathias, A. P., Ross, D. M., and Schachter, M., The distribution of 5-hydroxytryptamine, tetramethylammonium, homarine and other substances in sea anemones. *J. Physiol. (London)* **151**, 296 (1960).
226. Matzke, H. A., and Fedinec, A. A., The spread of tetanus toxin along the sciatic nerve of the rat. *Anat. Record* **121**, 335 (1955).
227. May, A. J., and Whaler, B. C., The absorption of *Cl. botulinum* type A toxin from the alimentary canal. *J. Physiol. (London)* **132**, 64P (1956).
228. May, A. J., and Whaler, B. C., The absorption of *Cl. botulinum* type A toxin from the alimentary canal. *Brit. J. Exptl. Pathol.* **39**, 307 (1958).
229. Meldrum, B. S., Depolarization of skeletal muscle by a toxin from cobra (*Naja naja*) venom. *J. Physiol. (London)* **168**, 49P (1963).
229a. Meldrum, B. S., The actions of snake venoms on nerve and muscle. The pharmacology of phospholipase A and of polypeptide toxins. *Pharmacol. Rev.* **17**, 393–445 (1965).
230. Meldrum, B. S., The mechanism of paralysis by cobra venom. Ph.D. Thesis, Oxford Univ. Press (Univ. London), London and New York, 1963.
230a. Mellanby, J., and van Heyningen, W. E., The role of ganglioside in the mode of action of tetanus toxin. *Biochem. Pharmacol.* **12** Suppl., 230 (1963).
231. Meyer, E. A., and Lamanna, C., Activity of Type A botulinal toxin and haemagglutinin exposed to proteolytic enzyme. *J. Bacteriol.* **78**, 175 (1959).
232. Miller, D. G., Massive anaphylaxis from insect stings. *Publ. Am. Assoc. Advan. Sci.* **44**, 117 (1956).
233. Mills, A. R., Poisonous fish in the South Pacific. *J. Trop. Med. Hyg.* **59**, 99 (1956).
234. Minervin, S. M., The results of many years' observations in the study of botulism. *J. Microbiol. Epidemiol. Immunobiol. (USSR) (Engl. Transl.)* **28**, 1403 (1957).
235. Minervin, S. M., Zhak, S. P., and Cherviakova, K. I., Suppression of the phagocytic property of leucocytes by botulinus toxin. *Zh. Mikrobiol. Epidemiol. Immunobiol.* **1956**, No. 6, 44 (1956). *Intern. Abstr. Biol. Sci.* **11**, 4688 (1958).
236. Miranda, F., "Purification et Caracterisation des Neurotoxines des Venins de Scorpions." Monograph, publ. by the author.

237. Miranda, F., and Lissitzky, S., Scorpamins: the toxic proteins of scorpion venoms. *Nature* **190,** 443 (1961).
238. Miranda, F., Rochat, H., and Lissitzky, S., Sur la neurotoxine du venin des scorpions. I: Purification a partir du venin de deux espèces de scorpions nord-Africains. *Bull. Soc. Chim. Biol.* **42,** 379 (1960).
239. Miranda, F., Rochat, H., and Lissitzky, S., Sur la neurotoxine du venin des scorpions. II: Utilisation de l'ectrophorèse sur papier pour l'orientation et le contrôle de la purification. *Bull. Soc. Chim. Biol.* **43,** 945 (1961).
240. Mohamed, A. H., and Zaki, O., Effect of the black snake toxin on the gastrocnemius-sciatic preparation. *J. Exptl. Biol.* **35,** 20 (1958).
241. Mohamed, A. H., and Zaki, O., A study of the effect of changing different ions in extracellular fluid on neuromuscular block caused by black snake toxin. *Indian J. Med. Res.* **47,** 636 (1959).
242. Morgan, F. G., The Australian Taipan, *Oxyuranus Scutellatus scutellatus* (Peters). *Publ. Am. Assoc. Advan. Sci.* **44,** 359 (1956).
243. Moroz-Perlmutter, C., Goldblum, N., de Vries, A., and Gitter, S., Detoxification of snake venoms and venom fractions by formaldehyde. *Proc. Soc. Exptl. Biol. Med.* **112,** 595 (1963).
243a. Mosher, H. S., Fuhrman, F. A., Buchwald, H. D., and Fischer, H. G., Tarichatoxin-Tetrodotoxin: A potent neurotoxin. *Science* **144,** 1100–1110 (1964).
244. Moussatché, H., Goncalves, J. M., Vieira, G. D., and Hasson, A., Pharmacological actions of two proteins from Brazilian rattlesnake venom. *Publ. Am. Assoc. Advan. Sci.* **44,** 275 (1956).
245. Murnaghan, M. F., Neuroanatomical site in tick paralysis. *Nature* **181,** 131 (1958).
246. Murnaghan, M. F., Site and mechanism of tick paralysis. *Science* **131,** 418 (1960).
247. Murtha, E. F., Pharmacological study of poisons from shellfish and puffer fish. *Ann. N.Y. Acad. Sci.* **90,** 820 (1960).
248. Murtha, E. F., Stabile, D. E., and Wills, J. H., Pharmacological effects of puffer poison. *J. Pharmacol. Exptl. Therap.* **122,** 247 (1958).
249. Nagai, J., Isolation of the poison of the Kugu fish by means of ion exchange. *Z. Physiol. Chem.* **306,** 104 (1956).
249a. Narahashi, T., Moore, J. W., and Scott, W. R., Tetrodotoxin blockage of sodium conductance increases in lobster giant axons. *J. Gen. Physiol.* **47,** 965–974 (1964).
250. Neumann, W., and Habermann, E., Paper electrophoresis separation of pharmacologically and biochemically active components of bee and snake venoms. *Publ. Am. Assoc. Advan. Sci.* **44,** 171 (1956).
251. Nigg, C., Hottle, G. A., Coriell, L. L., Rosenwald, A. S., and Beveridge, G. W., Studies on botulinum toxoid, types A and B. I Production of alum precipitated toxoids. *J. Immunol.* **55,** 245 (1947).
252. Nigrelli, R. F., ed., Biochemistry and pharmacology of compounds derived from marine organisms. *Ann. N.Y. Acad. Sci.* **90,** 615 (1960).
253. Nigrelli, R. F., and Jakowska, S., Effects of holothurin, a steroid saponin from the Bahamian sea cucumber (*Actinopyga agassizi*), on various biological systems. *Ann. N.Y. Acad. Sci.* **90,** 884 (1960).
254. North, E. A., and Doery, Hazel M., Inactivation of staphylococcal, tetanus and diphtheria toxins by ganglioside. *Brit. J. Exptl. Pathol.* **42,** 23 (1961).

255. Ohye, D. F., and Scott, W. J., Studies in the physiology of *Cl. botulinum* type E. *Australian J. Biol. Sci.* **10,** 85 (1957).

255a. Parsons, R. L., Hofmann, W. W., and Feigen, G. A., Mode of action of tetanus toxin on the neuromuscular junction. *Am. J. Physiol.* **210,** 84–90 (1966).

256. Patterson, R. A., Physiological action of scorpion venom. *Am. J. Trop. Med. Hyg.* **9,** 410 (1960).

257. Pearson, O. P., A toxic substance from the salivary glands of a mammal (short-tailed shrew). *Publ. Am. Assoc. Advan. Sci.* **44,** 55 (1956).

258. Pederson, H. O., Botulisme. *Nord. Veterinarmed.* **5,** 700 (1953).

259. Pedersen, J., and Christensen, A., Shock in botulism treated with dextran and blood. *Lancet* **II,** 560 (1952).

260. Pelloja, M., "Le Tétanos Expérimental par la Toxine Tétaninque," p. 299. Libraires Acad. Méd., Masson, Paris, 1951.

261. Peng, M-T., Effect of Formosan snake venoms on the depolarising action of acetylcholine at motor end plate. *T'ai-wan I Hsueh Hui Tsa Chih* **59,** 1073 (1960).

262. Perdrup, A., Electromyographic investigations on the mode of action of tetanus toxin. *Acta Pharmacol. Toxicol.* **2,** 121 (1946).

263. Perkins, W. E., and Tsuji, K., Sporulation of *Cl. botulinum.* II Effect of arginine and its degradation products on sporulation in a synthetic medium *J. Bacteriol.* **84,** 86 (1962).

264. Phillips, J. H., and Abbott, D. P., Isolation and assay of the nematocyst toxin of *Metridium senile fimbriatum. Biol. Bull.* **113,** 296 (1957).

265. Phelps, D. R., Stonefish poisoning. *Med. J. Australia* **I,** 293 (1960).

266. Polson, A., Joubert, J. F., and Haig, D. A., An electrophoretic examination of Cobra venoms. *Biochem. J.* **40,** 265 (1946).

267. Polson, A., and Sterne, M., Production of potent Botulinum toxins and formol toxoids. *Nature* **158,** 238 (1946).

268. Porges, N., Snake venoms; their biochemistry and mode of action. *Science* **117,** 47 (1953).

269. Potter, J. M., and Northey, W. T., An immunological evaluation of scorpion venoms. *Am. J. Trop. Med. Hyg.* **11,** 712 (1962).

270. Pratt, G. B., Wheaton, E., Bohrer, C. W., and Denny, C. B., Destruction of *Cl. botulinum* by ionising radiation. II Peas, chicken soup and pork in the frozen state. *Food Res.* **24,** 51 (1959).

271. Putnam, F. W., Lamanna, C., and Sharp, D. G., Physicochemical properties of crystalline *Cl. botulinum* type A toxin. *J. Biol. Chem.* **176,** 401 (1948).

272. Ralls, R. J., and Halstead, B. W., Moray Eel poisoning and a preliminary report on the action of the toxin. *Am. J. Trop. Med. Hyg.* **4,** 136 (1955).

272a. Rand, M. J., and Whaler, B. C., Impairment of sympathetic transmission by botulinum toxin. *Nature* **206,** 588–591 (1965).

273. Ranson, S. W., Local tetanus: Study of muscle tonus and contracture. *A.M.A. Arch. Neurol. Psychiat.* **20,** 663 (1928).

274. Rathmeyer, W., Paralysis caused by the digger wasp *Philanthus. Nature* **196,** 1148 (1962).

275. Reames, H. R., Kadull, P. J., Housewright, R. D., and Wilson, J. B., Studies on botulinum toxoids, types A and B. *J. Immunol.* **55,** 309 (1947).

276. Reid, H., Sea snakebites. *Brit. Med. J.* **II,** 73 (1956).

277. Reid, H., Report of an account of seasnakes of Malaya. *J. Trop. Med. Hyg.* **59,** 275 (1956).

278. Reid, H. A., Myoglobinuria and sea snakebite poisoning. *Brit. Med. J.* **I,** 1284 (1961).
279. Reid, H. A., Snakebite in Malaya. *In* "Venomous and Poisonous Animals and Noxious Plants of the Pacific Region" (H. L. Keegan and W. V. Macfarlane, eds.), p. 355. Macmillan (Pergamon), New York, 1963.
280. Rice, C. E., Pallister, E. F., Smith, L. C., and Reed, G. B., *Cl. botulinum* type A toxoids. *Can. J. Res.* **E25,** 167 (1947).
281. Rice, C. E., Smith, L. C., Pallister, E. F., and Reed, G. B., *Cl. botulinum* type B toxoids. *Can. J. Res.* **E25,** 175 (1947).
282. Rose, I., and Gregson, J. D., Evidence for a neuromuscular block in tick paralysis. *Nature* **178,** 95 (1956).
283. Rosenberg, P., and Podleski, T. R., Block of conduction by acetylcholine and d-tubocurarine after treatment of squid axon with cottonmouth moccasin venom. *J. Pharmacol. Exptl. Therap.* **137,** 249 (1962).
284. Rowson, K. E. K., The action of tetanus toxin in frogs. *J. Gen. Microbiol.* **25,** 315 (1961).
285. Russell, F. E., and Emery, J. A., Venom of the Weevers *Trachinus draco* and *Trachinus vipera. Ann. N.Y. Acad. Sci.* **90,** 805 (1960).
286. Sakaguchi, G., and Sakaguchi, S., Studies on toxin production of *Cl. botulinum* type E. III Characterization of the toxin precursor. *J. Bacteriol.* **78,** 1 (1959).
287. Sakaguchi, G., and Tohyama, Y., Studies on the toxin production of *Cl. botulinum* type E. I A strain of genus *Clostridium* having the action to promote type E botulinal toxin production in a mixed culture. *Jap. J. Med. Sci. Biol.* **8,** 247 (1955).
288. Sakaguchi, G., and Tohyama, Y., Studies on the toxin production of *Cl. botulinum* type E. II The mode of action of the contaminant organisms to promote toxin production of type E organisms. *Jap. J. Med. Sci. Biol.* **8,** 255 (1955).
289. Saunders, P. R., and Taylor, P. B., Venom of the lionfish *Pterois volitans. Am. J. Physiol.* **197,** 437 (1959).
290. Schantz, E. J., Biochemical studies on paralytic shellfish poisons. *Ann. N.Y. Acad. Sci.* **90,** 843 (1960).
291. Schantz, E. J., Studies on the paralytic poisons found in mussels and clams along the North American Pacific coast. *In* "Venomous and Poisonous Animals and Noxious Plants of the Pacific Region" (H. L. Keegan and W. V. Macfarlane, eds.), p. 75. Macmillan (Pergamon), New York, 1963.
292. Schantz, E. J., Mold, J. D., Stanger, D. W., Shavel, J., Riel, F. J., Bowden, J. P., Lynch, J. M., Wyler, R. S., Riegel, B., and Sommer, H., Paralytic Shellfish Poison: VI A procedure for the isolation and purification of the poison from toxic clam and mussel tissues. *J. Am. Chem. Soc.* **79,** 5230 (1957).
293. Schellenberg, D. B., and Matzke, H. A., The development of tetanus in parabiotic rats. *J. Immunol.* **80,** 367 (1958).
294. Schmidt, K. P., and Inger, R. F., "Living Reptiles of the World." Hamish Hamilton, London, 1957.
295. Schmidt, C. R., and Nank, W. K., Radiation sterilization of food. I Procedures for the evaluation of the radiation resistance of spores of *Cl. botulinum* in food products. *Food Res.* **25,** 321 (1960).

296. Schneider, M. D., Grecz, N., and Anellis, A., Sporulation of *Cl. botulinum* types A, B and E, *Cl. perfringens*, and putrefactive anaerobe 3679 in dialysis sacs. *J. Bacteriol.* **85**, 126 (1963).
297. Schöttler, W. H. A., On the toxicity of Scorpion venom. *Am. J. Trop. Med. Hyg.* **3**, 172 (1954).
298. Shvedov, L. M., Neutralisation of toxin formed in the alimentary tract in experimental toxico-infection with *Cl. botulinum*, Type A, by parenteral administration of antiserum. *J. Microbiol. Epidemiol. Immunobiol.* (*USSR*) (*Engl. Transl.*) **30**, 95 (1959).
299. Shvedov, L. M., Formation of toxin in the digestive tract of animals infected orally with a type A strain of *Cl. botulinum. J. Microbiol. Epidemiol. Immunobiol.* (*USSR*) (*Engl. Transl.*) **31**, 126 (1960).
300. Simmons, R. J., and Costilow, R. N., Enzymes of glucose and pyruvate catabolism in cells, spores and germinated spores of *Cl. botulinum. J. Bacteriol.* **84**, 1274 (1962).
301. Sinitsyn, V. A., Use of the indirect haemagglutination reaction in detection of botulinus toxins. *J. Microbiol. Epidemiol. Immunobiol.* (*USSR*) (*Engl. Transl.*) **31**, 408 (1960).
302. Sinitsyn, V. A., The use of the indirect haemagglutination test for determining *Cl. botulinum* toxins. II A modified method of the indirect haemagglutination test and a comparative evaluation of it with some tests used for detecting *Cl. botulinum* toxin. *J. Microbiol. Epidemiol. Immunobiol.* (*USSR*) (*Engl. Transl.*) **31**, 703 (1960).
303. Slotta, K., Further experiments on crotoxin. *Publ. Am. Assoc. Advan. Sci.* **44**, 253 (1956).
304. Southcott, R. V., Tropical jellyfish and other marine stingings. *Military Med.* **124**, 569 (1959).
305. Southcott, R. V., Coelenterates of medical importance. *In* "Venomous and Poisonous Animals and Noxious Plants of the Pacific Region" (H. L. Keegan and W. V. Macfarlane, eds.), p. 41. Macmillan (Pergamon), New York, 1963.
306. Stahnke, H. L., Some biochemical and pharmacological characteristics of *Centruroides sculpturatus* Ewing scorpion venom. *Biochem. Pharmacol.* **12**, Suppl., 187 (1963).
307. Stevenson, J. W., Bacterial neurotoxins. *Am. J. Med. Sci.* **235**, 317 (1958).
308. Su, C., Mode of curare-like action of cobra venom. *T'ai-wan I Hsueh Hui Tsa Chih* **59**, 1083 (1960).
309. Sverdlov, J. S., Action of tetanus toxin upon inhibitory mechanisms in spinal cord. *Biochem. Pharmacol.* **12**, Suppl., 230 (1963).
310. Takagi, A., Kawata, T., and Yamamoto, S., Electron microscope studies on ultrathin sections of spores of the *Clostridium* group, with special reference to the sporulation and germination process. *J. Bacteriol.* **80**, 37 (1960).
311. Thatcher, F. S., Robinson, J., and Erdman, I., The "vacuum pack" method of packaging foods in relation to the formation of the botulinum and staphylococcal toxins. *J. Appl. Bacteriol.* **25**, 120 (1962).
312. Thesleff, S., Supersensitivity of skeletal muscle produced by botulinum toxin. *J. Physiol.* (*London*) **151**, 598 (1960).
313. Tinkham, E. R., The deadly nature of gila monster venom. *Publ. Am. Assoc. Advan. Sci.* **44**, 59 (1956).

314. Treadwell, P. E., Jann, G. J., and Salle, A. J., Studies on factors affecting the rapid germination of spores of *Cl. botulinum*. *J. Bacteriol.* **76**, 549 (1958).
315. Tsuji, K., and Perkins, W. E., Sporulation of *Cl. botulinum*. I Selection of an aparticulate sporulation medium. *J. Bacteriol.* **84**, 81 (1962).
316. Tyler, H. R., Botulism. *Arch. Neurol.* **9**, 652 (1963).
317. Tyler, H. R., Physiological observations in human botulism. *Arch. Neurol.* **9**, 661 (1963).
318. Tyler, H. R., Botulinus toxin: effect on the central nervous system of man. *Science* **139**, 847 (1963).
319. van Heyningen, W. E., Toxic proteins. *In* "The Proteins" (H. Neurath and K. Bailey, eds.), Vol. II, Pt. A. Academic Press, New York, 1954.
320. van Heyningen, W. E., The fixation of tetanus toxin by nervous tissue. *J. Gen. Microbiol.* **20**, 291 (1959).
321. van Heyningen, W. E., Tentative identification of the tetanus toxin receptor in nervous tissue. *J. Gen. Microbiol.* **20**, 310 (1959).
322. van Heyningen, W. E., The relation between the fixation and inactivation of tetanus toxin by ganglioside. *Brit. J. Exptl. Pathol.* **42**, 397 (1961).
323. van Heyningen, W. E., The fixation of tetanus toxin by ganglioside. *Biochem. Pharmacol.* **12**, 437 (1963).
324. van Heyningen, W. E., The fixation of tetanus toxin, strychnine, serotonin and other substances by ganglioside. *J. Gen. Microbiol.* **31**, 375 (1963).
325. van Heyningen, W. E., and Arseculeratne, S. N., Exotoxins. *Ann. Rev. Microbiol.* **18**, 195 (1964).
326. van Heyningen, W. E., and Gladstone, G. P., The neurotoxin of *Shigella shiga*: production, purification and properties of the toxin. *Brit. J. Exptl. Pathol.* **34**, 202 (1953).
327. See ref. 230a.
328. van Heyningen, W. E., and Miller, P. A., The fixation of tetanus toxin by ganglioside. *J. Gen. Microbiol.* **24**, 107 (1961).
329. van Heyningen, W. E., and Woodman, R. J., The fixation of tetanus toxin by frog brain. *J. Gen. Microbiol.* **31**, 389 (1963).
330. Wagenaar, R. O., and Dack, G. M., Studies on the inactivation of type A *Cl. botulinum* toxin by irradiation with Cobalt-60. *Food Res.* **25**, 279 (1960).
331. Wagman, J., Isolation and sedimentation study of low M.W. forms of type A botulinum toxin. *Arch. Biochem. Biophys.* **50**, 104 (1954).
332. Wagman, J., Low molecular weight forms of type A botulinum toxin. II Action of pepsin on intact and dissociated toxin. *Arch. Biochem. Biophys.* **100**, 414 (1963).
333. Wagman, J., and Bateman, J. B., The behaviour of the botulinus toxins in the ultracentrifuge. *Arch. Biochem. Biophys.* **31**, 424 (1951).
334. Wagman, J., and Bateman, J. B., Botulinum type A toxin: properties of a toxic dissociation product. *Arch. Biochem. Biophys.* **45**, 375 (1953).
335. Webster, R. A., Centrally acting muscle relaxants in tetanus. *Brit. J. Pharmacol.* **17**, 507 (1961).
336. Welsh, J. H., Composition and mode of action of some invertebrate venoms. *Ann. Rev. Pharmacol.* **4**, 293 (1964).
337. Wentzel, L. M., Sterne, M., and Polson, A., High toxicity of pure botulinum type D toxin. *Nature* **166**, 739 (1950).
338. Werler, J. E., and Keegan, H. L., Venomous snakes of the Pacific area. *In* "Venomous and Poisonous Animals and Noxious Plants of the Pacific Region"

(H. L. Keegan and W. V. Macfarlane, eds.), p. 219. Macmillan (Pergamon), New York, 1963.

339. Whaler, B. C., Hemicholinium and botulinum toxin on sympathetic transmission. *Biochem. Pharmacol.* **12**, Suppl., 261 (1963).

340. Wheeler, W. M., A solitary wasp (*Aphilanthops frigidus* F. Smith) that provisions its nest with queen ants. *In* "Foibles of Insects and Men," p. 69. Knopf, New York, 1928. [Quoted by Beard (34).]

341. Whittaker, V. P., Pharmacologically active choline esters in marine gastropods. *Ann. N.Y. Acad. Sci.* **90**, 695 (1960).

342. Wiener, S., Stone fish sting and its treatment. *Med. J. Australia* **II**, 218 (1958).

343. Wiener, S., Observations on the venom of the stone fish (*Synanceja trachynis*). *Med. J. Australia* **I**, 620 (1959).

344. Wiener, S., Active immunization of man against the venom of the Australian Tiger snake (*Notechis scutatus*). *Am. J. Trop. Med. Hyg.* **9**, 284 (1960).

345. Wiener, S., Venom yields and toxicity of the venoms of male and female Tiger snakes. *Med. J. Australia* **47**, 740 (1960).

346. Wiener, S., Observations on the venom of the Sydney funnel-web spider (*Atrax robustus*). *Med. J. Australia* **II**, 693 (1961).

347. Wilson, V. J., Diecke, F. P. J., and Talbot, W. H., Action of tetanus toxin on conditioning of spinal motoneurones. *J. Neurophysiol.* **23**, 659 (1960).

348. Wilson, G. S., and Miles, A. A., "Topley and Wilson's Principles of Bacteriology and Immunity," 4th Ed., Vol. II, p. 1955. Arnold, London, 1955.

349. Wright, E. A., The effect of the injection of tetanus toxin into the central nervous system of rabbits. *J. Immunol.* **71**, 41 (1953).

350. Wright, E. A., Morgan, R. S., and Wright, G. P., The movements of toxin in the nervous system in experimental tetanus in rabbits. *Brit. J. Exptl. Pathol.* **32**, 169 (1951).

351. Wright, E. A., Morgan, R. S., and Wright, G. P., The site of action of the toxin in local tetanus. *Lancet* **2**, 316 (1952).

352. Wright, G. G., Duff, J. T., Fiock, M. A., Devlin, H. B., and Soderstrom, R. L., Immunity of toxins of *Cl. botulinum*. V. Detoxification of purified type A and type B toxins and the antigenicity of univalent and bivalent aluminum phosphate adsorbed toxoids. *J. Immunol.* **84**, 384 (1960).

353. Wright, G. P., Nerve trunks as pathways in infection. *Proc. Roy. Soc. Med.* **46**, 319 (1953).

354. Wright, G. P., The Neurotoxins of *Cl. botulinum* and *Cl. tetani*. *Pharmacol. Rev.* **7**, 413 (1955).

355. Yariv, J., and Hestrin, S., Toxicity of the extracellular phase of *Prymnesium parvum* cultures. *J. Gen. Microbiol.* **24**, 165 (1961).

356. Zacks, S. I., Metzger, J. F., Smith, C. W., and Blumberg, J. M., Localization of ferritin-labelled botulinus toxin in the neuromuscular junction of the mouse. *J. Neuropathol. Exptl. Neurol.* **21**, 610 (1962).

Author Index

Numbers in parentheses are reference numbers and indicate that an author's work is referred to although his name is not cited in text. Numbers in italics show the pages on which complete references are listed.

A

Aach, R. D., 406 (114), *447*
Abbott, B. C., 428 (1), 429 (1), *442*
Abbott, D. P., 430 (264), *455*
Abboud, F. M., 29 (1), 70, *81*, 198 (1, 163), *213*, *222*, 313 (1), *324*
Abel, F. L., 263 (1), 265 (1), 267 (1), *291*
Abel, J. J., 420, *442*
Ablad, B., 309 (98), *329*
Abrams, A., 401 (6, 177), 402 (6), *442*, *450*
Abreu, B. E., 29 (2), 75 (2), *81*, 365 (1, 226), *386*, *397*
Acheson, G. H., 180 (2), 182 (2), 210 (229), *213*, *226*, 258 (2), 259 (2), *291*, 320 (2), *324*, 333, 339 (126), 345 (126), 347 (126), 352 (126), 353 (126), 354 (126), 355, 356 (164), 361 (126), 364 (126), 367 (126), 368 (126), 370 (126), 371 (126), 372 (126), 373 (126), 374 (126), 377 (126), 379 (126), 380 (126), *392*, *394*, 420 (7), 422, *442*
Adam, K. R., 379 (2), *386*
Adams-Ray, J., 29 (3), 65 (238), *81*, *93*
Afonso, A., 332 (143), 333 (143), 334 (143), 335 (143), 336 (143), 337 (143), *393*
Agarwal, S. L., 247 (3), *291*
Ager, E. A., 406 (8), *442*
Ahlquist, R. P., 7 (1), 14 (2), 16 (2), 17 (2), 20 (2), *22*, 33 (237), 34 (5), 41, 44 (6), 47 (4), 48 (4), 54 (6), 58, 62, 71 (5), *81*, *93*, 133, *173*, 180 (3), 186, 192 (496), *213*, *241*, 244, 253 (5), 254 (5), 256 (6), 260 (5), 262 (4), 265 (5), 280 (4), 281 (6), *291*, 307, 308, 309 (54), 314, 316 (3), *324*, *327*
Ahmad, K., 374, 382 (1), *386*
Akcasu, A., 379 (96), 381, 382 (96), *391*
Alanis, J., 314 (6), *325*
Alcock, P., 113 (1, 2), *123*
Alender, C. B., 436 (26), *443*
Alexander, F., 141, *173*
Alexander, J. K., 121 (3), *123*
Alexander, W. M., 365 (1), *386*
Ali, Hanem I. E. S., 13 (39), 20 (39), *24*, 186 (4), 187 (4), *213*
Allen, W. J., 35, 36, 38, 72 (7), 74, 75 (7), *81*
Alleyne, G. A. O., 324 (7), *325*
Allwood, M. J., 39 (9), 42 (9), 59 (9), 80 (10), 81, *81*, 188 (5), *213*
Alousi, A. A., 196 (6), *213*
Alpers, H. S., 10 (20), 12 (20), *23*
Alston, E. J., 31 (123), 60 (123), *87*
Altszuler, N., 192 (13), 193 (14), 194 (473), 199 (13), *214*, *240*
Amatsu, H., 71, *81*
Ambache, N., 408, 409, 410 (16), 411 (9, 10, 12, 13), 412 (15), 413, 414 (10), 420 (18), 421 (19, 20), 422, 426 (19, 20), *442*, *443*
Ambanelli, U., 197 (86), *218*
Amemori, T., 199 (7), *214*
Anamenka, E., 48 (203), *91*, 251 (139), *298*
Anderson, H. L., 187 (132), *220*
Anderson, D. A., 264 (97), *296*
Anderson, R. B., 264 (116), 272 (116), 273 (116), 274 (116), 277 (116), *297*
Andrews, T. M., 37 (240), *93*
Andrews, W. H. H., 172, *177*, 205 (8), *214*
Anellis, A., 401 (21, 157, 296), *443*, *449*, *457*
Ang, M. K., 8 (6), *22*
Anichkov, S. V., 363 (4), *386*

Ankermann, H., 202 (9, 10), *214*
Annison, E. F., 181 (11), *214*
Antognetti, R. M., 206 (303), *230*
Antonio, A., 13 (39), 20 (39), *24*, 186 (4), 187 (4), *213*
Appleman, M. M., 182 (12), *214*
April, S. A., 184 (392), 199 (392), *235*, 318 (84), *329*
Aragon, P. R., 404 (209), *452*
Aranow, H., Jr., 256 (83), 272 (83), 284 (83), *295*
Aravindakshan, I., 439 (22), *443*
Archibald, K. M., 263 (202), *302*
Armitage, A. K., 145, *173*
Armstrong, D. T., 192 (13), 193 (14), 199 (13), *214*
Arnott, D. A., 401 (146), 402 (147), 403 (147), 404 (147), 405, 417 (147), *449*
Aronow, L., 249 (24), *292*, 353, *386*
Arora, R. B., 360 (127), 361 (127), 377 (6, 7, 9), 378 (6, 7, 8, 9, 10, 11, 206), *386*, *392*, *396*
Arthur, D. R., 428 (23), *443*
Arseculeratne, S. N., 400 (325), 418 (325), *458*
Asano, M., 435 (24), *443*
Ashmore, J., 183 (15), 198 (281, 282), 199 (15, 281, 282, 298), *214*, *229*, *230*, 318 (8, 56), *325*, *327*
Assali, N. S., 102 (83), *127*, 353 (13), 384 (12, 13, 14), 384 (221), *386*, *397*
Atkins, J. A., 432 (25), *443*
Atkinson, G., 102 (34), 113 (34, 35), 122 (34), *124*
Attar, H. J., 192 (158), *222*
Aujard, C., 192 (16), 195 (16), *214*
Aulsebrook, K. A., 212 (17), *214*
Avedon, M., 384 (113), *392*
Aviado, D. M., 54 (12), 59, 73, 75 (12), 77, *81*, 100, 102 (4, 31), 113 (4, 31), 121, 122 (4), *123*, *124*, 268 (7), 269 (7), *292*, 314 (14), 315 (14), *325*, 333 (21), 339 (16), 341, 342 (18, 21), 343 (18), 344 (20), 345 (17), 346 (17), 350 (15), 351 (17), 352 (20), 362 (19, 21), 363 (16), 375 (16), *387*
Axelrod, J., 9 (42), 10 (73), *24*, *25*, 132 (4), 133 (4, 71), 166 (64), *173*, *176*, 249 (24), *292*, 312 (43), *326*
Axelsson, J., 135 (5), 136, *173*
Azarnoff, D. L., 199 (215), *225*

B

Bach, L. M. N., 274 (38), *293*
Backmann, F., 55 (158), *89*
Bacq, Z. M., 30 (56), 31, *81*, *83*, 161, 163, 170, *173*
Bailey, D. M., 333 (21), *387*
Bainbridge, F. A., 35 (14), *81*
Baldwin, D. S., 54 (176), *90*
Baldwin, E. de F., 34 (124), 47 (124), 48 (124), *87*, 100 (52), 104 (52), 112 (52), 121 (52), *125*
Ball, E. G., 195 (173), 197 (18, 146, 172, 173, 227), *214*, *223*, *226*
Ball, M. F., 195 (39), *215*
Ballantine, D., 428 (1), 429 (1), *442*
Balzer, H., 188 (19), *214*
Bánhидy, F., 188 (447), 205 (447), *238*
Banner, A. H., 436 (26), *443*
Bannerjee, A. K., 213 (20), *214*
Barclay, A. E., 263 (256), *304*
Barclay, J. A., 44, *82*
Barcroft, H., 17 (3), *22*, 34, 35 (8), 36 (8), 37 (20), 38 (8), 40 (16), 48 (18), 51, 57, 58, *82*, 252 (8), 265 (8), *292*
Bardhanabaedya, S., 46 (133), 59 (133), *87*, 268 (47), *294*
Bardier, E., 44, *82*
Barer, G. R., 122 (5), *123*, 346 (24), 349 (24), 350 (24), 363 (23), *387*
Barger, G., 30 (22), 62, 69 (22), 79, *82*, 151, *175*, 243 (9), *292*
Barker, H. G., 77 (74), *84*
Barltop, J. A., 332 (167), 333 (167), 335 (167), *395*
Barme, M., 440, *443*
Barnes, J. H., 430 (28), *443*
Barnett, A. J., 35, 36, 48 (23), 50 (23), 51, 54, 65, *82*
Barr, J. S., 113 (86), *127*
Barron, A. L., 401 (29), *443*
Barsoum, G. S., 147, *173*

Bass, B. G., 100 (53), 104 (53), 105 (53), 112 (53), *125*
Bassett, D. L., 347 (162), 348 (162), 353 (162), *394*
Bateman, J. B., 403 (333, 334), 405, *458*
Battersby, E. J., 19 (4), *22*
Bauer, H., 212 (216), *225*
Bauer, R. O., 351 (208), 370 (84), 385 (212), *391, 396, 397*
Bauereisen, E., 254 (10), *292*
Baum, H., 202 (23), 203 (22), 205 (21), *214*
Baylis, J. H., 420 (31), 423 (30), 424 (31), *443*
Bean, J. W., 265 (11), 269 (130), *265, 298*
Beard, R. L., 427, 428 (34), 430, 431 (32), *443*
Bearn, A. G., 43, 53, *82*
Beck, J. C., 193 (55), 196 (388, 389), 197 (55), *216, 235*
Beck, R., 102 (83), *127*
Beckett, S. B., 184 (130), 209 (130, 131), *220,* 278 (61), *294,* 316 (25), *325*
Beckman, H., 71 (26), 76 (26), *82*
Begel, J. S., 401 (69), 402 (69), *445*
Bein, H. J., 63 (27), *82,* 362 (157), *394*
Belen'kii, M. L., 363 (4), *386*
Belford, J., 187 (26), 188 (24, 25), *215*
Belisle, C., 289 (242), *304*
Bell, J. F., 401 (221), *453*
Belleau, B., 246 (12, 13), *292*
Belocopitow, E., 182 (12), 187 (27), *214, 215*
Benfey, B. G., 248 (14, 15), *292*
Benforado, J. M., 332 (26), 339 (72), 345 (30), 346 (72), 347, 348, 349 (71, 72), 350 (26, 72), 351 (30), 352, 353 (30), 355 (26, 29), 356 (26), 357, 358 (26), 359 (27, 31), 360 (29), 361 (29), 369 (25), 371 (28), 372 (25), 382 (29), 386 (26), *387, 389, 390*
Benjamin, W., 193 (28), *215*
Bennett, A., 109 (70), *126,* 268 (175), *300*
Bentley, G. A., 45 (28), 67 (28, 29), *82,* 141, 144, *173*
Benzold, A. von, 331, 340, *387*
Berengo, A., 407, *443*
Berger, J. E., 196 (461), *239*
Berghout, J., 266 (184), *301*
Berglund, E., 21 (77), *25,* 102 (6, 7), 108 (7), 113 (6, 7), 120 (6), *123*
Bergmann, F., 428 (35), 429 (35, 36), *443*
Bergner, A. D., 428 (41), *444*
Bergström, S., 192 (436), 193 (29, 435), 194 (436), *215, 238*
Berlinger, F. G., 185 (153), 210 (153), *221*
Berne, R. M., 205 (30), *215,* 313 (9), *325*
Bernthal, T., 267 (16), *292*
Berry, E. L., 36 (167), *89*
Berry, G., 319 (86), 320 (86), *329*
Berry, J. L., 113 (1, 2), *123*
Berstein, M., 359 (41), 385 (41), 386 (41), *388*
Berthet, J., 185 (31), *215*
Bertler, Å., 8 (5), 19 (14), *22,* 62, 78 (31, 32), 81 (32), *82,* 131 (13, 14), *173*
Best, C. H., 204 (95), *218*
Best, M. M., 384 (46), *388*
Bevan, J. A., 345 (32), *387*
Beveridge, G. W., 401 (251), *454*
Beviz, A., 189 (32, 33), *215*
Bibler, R. H., 401 (111, 112), 402 (111, 112), 403 (111, 112), 405 (112), *447*
Billig, D. M., 49 (251), *93,* 109 (81), *127,* 269 (231), *303*
Billing, B., 43 (25), 53 (25), *82*
Binak, K., 104 (78), 105 (78), 109 (78), *126*
Binns, W., 386 (34), *388*
Bishop, G. H., 408, *443*
Bishop, J. S., 192 (13), 193 (14), 199 (13), *214*
Bizzi, A., 193 (34), 194 (34), *215*
Björklund, B., 407, *443*
Björntorp, P., 194 (36), 195 (35), 196 (37, 38), *213, 215*
Black, J. W., 309, 310 (10), 311 (10), 312 (10), 313, 314 (10), *325*

Black, M. M., 359 (35), 385 (35), 386 (35), *388*
Blackard, W. G., 195 (39), 197 (463), *215*, *239*
Blacket, R. B., 35 (23), 36 (23, 33), 48 (23), 49, 50 (23), 51 (23), 54 (23), *82*
Blaschko, H., 32, 78 (81), *82*, *85*
Blatteis, C. M., 201 (40), 203 (40), *215*
Blattner, R. J., 433, *443*
Bloom, F. E., 274 (17, 222), *292*, *303*, 347 (193), *396*
Blount, S. G., Jr., 269 (103), *296*
Blukoo-Allotey, J. A., 188 (41), *215*
Blum, F., 180 (42), *215*
Blumberg, H., 183 (292), 184 (292), *230*
Blumberg, J. B., 188 (490), *241*
Blumberg, J. M., 409 (356, *459*
Blumenfeld, S., 356 (199), 358 (199), *396*
Blumenthal, M. R., 323 (11), *325*
Bluntschli, H. J., 264 (18), 265 (18), *292*
Bock, K. D., 39, 52, *83*
Boehm, R., 333, 370, *388*
Bogdonoff, M. D., 197 (43), 198 (43), 199 (249), *216*, *227*
Bogen, E., 432 (40), *443*
Bohrer, C. W., 401 (97, 270), *446*, *455*
Bolton, B. L., 428 (41), *444*
Bonventre, P. F., 401 (42, 44, 45), 417, 418, *444*
Boréus, L. O., 271 (119), *297*
Borison, H. L., 344, 345 (38), 363 (37), 364, 365 (40), *388*
Boroff, D. A., 401 (46), 417, 418, *444*
Borst, H. G., 102 (6, 7), 108 (7), 113 (6, 7), 120, *123*
Boshart, C. R., 199 (44, 45, 46, 47), *216*
Boss, J. H., 439 (153), *449*
Bot, Gy., 183 (48), *216*
Botting, R., 315, *325*
Boucek, R. J., 117, 122 (56), *125*
Bouckaert, J. J., 45 (37), 73, *83*
Bouisset, L., 401 (48), *444*
Boura, A. L. A., 67, *83*, 152, 172 (15), *173*, *174*
Bousvaros, C. A., 109 (8), *126*
Boutwell, J. H., 209 (131), *220* 278 (61), 279 (61), *294*, 316 (25), *325*
Bovet, D., 244 (19), 255 (70), 256 (20, 21), 257 (19), 280 (19), *292*, *295*
Bovet-Nitti, F., 244 (19), 257 (19), 280 (19), *292*
Bowden, J. P., 428 (292), *456*
Bowen, H. F., 193 (362), *234*
Bowers, L. E., 401 (49), *444*
Boyd, A. M., 288 (22), *292*
Boyd, H., 248 (23), *292*
Boyd, G. H., Jr., 289 (208), *302*
Boyme, T., 209 (142), *221*
Bozler, E., 134, 149, 150, 153, *174*
Brackney, E. L., 54 (221), *92*
Bradley, S. E., 34, 43, 44, 54 (191), 71, 72, 73 (236), *83*, *90*, *93*, 264 (176), *300*
Braganca, B. M., 439 (22, 50), *443*
Brand, E. D., 365 (40), *388*
Brann, A. W., 274 (38), *293*
Braunwald, E., 18 (15), 21 (99), *22*, *26*, 63 (65), *84*, 205 (478), 206 (250), 206 (478), *227*, *240*, 311 (38), *326*
Brechbuhler, T., 439 (155), *449*
Breckenridge, C. G., 279 (122), *297*
Breed, E. S., 263 (153, 154), *299*
Brentano, C., 205 (49), *216*
Breuillard, J., 401 (48), *444*
Bridge, E. M., 181 (50), 202 (50), *216*
Briggs, A. H., 212 (51), 216
Briggs, L. H., 332 (128), 360 (128), *392*
Brodie, B. B., 249 (24), 278 (25), *292*
Brodie, O. J., 20 (95), *26*
Brodie, T. G., 44, *83*
Brody, T. M., 183 (208, 209), 184 (208), 185 (208), 186 (368), 187 (208, 209, 368), 188 (209), 189 (209, 297, 368), 190 (52, 108, 109), *216*, *225*, *230*, *234*, 266 (26, 31, 244), *293*, *304*
Brofman, B. L., 122 (9), 123
Bromer, A. W., 113 (86), *127*
Bronfenbrenner, J., 403, 408, 416, *443*, *444*

Bronsky, D., 359 (41), 385 (41), 386 (41), *388*
Brooker, W. D., 199 (53), *216*
Brooks, C. McC., 3 (7), 5 (8, 60), 6 (8, 60, 91), 8 (6, 92), 13 (83), 14 (33), 21 (33), *22, 25, 26,* 259 (235), 278 (235), *303,* 320 (31), 321 (31), *326,* 358 (41a), 369 (41a), 372 (41a), *388*
Brooks, V. B., 409, 425, *444*
Brown, G. L., 130, *174,* 248 (27), *293*
Brown, H. O., 259 (185), 290 (185), *301*
Brown, M. S., 437 (57), *444*
Brown, R. H., 197 (290), *229*
Brown, R. V., 441 (58), *444*
Brown, S. J., 192 (390), 195 (390), 198 (390), 199 (391), *235*
Brown-Sequard, M. E., 30 (42), *83*
Bruce, R. A., 188 (490), 192 (54), *216, 241*
Bruner, H. D., 98 (10), *123*
Brunjes, S., 283 (128), 285 (28, 128), *293, 298*
Brust, A. A., 353 (13), 384 (13), *386*
Bryan, J. H., 346 (155), *394*
Bryant, R. D., 384 (42), 385 (42), *388*
Bucherl, E., 269 (29), *293*
Bucht, H., 54 (271), *94*
Buchwald, H. D., 436 (243a), *454*
Buckle, R. M., 193 (55), 197 (55), *216*
Buckley, E. E., 428 (60), *444*
Bücherl, W., 432, *444*
Bueding, E., 135 (5), 136 (5), 159, *173, 174,* 190 (56), *216, 238*
Bülbring, E., 190 (56), *216*
Buffoni, F., 188 (57), *216*
Bulatova, T. I., 408 (61), *444*
Bulbring, E., 31 (43), 60, *83,* 135 (5, 21), 136 (5), 142, 159 (19), *174*
Buniva, G., 197 (102), *219*
Burack, W. R., 8 (98), *26*
Burch, G. E., 65 (146, 233), 66, *83, 88, 93,* 109 (11), *123,* 211 (280), *229*
Burgen, A. S. V., 282 (30), *293,* 408, 409, *445*
Burke, J. M., 428 (63), *445*
Burks, A. L., 29 (2), 75 (2), *81*
Burn, J. H., 9 (10, 11), 18, *22,* 31 (43), 36 (53), 40, 49, 53, 54, 60, 62 (45, 54), 63, 64, 65, 79, *83,* 143, 150, 151, 162, 164, 165, 166, 167, 169 (28), *174, 175,* 412 (65), 413, *445*
Burnett, C. H., 349 (74), 383 (74), 384 (74), *390*
Burns, B. D., 367 (43), *388*
Burns, J. J., 184 (392), 199 (58, 392), *235,* 318 (13, 84), *325, 329*
Burnstock, G., 159, *174,* 210 (59), 212 (59), *216,* 248 (23), *292*
Burridge, W., 15 (12), *22*
Burton, A. C., 42, *83,* 98 (12), 102 (74), 103, *123, 126*
Buschke, W., 280 (75), *295*
Buskirk, E. R., 199 (433), 205 (433), *237*
Butcher, R. W., 182 (382), 188 (382), 189 (382), 196 (60), *216, 235,* 278 (248), *304*
Butler, W. M., Jr., 278 (25), *292*
Byers, S. O., 195 (149), *221*
Byushuk, N. S., 185 (61), 187 (61), *217*

C

Caddell, H. M., 289 (208), *302*
Cahill, G. F., Jr., 192 (375), 197 (62, 267), *217, 228, 234*
Cairncross, K. D., 188 (398), *235*
Cairoli, V. J., 321 (81), *328*
Calliauw, L., 342 (150), 343 (150), 344 (44), 352 (44), 353, 362 (44), *388, 394*
Calvert, D. N., 199 (53), *216,* 266 (26, 31), *293*
Cameron, W., 264 (42), *293*
Cammack, K. A., 403, 404, 405, *445*
Campbell, C. C. R., 406 (110), *447*
Campbell, C. H., 439 (68), *445*
Campbell, G., 248 (23), *292*
Campos, H. A., 19 (13), *22*
Cannon, B. W., 30 (56, 59), 35, 36, 43 (58), *83, 84,* 252 (165), *300*
Cappelli, V., 184 (164), 187 (164), 204 (164), *222*
Cardella, M. A., 401 (69, 70), 402 (69, 70), 403 (70), 405, *445*
Carey, J. E., 439 (72), 440 (71, 72), *445*
Carlisle, D. B., 437, *437*

Carlson, L. A., 192 (64, 66), 193 (29, 63, 65, 67), 194 (63, 65, 67, 68), 207 (192), *215, 217, 224*
Carlson, L. D., 204 (210, 211, 340), *225*
Carlsson, A., 8 (5), 19, *22,* 62 (30), 78, *82, 84,* 132 (32), *174*
Carmichael, H. T., 35, *86*
Carr, L., 198 (281, 282), 199 (281, 282), *229,* 318 (56), *327*
Carrea, R., 425 (75), *445*
Carter, S. A., 289 (186), *301*
Cascio, G., 200 (397), *235*
Case, R. B., 21 (77, 99), *25, 26,* 205 (478), 206 (478), *240*
Caskey, W. H., 122 (9), *123*
Casper, J., 441 (152), *449*
Castello, S., 197 (86), *218*
Castillo, C. A., 78 (211), 80 (211), *91*
Castro de la Mata, R., 314 (14), 315, *325*
Catalano, P. M., 37 (82), 50 (82), *85*
Caudwell, G. C., 260 (149), *260*
Caughey, J. E., 377 (177), 380 (177), *395*
Cavalca, L., 183 (69), *217*
Cavanagh, J. B., 400 (76), *445*
Celander, O., 261 (32), 262 (32), 264 (32), 265 (32), 266 (32), *293*
Čepelik, J., 186 (479), 200 (479), *240*
Cerletti, A., 251 (218), 252 (250), 281 (219), *303, 304,* 339 (16), 343 (16), 351 (65), 352 (16, 65), 363 (16), 375 (16), *387, 389*
Černohorský, M., 186 (479), 200 (479), *240*
Cervoni, P., 161 (69), 164, 166 (69), 169 (69), *174, 176*
Chalian, W., 420 (4), *442*
Challoner, D. R., 195 (70), 206 (70, 71), *217*
Chamberlin, P. E., 202 (176), *223*
Chan, G. C. M., 245 (187), 248, 187), 258 (187), *301,* 312 (73), *328*
Chang, C. C., 439 (77, 78), 440 (78, 78a), *445*
Chang, D. K., 62, *94,* 167, 168, *177*
Chang, H., 406 (107), *447*
Chang-Shaw Jang, 169, 170 (35), *175*
Chanley, J. D., 435 (142, 143), *448*
Chargaff, E. C., 31 (123), 60 (123), *87*
Chasis, H., 44, *84*
Chen, K. K., 68, 69 (62), 71 (62), 72, 73, *84*
Chenoweth, M. B., 259 (81), *295*
Cherkes, A., 192 (160a), *222,* 318 (33), *326*
Cherkes, A. I., 188 (72), *217*
Cherry, R. O., 439 (188), *451*
Chertkova, F. A., 403 (79), *445*
Cherviakova, K. I., 408 (235), *453*
Chesrow, E. J., 359 (41), 385 (41), 386 (41), *388*
Chess, D., 254 (33), 279 (33), 282 (33), *293*
Cheung, W. Y., 188 (73), *217*
Chi, Y.-M., 183 (339), 185 (339), 190 (248), 191 (248), *227, 232*
Chidsey, C. A., 18 (15), *22,* 63, *84,* 311 (38), 312 (37), *326*
Chiu, S., 196 (388, 389), *235*
Chlouverakis, C., 198 (74), *217*
Christensen, A., 410, *455*
Christensen, H. E., 161, *178*
Christensen, L., 279 (34), 291 (34), *293*
Christy, H. W., 268 (141), *298*
Churchill-Davidson, H. C., 54 (67), 74, 75 (67), *84*
Cicardo, V. H., 352 (45), *388*
Claassen, V., 184 (75), *217,* 317 (15), *325*
Clark, B., 189 (180), *223*
Clark, J. K., 77 (74), *84*
Clark, R. E., 311 (40), 314 (40), *326*
Clark, W. B., 280 (35), 291 (35), *293*
Clark, R. E., 205 (185), *223*
Clarke, G. A., 43 (68), *84*
Clausen, C. P., 428 (80), *446*
Clegg, P. C., 155, *175*
Clément, G., 192 (76), *217*
Clifford, J. E., 78 (211), 80 (211), *91*
Cobb, L. A., 192 (54), *216*
Cobbold, A., 267 (36), *293*
Cobbold, A. F., 40 (16), 42, 51 (114), 57, 58, 59 (69, 114), 61, *82, 84, 86,* 185 (77), 188 (5), 204 (77), *213, 217*

Codegoni, A. M., 193 (34), 194 (34), *215*
Coe, W. S., 384 (46), *388*
Cohen, G., 100 (53), 104 (53), 105 (53), 112 (53), *125*
Cohn, J. N., 102 (80), *127*
Coleman, I. W., 416 (81), *446*
Collier, H. D., 109 (13), *123*
Colville, K. I., 184 (392), 199 (58, 392), *216, 235,* 318 (13, 84), *325, 329*
Comroe, J. H., 9 (16), 10 (16), 20 (16), *23,* 333 (51), 340, 344, 362 (51), *388*
Condon, E., 48, *84*
Conner, P. K., 365 (47), *388*
Cooke, W. T., 44, *82*
Cooper, C. J., 50 (72), 51, 52 (72), *84*
Cooper, T. W., 58 (270), 61 (270), *94,* 9 (17, 18), *23,* 264 (262), *305*
Coraboeuf, E., 372 (222), *397*
Corcoran, A. C., 59 (73), *84,* 384 (48), *388*
Cori, C. F., 12, *23,* 180, 181 (78), 182 (443), 187 (245, 246), 188 (89, 234), 191 (78), *217, 218, 226, 227, 238*
Cori, G. T., 12, *23*
Correll, J. W., 183 (79), 199 (79), *217*
Coriell, L. L., 401 (251), *454*
Corkill, N. L., 441 (82, 83), *446*
Corley, R. W., 349 (104), 372 (104), 383 (104), 384 (103), 385 (104), *391*
Cornman, I., 435 (84), *446*
Costa, E., 274 (17, 222), *292, 303*
Costilow, R. N., 401 (85, 300), *446, 457*
Cotten, M. de V., 258 (37), *293*
Cottle, W. H., 203 (80), *217*
Cournand, A., 108 (46), 122 (9), *123, 125*
Courtois-Suffit, M., 421 (86), *446*
Courville, D. A., 428 (87), *446*
Coxe, J. W., 113 (82), *127*
Craig, A. B., Jr., 209 (83, 84), 210 (81, 82), *218*
Craig, J. W., 182 (85), *218*
Crandall, M., 190 (272), *228*
Crane, M. C., 285 (28), *293*
Cranefield, P. F., 4, 6 (46), 14 (46), *24,* 319 (44), *326,* 358 (99), 359 (99), *391*
Cranmer, J. I., 274 (38), *293*
Credner, K., 79 (157), *89*
Crescitelli, F., 428 (88), *446*
Crosley, A. P., 77, *84*
Crout, J. R., 8 (88), 10 (20), 12 (20), 19 (88), *23, 26*
Crumpton, C. W., 78 (211), 80 (211), *91*
Culbertson, J. W., 251 (73), *295,* 349 (74), 383 (74), 384 (74), *390*
Cummings, J. R., 406, *449*
Currens, J. H., 349 (172), 383 (172), 384 (49, 172), 385 (49), *388, 395*
Curtis, D. R., 3 (7), *22,* 425 (56, 89), *444, 446*
Cusick, G., 36 (136), *88*
Csapo, I. A., 152, 158, *175*
Cucurachi, L., 197 (86), *218*

D

Dack, G. M., 401 (330), 414, *446, 458*
Daggett, W. M., 17 (94), *26,* 211 (87), *218*
Dale, A. S., 98 (15), *123*
Dale, H. H., 30 (22, 75), 40, 62, 68, 69 (22, 76), 70, 79, *82, 84, 85,* 133, 148, 151, 169, *175,* 243 (9), 244 (39), 249, 258 (39), 266, 279 (39), 280 (39), 282 (39), *292, 293*
Dale, N., 324 (92), *329*
Daly, C., 77 (150), *88*
Daly, I. de B., 98, (19, 22, 23), 101 (20, 21), 102 (24), 112 (16), 113 (1, 2, 18, 19, 24), 122 (17), *123, 124*
Daly, M. de Burgh, 267 (40), *293*
d'Amico, G., 185 (153), 210 (153), *221*
Dandiya, P. C., 377 (9), 378 (9), *386*
Danforth, W. H., 182 (88), 188 (89, 90), 189 (90), *218*
Daniel, B. N., 212 (92), *218*
Daniel, E. E., 158 (42), *175,* 211, 212 (92, 93, 94), *218*
Daniel, A., 196 (389), *235*
Daniel, P. M., 263 (256), *304*

Danielopolu, D., 256 (41), *293*
Darby, G. E., 406 (108), *447*
Das, P. K., 378 (10), *386*
Dashe, A. M., 384 (113), *392*
Davey, M. J., 18 (21), *23*
Davidson, I. W. F., 204 (95), *218*
Davidson, J. R., 343 (185), 351 (185), *395*
Davies, J. R., 413 (91), 421, 423 (92), 425 (92), 427 (93), *446*
Davies, R., 268 (56), *294*
Davies, R. O., 264 (42), *293*
Davies, B. N., 130 (18), *174*
Davis, A. H., 187 (132), *220*
Davis, D. A., 319 (70), *328*
Davis, E. J., 188 (96), *218*
Davis, J. E., 54 (230), 60 (230), *92*
Davis, L. D., 208 (97), *218*
Davoren, P. R., 182 (99), 191 (98), *218*
Dawes, G. S., 201 (100), 203 (100), *219*, 256 (43), 259 (43, 44), *293*, 333 (51), 340, 342 (51, 52), 344 (52, 54), 345, 348 (53), 362 (51), 374, 379, 382 (50), *386*, *388*, *389*
Dawkins, M. J. R., 194 (101), 207 (101), *219*
Dawkins, O., 212 (92), *218*
Day, H. T., 187 (273), *228*
Day, M. D., 67 (79), *85*, 143, *175*
Deal, C. P., 54 (80, 133), 59 (133, 135), *85*, *87*
Deal, C. P., Jr., 265 (45), 266 (94), *293*, *296*
deBeer, E. J., 54 (12), 59 (12), 73 (12), 75 (12), 77 (12), *81*
de Bodo, R. C., 192 (13), 193 (14), 199 (13), *214*
De Caro, L. G., 197 (102), *219*
Deeds, F., 332 (229), *398*
DeFazio, V., 104 (78), 105 (78), 109 (78), *126*
DeGroot, C. A., 184 (103, 466), *219*, *239*
de la Londe, I. S., 39 (182), 40, 41 (180, 182), 66 (181), *90*, 188 (104), *219*
DeLange, R. J., 182 (255), *227*
de Largy, C., 50 (190), 60, *90*
Deliwala, C. V., 369 (130), 370 (130), *393*
del Magelhaes, O., 433 (96), *446*
del Missier, P., 6 (74), *25*
DeLong, S. L., 280 (46), *294*
del Pozo, E. C., 433 (95), *446*
Demis, D. J., 37 (82), 50 (82), 78 (81), *85*
Denison, A. B., 41, 46, 55 (134), 58 (138, 270), 59 (133, 282), 61 (138, 270), *87*, *88*, *94*, *95*
Denison, A. B., Jr., 262 (240), 264 (97, 262), 266 (92), 267 (91), 268 (47), *294*, *296*, *304*, *305*
Denisova, I. A., 403 (79), *445*
Dennis, E. W., 121 (3), *123*
Denny, C. B., 401 (97, 270), *446*, *455*
De Pasquale, N. P., 109 (11), *123*
Depierre, F., 17 (75), *25*
Depocas, F., 201 (106), 204 (105), *219*
Depoorter, A. E., 35 (23), 36 (23), 48 (23), 50 (23), 51 (23), 54 (23), *82*
Dertunger, B. L., 56 (185), 57 (185), 58 (185), *90*
DeVleeschhouwer, G., 352, *391*
Devlin, H. B., 401 (352), *459*
de Vries, A., 439 (153, 192, 243), 441 (151, 152), *449*, *451*, *454*
de Wardener, H. E., 54 (67), 75 (67), *84*
Dexter, L., 109 (64), *126*
Dhalla, N. S., 155 (91), *177*, 206 (418), *237*
Diamond, J., 190 (52, 108, 109), *216*, *219*
Dickinson, C. J., 324 (7), *325*
Dickman, S. R., 181 (110), *219*
Dickens, F., 408, 409, *445*
Dickson, E. C., 408, 409, *446*
Diecke, F. P. J., 425 (347), *459*
Dil, A. H., 345 (17), 346 (17), 351 (17), *387*
Diniz, C. R., 433 (101), *446*
Dirken, M. N. J., 121 (25), *124*
DiStefano, V. A., 184 (384), *235*
Dixon, R. L., 185 (11), *219*
Dixon, W. E., 44, 68, 69 (76), 70, *83*, *85*
Dock, D. S., 109 (64), *126*
Dodd, A., 212 (94), *218*

Dodge, E., 429 (218), *453*
Dodge, H. T., 122 (26), *124*
Dörner, J., 355 (29), 360 (29), 361 (29), *387*
Doery, Hazel M., 426 (254), *454*
Dokukin, A. V., 342 (55), *389*
Dole, V. P., 192 (112), *219,* 263 (202), *302,* 318 (16), *325*
Dolejšová, K., 187 (217), 199 (336), 200 (337, 481), *225, 232, 240*
Dolman, C. E., 400, 401 (146), 402 (147), 403 (147), 404 (147), 405, 406 (102–108, 110), 407, 417 (147), *442, 447, 449*
Donal, J. S., 34 (259), 71 (259), 72 (259), *94*
Donald, D. E., 98 (27, 28), *124,* 311 (17), 312 (17), 313, *325*
Dongen, K. van, 256 (48), 260 (48), *294*
Dontas, A. S., 248 (49), *294,* 344, 349, 351 (56), *389*
Doray, B. H., 186 (420a), *237*
Dorner, J., 41, 53, *85*
Dornhorst, A. C., 310 (19), 311 (19), 324 (7, 18), *325,* 39 (84), *85*
Doss, D., 204 (113), *219*
Douglas, D. E., 195 (204), *225*
Douglas, W. W., 162 (44), *175*
Dow, S., 101 (61), *126*
Downing, S. E., 351 (57), *389*
Doyle, A. E., 384 (58), *389*
Draper, M. H., 6 (22), *23*
Draskóczy, P. R., 8 (98), *26*
Dreisbach, R. H., 213 (114), *219*
Dresel, P. E., 209 (115), 210 (115), *219,* 258 (50), 259 (51, 53), 260 (52), 278 (52), *294,* 319 (20), 321, *325,* 378 (165), 378 (165), *394*
Drill, V. A., 4 (23), 8 (23), 20 (23), *23*
Drummond, G. I., 188 (116), *219*
Drury, D. R., 181, *219*
D'Silva, J. L., 208 (107), *219,* 316 (22), *325*
DuBose, H. H., 255 (96), 287 (93), *296*
Dudarenko, G. V., 403 (79), *445*
Dudel, J., 14 (24), *23,* 210 (118), *219*
Duff, J. T., 401 (69, 70, 111, 112, 130, 154, 352), 402 (69, 70, 111, 112, 130), 403 (70, 111, 112, 113, 130, 154), 404 (130), 405 (70), 417 (113, 130), *445, 447, 448, 449, 459*
Duff, R. S., 38, *85,* 264 (54), *294*
Duggan, J. W., 280 (35), 290 (35), *293*
Duke, H., 101 (20), *124*
Dumke, P. R., 45 (86), 48 (86), 75, *85*
Duncan, D. G., 321, *325*
Duncan, L., 188 (116), *219*
Duncanson, D., 51, *85*
Dungan, K. W., 309 (23), 323 (55), *325, 327*
Dunn, A., 192 (13), 193 (14), 199 (13), *214*
Durant, R. C., 435 (141), *448*
Dury, A., 194 (119), *219*
Dzúrik, R., 191 (120, 252), *219, 227*

E

Eadie, G. A., 406 (114), *447*
Eagle, E., 34 (259), 71 (259), 72 (259), *94*
Eakins, K. E., 41, 56 (88), *85*
Eastman, P. F., 421 (115), *447*
Eaton, R. P., 192 (122, 123), 194 (121), *220*
Eccles, J. C., 425 (56, 116), *444, 447*
Eccles, R. M., 281 (55), *294*
Eckart, G. E., 102 (80), *127*
Eckenhoff, J. E., 268 (56), *294*
Eckstein, J. W., 29 (1), 70, *81,* 198 (1, 163), *213, 222,* 271 (57), *294,* 313 (1), *324*
Eckstein, R. W., 267 (58), *294*
Edholm, O. G., 35 (8), 36 (8), 38 (8), 51 (87), *81, 85*
Edman, K. A. P., 153, 155, 157, *175*
Edmondson, J. H., 193 (124), *220*
Edmunds, C. W., 408, *447*
Edwards, E. A., 287 (59, 76), 288 (59, 76), *294, 295*
Edwards, J. E., 99 (29), *124*
Edwards, W. S., 113 (30), *124*
Eid, C. H., 260 (198), 278 (198), *301*
Eik-Nes, K., 181 (110), *219*
Ek., J., 54 (271), *94*
Ekelund, L.-G., 207 (192), *224*

Eklund, H. W., 401 (213, 214), 402 (214), 403 (213), *452*
Ekmanner, S., 50 (89), *85*
Elder, J. T., 184 (125), *220*
Elek, S. R., 385 (59), *389*
Eliakim, M., 102 (31), 113 (31), *124*
Elisová, K., 187 (217), 198 (338, 482), 199 (482), *225, 232, 240*
El-Khanagry, H. A., 203 (22), 205 (21), *214*
Ellestad, M. H., 269 (60), 290 (60), *294*
Elliott, F. S., 210 (126), *220*
Elliott, H. W., 29 (2), 75 (2), *81*
Elliott, P. M., 384 (58), *389*
Elliott, T. R., 30, 44, *85*
Ellis, S., 12, 13 (25), *23,* 180 (128), 181 (128), 183 (127), 184 (130, 136), 186 (128, 134, 236), 187 (132, 136, 235, 236), 189 (235, 464a), 192 (133, 136), 198 (133), 199 (133, 136, 236), 200 (128), 205 (128), 206 (128), 207 (236), 208 (129), 209 (130, 131, 132a), 210 (132a), *220, 226, 239,* 278 (61), 278 (61), *294,* 316 (25), 317 (24), 318 (24), *325*
Ellsworth, H. C., 31, *94*
Emanuel, D. A., 271 (105), *297*
Emerson, G. A., 260 (62), *294*
Emerson, K., Jr., 263 (202), *302*
Emery, J. A., 437, *456*
Emmelin, N. G., 281 (30), *293,* 410, *447*
Emmons, P., 432 (120, 121), 433 (120, 121), *447*
Endean, R., 428 (122a), 435 (122, 123), *447*
Enderby, G. E., 268 (56), *294*
Engel, F. L., 193 (308), 195 (39), 197 (279, 463, 464), 198 (487), *215, 229, 230, 239, 240,* 318 (26), *325*
Engelberg, H., 196 (135), *220*
Engelhardt, A., 55 (158), *89*
Engelman, K., 18 (49), *24*
Ensen, Y., 13 (83), *26*
Enson, Y., 259 (235), 278 (235), *303*
Erdman, I., 401 (311), *457*
Erlanger, J., 35 (91), *85,* 266 (63), 289 (63), *294*
Erliy, D., 209 (316), 210 (316), *231,* 321 (27), *326*
Ernstene, A. C., 113 (86), *127*
Esplin, D. W., 433 (124), *447*
Essex, H. E., 428 (125), *448*
Estandia, A., 324 (36), *326*
Estes, E. H., Jr., 197 (43), 198 (43), *216*
Etzensperger, J., 373 (61), 374, *389*
Eusebi, A. J., 184 (136), 186 (134), 187 (136), 192 (136), 199 (136), 209 (132a), 210 (132a), *220*
Evans, C. L., 282 (65), *294*
Evans, D. H. L., 157, *175*
Evans, E. A., 420 (3), *442*
Evans, H. E., 431 (126), *448*
Evans, J. D., 193 (350), *233*
Evans, J. I., 38 (144), *88*
Evans, W. H., 194 (332), *232*
Everett, J. W., 276 (150, 223), *299, 303*
Ewing, P. L., 102 (34), 113 (34, 35), 122 (34), *124*
Eyzaguirre, C., 379 (62), *389*
Exton, J. H., 181 (137), *220*
Eymer, K. P., 192 (408), 194 (408), *236*
Ezaki, Y., 99 (84), *127*

F

Faber, M., 31 (123), 60 (123), *87*
Fain, J. N., 197 (138), *221,* 183 (314), 187 (314), 199 (314), *231,* 277 (155), 278 (155), *299,* 317 (61), 318 (61), *327*
Fairbanks, V. F., 344 (38), 345 (38), 363 (37), 364, 365 (38), *388*
Falck, B., 131 (13), *173*
Falk, G., 374 (63), *389*
Farah, A., 258 (2), 259 (2), *291,* 320 (2), 323 (28), *324, 326*
Farber, L., 430 (127), *448*
Farkas, T., 193 (139), *221*
Farmer, J. B., 18 (21), *23,* 315 (12), *325*
Farrand, E. A., 43, 53 (99), *86*
Farrar, C. B., 343 (185), 351 (185), *395*

Farrel, J. E., 259 (235), 278 (235), *303*

Farrell, J. E., 13 (83), *26*

Fassina, G., 197 (140), 198 (140), *221*

Fazekas, J. F., 77 (150), *88*, 268 (66), *294*

Fedinec, A. A., 421 (226), *448*

Feeley, J. W., 102 (36), 109 (36), 113 (36), *124*

Feigen, G. A., 369 (102), *391*, 420 (255a), 421 (129), 422 (255a), *448*, *455*

Feigelson, E. B., 192 (141), 193 (141), 195 (141), *221*

Feinleib, M. R., 186 (26), 188 (24, 25), *215*

Felkai, B., 251 (107), 269 (107, 108), 270 (107), 290 (107, 108), *297*

Fellows, E. J., 246 (157), *299*

Felts, J. M., 192 (162), *222*

Fenn, W. D., 13, *23*

Ferguson, D., 98 (28), *124*

Fernándes-Morán, H., 4 (27), *23*

Fernandez, E., 351 (65), 352 (65), *389*

Ferreira, H. M., 410 (16), *442*

Ferris, E. B., 353 (13), 384 (13), *386*

Fewings, J. D., 50 (72), 51 (72), 52 (72), *84*

Field, E. J., 46 (100), *86*

Field, J. B., 191 (360), *233*

Finder, A. G., 209 (142, 416), *221*, *236*

Fine, J., 109 (43), *125*

Fine, M. B., 194 (143), *221*

Fink, L. D., 164 (34), *174*

Finkelstein, J. L., 192 (410), 236

Finkleman, B., 142, *175*

Finley, K. H., 45 (106), 46 (106), *86*

Finnerty, F. A., Jr., 268 (66), *294*

Finesinger, J., 48, *86*

Fiock, M. A., 401 (130, 154, 352), 402 (130), 403 (130, 154), 404 (130), 405, 417 (130), *448*, *449*, *459*

Firor, W. M., 419 (131), 420 (4), 424 (131), *442*, *448*

Fischer, H. G., 436 (243a), *454*

Fisher, R. B., 206 (144), *221*

Fishman, A. P., 98 (37, 38), 99 (39), 100 (53), 101 (37), 104 (53), 105 (53), 108 (66), 109 (66), 111, 112 (37, 53), *124*, *125*, *126*, 262 (154), *299*

Firsch, E. F., 9 (18), *23*

Fizette, N. B., 195 (145, 197), *221*, *224*

Flacke, W., 332 (68), 338 (68, 69, 70), 339 (72, 151), 345 (30), 346 (72), 347 (30), 348 (30), 349 (71), 350 (72), 351 (30), 352 (30), 353 (30), 366, 367 (68, 69, 70), 368 (69), 369 (68), 370 (70), 372 (68), 375, 376 (65, 69), 377 (68), 378 (66), 379 (67, 68), 380 (68), 382 (68), *387*, *389*, *390*, *394*

Flatt, J. P., 197 (146), *221*

Fleckenstein, A., 13, *23*

Fleckenstein, B., 164, *175*

Fleisher, J. H., 436 (132, 133), *448*

Fleishman, M., 271 (105), *297*

Fleming, J. W., 121 (88), *127*, *268* (268), *305*

Fleming, W. W., 169, *175*, 184 (147, 239), *221*, *226*, 311 (29)

Flinn, R. B., 197 (62, 267), *217*, *228*

Flock, E. V., 283 (214), 285 (214), *302*

Florey, H., 45, *86*

Flynn, J. E., 432 (25), *443*

Foá, P. P., 185 (153), 210 (153), *221*

Fog, M., 46 (103), *86*

Foggie, P., 98 (19), 113 (19, 40), 122 (17), *123*, *124*, *125*

Folk, B. P., 379 (62), *389*

Folkow, B., 32 (104), 38, 50, 54, *86*, 248 (68), 261 (68), 262 (67), 267 (36), *293*, *295*

Fomon, S. J., 263 (132), 264 (132), *298*

Forbes, A. S., 45, 46, *86*

Ford, R. V., 262 (69), *295*, 383 (14), 385 (161), *394*

Forney, R. B., 192 (241), 198 (242), *227*

Foster, R., 152, *175*

Fourneau, E., 255 (70), *295*

Fouts, J. R., 185 (11), *219*

Fowler, N. D., 17 (47), 18 (48), 19, *24*

Fowler, N. O., 78, *89*, 98 (42), 104 (41), 105 (41), *125*

Fox, A., 212 (449), *238*

Fox, S. M., 79 (162), 80 (162), *89*

Fraenkel-Conrat, H., 441 (134), *448*
Frank, E. D., 109 (43), *125*
Frank, G. B., 367 (43), 374 (73), *388, 390*
Frank, H. A., 109 (43), *125*
Franklin, D., 346 (192), *396*
Franklin, K. J., 113 (44), *125*, 263 (256), *304*
Fredericq, H., 161, 163, *173*
Freedman, D. X., 273 (71), *295*
Freedman, H., 35 (108), 36 (108), *86*
Freeman, N. E., 35 (108), 36 (108), *86*, 289 (72), *295*
Freeman, N. L., 408, *448*
Freeman, S E., 188 (398), *235*
Freis, E. D., 102 (79, 80), 110 (79), 113 (79), *127*, 185 (148), *221*, 269 (213), 251 (73), *295, 302*, 347 (75), 349 (74), 363 (75), 383 (74), 384 (74), 385 (75), *390*
French, G. N., 258 (2), 259 (2), *291*, 320 (2), *324*
Frenkel, H., 44, *82*
Freyberger, W. A., 53 (140), *88*, 259 (161), *299*, 320 (64), 321 (64), *327*, 343 (86, 87), 344 (86), 351 (86), 352 (86), *390*
Friedberg, L., 113 (45), 116, 122 (45), *125*, 256 (133), 269 (74), *295, 298*
Friedberg, S. L., 190 (248), 191 (248), *227*
Friedemann, U., 423 (138, 140), 424 (136, 139), *448*
Friedenwald, J. S., 280 (75), *295*
Friedlich, A. L., 349 (172), 383 (172), 384 (172), *395*
Friedman, M., 195 (149), *221*
Friedman, S. M., 210 (220), *225*, 279 (241), *304*
Friend, D. G., 287 (76), 288 (76), *295*
Friess, S. L., 435 (141, 142, 143), *448*
Fritts, H. W., Jr., 108 (46), *125*
Fritz, I. B., 181 (150), *221*
Froberg, S., 278 (77), *295*
Fröberg, S., 192 (152), 193 (151), 194 (151), 199 (151), *221*
Fröhlich, A., 62 (109), *86*, 167, *175*
Frost, J., 38 (105), 50 (105), 54 (105), *86*
Fuentes, J., 355 (29), 360 (29, 77), 361 (29), 378 (76, 77), 382 (29), *387, 390*
Fuhrman, F. A., 436 (243a), 437 (184), *451, 454*
Fujita, E., 338 (141), *393*
Fujita, T., 213 (329), *232*
Fukuda, A., 181 (415), *236*
Fulthorpe, A. J., 426, *448*
Fulton, R. M., 324 (7), *325*
Furchgott, R. F., 8 (29), 13, 14 (35), 15 (35), 19 (29), *23*, 133, 134 (53), 138, 161 (69), 166 (69), 169 (69), *175, 176*, 247 (78), 248 (78), 280 (79), 281 (80), *295*, 318, *326*
Furman, R. H., 196 (37, 38), *215*

G

Gaddum, J. H., 20 (31), *23*, 31, 54, 62, *86*, 113 (47, 48), *125*, 147, 156, 169, *173, 175*
Galambos, É., 204 (363), *234*
Galansino, G., 185 (153), 210 (153), *221*
Gamble, C. J., 34 (259), 71 (259), 72 (259), *94*
Gans, J. H., 194 (154), *221*
Gant, M., 194 (230), *226*
Ganz, A., 17 (32), *23*
Garattini, S., 193 (34), 194 (34), *215*
Garb, S., 17 (32), *23*, 259 (81), *295*
Garber, S. T., 353 (13), 384 (13), *386*
Garbus, J., 199 (301), *230*
Garcia, L. A., 199 (391), *235*
Gardiner, J. E., 163, *176*
Gargouil, Y. M., 372 (222), *397*
Garland, R. B., 195 (155), *221*
Garvey, A. H., 266 (92), *296*
Gaskell, P., 51 (17), *82*
Gasser, H. S., 35 (91), *85*, 266 (63), 289 (63), *294*
Geiling, E. M. K., 339, *395*
Geissman, T. A., 428 (88), *446*
Gellhorn, A., 193 (28), *215*
Gellhorn, E., 345 (78), *390*
Gendon, I. Z., 401 (145), 403 (145), *449*
Genther, G. H., 369 (102), *391*, 421 (129), *448*

George, H. W., 368, 377 (129), 378 (129), *392*
Gerard, R. W., 273 (137), *298*
Gerchen, G., 159 (19), *174*
Germon, W. J., 113 (86), *127*
Gershfeld, N. L., 381 (80, 205), *390, 396*
Gerszi, K. E., 186 (396), *235*
Gerwing, J., 401 (146), 402 (147), 403 (147), 404 (147), 405, 417 (147), *449*
Gessert, C. F., 191 (393, 394), 213 (393, 394), *235*
Ghiretti, F., 434 (148), *449*
Gho, B. K., 184 (466), *239*
Ghosh, B. N., 439 (149), *449*
Giardina, A., 199 (167, 168), *222*
Giarman, N. J., 185 (278), *229*, 273 (71), *295*
Gibbs, E. L., 46 (113), *86*
Gibbs, F. A., 46, *86*
Gibson, W., 17 (105), *27*
Gilardi, F., 183 (69), *217*
Gilbert, J. L., 3 (7), 8 (6), 14 (33), 21 (33), *22, 23*, 320, 321 (31), *326*
Gilbert, R. P., 102 (49), 113 (49), *125*
Gilding, H. P., 265 (220), 267 (220), *303*
Gillespie, J. A., 287 (82), *295*
Gillespie, J. S., 130 (18), 136, 143 (59), *174, 176*, 248 (27), *293*, 413, *449*
Gillespie, L., 37 (226), *92*
Gilmore, J. P., 53 (256), *94*, 206 (476), *240*, 314 (89), *329*
Gilot, J., 198 (330), *232*
Ginsburg, J., 39 (9), 42 (9), 51 (114), 57, 58 (69), 59 (9, 69, 114), 61, 80 (10), 81, *81, 84, 86*, 185 (77), 204 (77), *217*, 264 (54), 271 (233), *294, 303*
Ginzell, K. H., 102 (50), 113 (50), *125*
Giotti, A., 188 (57), *216*
Girout, R., 421 (86), *446*
Gitter, S., 439 (153, 192, 243), 441 (151, 152), *449, 451, 454*
Giuntini, C., 109 (51), *125*
Gladstone, G. P., 400 (326), *458*
Glass, H. G., 351 (144), *393*
Glassman, H. N., 405, *452*
Glick, G., 122 (73), *126*, 311 (38), *326*
Glitsch, H. G., 211 (156), *222*
Glockling, B., 205 (8), *214*
Glover, W. E., 37 (119), 39 (115), 41 (116), 42, 49, 54 (118), 61, *86, 87*, 188 (157), *222*
Goetz, R. H., 264 (18), 265 (18), *292*
Gold, M., 192 (158), 193 (425), 194 (159), *222, 237*
Goldberg, G. I., 79 (163), 80 (163), *89*
Goldberg, L. I., 79 (162, 219), 80 (162), *87, 89, 92*
Goldblum, N., 439 (153, 243), *449, 454*
Goldenberg, M., 31 (123), 34, 47, 48 (124), 60, *87*, 100 (52), 104 (52), 112 (52), 121 (52), *125*, 256 (83), 272 (83), 284 (83), *295*
Goldfien, A., 193 (193), 199 (193), *224*, 318 (41), *326*
Goldfischer, J. D., 251 (84), *295*
Goldring, R. M., 100 (53), 104 (53), 105 (53), 112 (53), *125*
Goldring, S., 366 (81), *390*
Goldring, W., 44 (61), *84*
Goldstein, L., 275 (85, 174), *295, 300*
Golenhofen, K., 39, *87*
Gomez Alonso de la Sierra, B., 21 (89), *26*
Gomez, D. M., 262 (154), *299*
Gommi, B. W., 213 (491), *241*
Goncalves, J. M., 433 (101), 441 (244), *446, 454*
Goodall, McC., 63 (126), 78 (126, 127), *87*
Goodford, P. J., 212 (216), *225*
Goodman, H. M., 193 (124), 198 (160), *220, 222*, 318 (32), *326*
Goodman, L. S., 245 (188), 246 (189), 247 (189), 265 (189), 266 (189), 267 (189), 274 (189, 190), 277 (189), 279 (189), 280 (189), *301*, 365 (40), *388*
Goodwin, L. G., 31, *86*
Gordon, E., 133 (71), *176*
Gordon, M., 401 (154), 403 (154), *449*
Gordon, R. S., Jr., 192 (160a), *222*, 318 (33), *326*
Gordon, W., 35, *87*
Gorin, E., 194 (411), 236
Gorini, M., 197 (102), *219*

Gorten, R., 57, *87*
Goth, 347, 352, 353, *390*
Goto, Y., 188 (161), 205 (161), *222*
Gottfried, C., 401 (69, 70, 112), 402 (69, 70, 112), 403 (70), 405 (70, 112), *445, 447*
Gourzis, J. T., 264 (191), 270 (191), 271 (191), 289, *301*, 365 (83), 370 (84), 385 (83), *390*
Gousios, A., 192 (162), *222*
Goutier, R., 375 (85), 376 (85), *390*
Gowdey, C. W., 253 (86), 254 (86), *295*
Grafova, V. N., 420 (202), 423 (200), 424 (201, 202, 203), *451, 452*
Graham, J. D. P., 149, *176*, 245 (88), 248 (87), *296*
Graham, M. H., 198 (163), *222*
Graikoski, J. T., *451*
Grana, E., 184 (164), 187 (164), 204 (164), *222*
Granata, L., 313 (34), *326*
Grandjean, T., 324 (35), *326*
Granger, H. R., 56 (185, 254), 57 (185), 58 (185), *90, 94*
Grant, J. I., 251 (139), *298*
Grant, R. T., 38, *87*
Grant, W. M., 279 (89), *296*
Grasset, E., 439 (155), *449*
Gray, G., 204 (211), *225*
Gray, H. H., 439 (156), *449*
Gray, J. A. B., 162 (44), *175*
Grayson, J., 43, 44, 46 (100), 53, 54 (132), *86, 87*
Grecz, N., 401 (157, 296), *449, 457*
Greeff, K., 55 (158), *89*
Green, A. F., 67, *83*, 152, 172 (15), *173, 174*
Green, D. M., 36 (136), *88*
Green, H. D., 37 (137), 41, 42, 46, 50 (137), 54 (80, 133, 230), 55 (134), 58 (138, 270), 59 (135, 137, 282), 60 (230), 61 (270), *85, 87, 88, 92, 94, 95*, 253 (211), 254 (96, 129, 164), 262 (240), 264 (90, 95, 97, 262), 265 (45, 90, 129) 266 (92, 94, 98), 267 (91, 96, 129, 164), 268 (47, 96), 287 (96), *294, 296, 298, 300, 302, 304, 305*
Green, K. G., 324 (7), *325*
Greene, D. G., 34 (124), 47 (124), 48 (124), *87*, 100 (52), 104 (52), 112 (52), 121 (52), *125*
Greene, N. M., 188 (165), *222*
Greenfield, A. D. M., 39 (115), 41, 50 (190), 60 (190), *86, 90*
Greenspan, K., 321 (99), *329*
Gregg, D. E., 313 (34), *326*
Gregory, R., 109 (70), *126*, 268 (175), *300*
Gregson, J. D., 427, 432 (158, 159), 433, *449*
Grieff, K., 154, *176*
Griffith, F. R., Jr., 40 (139), *88*, 180, 202 (419), *222, 237*
Griffith, G. C., 385 (59), *389*
Griffith, W., 343 (185), 351 (185), *395*
Grillo, S. A., 248 (15), *292*
Grimson, K. S., 260 (99), *296*
Grivas, J. C., 338 (141), *393*
Grizou, V., 401 (48), *444*
Grodko, N. S., 403 (79), *445*
Gromokovskaya, M. M., 413 (160), *449*
Gross, F., 63 (27), *82*, 253 (100), *296*
Grossman, A., 14 (35), 15 (35), *23*
Grossman, R. G., 339 (223), 343 (223), 344 (223), 345 (223), 351 (223), 352 (223), 360 (223), *397*
Grossman, S. P., 275 (101, 102), *296*
Grover, R. F., 269 (103), *296*
Gruenfeld, N., 336 (142), 338 (142), 370 (142), 376 (142), 379 (142), *393*
Gruhzit, C. C., 53, *88*, 343 (86), 344 (86), 351 (86), 352 (86), *390*
Guarnieri, E., 199 (167, 168), *222*
Guillemin, R., 276 (104), *296*
Guillet, P., 256 (131), *298*
Gujral, P. K., 338 (88, 89), 354 (89), 370 (88) 379 (88), 382 (88), *390*
Gump, W. S., 245 (192), 247 (192), *301*
Gunnells, J. C., 57 (129), *87*
Gunning, A. J., 122 (5), *123*
Gunning, R. E. L., 37 (167), 44, 45, *89*
Gunnison, J. B., 406, *449*
Gurd, M. R., 78, *88*, 149, *176*
Gustavson, R. G., 148 (101), *178*

Gutman, A., 193 (412), 196 (169), *222, 236*
Guyton, A. C., 408, 409, 410, *449*

H

Haas, H. G., 211 (156), *222*
Haast, W. E., 439 (163), *449*
Habermann, E., 430 (250), 431 (164, 250), *450, 454*
Haddy, F. J., 271 (105), *297*
Hadidian, Z., 441 (165), *450*
Haeger, K., 248 (68), 261 (68), *295*
Hagen, J. H., 180 (175), 194 (174), 195 (173, 175), 196 (171), 197 (172, 173), 206 (170), *222, 223*
Hagen, P. B., 180 (175), 194 (174), 195 (175), *223*
Haid, B., 258 (169), *300*
Haig, D. A., 439 (266), *455*
Haight, A. S., 185 (492), *241*
Haimovici, H., 282 (106), *297*
Haist, R. E., 277 (115), *297*
Hajdu, S., 15 (36), 16 (37), *23*
Hall, G. E., 324 (62), *327*
Hall, L. S., 59 (135), *88,* 266 (94), *296*
Hall, V. E., 202 (176), *223*
Hall, W. J., 18 (38), *24*
Hallmann, G., 366, *396*
Halmágyi, D., 251 (107), 269 (107, 108), 270 (107), 290 (107, 108), *297*
Halperin, M. H., 251 (73), *295,* 349 (74), 383 (74), 384 (74), *390*
Halstead, B. W., 428 (87), 429, 435 (272), 436 (168, 174), *446, 450, 455*
Hamberg, U., 31 (96), *85*
Hamburger, J., 193 (177), *223*
Hamilton, M., 288 (109), *297*
Hamilton, M. D., 65 (24), *87*
Hamilton, P. B., 263 (202), *302*
Hamilton, W. F., 99 (54), 113 (54), 116, *125,* 33, 58 (142), *88, 93,* 289 (208), *302*
Hamilton, W. F., Jr., 289 (208), *302*
Hamilton, W. K., 271 (57), *294*
Hammermeister, K. E., 188 (178), *223*
Hammerstrom, R. N., 266 (184), *301*
Hamon, D. P. G., 333 (22), *387*
Hamosh, M., 318 (102), *329*
Hampil, B., 420 (3, 5), *442*
Hanaford, S. W., 53 (256), *94*
Handford, P. M., 401 (182), *450*
Handley, C. A., 54 (215, 218), 77 (215), *92,* 258 (123), 259 (123), 262 (110, 111, 172), 263 (111, 173), *297, 300*
Handovsky, H., 272 (112), *297*
Hannon, J. P., 193 (179), *223*
Harakal, C., 68, 69 (143), 70, *88*
Hapke, H. J., 363 (91), *390*
Hardman, H. F., 321 (57), *327*
Hardman, J. G., 184 (181), 187 (181), 189 (180), 198 (181), *223*
Harel, L., 195 (181a), *223*
Harlan, W. R., 193 (470), *239*
Harris, A. S., 324 (36), *326*
Harris, L. S., 378 (92), *391*
Harris, T. D., 365 (40), *388*
Harrison, D. C., 18 (15), *22,* 63 (65), *84,* 109 (64), *126,* 311 (38), 312 (37), *326*
Harrison, C. S., 436 (132, 133), *448*
Harrison, F., 347, 352, 353, *390*
Harrison, T. R., 71 (280), *95*
Harry, J., 409, *450*
Hart, J. S., 205 (182), 207 (182), *223*
Hartman, F. A., 38, *88*
Hartung, W. H., 3, 8 (40), *24*
Harvey, A. M., 420, *450*
Harvey, R. M., 109 (51), *125*
Harvey, S. C., 185 (183), *223,* 246 (113), 247 (3), 273 (113), 277 (114), *291, 297,* 317 (39), *326*
Hashimoto, K., 205 (185), *223,* 313, 314 (40), *326*
Hasselblatt, A., 184 (184), *223*
Hassencamp, E., 35, *88*
Hasson, A., 441 (244), *454*
Haugaard, N., 13 (39), 20 (39, 43), *24,* 180 (187), 186 (4), 187 (4), 188 (188, 201, 257), 189 (188, 201), *213, 223, 224, 227*
Hausberger, F. X., 192 (189, 190), *224*
Havel, R. J., 180 (191), 192 (162, 191), 193 (193), 199 (193), 207, *224,* 318 (41), *326*

Hawkins, D. F., 311 (29), *326,* 360 (93, 94), 361 (93), *391*
Hawkins, R. D., 277 (115), *297*
Haynes, F. W., 109 (64), *126*
Hazard, R., 183 (194), *224,* 359 (95), *391*
Headings, V. E., 212 (195), *224*
Hebb, C. O., 98 (19), 101 (20, 21), 102 (58), 113 (19, 48, 55, 58), 122 (55), *124, 125, 126*
Hecht, H., 104 (75), 105 (75), *126*
Hecht, H. H., 264 (116), 272 (116), 273 (116), 274 (116), 277 (116), *297*
Heckly, R. J., 403 (172, 175), 404, 405 (175), 415 (175), *450*
Heemstra, H., 121 (25), *124*
Hegglin, R., 313, *326*
Heilbrunn, L. V., 14 (41), *24*
Heimberg, M., 195 (145, 197), *221, 224*
Heinemann, H. O., 196 (495), *241*
Helfrich, P., 436 (26), *443*
Hellmann, K., 163 (56), *176*
Hellems, H. K., 104 (78), 105 (78), 109 (78), *126*
Hellerstein, H. K., 122 (9), *123*
Helmer, P. R., 208 (97), *218*
Helmich, H., 362 (157), *394*
Helmreich, E., 187 (246), 188 (89, 234), *218, 226, 227*
Hemingway, A., 202 (198), 203 (198), *224*
Henderson, A. M., 186 (424), *237*
Hendrix, J. P., 45, 73, *93,* 260 (99), *296*
Henneman, D. H., 181 (199), *224*
Henry, J. W., 261 (193), *301*
Hensel, H., 39 (36), 52 (36), *83*
Hermann, H., 254 (117), *297*
Hermansen, K., 154, *176*
Herman, M. S., 187 (199a), *224*
Herms, W. B., 428 (173), *450*
Héroux, O., 204 (200), *224*
Herr, F., 379 (96), 381, 382 (96), *391*
Herring, B., 191 (360), *233*
Herring, D. A., 366 (149), *394*
Hershberger, R. L., 121 (3), *123*
Herting, G., 166, *176*
Hertting, G., 9 (42), *24,* 312 (43), *326*
Herwitz, G. K., 57 (171), *89*
Hess, M. E., 20 (43), *24,* 180 (187), 188 (188, 257), 188 (189, 201), *223, 224, 227,* 342 (18), 343 (18), *387*
Hessel, D. W., 428 (87), 436 (174), *446, 450*
Hetényi, G., Jr., 251 (107), 269 (107), 270 (107), 290 (107), *297*
Heymans, C., 352, *391*
Hibbs, R. G., 65 (146, 233), *88, 93*
Highman, B., 194 (300), 199 (301), *230*
Hildebrand, G. J., 403 (172, 175), 404, 405 (175), 415 (175), *450*
Hildes, J. A., 40, *88*
Hill, I. D., 324 (7), *325*
Hillarp, N. Å., 32 (148), 47 (148), *88,* 131 (13, 14), *173*
Hillyard, I. W., 323 (55), *327*
Hilton, S. M., 37 (149), *88*
Himwich, H. E., 77 (150), *88*
Hines, H. M., 51 (169), *89*
Hinkle, L. E., Jr., 197 (361), *233*
Hinshaw, L. B., 102 (49), 113 (49), *125*
Hirose, T., 345 (98), *391*
Hirschman, J. C., 117, 122 (56), *125*
Hirt, L., 331, 340 (33), *387*
Ho, P.-P., 194 (470), *240*
Ho, R. J., 195 (202), 196 (60), *216, 224*
Ho, S. J., 195 (203), *224*
Hodge, R. L., 49, 50 (72), 51 (72), 52 (72), 65, 67, *84, 88*
Hodgeson, N. B., 430 (176), *450*
Hodgkin, A. L., 4, *24*
Höyem, T., 401 (178), *450*
Hökfelt, B., 32 (148), 47 (148), *88*
Hoff, H. E., 279 (122), *297*
Hoffman, B. F., 4, 5 (8), 6(8, 46), 13 (83), 14 (42), *22, 24, 26,* 259 (235), 278 (235), *303,* 319 (44), 321 (99, 100), 322 (90, 91), *326, 329,* 358 (41a, 99), 359 (99), 369 (41a), 372 (41a), *388, 391*
Hoffmann, P., 367, *391*
Hofmann, A., 250 (245, 246), *304*
Hofmann, W. W., 369 (102), 376, *391,* 420 (255a), 421 (129), 422 (255a), *448, 455*

Hoijer, D. J., 201 (420), *237*
Holcomb, A. K., 14 (64), *25*, 320 (67), 321 (67), *328*
Holland, W. C., 212 (51), *216*
Hollander, A., 423 (138, 140), 424 (138, 139), *448*
Hollander, W., 190 (203a), *224*
Hollenberg, C. H., 193 (369), 195 (204), 196 (205), *225*, *234*
Hollenberg, N. K., 263 (118), 264 (42, 118, 120), 265 (118, 120), 266 (118), 271 (118, 119), 289 (118), *293*, *297*
Hollett, C. R., 196 (206), *225*
Holling, H. E., 38, *89*
Holman, M. E., 159 (32), *174*
Holmes, F., 268 (129), *297*
Holmes, J. C., 17 (47), 18 (48, 19, *24*, 78, *89*
Holmgren, A., 207 (192), *224*
Holton, P., 31, *89*
Holtz, P., 31, 55, 79, *89*, 113 (47), *125*, 132, 154, *176*, 194 (207), 197 (207), *225*
Holzbauer, M., 156, *176*
Honig, C. R., 209 (84), *218*
Hoobler, S. W., 265 (269), *305*, 349 (104), 372 (104), 383 (104), 384 (103), 385 (104), *391*
Hornbrook, K. R., 183 (208, 209), 184 (208), 185 (208), 186 (368), 187 (208, 209, 368), 188 (209), 189 (209, 368), *225*, *234*
Horning, M. G., 278 (25), *292*
Hornykiewicz, O., 79 (160), *89*
Horvath, S. M., 43 (99), 53 (99), 76 (161), *86*, *89*, 122 (57), *125*
Horwitz, D., 18 (49), *24*, 79, 80 (162, 163), *89*, 185 (333), 197 (333), 198 (333), *232*
Hoshi, T., 14 (62), *25*
Hoskins, D., 414, *446*
Hoskins, R. G., 37, 44, 45, *89*
Hossli, G., 17 (50), *24*
Hottenstein, D., 20 (43), *24*, 189 (201), *224*
Hottle, G. A., 401 (6, 177, 178, 251), 402 (6), *442*, *450*, *454*
Housewright, R. D., 401 (275), *455*
Howard, A., 366 (149), *394*
Howard, J. G., 400 (76), *445*
Howard, J. W., 57, *90*
Howard, R. M., 285 (207), *302*
Howard, W. B., 264 (95), *296*
Howells, J. E., 188 (346), *233*
Hoyer, B. H., 401 (221), *453*
Hruza, Z., 193 (221), *225*
Hsieh, A. C. L., 204 (210, 211), *225*
Hüter, J., 212 (216), *225*
Hufnagel, C. A., 102 (79), 110 (79), 113 (79), *127*
Huggins, R. A., 253 (5), 254 (5), 258 (123), 259 (123), 260 (5), 262 (172), 263 (173), 264 (5), 279 (122), *291*, *297*, *300*
Hughes, F. W., 192 (241), 198 (242), *227*
Hughes, L. E., 433 (124), *447*
Hughes, R., 410, *450*
Humphreys, J., 50 (168), *89*
Hull, D., 194 (101), 201 (212), 202, 203 (212), 204 (212), 207 (101, 214), 208 (213, 214), *219*, *225*
Hunninghake, D. B., 199 (215), *225*
Hunt, C. C., 367 (105), *391*
Hunt, J., 212 (93, 94), *218*
Hunter, J., 199 (301), *230*
Hunter, R. B., 31 (273), *94*
Hurst, P., 324 (7), *325*
Hutcheon, D. E., 53, 54, *83*, 166, 174
Hutter, C. P., 248 (140), *298*
Hutter, D. F., 6 (51, 52), 14 (51, 52), *24*
Hutter, O., 421 (181), *450*
Huvos, A., 313 (34), *326*
Huxley, A. F., 4, *24*
Hyland, J. W., 109 (64), *126*
Hyman, A. L., 109 (11), *123*
Hyman, C., 287 (267), *305*
Hynie, S., 186 (479), 187 (217, 218), 198 (334, 482), 199 (254, 355, 336, 406, 482), 200 (337, 479, 480, 481), *225*, *227*, *232*, *236*, *240*

I

Iglauer, A., 57 (171), *89*
Imai, S., 205 (185), *223*, 313 (40), 314 (40), *326*
Imig, C. J., 51, *89*
Indevine, D., 268 (56), *294*
Ing, H. R., 152 (50), *175*

Inger, R. F., 438 (294), 439 (294), 441 (294), *456*
Ingram, M., 400 (182a), 401 (182, 183), *450, 451*
Innes, I. R., 247 (125, 126), 251 (124), *298*, 360 (106, 107), *391*
Ionides, C. J. P., 441 (83), *446*
Iriye, T. T., 191 (219), *225*
Isaacson, A., 374 (196), *396*
Issekutz, B., Jr., 192 (319), 194 (159), *222, 231*
Ito, R., 321 (81), *328*
Itoh, M., 435 (24), *443*
Iványi, J., 251 (107), 269 (107, 108), 270 (107), 290 (107, 108), *297*

J

Jacob, S., 109 (43), *125*
Jackson, T. W., 58 (138), 61 (138), *88*
Jacques, S., 194 (230), *226*
Jakowska, S., 435 (253), *454*
James, L. F., 386 (34), *388*
James, T. N., 14 (53), *24*, 311 (45, 46), *326, 327*
Jameson, A. G., 100 (53), 104 (53), 105 (53), 112 (53), *125*
Jamieson, J. D., 210 (220), *225*
Jann, G. J., 401 (314), *458*
Jansky, L., 205 (182), 207 (182), *223*
Jarisch, A., 340, 344, 346, 363 (108), *391*
Jeffcoate, T. N. A., 251 (127), *298*
Jelinkova, M., 193 (221), *225*
Jellinek, M., 9 (18), *23*
Jenkinson, D. H., 211 (222), *226*
Joel, C. D., 195 (223), *226*
Joels, N., 342 (174), 346, *395*
Jörgensen, G., 183 (225), *226*
Johns, V. J., Jr., 283 (128), 285 (28, 128), *293, 298*
Johnson, A. D., 36 (136), *88*
Johnson, D. H., 43, 53, *87*
Johnson, G. E., 201 (402), 204 (224), *226, 236*
Johnson, H. D., 255 (129), 265 (129), 267 (129), *298*
Johnson, P., 191 (360), *233*
Johnson, P. C., 269 (130), *298*
Johnson, R., 199 (283), *229*
Johnson, W. S., 333 (22), *387*
Johnston, J. H., 50 (168), *89*
Johnstone, M., 324 (47), *327*
Jona, E., 102 (63), 113 (63), *126*
Jonas, A. F. J., 420 (5), *442*
Jones, G. T., 273 (236), *304*
Jones, J. V., 344 (111), *392*
Jones, W. R., 331 (225), 338 (225), 363 (225), 365 (225), *397*
Jordan, E. J., 185 (492), *241*
Jordan, F., 256 (131), *298*
Joseph, J., 420 (31), 424 (31), *443*
Joseph, N., 34 (259), 71 (259), 72 (259), *94*
Josephson, B., 54 (271), *94*
Joubert, J. F., 439 (266), *455*
Jourdan, F., 45 (37), 73, *83*
Joy, R. J. T., 204 (226), *226*
Juhász, Nagy, A., 268 (251), *304*
Jungas, R. L., 197 (18, 227), *214, 226*

K

Kabal, J., 195 (228), *226*
Kabanova, Ye. A., 408 (61), *444*
Kabza, T. G., 349 (104) 372 (104), 383 (104), 384 (103), 385 (104), *391*
Kadull, P. J., 401 (275), *455*
Kahn, J. B., Jr., 210 (229), *226*, 355, *397*
Kaiser, G. A., 206 (250), *227*
Kalow, W., 342 (18), 343 (18), *387*
Kameyama, S., 14 (62), *25*
Kanameishi, D., 185 (153), 210 (153), *221*
Kaniike, K., 209 (452), *238*
Kanno, T., 344, 363 (216), 364, *397*
Kao, C. Y., 437 (184), *451*
Kaplan, A., 194 (230), *226*, 363 (168), *395*
Kaplan, S. A., 263 (132), 264 (132), *298*
Kapper, A., 48 (170), *89*
Kappert, A., 204 (232), *226*
Kappey, F., 202 (231), *226*
Karis, J., 321 (100), *329*
Karlberg, P., 200 (233), *226*
Karmen, A., 192 (141), 193 (141), 195 (141), *221*
Karpatkin, S., 188 (234), *226*
Kats, F. M., 403 (79), *445*

Katsui, N., 336 (142), 338 (142), 370 (142), 376 (142), 379 (142), *393*

Katz, L. N., 14 (101), *27*, *113* (45), 116 (45), 122 (45), *125*, 256 (133, 134), 269 (74), *295*, *298*

Katz, R., 21 (104), *27*

Kaufman, J., 57, *89*

Kauntze, R., 365 (112), 384 (112), 385 (112), *392*

Kavaler, F., 7 (54), 8 (6), 15 (55, 56), *22*, *24*

Kawata, T., 401 (311), *457*

Kay, H. B., 65 (24), *82*

Keach, L. M., 58 (138), 61 (138), *88*

Keegan, H. L., 428 (185), 439 (338), *451*, *458*

Keele, C. A., 45 (172), *89*

Kegeles, G., 401 (6), 402 (6), 403 (186), 405, *442*, *451*

Keiper, G. F., 408, *447*

Kellaway, C. H., 439 (187, 188), *451*

Keller, C. J., 45 (173), *89*

Kemp, R. G., 182 (255), *227*

Kempe, L. L., 401 (42, 44, 45), 417, 418, *444*, *451*

Kenan, L. F., 264 (95), *296*

Kennard, J. H., 149, *176*

Kenney, R. A., 44, *82*

Kenny, A. D., 184 (147, 239), 187 (238), 191 (237), 213 (238), *221*, *226*

Kennedy, B. L., 186 (134, 236), 187 (235, 236), 189 (235), 192 (133), 198 (133), 199 (133, 236), 207 (236), *220*, *226*

Kepchar, J. H., 37 (137), 41, 42, 50 (137), 55, 59 (137), *88*, 267 (96), 268 (96), *296*

Kermani, M. H., 316 (58), *327*

Kerpekar, S., 8 (29), 19 (29), *23*

Kerpel, S., 197 (240, 413), *227*, *236*

Kerr, D. E., 406 (107), *447*

Kert, M. J., 384 (113), *392*

Kerwin, J. F., 245 (258), 246 (157), *299*, *305*

Kety, S. S., 55, 75 (245), *89*, *93*

Keys, A., 76 (175), *90*

Khan, A. U., 192 (241), 198 (242), *227*

Kibler, R. F., 186 (243), *227*

Kiebel, G., 367 (114), 378 (114, 195), 379 (114), *392*, *396*

Kilburn, K. H., 183 (244), *227*

Killos, P. J., 436 (132, 133), *448*

Kim, Y. I., 319 (82), *328*

Kindler, S. H., 401 (190), *451*

King, B. D., 47, 55 (177), *90*

King, S. E., 54 (176), *90*

Kingston, C. W., 430 (191), *451*

Kini, M. M., 379 (115), 383 (115), *392*

Kinsman, J. M., 384 (46), *388*

Kipnis, D. M., 187 (245, 246), 194 (400), *227*, *236*

Kirpekar, S. M., 161, 166, 169, *176*

Kirshner, N., 78 (127), *87*, 132, *176*

Kissin, M., 35, *93*

Kitchen, T., 266 (98), *296*

Kits van Heijningen, A. J. M., 187 (247), *227*

Kjellmer, I., 267 (36), 293

Klainer, L. M., 190 (248), 191 (248), *227*

Klatskin, G., 185 (278), *229*

Klein, R. J., 197 (43), 198 (43), 199 (249), *216*, *227*

Klerer, J., 401 (111, 112), 402 (111, 112), 403 (111, 112), 405 (112), *447*

Kline, N. S., 273 (159), *299*

Klocke, F. J., 206 (250), *227*

Kloep, L. P., 195 (345), *233*

Knapp, D. W., 76 (161), *89*, 122 (57), *125*

Knobil, E., 198 (160), *222*, 318 (32), *326*

Kobayashi, M., 109 (70), *126*, 268 (175), *300*

Kobota, S., 71, *81*

Koch, R. B., 400 (21), *443*

Kochwa, S., 439 (192), 441 (151, 152), *449*, *451*

Koepchen, H. P., 352 (147), 363 (147), *394*

Koepp, W., 79 (157), *89*

Kohn, A. J., 435 (193, 194), *451*

Kolb, E. J., 377 (116), 385 (116), *392*

Komalahiranya, A., 379 (117), *392*

Komrad, E. L., 317 (48), *327*

Koneczny, O., 184 (477), *240*

Konttinen, A., 198 (251), *227*

Konzett, H., 17 (3), *22,* 48 (18), 51, 56, 57, 58, *82, 90,* 102 (58), 113 (55, 58), *125, 126,* 252 (8, 135), 265 (8), 281 (219), *292, 298, 303*

Kopin, I. J., 9 (57), 10 (57), 17 (57), *24,* 133 (71), 166 (64), *176*

Kopetz, K., 192 (408), 194 (408), *236*

Koppanyi, T., 251 (263), *305*

Korein, J., 377 (116), 385 (116), *392*

Korman, H., 109 (43), *125*

Korner, P. I., 263 (136), *298*

Korol, B., 13 (63), *25*

Kosterlitz, H. W., 360 (106), 361 (118), *391, 392*

Kosman, M. E., 273 (137), *298*

Kot, P. A., 102 (80), *127*

Kottegoda, S. R., 102 (50), 113 (50), *125*

Kovtunovitch, L. G., 408, *451*

Kraatz, C. P., 369 (119), *392*

Krajči-Lazáry, B., 191 (120, 252), *219, 227*

Krake, J. J., 200 (320), *231*

Kramer, K., 263 (138), *298*

Krause, I., 184 (305), 210 (305), *230*

Kravchenko, A. T., 407 (196), *451*

Krayenbuhl, H. P., 313 (42), *326*

Krayer, D., 8 (70), *25*

Krayer, O., 180 (253), 182 (253), 183 (253), *227,* 332 (128), 333 (124), 338 (134), 339 (126, 151), 340 (125), 345 (126, 136), 347 (126, 162), 348 (162), 351, 352 (126), 353 (126, 162), 354 (126, 163) 359, 360 (106, 107, 120, 121, 122, 123 127, 128, 131, 132, 133, 135), 361 (118, 120, 126, 127), 363 (126), 365, 367 (126), 368 (126), 369 (130), 370 (126), 371 (126), 372 (126), 373 (126), 374 (126), 377 (126, 129), 378 (123, 129), 379 (126), 380 (126), 383 (159), 385 (124), 386 (159), *392, 393, 394,* 441 (197), *451*

Krčíková, D., 199 (254, 406), *227, 236*

Krebs, E. G., 182 (255), 187 (365, 366), 188 (178), *223, 227, 234*

Krishnaswamy, N. R., 378 (11), *386*

Kruta, U., 14 (58), *24*

Kryzhanovskii, G. N., 420 (199, 202), 423 (200), 424, 425 (198), *451, 452*

Kuffler, S. W., 367 (105, 137), 373, *391, 393*

Kuida, H., 102 (49), 113 (49), *125*

Kukovetz, W. R., 188 (188, 256, 257), 189 (188, 256, 258, 259), *224, 227*

Kulaev, B. S., 342 (139), *393*

Kuna, A., 191 (219), *225*

Kundel, H., 193 (28), *215*

Kunkle, P., 38 (179), *90*

Kupchan, S. M., 331 (225), 332 (143), 333, 334, 335, 336 (140, 142), 337, 338 (141, 142, 225), 363 (225), 365 (225), 369 (130), 370 (130, 142), 376 (142), 379 (142), *393, 397*

Kuriyama, H. A., 135, 158, 159 (19), *174, 175*

Kurogochi, Y., 209 (452, 453), *238,* 239

Kuale, J., 311 (17), 312 (17), 313 (17), *325*

Kuale, W. F., 283 (214), 285 (214), *302*

Kvam, D. C., 184 (261), 194 (260), 199 (260, 261), *228*

Kwiatkowski, H., 20 (31), *23,* 62, *86*

L

Labate, J. S., 150, 152, *176*

Lacroit, E., 188 (262, 276), 189 (263, 276), *228*

LaForge, M., 258 (123), 259 (123), *297*

Laing, W. B., 406 (110), *447*

Lamanna, C., 400, 401 (213, 214), 402 (214), 403 (172, 175), 404 (204, 209, 211, 212, 220, 231), 405 (175, 210, 271), 407, 411 (208), 413 (206, 207, 215), 414, 415 (175), 416 (206), *452, 453*

Lamont, A., 419 (131), 424 (131), *448*

Lanari, A., 425 (75), *445*

Landa, J. F., 374, *389*

Landgren, S., 344 (108), 363 (108), *391*

Lands, A. M., 7 (59), *25,* 56 (254), 57 (185), 58, *90, 94,* 251 (139), *298*

Lane, C. E., 429 (216, 218), *453*

Lane, R. F., 406 (108), *447*

Lang, G., 320 (31), 321 (31), *326*

Lange, G., 5 (60), 6 (60), 8 (6), 14 (33), 21 (33), *22, 23, 25*
Lange, R. L., 104 (75), 105 (75), *126*
Langemann, H., 78 (187), *90*
Langford, H. G., 49, *90*
Langley, J. N., 30, *90*
Languth, H. W., 413 (222), *453*
Lanier, J. T., 255 (129), 265 (129), 267 (129), *298*
Larner, J., 182 (85), *218*
Lansing, A. M., 349 (224), 355 (224), *397*
Larsell, O., 101 (59, 60, 61), *126*
Larsen, R., 43 (99), 53 (99), *86*
Larson, A., 268 (56), *294*
Larson, A. M., 193 (179), *223*
Latham, W., 54 (191), *90*
Laubender, W., 184 (264), *228*
Laurence, D. R., 67 (192), *90*, 324 (7, 18, 19), *325*, 418, *453*
Lazaro, E. J., 343 (190), 349 (189), *396*
Leach, E. H., 65 (51), *83*, 162 (24), *174*
Leblanc, J. A., 201 (266), 204 (265), *228*
Leboeuf, B., 197 (62, 267), *217, 228*
Leduc, J., 201 (268), *228*
Lee, C. Y., 440, *445*
Lee, F. C., 420 (3), *442*
Lee, K. S., 13, *23*, 205 (269), 206 (269), *228*
Lee, T. D., 102 (36), 109 (36), 113 (36), *124*
Lee, W. C., 323 (10, 11), *327*
Lee, W. H., 289 (242), *304*
Lees, P., 315 (51), *327*
Leffkowitz, M., 441 (151), *449*
Lei, B. W., 184 (270), *228*
Lembeck, F., 156, *157*
Lénárd, G., 188 (447), 205 (447), *238*
Lennox, W. G., 46 (113), *86*
Leonard, E., 16 (37), *23*
Leonard, F., 248 (140), *298*
Leonard, S. L., 186 (275), 187 (273), 190 (271, 272, 274), *228*
Lerke, P., 430 (127), *448*
Leroy, G. V., 268 (141), *298*
Lessin, A. W., 409, 411, *442*
Leusen, I., 188 (276), 189 (263, 276), *228*
Lever, A. F., 49, 50, *91*
Levey, H. A., 3 (7), *22*
Levi, G., 441 (152), *449*
Levin, F. M., 210 (126), *220*
Levine, H. D., 385 (148), *394*
Levine, O. R., 108 (66), 109 (66), 111 (66), *126*
Levine, R., 181 (150), *221*
Levine, R. A., 185 (277, 278), 186 (277), *229*
Levine, R. J., 291 (142), *298*
Levitt, G., 35, *87*
Levy, A. C., 193 (278a), 198 (278a), *229*
Levy, B., 256 (6), 281 (6), *291*, 308, 309 (54), 316 (52), *324, 327, 329*
Lewandowsky, M., 30, *91*, 164, *176*
Lewis, G. P., 37 (149), *88*
Lewis, J. J., 213 (20), *214*, 374, 379, 382 (3), *386, 393, 394*
Lewis, R. A., 349 (224), 355 (224), *397*
Lewis, M. L., 109 (51), *125*
Li, T. H., 339 (16), 342 (18), 343 (16, 18), 352 (16), 362 (19), 363 (16), 374 (16), *387*
Libet, B., 281 (55), *294*
Lichty, J. A., 401 (178), *450*
Liddle, G. W., 29 (2), 75 (2), *81*
Liebow, L. M., 267 (58), *294*
Ligou, J. C., 99 (69), *126*, 202 (343), *232*
Liljedahl, S.-O., 192 (66), 193 (65), 194 (65), *217*
Lilienthal, J. L., Jr., 379 (62), *389*
Lilienthal, S. L., 99 (62), *126*
Liljestrand, A., 252 (143), *298*
Lilla, L., 184 (164), 187 (164), 204 (164), *222*
Lillehei, R. C., 289 (145), *299*
Lim, R. K. S., 351, *393*
Lincová, D., 186 (479), *240*, 200 (479), *240*
Linder, E., 256 (134), *298*
Lindquist, M., 78 (60), *84*
Lindsay, L. A., 199 (58), *216*, 318 (13), *325*
Linenthal, A. J., 17 (105), *27*

Linhart, J. W., 197 (43), 198 (43), *216*
Lipner, H. J., 204 (399), *230*
Lippold, O. C. J., 420 (18), 422, *442*
Lish, P. M., 184 (261), 199 (261), *228*, 309 (23), 323 (55), *325, 327*
Lishajko, F., 78 (97), *85*
Lissitzky, S., 433 (237, 238, 239), *454*
Lister, R. E., 374, 379, *393, 394*
Litter, J., 251 (73), *295*, 349 (74), 383 (74), 384 (74), *390*
Liu, C. K., 102 (63), 113 (63), *126*
Livni, E., 439 (153), *449*
Lobb, A., 36 (136), *88*
Lockett, M. F., 315 (12, 51), *325, 327*
Lockwood, M. A., 202 (419), *237*
Lockett, M. F., 17 (61), *25*, 41, 56 (88, 196, 197), *85, 91*, 137, *177*
Loeschcke, H. H., 352 (147), 363 (147), *394*
Loew, E. R., 317 (48), *327*
Loewi, O., 30 (198), 62 (109), *86, 91*, 167, *175*
Long, C., 67 (279), *95*
Long, P. H., 408, *447*
Longerbeam, J. K., 289 (144), *299*
Lopez, E., 197 (279), *229*, 314 (6), *325*
Love, W. C., 183 (15), 198 (281, 282), 199 (15, 281, 282, 283), 211 (280), *214, 229*, 318 (8, 56), *325, 327*
Lovenberg, W., 18 (49), *24*
Lowe, C. V., 186 (420a), *237*
Lowe, R. D., 39 (200), 40 (202), 42, 59 (200), 61, *91*, 185 (364), 199 (364), *234*, 317 (77), 318 (77), *328*
Lowenthal, J. P., 404 (211, 212, 220), 407, *452, 453*
Lowett, A., 248 (23), *292*
Loxterman, P. B., 190 (318), *231*
Loyke, H. F., 384 (103), *391*
Lu, H. H., 5 (60), 6 (60), *25*
Lucchesi, B. R., 321 (57), *327*
Luck, C. P., 102 (24), 113 (24), *124*
Luduena, F. P., 48 (203), 56 (186), *90, 91*, 251 (139), *298*
Luis, A. S., 109 (51), *125*
Luisada, A. A., 102 (63), 113 (63), *126*
Lum, B. K. B., 254 (146), 260 (146), *299*, 316 (58), *327*
Lunbberg, A., 281 (147), *299*
Lundholm, L., 40 (204), 41, *91*, 142, 155, *177*, 189 (284, 284a, 286, 287), 203 (285, 288, 289), *229*
Luria, M. N., 122 (73), *126*
Luthy, E., 313 (42), *326*
Lyman, H., 35, 36, *84*
Lynch, J. M., 428 (292), *456*
Lynn, W. S., 197 (290), *229*
Lyon, J. B., Jr., 188 (291), *229*
Lyons, R. H., 359 (35), 385 (35), 386 (35), *388*

M

McAuliff, J. P., 183 (292), 184 (292), *230*
McCall, M. L., 383 (153), *394*
MacCannell, K. L., 259 (51), *294*
McCarthy, D. A., 356, 358 (210), *397*
McCarthy, H. M., 56 (185), 57 (185), 58 (185), *90*
McCartney, E., 382 (154), *394*
McCarty, L. P., 323 (49), *327*
McChesney, E. W., 183 (292), 184 (292), *230*
McClure, D. A., 183 (295), *230*
McConn, R. G., 365 (47), *388*
McCorry, R. L., 50 (190), 60 (190), *90*
McCutcheon, R. S., 183 (293, 294), 184 (270), 187 (293, 294), *228, 230*
MacDonald, I., 99 (67), 102 (67), *126*
MacDonald, M. A., 408, 409, 410, *449*
McDonald, R. H., 79, *92*
McDougal, M. D., 137, 138, 139, 140, 153, *177*, 281 (156), *299*
McDowall, R. J. S., 51, *92*
McEachern, C. G., 324 (62), *327*
McElroy, O. E., 401 (213, 214), 402 (214), 403 (213), *452*
McElroy, W. T., Jr., 192 (426, 427), 194 (426, 427), 199 (296), *230, 237*, 318 (63), *327*
Macfarlane, W. V., 428 (185), *451*
McGinty, J. F., 349 (172), 383 (172), 384 (172), *395*
MacGregor, D. F., 167, *177*
McGregor, M., 102 (6, 7), 108 (7), 113 (6, 7), 120 (6), *126*
McGuire, J., 104 (41), 105 (41), *125*
McGuire, L. B., 109 (64), *126*

McIntyre, A. R., 191 (393, 394), 213 (393, 394), *235*
McKay, E. A., 247 (227), *303*
McKee, M. T., 401 (221), *453*
MacKenna, B. R., 143 (59), *174*, 413, *449*
McKinsey, J. J., 188 (90), 189 (90), *218*
Mackintosh, J., 420 (31), 423 (30), 424 (31), *443*
McKnight, R. L., 319 (70), *328*
MacLean, L. D., 54 (221), *92*
McLain, P. L., 346 (155), *394*
McLaughlin, J. J. A., 428 (63), *445*
McLean, L. D., 289 (145), *299*
McLean, R. A., 246 (157), *299*
McLennan, H., 432 (120, 121), 433 (120, 121), *447*
MacLeod, J. A., 264 (97), *296*
MacLeod, R. M., 197 (290), *229*
McNarr, J. D., 385 (59), *389*
McNary, J. E., 195 (345), *233*
McNay, J., 262 (158), *299*
McNeill, J. H., 189 (297), *230*
McMichael, J., 34, 43 (222), *92*
Maddock, W. O., 279 (148), *299*
Madison, L., 55 (250), *93*
Maengwyn-Davies, G. D., 251 (263), *305*
Märki, F., 438, *453*
Mager, J., 401 (190), *451*
Magladery, J. W., 513 (222), *453*
Magnussen, T., 78 (60), *84*
Mahler, R., 199 (298), *230*
Mahon, W. A., 63, 68 (209), *91*
Maickel, R. P., 278 (25), *292*
Mailman, R. H., 384 (113), *392*
Maison, G. L., 351 (208, 209, 213), 354 (207), 386 (169), *395, 396, 397*
Makman, M. H., 184 (299), 185 (299), *230*
Maling, H. M., 194 (300), 199 (301), *230*, 278 (25), *292*
Malkin, M. F., 192 (390), 195 (390), 198 (390), 199 (391), *235*
Mallov, S., 196 (6), *213*
Malton, S. D., 259 (161), *299*, 320 (64), 321 (64), *327*
Mandoki, J. J., 360 (131), *393*
Mangolis, L., 29 (2), 75 (2), *81*
Mann, M., 130, 147, *177*
Mannaioni, P. F., 323 (59), *327*
Manning, G. W., 260 (149), *260*, 324 (62), *327*
Mansfield, P. R., 211 (87), *218*
Manson, J., 40 (180), 41 (180), *90*, 188 (104), *219*
Manson, W., 102 (83), *127*
Mansour, T. E., 182 (302), *230*
Mantegazza, P., 65, *91*
Marchett, G. V., 206 (303), *230*
Marchisotto, J., 428 (63), *445*
Marcou, I., 256 (41), *293*
Margolies, A., 34 (259), 71 (259), 72 (259), *94*
Margolin, E. G., 385 (148), *394*
Margolis, S., 197 (434), *237*
Markee, J. E., 276 (150, 223), *299, 303*
Marks, P. A., 54 (191), *90*
Marquardt, P., 183, 184 (305), 188 (304), 209 (306), 210 (305, 306), *230*
Marrazzi, A. S., 273 (151), *299*
Marsh, D. F., 57 (207), 58 (207), *91*, 366 (149), *394*
Marshall, J. M., 158, 159, *177*
Marshall, N. B., 193 (307, 308), *230*
Marson, F. G. W., 54 (208), *91*
Martin, K., 213 (309), *230*
Martin, W. R., 257 (152), *299*
Martini, L., 342 (150), 343 (150), *394*
Marzoni, F. A., 260 (99), *296*
Mashford, M. L., 63, 68, *91*
Mason, D. T., 37 (226), *92*, 311 (38), *326*
Mason, G. I., 45 (106), 46 (106), *86*
Masoro, E. J., 201 (310), *231*
Massullo, E. A., 102 (79), 110 (79), 113 (79), *127*
Master, A. M., 285 (171), *300*
Matallana, A., 339, *394*
Matheson, F., 436 (224), *453*
Mathias, A. P., 430 (225), *453*
Matsuda, K., 14 (62), *25*
Matsumoto, S., 205 (311), *231*
Matton, G., 343 (152), *394*
Mattingly, T. W., 288 (170), *300*
Matz, L. R., 65, *91*
Matzke, H. A., 421 (226, 293), *453, 456*

Maxwell, G. M., 78, 80, *91*
Maxwell, M. H., 262 (154), 263 (153, 154), *299*
May, A. J., 414, 415 (228), *453*
May, L. G., 109 (70), *126,* 268 (175), *300*
Mayer, S. E., 182 (488), 183 (314), 184 (181), 187 (181, 314, 488), 188 (312, 313), 189 (180, 313, 488), 190 (488), 198 (181), 199 (314), *223, 231, 240,* 277 (155), 278 (155), *299,* 312, 317 (61), 318 (61), *327*
Mazurkiewicz, I., 13 (63), *25*
Medinets, H. E., 273 (159), *299*
Meek, W. J., 68, 69 (62), 71 (62), 72, 73, *84,* 260 (198), 278 (198), *301,* 316 (75), *328*
Meesmann, W., 346 (156), *394*
Mehlman, B., 202 (343), *232*
Meier, R., 63 (27), *82,* 253 (100), *296,* 362 (157), *394*
Meilman, E., 360 (127), 361 (127), 383 (159), 384 (158), 386 (159), *392, 394*
Meinertz, H., 195 (315), *231*
Meldrum, B. S., 439 (229, 229a, 230), 440, *453*
Mellanby, J., 427 (230a), *453*
Mellander, S., 267 (36), 270 (160), 271 (160), *293, 299*
Melmon, K., 37 (226), *92*
Melson, F., 366, *394*
Melville, K. I., 13 (63), *25,* 31, *92*
Mendez, C., 209 (316), 210 (316), *231,* 360 (131), *393*
Mendez, R., 321 (27), *326*
Meng, H. C., 195 (202, 203), 196 (60), *216, 224*
Menon, T., 210 (445), *238*
Mercantini, E. S., 65, *92*
Merendino, K. A., 188 (490), *241*
Merlo, L., 206 (303), *230*
Merrick, A. W., 188 (317), *231*
Merrill, J. P., 385 (148), *394*
Mestyán, G., 201 (100), 203 (100), *219*
Metraux, J., 285 (171), *300*
Mettler, F. A., 273 (159), *299*
Metzger, J. F., 409 (356), *459*
Meyer, E. A., 404 (231), *453*
Meyer, K. F., 406, *449*
Meyers, C. E., 413 (215), *452*
Meyers, F. H., 109 (13), *123*
Milch, L. J., 190 (318), *231*
Miles, A. A., 419 (348), *459*
Miles, B. E., 54 (67), 75 (67), *84*
Miller, C. C., 35 (108), 36 (108), *86*
Miller, D. G., 430 (232), *453*
Miller, H., 17 (67), *25,* 319, *328*
Miller, H. I., 192 (319), 194 (159), *222, 231*
Miller, J. M., 193 (177), *223*
Miller, J. W., 316, *328*
Miller, L. C., 48 (203), 54 (215), 77, *91, 92*
Miller, L. L., 185 (421), *237*
Miller, P. A., 426 (328), *458*
Miller, S. I., 383 (161), 385 (161), *394*
Miller, W. L., 200 (320), *231*
Miller, W. S., 101 (65), *126*
Mills, A. R., 435, *453*
Milnor, W. R., 102 (36), 109 (36), 113 (36), *124*
Minervin, S. M., 407, 408 (235), *453*
Mironda, F., 433 (236, 237, 238, 239), *453, 454*
Mise, J., 121 (3), *123*
Mitchell, J. H., 7 (78), *26,* 351 (57), *389*
Mitchell, L. R., 435, 436 (168), *450*
Mobray, J. F., 49 (193), 50 (193), *91*
Moe, G. K., 53 (140), *88,* 209 (316), 210 (316), *231,* 259 (161), *299,* 320 (64), 321 (64), *327,* 343 (86, 87), 344 (86), 347 (162), 348 (162), 351 (86), 352 (86), 353 (162), 354 (163), *390, 394*
Moës, A., 198 (330), *232*
Møller, E., 283 (163), *300*
Moffitt, R. L., 351 (144), *393*
Mohamed, A. H., 439 (240, 241), 440 (240, 241), *454*
Mohme-Lundholm, E., 141, 142, 155, *177,* 187 (324), 189 (32, 33, 284, 284a, 286, 287, 322), 190 (321, 322, 323), 203 (285), *215, 229, 231,* 278 (162), *300*
Moister, F. C., 251 (73), *295,* 347 (75), 363 (75), 385 (75), *390*
Mold, J. D., 428 (292), *456*
Molner, J. G., 406 (114), *447*

Mongar, J. L., 40, *92*
Montes, G., 345 (136), 351 (136), *393*
Moore, B., 35 (213), *92*
Moore, D. E., 401 (111, 112), 402 (111, 112), 403 (111, 112), 405 (112), *447*
Moore, J. I., 320 (67), 321 (65, 67), *328*
Moore, J. C., 49 (251), *93*, 109 (81), *127*, 269 (231), *303*
Moore, J. I., 14 (64), *25*
Moore, J. W., 436 (249a), *454*
Moore, P. E., 255 (164), 267 (164), *300*
Moore, R. E., 200 (233), 201 (325, 326, 327, 328), 202 (23, 325, 326, 326a, 328), 203 (22, 326, 326a), 204 (326), 205 (21), *214, 226, 231, 232*
Moore, R. M., 252 (165), *300*
Moore, W. W., 276 (166), *300*
Morad, M., 15 (56), *24*
Morales, A. G., 355, 356 (164), *394*
Moran, N. C., 14 (64), *25*, 183 (314), 187 (314), 188 (313), 189 (313), 199 (314), *231*, 258 (37, 167, 168), 277 (155), 278 (155), *293, 299, 300*, 309 (98), 310 (68), 311 (68), 312 (66, 68, 69), 317 (61), 318 (61), 320, 321 (67), *327, 328, 329*, 343 (166), 344 (166), 352 (166), 388 (165), 379 (165), *394, 395*
Morgan, F. G., 440 (242), *454*
Morgan, H. E., 182 (382), 188 (382), 189 (382), *235*
Morgan, K. J., 332 (167), 332 (167), 335 (167), *395*
Morgan, R. S., 413 (91), 420 (31, 351), 421 (19, 20), 423 (30, 92, 350, 351), 424 (31), 425 (92), 426 (19, 20), 427 (93), *443, 446*
Morii, H., 213 (329), *232*
Morkin, E., 108 (66), 109 (66), 111 (66), *126*
Moroz-Perlmutter, C., 439 (153, 243), *449, 454*
Morris, J. A., 102 (83), *127*
Morris, L. E., 258 (169), *300*
Morse, R. A., 258 (123), 259 (123), *297*
Morton, I. K. M., 211 (222), *226*
Morton, J. V., 181 (150), *221*
Moschos, C. B., 194 (373), *234*
Moser, M., 285 (171), 288 (170), *300*
Mosey, L., 363 (168), 386 (169), *395*
Mosher, H. S., 436 (243a), 437 (57), *444, 454*
Mosimann, W., 339 (72), 345 (30), 346 (72), 347 (30), 348 (30), 349 (71, 72), 350 (72), 351 (30), 352 (30), 353 (30), *387, 389, 390*
Mosovich, L. L., 186 (420a), *237*
Mott, J. C., 342 (52), 344 (52), 345 (53), 348 (53), *388, 389*
Mouillé, P., 183 (194), *224*, 359 (95), *391*
Moussatché, H., 441 (244), *454*
Moutschen, J., 198 (330), *232*
Moyer, J. H., 54 (215, 218), 77 (215), *92*, 262 (69, 110, 111, 172), 263 (111, 173), *295, 297, 300*, 365 (47), 383 (161), 385 (161), *388, 394*
Mühlbachová, E., 187 (217, 218), 198 (334, 338, 482), 199 (254, 335, 336, 406, 482), 200 (337, 480, 481), *225, 227, 232, 236, 240*
Mueller, P., 356 (199), 358 (199), *396*
Mueller, P. S., 185 (333), 194 (331, 332), 197 (333), 198 (333), *232*
Muñoz, C., 275 (85, 174), *295, 300*
Munro, A. F., 140, *177*
Murad, F., 183 (339), 185 (339), *232*
Murakami, L., 400, *447*
Murdaugh, H. V., Jr., 122 (26), *124*
Murnaghan, M. F., 360 (170, 171), *395*, 433 (245, 246), *454*
Murphy, Q. R., Jr., 208 (97), *218*, 260 (198), 263 (1), 265 (1), 267 (1), 278 (198), *291, 301*, 316 (75), *328*
Murray, W. J., 319 (70), *328*
Murtha, E. F., 428 (247), 436 (247, 248), *454*
Mushet, G., 14 (64), *25*, 320 (67), 321 (67), *328*
Muskus, A., 21 (89), *26*
Myers, G. B., 286 (271), *305*
Myers, G. S., 349 (172), 383 (172), 384 (49), 384 (172), 385 (49), *388, 395*
Myers, J. D., 186 (246), *227*

N

Nadas, A. S., 269 (221), *303*
Nadeau, G., 204 (265), *228*
Nadeau, R. A., 14 (53), *24,* 311 (45, 46), *326, 327*
Nagai, J., 436 (249), *454*
Nagasaka, T., 204 (340), *232*
Nagasawa, J., 212, 213 (342), *232*
Nahas, G. G., 99 (67, 68, 69), 102 (67, 68), *126,* 202 (343, 451), *232, 238*
Nakao, K., 213 (329), *232*
Nakatani, G., *232*
Nalefski, L. A., 268 (141), *298*
Nank, W. K., 401 (295), *456*
Napoli, M. D., 365 (176), *395*
Napolitano, L., 195 (345), *233*
Narahara, H. T., 188 (359), *233*
Narahashi, T., 436 (249a), *454*
Narayana, B., 98 (15), 113 (2), *123*
Nash, V. L., 56 (185), 57 (185), 58 (185), *90*
Nasmyth, P. A., 18 (65), 19, *25,* 63, *92,* 172, *177*
Nathanson, M. H., 17 (67), *25,* 319, *328*
Navratil, E., 30 (198), *91*
Nayler, W. G., 13 (68), *25,* 188 (346, 347), *233*
Naylor, J., 196 (388), *235*
Nehlman, B., 99 (69), *126*
Neil, E., 45 (172), *89,* 341 (173), 342 (173, 174), 344 (108), 346, 363 (108), *391, 395*
Nelson, G. H., 192 (496), *241*
Nelson, R. A., 109 (70), *126,* 268 (175), *300*
Nesbit, R. M., 421 (115), *447*
Nestel, P. J., 192 (436), 193 (348, 435), 194 (348, 436), 199 (433), 205 (433), *232, 233, 237, 238*
Neumann, W., 430 (250), 431 (250), *454*
Newman, A. J., 385 (175), *395*
Newman, E. V., 19 (4), *22*
Ngai, S. H., 339 (223), 343 (223), 344 (223), 345 (223), 351 (223), 352 (223), 360 (223), *397*
Nickel, J. F., 264 (176), *300*
Nickerson, M., 185 (183), 209 (115), 209 (115), *219, 223,* 244 (177), 245 (177, 180, 181, 187, 188, 192), 246 (113, 182, 189, 195), 247 (179, 180, 182, 189, 192), 248 (49, 178, 187), 249 (182), 252 (234), 254 (146), 257 (177), 258 (177, 187, 194, 196), 259 (51, 185, 194, 196), 260 (52, 177), 261 (193), 264 (42, 191), 265 (189, 269), 266 (184, 189, 272), 267 (189), 270 (191), 271 (191), 273 (113, 178), 274 (189, 190), 277 (114, 189), 278 (52, 177), 278 (189), 280 (177, 189), 281 (177), 289 (186, 272), 290 (185), *293, 297, 299, 300, 301, 303, 305,* 312 (73), 317 (39, 72), 320 (74) 321 (74), *326, 328*
Niederland, T. R., 191 (120, 252), *219, 227*
Niemeyer, H., 183 (349), *233*
Nigg, C., 401 (178, 251), *450, 454*
Nigrelli, R. F., 428 (252), 435 (142, 253), *448, 454*
Nilsson, J., 19 (14), *22*
Nisell, O. I., 102 (71), 113 (71, 72), *126*
Nishiue, T., 209 (453), *239*
Nissell, O. I., 269 (197), *301*
Noach, E. L., 184 (75), *217,* 317 (15), *325*
Noelle, H., 183 (225), *226*
Noll, L., 384 (221), *384*
Noltie, H. R., 181 (50), 202 (50), *216*
Nomaguchi, G. M., 246 (195), 258 (194), 259 (194), 261 (193), *301,* 320 (74), *328*
Norcia, L. N., 193 (350), *233*
Norcross, N. C., 45, 46 (225), 73 (225), *92*
Nordenstam, H., 29 (3), 65 (238), *81, 93*
Norman, L. R., 17 (105), *27*
North, E. A., 426 (254), *454*
Northey, W. T., 433 (269), *455*
Northrop, G., 186 (351, 352, 353), *233*
Nunn, D. B., 288 (242), *304*
Nusser, E., 346 (24), 349 (24), 350 (24), 363 (23), *387*
Nylin, G., 48 (170), *89,* 204 (232), *226*

O

Oakley, C., 122 (73), *126*
Oates, J. A., 37, *92*
O'Brien, G. S., 260 (198), 278 (198), *301*, 316 (75), *328*
Ochs, L., 55 (250), *93*
O'Dell, T. B., 365 (176), *395*
Odell, W. D., 197 (357), *233*
Ogawa, S., 35, 44, *92*
Ogg, J., 283 (214), 285 (214), *302*
Ohler, E. A., 276 (199), *302*
Ohye, D. F., 401 (255), 406, 418 (255), *455*
Okinaka, S., 213 (329), *232*
O'Leary, J. L., 366 (81), *390*
Oliver, G., 30, 43, 44, 45, *92*
Oliver, T. K., Jr., 200 (233), *226*
Olson, W. H., 269 (60), 290 (60), *294*
O'Neill, J. J., 428 (41), *444*
O'Neil, J. R., 349 (172), 383 (172), 384 (172), *395*
Opitz, K., 184 (354), *233*
Orbison, J. A., 288 (170), *300*
Orestano, G., 204 (355), *233*
Orias, O., 5 (8), 6 (8), *22*, 358 (41a), 369 (41a), 372 (41a), *388*
Orimo, H., 213 (329), *232*
Orö, L., 192 (152), 193 (29, 67, 151), 194 (67, 68, 151), 199 (151), *215*, *221*, 278 (77), *295*
Orskov, S. L., 210 (356), *233*
Orth, O. S., 258 (200), 259 (200), *302*
Orth, R. D., 193 (358), 197 (357), *233*
O'Shea, J., 248 (23), *292*
Otsuka, M., 14 (69), *25*
Ottis, K., 54, 60 (230), *92*, 266 (98), *296*
Ourisson, P., 338 (134), 360 131), *393*
Øye, I., 182 (382), 188 (382), 189 (382), *235*, 278 (248), *304*
Özand, P., 188 (359), *233*

P

Paasonen, M. K., 8 (70), *25*
Pachomov, N., 377 (177), 380 (177), *395*
Paes de Carvalho, A., 6 (71), *25*
Page, I. H., 36, 59 (73), *84*, *94*, 198 (403, 404), 199 (403, 405), *236*, 278 (225), *303*, 318 (85), *329*, 351, *397*
Paget, G. E., 310 (76), *328*
Paintal, A. S., 342 (179, 180), 344 (179), 362 (178), 368 (180), 372 (180), 374 (179), 379, *395*
Pallister, E. F., 401 (280, 281), *456*
Palm, D., 188 (19), *214*
Paoletti, R., 193 (139), *221*
Pappenheimer, J. R., 270 (201), *302*
Papper, E. M., 72 (252), 77 (252), *93*, 264 (176), *300*
Park, A. M., 413 (222), *453*
Park, C. R., 181 (137), *220*
Parkerson, G. H., Jr., 276 (224), *303*
Parks, V. J., 40 (180), 41 (180), *64*, 66 (181, 231), 72 (231), 75, *90*, *92*, 188 (104), *219*
Parks, R. E., Jr., 186 (351, 352, 353), *233*
Parnas, I., 428 (35), 429 (35, 36), *443*
Parsons, R. L., 420 (255a), 422 (255a), *455*
Pastan, I., 191 (360), *233*
Patel, D. J., 102 (74), 103, 104 (75), 105 (75), *126*
Paton, A., 57, 58 (69), 59 (69), *84*, 185 (77), 204 (77), *217*
Paton, W. D. M., 144, *177*
Patrick, R. W., 9 (42), *24*
Patterson, R. A., 433 (256), *455*
Paul, M. H., 17 (105), *27*, 269 (221), *303*
Paul, P., 192 (319), *231*
Pearson, O. P., 441 (257), *455*
Pearson, R. S. B., 38, *87*
Peart, W. S., 37 (240), 49 (193), 50 (193), 54 (112), *86*, *91*, *93*
Peckham, N. H., 436 (174), *450*
Pederson, H. O., 406, 410, *455*
Pelloja, M., 419, *455*
Pelletier, M. H., 57 (207), 58 (207), *91*
Peng, M. T., 363 (181), 364 (181), *395*, 439 (261), *455*
Penick, S. B., 197 (361), *233*
Penna, M., 17 (32), *23*, 314 (14), 315 (14), *325*
Pennefather, J. N., 147, *177*

Pennes, H. H., 75 (245), *93*
Perdrup, A., 420, *455*
Pérez, N., 183 (349), *233*
Perkins, M. E., 258 (167, 168), *300*, 310 (68), 311 (68), 312 (68, 69), *328*, 343 (166), 344 (166), 352 (166), 378 (165), 379 (165), *394*, *395*
Perkins, W. E., 401 (97, 263, 315), *446*, *455*, *458*
Perl, W., 199 (391), *235*
Perlmutter, C., 439 (192), *451*
Perrine, J., 199 (44, 45), *216*
Perry, W. F., 193 (362), *234*
Persson, H., 50 (89), *85*
Pesch, L. A., 185 (278), *229*
Peskin, G. W., 342 (18), 343 (18), *387*
Peterson, N. S., 421 (129), *448*
Petrovskaia, B., 113 (76, 77), *126*
Pevnitskii, L. A., 420 (202), 423 (200) 424 (201, 202, 203), *251*, *452*
Pfaff, W. W., 192 (141), 193 (141), 195 (141), *221*
Pfeifer, A. K., 204 (363), *234*
Pflug, E., 205 (49), *216*
Phelps, D. R., 436 (265), *455*
Philip, C. B., 433 (124), *447*
Philipson, J. B., 68 (209), *91*
Phillips, J. H., 65 (146, 233), 66, *83*, *88*, *93*, 430 (264), *455*
Phillips, R. A., 263 (202), *302*
Philpot, F. J., 165 (25), *174*
Pickering, G. W., 35, 36 (33), 49 (33), *82*, *93*
Pickford, M., 54 (235), *93*
Pierson, J. C., 46 (246), 93
Pilcher, C., 71 (280), *95*
Pilkington, T. R. E., 185 (364), 199 (364), *234*, 317 (77), 318 (77), 324 (7), *325*, *328*
Pines, K. L., 34 (124), 47 (124), 48 (124), *87*, 100 (52), 104 (52), 112 (52), 121 (52), *125*
Pircio, A., 339, *395*
Pirré, A., 199 (45, 46, 47), *216*
Pitman, C. R. S., 441 (83), *446*
Plampin, J. N., 339 (194), *396*
Podleski, T. R., 441 (283), *456*
Pöch, G., 189 (258, 259), *228*
Poisner, A. M., 323 (78), *328*
Poley, G. W., 332 (229), *398*
Polgar, A. A., 420 (202), 423 (200), 424 (201, 202, 203), *451*, *452*
Poli, J. F., 102 (63), 113 (63), *126*
Porter, C. C., 9 (72), *25*
Porter, J., 188 (291), *229*
Posner, J. B., 187 (365, 366), *234*
Polson, A., 401 (337), 439 (266), *455*, *458*
Pongratz, E., 439 (155), *449*
Pontius, R. G., 342 (20), 344 (20), 352 (20), 362 (19), *387*
Porges, N., 428 (60), 439 (268), *444*, *455*
Potter, J. M., 433 (269), *455*
Potter, L. F., 10 (73), *25*
Pouliot, M., 201 (266), *228*
Pound, E., 343 (185), 351 (185), *395*
Powell, C. E., 157, *177*, 244 (203), *302*, 307, 311 (79), 314 (79), *324*, *328*
Prandoni, A., 288 (170), *300*
Pratt, G. B., 401 (270), *455*
Presser, C., 184 (264), *228*
Preston, J. E., 183 (15), 199 (15), *214*, 318 (8), *325*
Prévot, A. R., 417, *444*
Price, W. M., 202 (198), 203 (198), *224*
Prichard, B. N. C., 324 (7), *325*
Prichard, M. M. L., 263 (256), *304*
Primrose, J., 279 (204), 291 (204), *302*
Prosser, C. L., 159 (32), *174*
Provasoli, L., 428 (63), *445*
Prystowsky, H., 384 (14), *386*
Puloka, T., 436 (224), *453*
Purinton, C. O., 35 (217), 92
Purkhold, A., 63 (98), *86*
Purser, S. H., 40, *88*
Putnam, F. W., 405, *455*
Putnam, T. J., 46, *86*
Pytasz, M., 191 (367), *234*

Q

Quastel, J. H., 379 (115), 383 (115), *392*
Quinn, P. V., 186 (368), 187 (368), 189 (368), *234*

R

Raben, M. S., 193 (369), 196 (205), *225, 234*
Radojković, J., 183 (349), *233*
Rahdert, E., 365 (226), *396*
Rajasalmi, M., 198 (251), *227*
Rall, T. W., 180 (444), 183 (339), 185 (31, 339, 371), 190 (248), 191 (248), 210 (445), *215, 227, 232, 238*
Ralls, R. J., 435 (272), *455*
Rall, T. W., 312, *328*
Ramey, E. R., 187 (199a), 193 (278a), 195 (228), 198 (278a), *224, 226, 229*
Rand, M. J., 18, *22*, 36 (53), 49, 63, 64, 65 (51), 67 (79), 79, *83, 85*, 143, 147, 150, 151, 162 (24), 166, 169 (28), *174, 177*, 412 (65), 413, *445*
Randall, B. F., 51 (169), *89*
Randall, L. O., 255 (205), *302*
Randle, P. J., 195 (155), *221*
Ranges, H. A., 34, 44 (61), 71, 72, 73 (236), *84, 93*
Rankin, V. M., 279 (148), *299*
Ransom, F., 382 (154), *394*
Ranson, S. W., 420 (273), *455*
Rapport, D., 43 (58), *84*
Rathmeyer, W., 431 (274), *455*
Ratnoff, O. D., 420 (7), 422, *442*
Rawson, C. W., 44 (6), 54 (6), *81*
Raynaud, M., 417, *444*
Reale, A., 48 (170), *89*, 204 (232), *226*
Reames, H. R., 401 (275), *455*
Reardon, M. J., 260 (99), *296*
Rechnic, J., 439 (153, 192), 441 (152), *449, 451*
Redisch, W., 285 (207), 288 (264), *302, 305*
Reed, G. B., 401 (29, 280, 281), *443, 456*
Reeves, J. T., 269 (103), *296*
Regan, T. J., 104 (78), 105 (78), 109 (78), *126*, 188 (372), 189 (372), 194 (373), 211 (372), *234*
Regazzini, A., 196 (374), *234*
Reich, K., 428 (35), 429 (35, 36), *443*
Reid, H., 440 (277), 441 (276, 277), 441 (278, 279), *455, 456*
Reid, L. C., 6 (74), *25*
Reilly, J., 17 (75), *25*, 321 (81), *328*
Reiter, M., 355 (183), 360 (133), 361 (183), 382, *393, 395*
Remensnyder, J. P., 351 (57), *389*
Remington, J. W., 33, 58 (142), *88, 93*, 289 (208), *302*
Renkin, E. M., 270 (209, 210), *302*
Rennick, B. R., 259 (161), *299*, 320 (64), 321 (64), *327*
Renold, A. E., 192 (375), *234*
Renson, J., 170, *173*
Reshef, L., 195 (376), *234*
Reuse-Blom, S., 355 (184), 361 (184), *395*
Reuter, H., 212 (377, 378), *234*
Rezepov, F. F., 407 (196), *451*
Rhodin, J., 65 (238), *93*
Rhodin, J. A. G., 6 (74), *25*
Rice, C. E., 401 (280, 281), *456*
Richards, A. B., 365 (1, 225), *386, 397*
Richards, A. N., 40, *85*
Richardson, A. P., 343 (166, 185), 344 (166), 351 (185), 352 (166), 378 (165), 379 (165), *394, 395*
Richardson, A. W., 253 (211), 255 (164), 267 (164), *300, 302*
Richardson, J. C., 50 (168), *89*
Richardson, K. C., 65, *93*
Richter, H., 340 (109), *391*
Riegel, B., 428 (292), *456*
Riehl, J. L., 257 (152), *299*
Rieker, M., 8 (29), 19 (29), *23*
Riel, F. J., 428 (292), *456*
Riggilo, D. A., 184 (261), 199 (261), *228*
Riker, W. F., Jr., 17 (75), *25*, 319 (82), *328*
Riker, W. K., 343, 362, *396*
Riley, R. L., 99 (62), *126*
Riley, W. D., 182 (255), *227*
Rimmer, A. D., 193 (379), *234*
Ringler, I., 199 (44, 45, 46, 47), *216*
Ritchie, G., 258 (200), 259 (200), *302*
Rivier, J.-L., 324 (35), *326*
Rizack, M. A., 196 (380, 381), *235*
Roberts, G., 253 (211), *302*
Roberts, J., 17 (75), *25*, 319, 321 (81), *328*
Roberts, T. A., 400 (182a), *450*
Robertson, J. I. S., 37, *93*

S

Sjoerdsma, A., 18 (49), *24,* 37 (226), 79 (163), 80 (163), *87, 89, 92,* 291 (142), *298*
Skarin, A. T., 202 (419), *237*
Skinner, S. L., 37 (255), 39, 40 (180), 52 (255) 64 (231), 65, 66 (181, 231, 232, 278), 72 (231), 75 (231), *90, 91, 92, 94,* 188 (104), *219*
Skoglund, K.-H., 48 (170), *89,* 204 (232), *226*
Skulberg, A., 401 (179), *450*
Slater, I. H., 157, *177,* 244 (203), 273 (236), *302, 304,* 307, 311 (79), 314 (79), *324, 328*
Slotta, K., 441 (303), *457*
Smirk, F. H., 384 (58), *389*
Smith, C. M., 377 (227), 378 (227), *397*
Smith, C. W., 409 (356), *459*
Smith, D. F. G., 282 (65), *294*
Smith, D. J., 113 (82), *127*
Smith, E., 369 (25), 372 (25), *387*
Smith, E. R., 18 (84), *26*
Smith, H. W., 44 (61), *84,* 262 (154), 263 (153, 154), *299*
Smith, L. C., 401 (280, 281), *456*
Smith, O., 346 (192), *396*
Smith, R. E., 201 (420), *237*
Smith, R. W., 102 (83), *127*
Smith, R. W., Jr., 193 (177), *223*
Smith, S. M., 258 (196), 259 (196), *301*
Smith, T. C., 199 (44, 45), *216*
Smith, T. H. F., 255 (205), *302*
Smythe, C. McC., 53 (256), *94,* 264 (176), *300*
Snyder, C. H., 256 (83), 272 (83), 284 (83), *295*
Sobotka, H., 435 (142, 143), *448*
Sodeman, W. A., 432 (25), *443*
Soderstrom, R. L., 401 (352), *459*
Soffer, A., 284 (237), *304*
Sokal, J. E., 185 (421), 186 (396, 420a, 423, 424), 187 (422), *235, 237*
Sokoloff, L., 46, 47 (177), 55 (177), 60 (257), 73, 77, *90, 94,* 267 (238), *304*
Solomon, R. J., 406 (114), *447*
Sommer, L. S., 269 (221), *303*
Sonnenblick, E., 14 (85), *26*
Sonnenschein, R. R., 282 (239), *304*
Soto-Rivera, A., 270 (201), *302*
Southcott, R. V., 430 (191, 304), *451, 457*
Späth, M., 209 (306), *230*
Spencer, M. P., 44 (258), *94,* 262 (240), *304*
Spitzer, J. J., 192 (158, 410, 426, 427), 193 (425), 194 (159, 426, 427), 199 (296), *222, 230, 236, 237,* 318 (63), *327*
Spoelstra, A. J.-G., 201 (428), 203 (428), *237*
Sproull, D. H., 184 (184, 429, 430), *223, 237*
Spühler, O., 185 (431), *237*
Spuhler, O., 384 (235), 385 (235), *398*
Spurr, C. L., 262 (69), 295
Sréter, F. A., 279 (241), *304*
Stabile, D. E., 436 (248), *454*
Stahnke, H. L., 433 (306), *457*
Stallworth, J. M., 289 (242), *304*
Standaert, F. G., 319 (82), *328,* 435 (142, 143), *448*
Stanford, C. F., 61 (120, 121), *87*
Stanger, D. W., 428 (292), *456*
Stanton, J. R., 185 (148), *221,* 251 (73), *295,* 347 (75), 349 (74), 363 (75), 383 (74), 384 (74), 385 (75), *390*
Starr, I., 34, 48, 71, 72, *82, 94*
Staub, H., 40, 59 (260), *94*
Stead, E. A., 38 (179), 57 (129), *87, 90*
Stearns, N. S., 354 (207), *396*
Steele, J. M., 285 (207), 288 (264), *302, 305*
Steele, R., 192 (13), 193 (14), 199 (13), *214*
Stehle, R. L., 31, *94*
Stein, A. A., 183 (385), 184 (385), *235*
Stein, J. A., 262 (257), *304*
Stein, O., 197 (432), *237*
Stein, Y., 197 (432), *237*
Steinberg, D., 192 (123, 141, 436, 462), 193 (141, 414, 435), 194 (414a, 436), 195 (70, 141), 196 (461), 197 (434, 462), 198 (462), 199 (433), 205 (433), 206 (70, 71), *217, 220, 221, 236, 237, 238, 239*

Steinitz, F. S., 113 (45), 116 (45), 122 (45), *125*, 269 (74), *295*
Stephenson, J. S., 309, 310 (10), 311 (10), 312 (10), 313, 314 (10), *325*
Stephenson, R. P., 247 (243), *304*
Stern, P. A., 266 (244), *304*
Stern, R., 187 (365, 366), *234*
Sterne, M., 401 (337), *455*, *458*
Stevenson, J. W., 400, 418 (307), *457*
Stewart, J. T., 188 (90), 189 (90), *218*
Stewart, T., 51 (87), *85*
Stillman, P. H., 285 (207), *302*
Stitzel, R. E., 19 (13), *22*
Stock, K., 194 (207), 197 (207), 198 (484, 485, 486), 199 (437), *225*, *238*, *240*
Stock, J. P. P., 324 (92), *329*
Stoelting, R., 199 (283), *229*
Stoll, A., 250 (245, 246), *304*
Stoltzenberger-Seidel, M., 183 (438), *238*
Stone, C. A., 9 (72), *25*
Stopp, P. E., 258 (37), *293*
Strand, O., 192 (436), 194 (436), *238*
Strata, A., 197 (86), *218*
Strömblad, B. C. R., 206 (439), *238*
Strubelt, O., 202 (440), 204 (441, 442), *238*
Stuart, D., 202 (198), 203 (198), *224*
Study, R. S., 262 (247), 263 (247), *304*
Stutzman, J. W., 351 (208, 209), 386 (169), *395*, *396*, *397*
Su, C., 439 (308), *457*
Suckling, E. E., 5 (8), 6 (8), 8 (6), *22*, 358 (41a), 369 (41a), 372 (41a), *388*
Susina, S. V., 319 (93), *329*
Sussman, K. E., 193 (414), 194 (414a), *236*
Sutherland, E. W., 180 (444), 182 (99, 382, 443, 446), 183 (339), 184 (299), 185 (31, 299, 339, 371), 188 (382), 189 (382), 190 (248), 191 (98, 446), 196 (60), 197 (446), 210 (445), *215*, *216*, *218*, *227*, *230*, *232*, *235*, *238*, 278 (248), *304*, 312, *328*
Sutherland, V., 29 (2), 75 (2), *81*
Sutter, M. C., 259 (53), 264 (249), 271 (249), *294*, *304*
Sutton, G. C., 48 (170), *89*, 204 (232), *226*, 252 (250), *304*
Svedmyr, N., 187 (324), 203 (288, 289), *229*, *231*
Sverdlov, J. S., 425 (309), *457*
Swain, H. H., 320, 321 (65), *328*, 356, 358 (210), *397*
Swaine, C. R., 339 (72), 345 (30), 346 (72), 347 (30), 348 (30), 349 (71, 72), 350 (72), 351 (30), 352 (30), 353 (30), 367 (232), 368 (232), 371 (232), 373 (232), 376, 377, 379 (232), *387*, *389*, *390*, *398*
Swan, A. A., 113 (48), *125*
Swan, H. J. C., 35, 36 (20), 37 (263), 38, 43 (263), 44, 48, 50 (262), 54 (132), 74, 75, *84*, *85*, *87*, *94*, 252 (8), 264 (8), *292*
Swan, K. C., 279 (34), 291 (34), *293*
Swiss, E. D., 351 (213), 363 (211), 365 (211), 385 (212), *397*
Sydow, V. L., 44 (6), 54 (6), *81*
Szabó, E., 183 (48), *216*
Szekeres, L., 188 (447), 205 (447), *238*
Szentiványi, M., 268 (251), *304*
Szilágyi, T., 183 (48), *216*
Szücs, Z., 269 (108), 290 (108), *294*

T

Tabor, C. G., 266 (92), *296*
Taborska, J., 191 (367), *234*
Taeschler, M., 252 (250), *304*
Tainter, M. L., 62 (54), 68, 69 (265), *83*, *94*, 167, 168, *177*, 251 (139), *298*
Takagi, A., 401 (310), *457*
Takagisi, T., 210 (450), *238*
Takasaki, K., 343 (214), *397*
Takino, M., 99 (84), *127*
Tal, E., 195 (454), *239*
Talbot, W. H., 425 (347), *459*
Tamai, T., 210 (450), *238*
Tanaka, K., 344, 345 (98), 363 (216), 364, 365, 366, *391*, *397*
Taneja, G. C., 254 (252), 282 (252), 283 (252), *304*
Tanino, S., 209 (452, 453), *238*, *239*
Tanz, R. D., 323 (95), *329*
Tarlov, I. M., 423 (138), 424 (138), *448*
Tatum, E. L., 10 (20), 12 (20), *23*

Taylor, J. P., 44 (6), 54 (6), *81*
Taylor, P. B., 436 (289), *456*
Taylor, R. D., 36, *94,* 351, *397*
Taylor, S. R., 374 (196), *396*
Taylor, W. J., 186 (243), *227*
Taymor, R. C., 285 (171), *300*
Teasdall, R. D., 413 (222), *453*
Tényi, M., 269 (108), 290 (107), *297*
Terranova, R., 356 (199), 358 (199), *396*
Texter, E. C., Jr., 285 (207), *302*
Thatcher, F. S., 401 (311), *457*
Thesleff, S., 157 (46), *175,* 409, 410, *457*
Thiele, W., 254 (253), *304*
Thomas, L. J., Jr., 15 (86), *26*
Thompson, J. W., 41 (202), 65 (51), *83, 91,* 161, 162 (24), 163 (56), 167, 170, *174, 176, 177, 178*
Thompson, R. H., 199 (433), 205 (433), *237*
Thomson, A. E., 264 (42), *293*
Thornley, M. J., 401 (183), *451*
Tidball, M. E., 142, *178*
Tillgren, N., 251 (254), *304*
Tillotson, R. F., 324 (36), *326*
Tinkham, E. R., 441, *457*
Titterington, E., 317 (77), 318 (77), *328*
Tizard, J. P. M., 202 (409), 203 (409), 207 (409), *236*
Tobian, L., 212 (449), *238*
Török, T., 188 (447), 205 (447), *238*
Tohyama, Y., 401 (287, 288), 418 (287, 288), *456*
Toida, N., 210 (450), *238*
Tomchick, R., 132 (4), 133 (4), *173*
Tomich, M., 406 (110), *447*
Torp, A., 131 (13), *173*
Torres H. N., 182 (12), *214*
Totaro, J. A., 9 (72), *25*
Townsend, C. T., 401 (97), *446*
Tozzi, S., 316, *329*
Trapold, J. H., 350 (218), *397*
Trautwein, W., 6 (52), 14 (24, 52), *23, 24,* 211 (118, 156), *219, 222,* 333 (219), *396*
Treadwell, P. E., 401 (314), *458*
Trendelenburg, U., 8 (88), 12 (87), 19 (87), 21 (89), *26,* 64, *94,* 142, 165 (25), 167, 168, 169, *174, 175, 178,* 323 (97), *329*
Trevan, J. W., 35 (14), *81*
Triggle, D. J., 246 (13), *292*
Triner, L., 202 (451), *238*
Tripod, J., 34 (212), 53 (212), 63 (27), *82, 91,* 253 (100), 274 (255), *296, 304*
Trounce, J., 365 (112), 384 (112), 385 (112), *392*
Trueta, J., 263 (256), *304*
Tryer, J. H., 102 (85), 113 (85), *127*
Tsuji, K., 401 (263, 315), *455, 458*
Tsujimoto, A., 209 (452, 453), *238, 239*
Tullar, B. F., 31, 56 (186), *90, 94*
Turino, G. M., 100 (53), 104 (53), 105 (53), 112 (53), *125*
Turnbull, G. L., 342 (18), 343 (18), *387*
Tuttle, R., 323 (28), *326*
Tyler, C., 65 (206), *91*
Tyler, H. R., 413, *458*
Tzur, R., 195 (454), *239*

U

Udenfriend, S., 8 (90), *26*
Uei, I., 205 (185), *223,* 311 (40), 314 (40), *326*
Uhle, F. C., 338 (134), 378 (92), *391, 393*
Ullman, T. D., 262 (257), *304*
Ullyot, G. E., 245 (258), *305*
Underwood, M. C., 201 (326, 327, 328), 202 (23, 326, 326a, 328), 203 (326, 326a), 204 (326), *214, 231, 232*
Unna, K. R., 257 (152), *299,* 317 (93), *329*
Usardi, M. M., 193 (139), *221*
Ushakova, A. A., 403 (79), *445*
Ushiyama, J., 6 (91), 8 (92), *26*
Uvnäs, B., 38 (105), 50 (105), 54 54 (105), *86,* 248 (68), 261 (68), 264 (120), 265 (120), 282 (259), *295, 297, 305*

V

Valadares, J. R. E., 188 (116), *219*
Van Deripe, D. R., 309 (98), *329*

Van Der Pol, M. C., 184 (455), *239*
Van Dyke, H. B., 148 (101), *178*
Vane, J. R., 134, 140, 144, 145 (103), 146, *173, 177, 178,* 180 (457), *239*
van Heyningen, W. E., 400 (319), 418 (325), 419 (319), 421 (129), 426 (321, 322, 323, 324, 328, 329), 427 (230a, 329), *448, 453, 458*
Van Maanen, E. F., 360 (135), *393*
Van Roy, F. P., 184 (456), 185 (456), *239*
Van Slyke, D. D., 263 (202), *302*
Varagić, V., 152 (50), *175*
Vass, C. C., 51, *84*
Vassale, M., 321 (99, 100), *329*
Vaughan, M., 192 (436, 462), 193 (435), 194 (436), 196 (458, 459, 460, 461), 197 (434, 460, 462), 198 (462), *237, 238, 239*
Vaughan, Williams, E. M., 321 (87, 101), 322 (88), *329*
Verdy, M., 192 (66), *217*
Verhonick, P. J., 37 (82), 50 (82), *85*
Verity, M. A., 345 (32), *387*
Verner, J. V., Jr., 197 (463, 464), *239*
Vertua, R., 193 (139), *221*
Vial, J., 254 (117), *297*
Vick, R. L., 355, *397*
Vieira, G. D., 441 (244), *454*
Villarreal, R., 319 (86), 320 (86), *329*
Vincent, N. H., 186 (134), 188 (41), 189 (464a), *215, 220, 239*
Violante, A., 76 (175), *90*
Visscher, M. B., 54 (221), *92,* 102 (49), 113 (49), *125*
Vizi, E. Sz., 204 (363), *234*
Vleeschhouwer, G., 256 (260), *305*
Vogel, G., 181 (465), *239*
Vogel, U., 181 (465), *239*
Vogt, E., 99 (54), 113 (54), 116 (54), *125*
Vogt, M., 54 (112), *86,* 156, *176*
Volle, R. L., 379 (117), *392*
von Euler, U. S., 3 (93), 12 (93), *26,* 31 (92, 96), 32 (94, 104), 47 (94), 52, 53, 63 (98), 66, 78 (97), *85, 86,* 100 (32), 101 (33), *124,* 131 (105), 147, *178,* 252 (64), *294*
Von Ludány, G., 122 (17), *123*
von Meier, R., 34 (212), 53, *91*
Voskian, J., 384 (221), *397*
Vrij, Jzn. C., 184 (466), *239*

W

Waaler, B. A., 98 (23), *124*
Waddell, A. W., 211 (467), *239*
Wadström, L. B., 193 (468), *239*
Wagenaar, R. O., 401 (330), *458*
Wagley, P. F., 428 (41), *444*
Wagman, J., 403 (332, 333, 334), 405, 414 (331, 332), 415, *458*
Wagner, M., 193 (28), *215*
Waldeck, B., 78 (60), *84*
Walder, D. N., 287 (261), 288 (261), *305*
Walker, H. A., 343 (185), 351 (185), *395*
Walker, H. G., 38 (144), *88*
Walker, J. M. G., 211 (469), *239*
Wallace, G., 17 (94), *26*
Wallace, J. M., 193 (470), *239*
Wallon, G., 372, *397*
Walters, M., 285 (171), *300*
Walters, P. A., 58, 61, *94*
Walters, P. A., Jr., 264 (262), *305*
Walton, R. P., 20 (95), *26*
Waltz, D. T., 251 (263), *305*
Wang, C. Y., 185 (183), *223,* 277 (114), *297,* 317 (39), *326*
Wang, S. C., 339 (223), 343 (223), 344, 345 (223), 351, 352 (223), 360 (223), 363 (181), 364 (181), *397*
Warnke, R. D., 286 (271), *305*
Watts, D. T., 185 (471), *240*
Watts, J. A., 54 (235), *93*
Waud, R. A., 349 (224), 355 (224), *397*
Waugh, J. M., 283 (214), 285 (214), *302*
Waugh, W. H., 212 (472), *240*
Watman, D., 199 (215), *225*
Wearn, J. T., 113 (86), *127*
Weaver, L. C., 331 (225), 338 (141, 225), 363 (225), 364 (1), 365 (225, 226), *386, 393, 397*
Weber, J. F., 184 (466), *239*
Webster, R. A., 418, 420 (335), *453, 458*
Wechsler, R. L., 47 (177), 55 (177), *90*

Weidmann, S., 4, 5 (96), 6 (22), *23*, *26*
Weil, R., 194 (473), *240*
Weiner, N., 8 (98), *26*, 168, *178*, 180 (474), *240*
Weinges, K. F., 192 (408), 194 (408), *236*
Weise, H., 185 (475), *240*
Weisfeldt, M. L., 206 (476), *240*
Weiss, A. J., 342 (18), 343 (18), *387*
Weiss, C., 379 (2), *386*
Weiss, S., 38 (179), *90*
Weissler, A. M., 57 (129), *87*
Weiszbecker, L., 184 (477), *240*
Weizel, H. A. E., 109 (43), *125*
Welch, A. D., 78 (81), *85*
Welch, G. H., 21 (99), *26*, 205 (478), 206 (478), *240*
Welsh, J. H., 428 (336), 430 (336), *458*
Wendling, M. G., 198 (1), *213*
Wendt, V. E., 193 (386), *235*
Wenke, M., 186 (479), 187 (217, 218), 198 (334, 338, 482), 199 (335, 336, 406, 482), 200 (337, 479, 480, 481), *225*, *232*, *236*, *240*
Wentzel, L. M., 401 (337), *458*
Wenzel, D. G., 377 (227), 378 (227), *397*
Werler, J. E., 439 (338), *458*
Werko, L., 54 (271), *94*
Wertheimer, E., 192 (483), *240*, 318 (102), *329*
Wertheimer, L., 288 (264), *305*
West, C. D., 263 (132), 264 (132), *298*
West, G. B., 31 (273), 47 (272), 78 (253), *93*, *94*, 130, 137, 138, 139, 140, 147, 150, 151 (107), 152, 153, 156, *177*, *178*, 281 (156), *299*
West, J. W., 346 (228), *398*
West, T. C., 164 (34), *174*
Westcott, R. N., 104 (41), 105 (41), *125*
Westcott, W. C., 161, *178*
Westermann, E., 78 (274), *95*, 194 (207), 197 (207), 198 (484, 485, 486), 199 (437), *225*, *238*, *240*
Whaler, B. C., 410, 412, 413, 414 (228), *450*, *453*, *455*
Wheatley, D., 260 (265), 269 (265), 290 (265), *305*
Wheaton, E., 401 (270), *455*
Whelan, R. F., 37 (255, 276), 38 (276), 39 (182), 40 (180, 277), 41 (182), 50 (72, 190), 51 (17, 72), 52 (72, 93, 255), 60 (190), 64 (231), 65, 66 (181, 231, 232, 278), 72 (231), 75 (231), *82*, *84*, *88*, *90*, *92*, *93*, *94*, *95*, 188 (104), *219*
Wheeler, W. M., 431 (340), *459*
Whitby J. L., 400 (76), *445*
Whitby, L. G., 166 (64), *176*, 312 (43), *326*
Whitcomb, E. R., 435 (142, 143), *448*
White, C. A., 344 (38), 345 (38), 365 (38), *388*
White, J. E., Jr., 197 (279), 198 (487), *229*, *240*, 318 (26), *325*
White, J. M., Jr., 258 (169), *300*
White, P. D., 384 (49), 385 (49), *388*
Whittaker, V. P., 435 (341), *459*
Whittenberger, J. L., 102 (6), 113 (6), 120 (6), *123*
Wick, A. N., 181, *219*
Widdicombe, J. G., 342 (52), 344 (52, 54), 345 (53), 348 (53), *388*, *389*
Wiener, S., 432 (346), 435 (194), 436 (342), 439 (344), 440 (345), *451*, *459*
Wiercinski, F. J., 14 (41), *24*
Wiest, W. G., 181 (110), *219*
Wiggers, C. J., 14 (100, 101), *27*, 267 (58), *294*
Wilkins, R. W., 185 (148), *221*, 251 (73), *295*, 349 (74), 383 (74), 384 (74), *390*
Will, L., 199 (44, 45), *216*
Williams, B. J., 182 (488), 187 (488), 189 (488), 190 (488), *240*, 312 (103), *329*
Williams, F. F., 439 (188), *451*
Williams, F. L., 264 (266), 271 (266), *305*
Williams, M. A., 199 (301), *230*
Williams, M. H., Jr., 98 (87), *127*
Williams, O. B., 401 (49), *444*
Williams, R. H., 192 (54), 193 (358), 194 (143), 197 (357), *216*, *221*, *233*
Williams, W. O., Jr., 266 (92), *296*

Williamson, J. R., 188 (73, 489), 206 (144), *217, 221, 241*
Wills, J. H., 436 (248), *454*
Wilson, C. P., 71, *95*
Wilson, G. M., 35 (23), 36 (23, 33), 48 (23), 49 (33), 50 (23), 51 (23), 54 (23), *82*, 288 (109), *297*
Wilson, G. S., 419 (348), *459*
Wilson, J. B., 401 (275), *455*
Wilson, J. K., 251 (127), *298*
Wilson, R., 67 (279), *95*
Wilson, R. H., 332 (229), *398*
Wilson, V. J., 425 (347), *459*
Wimsatt, W. A., 186 (275), *228*
Winegrad, S., 14 (102), 15 (102), *27*
Winer, B. M., 339 (230, 231), 365 (231), 377 (230), 384 (230, 231), 385 (230, 231), *398*
Winer, M. L., 439 (163), *449*
Wingfield, B. H., 401 (70), 402 (70), 403 (70), 405 (70), *445*
Wingo, C. W., 432 (25), *443*
Winsor, T., 287 (267), *305*
Winter, G., 181 (465), *239*
Winterscheid, L. C., 188 (490), *241*
Wirsén, C., 192 (66), *217*
Wirz, E., 53 (212), *91*
Witham, A. C., 121 (88), *127*, 268 (268), *305*
Witkin, L., 268 (66), *294*
Witkop, B., 438, *453*
Witt, P. N., 356, 359 (31), 367 (232), 368 (232), 371 (232), 373 (232), 376, 377, 379 (232), *387, 398*
Wnuck, A. L., 54 (12), 59 (12), 73 (12), 75 (12), 77 (12), *81*
Wölpert, K., 154, *176*
Wohl, A., 183 (385), 184 (385), *235*
Wolff, H. G., 95
Wollenberger, A., 382 (233), 383 (234), *398*
Wolochow, D. A., 68 (209), *91*
Wood, E. H., 345 (136), 351 (136), *393*
Wood, M., 248 (23), *292*
Woodbury, R. A., 253 (5), 254 (5), 260 (5), 265 (5), *291*
Woodbury, J. W., 4, 14 (103), *27*
Woodbury, R. A., 99 (54), 113 (54), 116 (54), *125*
Woodman, R. J., 426 (329), 427 (329), *458*
Woodward, D. J., 265 (269), *305*
Woolley, D. W., 213 (491), *241*
Wright, E. A., 413 (91), 419 (349), 420 (351), 421, 423 (92, 350, 351), 424 (349), 425 (92), 427 (93), 439 (72), 440 (71, 72), *445, 446, 447, 459*
Wright, G. G., 401 (111, 112, 352), 402 (111, 112), 403 (111, 112, 113), 405 (112), 417 (113), *447, 459*
Wright, G. P., 400, 406, 414, 418 (354), 420 (31, 351), 421 (19), 423 (30), 423 (92, 350, 351), 424 (31), 425 (92), 426 (19, 20), *443, 459*
Wright, J. E., 13 (68), *25*, 188 (347), *233*
Wright, P. A., 185 (492), *241*
Wright, S., 252 (270), *305*
Wunsch, R. E., 286 (271), *305*
Wyler, R. S., 428 (292), *456*
Wylie, W. D., 54 (67), 75 (67), *84*
Wyss, St., 384 (235), 385 (235), *398*

Y

Yago, N., 205 (185), *223*, 313 (40), 314 (40), *326*
Yamamoto, S., 401 (311), *457*
Yard, A. C., 266 (272), 289 (272), *305*
Yarinsky, A., 401 (130, 154), 402 (130), 403 (113, 130, 154), 404 (130), 405, 417 (113, 130), *447, 448, 449*
Yariv, J., 429 (355), *459*
Yasukata, M., 345 (98), 391
Yasuo, A., 185 (493), *241*
Yeh, B. K., 322 (91), *329*
Yein, C. S., 258 (169), *300*
Yelnosky, J., 21 (104), 27
Yonkman, F. F., 254 (33), 279 (33), 282 (33), *293*
Yoshioka, T., 345 (98), 391
Youmans, P. L., 41, 59 (282), *95*
Youmans, W. B., 279 (148), *299*
Young, L. N., 439 (68), *445*
Yu, D. H., 205 (269), *228*
Yu, P. N., 122 (73), *126*
Yunis, A. A., 188 (178), *223*

Z

Zacks, S. I., 409, *459*
Zadina, R., 14 (58), *24*
Zaimis, E., 65 (206), 66 (283), *91, 95*
Zaki, O., 435 (240, 241), 440 (240, 241), *454*
Zakusov, V. V., 342 (236), *398*
Zarzycki, J., 191 (367), *234*
Zatman, L. J., 408, 409, *445*
Zhak, S. P., 408 (235), *453*
Zierler, K. L., 379 (62), *389*
Zimmer, J. G., 37 (82), 50 (82), *85*
Zimmerman, B. G., 313 (1), *324*
Zimmerman, H. A., 121 (89), *127*
Zimmerman, J., 8 (82), *26*
Zimmerman, J. H., 332 (143), 333 (143), 334 (143), 335 (143), 336 (143), 337 (143), *393*
Zodrow, W. W., 323 (49), *327*
Zoll, P. M., 17 (105), *27*
Zoltzman-Nirenberg, P., 8 (90), *26*
Zondek, S. G., 212, *241*
Zotterman, Y., 344 (108), 346, 363 (108), *391*
Zschiesche, L. J., 113 (86), *127*
Zsoldes, S. J., 196 (495), *241*
Zsótér, T., 269 (108), 290 (108), *297*
Zuger, B., 423 (140), 424 (139), *448*
Zuspan, F. P., 192 (496), 193 (496), *241*

Subject Index

A

Acetylcholine, 254, 376
 blood vessels, 166
 botulism, 408–410
 cocaine, 167, 168
 free fatty acids, 198
 haloalkylamines, 248
 inotropic action, 15
 intestine, 142
 lateral olfactory tract, 274
 membrane polarization, 136
 nictitating membrane, 162–165, 170
 norepinephrine release, 9
 stomach, 145
 superior cervical ganglion, 161
 sympathetic activity, 11, 143
 sympathetic ganglia, 10
 uterus, 154
Acetylcholinesterase, 163, 282, 283, 323
Acetylstrophanthidin, 321
ACTH (adrenocorticotropic hormone), 276, 318
Addison's disease, 264
Adenosine, 15, 146
Adenosine-3,5′-monophosphate, 182, *see also* Cyclic AMP
Adenosine triphosphate, 9, 16
Adenyl cyclase system, 183
 β-adrenotropic receptors, 191
 ATP, 182
 blood vessels, 190
 catecholamines, 191
 cyclic AMP, 182, 191
 DCI, 185
 epinephrine, 190, 191
 ergotamine, 185
 ISO, 191
 metabolic responses, 278
 norepinephrine, 191
ADH, *see* Antidiuretic hormone
Adipose tissue
 amphetamine, 198
 cyclic AMP, 200
 DCI, 199
 dihalophenylethylamine, 199
 dopamine, 198
 enzymes, 196
 ephedrine, 198
 epinephrine, 197
 free fatty acids, 195
 glucose, 193
 ISO, 197
 lipase, 194
 lipid, 192
 metabolism, 196
 α-methylnorepinephrine, 198
 norepinephrine, 197, 198
 phentolamine, 198
 phenylephrine, 198
 pronethalol, 199
 triglycerides, 193
 tyramine, 198
Adrenal gland
 arterenol, 31, 78
 circulatory stress, 32
 dopamine, 78
 epinephrine, 31, 78
 hypothalamus, 32
 isoproterenol, 17
 metabolic stress, 32
Adrenaline (epinephrine), 1, 3, 138
 blood vessels, 261, 271
 carcinoid syndrome, 291
 central nervous system, 272–275
 coronary vessels, 268
 EEG, 275
 ethoxybutamoxane, 273
 heart, 258–260
 intestinal muscle, 280, 281
 metabolic responses, 277, 278
 muscle, blood vessels, 266, 267
 nictitating membrane, 162
 ovulation, 276
 pressor action, 62
 pulmonary blood vessels, 268, 269
 renal circulation, 264
 salivary glands, 282
 skin circulation, 264
 splanchnic blood vessels, 265
 spleen, 266
 sweating, 282
 tolazoline, 254
 uterus, 280

Adrenaline diabetes, 180
Adrenalone, 138, 161, 170
Adrenergic blockade, 269
α-Adrenergic blockade
  hyperglycemia, 209
  hyperkalemia, 209
  metabolic responses, 277
  ovulation, 276
  postural hypotension, 272
  renal circulation, 262, 263
  therapeutic use, 283
Adrenergic blocking agents, 210, 288
α-Adrenergic blocking agents, 190, 243, 244
  azapetine, 184, 255
  benzodioxans
    dibozane, 184, 256
    piperoxan, 255
    prosympal, 255
  Dibenamine, 184
  dibenzazepines, 255
  epinephrine, 209
  effector responses
    central nervous system, 272–277
    eye, 279
    glands, 282
    heart, 258–260
    intestine, 280, 281
    metabolic responses, 277–279
    uterus, 280
    vasculature, 260–272
  ergot alkaloids
    dihydroergotamine, 250
    ergotamine, 250
    ergotoxine, 250
    hypergine, 250
  haloalkylamines, 245
    acetylcholine, 248
    administration, 246
    Dibenamine, 245
    Dibenyline, 246
    Dibenzyline, 246
    dose-response curves, 247
    histamine, 248
    5-hydroxytryptamine, 247
    imidazoline, 252
      phentolamine, 253
      tolazoline, 253
    mechanism of action, 246
    phenoxybenzamine, 246, 247
    N-phenoxyisopropyl-*N*-benzyl-β-chlorethylamine, 246
  Hydergine, 184
  hyperglycemia, 209
  hyperkalemia, 209
    other drugs
      chlorpromazine, 257
      corynanthine, 257
      ethyl yohimbine, 257
      phenothiazines, 257
      yohimbine, 257
  phenoxybenzamine, 184
  phentolamine, 184
  prisoline, 184
  yohimbine, 184
    therapeutic use
      hypertension, 285
      other conditions, 29
      peripheral vascular disease, 286–289
      pheochromocytoma, 283, 284
      shock, 289
β-Adrenergic blocking agents
  DCI, 244, 307
  dichloroisoproterenol, 183, 185, 307, 309
  dihydroergocornine, 308
  dihydroergotamine, 308
  epinephrine antagonists, 186, 209
  ethylnorepinephrine, 308
  hyperglycemia, 209
  hyperkalemia, 209
  IMA, 186, 199
  isoprophenamine, 309
  N-isopropylmethoxamine, 184
  N-isopropylphenylethanolamines, 309
  methanesulfonanilide, 309
  methoxyphenamine, 308
  MJ-1999, 184, 186
  pronethol, 184, 186, 309
Adrenergic drugs
  action, 8, 21, 22
  classification, 8
  conduction, 6
  injured hearts, 8
  inotropic effects, 14
  metabolism, 179
  monamine oxidase, 8
  norepinephrine, 8
  pacemaker cells, 6

plasma membrane, 5
pulmonary circulation, 97
receptors, 7, 8
smooth muscle, 129
systemic circulation, 29
Adrenergic receptors, 182
central nervous systems, 276
ephedrine, 20
hepatic, 186
muscle glycogenolysis, 187
α-potassium, 209
Adrenocorticotropic hormone, *see* ACTH
β-Adrenotropic receptor, 191
Aglycones, 354
Alderlin, *see* Pronethalol
Alkaloids, semisynthetic, 338
Alkamines, 354
Alkavervir, *see* Veriloid
Amine oxidase, 16, 62
blood vessels, 165, 166
catecholamines, 131
cocaine, 167, 172
ephedrine, 20
iproniazid, 16, 131, 166, 167
nictitating membrane, 165
sensitization, 170
Amines
chemical structure, activity, 140
sympathomimetic, species, 137, 138
Amino-ethanol-catechol, *see* Arterenol
Aminophylline, 20
p-Aminosalicylic acid, 194
AMP (adenosine monophosphate), 185
Amphetamine (Benzedrine), 4, 29, 66, 122, 138
adipose tissue, 198
analeptic, 275
arterenol, 63
blood glucose, 184
blood pressure, 74
brain, 191
breakdown, 73
cardiac output, 74
central nervous system, 21
circulation, 74
cerebral, 75
kidney, 75
skeletal muscle, 75
skin, 74
effector sensitization, 170, 172
formation, 73
heart, 21
D-isomer, 74
lipolytic activity, 198
nictitating membrane, 164, 170
oxygen consumption, 204
peripheral resistance, 74
phosphorylase, 191
reserpine, 63, 204
stomach, 134, 145, 146
structure, 73
sympathetic activity, 11
Amphibia, 437
kokoi toxin, 438
tauchatoxin, 437
Amylase, 206
Analeptic, 74, 275, 363
Andromedotoxin
A-V nodal discharge, 357
bigeminal rhythm, 357
myocardial conduction, 356
Purkinje conduction, 356
refractory period, 357
S-A nodal discharge, 357
ventricular tachycardia, 357
veratrinic responses, 379
Anectine, *see* Succinylcholine
Angeloylzygadenine, 334
Anginal attack, 324
Angina pectoris, 251
Angiotensin, 210
Annelida, 430
Ansolysen, *see* Pentolinium
Antiaccelerator action, 359
Anticholinesterases, 10, 410
Antidiuretic hormone (ADH), 318
Antihistamines, 362
Antihistaminic action, 248
Antihistaminics, 189, 253, 317
Apomorphine emesis, 273
Apresoline, *see* Hydralazine
Aramine (metaraminol), 4
Aranthol, 21
Arfonad, *see* Trimethaphan
Arrhythmia, cardiac, 319–321
Arterenol (amino-ethanol catechol; norepinephrine, noradrenaline, B.P.), 29, 42, 60, 61, 63, 65, 67
adrenal gland, 31, 65
amphetamine, 63

atropine, 48
blood pressure, 48, 61, 74
breakdown, 47
cardiac output, 47, 48
chemical structure, 47
circulation
intestinal, 53
kidney, 54
liver, 53
skeletal muscle, 50, 61
skin, 50
spleen, 54
Dibenamine, 51
dopamine, 78, 79
ephedrine, 63
epinephrine, 60
formation, 47
heart rate, 60
mephentermine, 63
peripheral resistance, 50
phenylethylamine, 63
reserpine, 62, 79
sympathectomy, 64
transmitter substance, 31
tryptamine, 63
tryamine, 63
vasoconstriction, 64
vasodilator substance, 49
vasomotor tone, 32, 66
Ascorbutic acid, 194
Assay methods, 145, 147
Atherosclerosis, 288
ATP, 144, 159, 182, 186
Atropine, 150, 253, 254, 345
amphetamine, 74
arterenol, 48
botulism, 410
ephedrine, 71
germerine, 347, 348
ileum, 141
intestinal muscle, 281
nictitating membrane, 161–163
papillary muscle, 323
splanchnic blood vessels, 265
sweating, 283
uterus, 152
vagal blockade, 248
veratrum alkaloids, 365
Azacyclonol (Frenquel), 273
Azamethonium (Pendiomid), 10
Azapetine (Ilidar; 6-allyl-6,7-dihydro-5*H*-dibenz(c,e)azepine)
α-adrenergic blocker, 255
blood glucose, 183, 184
central nervous system, 215
coronary vessels, 268
diarrhea, 255
g.i. motility, 255
muscle, blood vessels, 266, 267
peptic ulcers, 255
renal circulation, 262
side effects, 255
skin circulation, 265
splanchnic blood vessels, 265, 266
sympathetic activity, 11
vasodilation, 255

B

Banthine, *see* Methantheline
Benodaine, *see* Piperoxan
Benzedrine, *see* Amphetamine
Benzedrex, *see* Propylhexedrine
Benzodioxans, 244, 255
blood vessels, 256
bronchi, 256
central nervous system, 256, 272
circulation, 256
coronary vessels, 268
g.i. musculature, 256
heart, 256, 259, 260
intestinal muscle, 281
nictitating membrane, 256
side effects, 256, 257
uterus, 256, 280
Benzothiadiazine diuretics, 384
5-Benzyloxygramine, 157
Bethanidine, 67
Bezold-Jarisch effect, 340
afferent pathways (B, C, fibers), 344
anesthetics, 345
atropine, 345
baroreceptors, 344, 345
calcium, 379
central connections, 345
citrate, 379
efferent pathways, 345
physiological role, 346
receptors, 342
vasodilation, 345
veratridine, 379

Bistrium, *see* Hexamethonium
Blood flow
 cerebral, 268
 germerine, 348
 nutrient flow, 269
  noradrenaline, 270
  phenoxybenzamine, 270
  sympathetic innervation, 270
 oxygen extraction, 270
 precapillary sphincters, 270
 ^{86}Rb, 270
 thoroughfare pathways, 269
Blood glucose, 182, *see also* Glucose
 calorigenic effect, 207
 cyclic AMP, 209
 ephedrine, 184
 epinephrine, 182–184
 glycogenolysis, liver, 181
 insulin, 193
 isoproterenol, 183, 185
 kidney, 181
 lactate, 181
 methoxamine, 184
 norepinephrine, 183, 184, 193
 skeletal muscle, 181
 species, 183–185
Blood lactate
 calorigenic effect, 207
 catecholamines, 187
 cocaine, 187
 dibozane, 187
 DCI, 187
 epinephrine, 186–188
 ergotamine, 187
 ethylnorepinephrine, 187
 IMA, 187
 isoproterenol, 186
 MJ-1999, 187
 norepinephrine, 186, 187
 phenoxybenzamine, 187
 species, 186–188
Blood sugar, *see* Blood glucose
Blood vessels
 acetylcholine, 166
 adenyl cyclase system, 190
 adrenaline, 261, 271
 amine oxidase, 165, 166
 catecholamines, 261
 cerebral vascular bed, 267
 coronary vessels, 268
 denervation, 165, 166
 DHE, 189
 dibenamine, 189, 261
 dihydroxyacetone phosphate, 189
 epinephrine, 165, 166, 189, 190
 ergot alkaloids, 251
 fructose-1,6-diphosphate, 189
 glucose-6-P, 189
 glycogenolysis, 189
 haloalkylamine, 261
 kidney, 262
 lactate, 189
 mucopolysaccharide, 190
 norepinephrine, 165, 166, 261
 nutrient blood flow, 269
 phenoxybenzamine, 271
 phentolamine, 271
 phosphorylase, 189
 polyephedrine, 261
 postcapillary vessels, 270
 potassium, 189
 pseudocholinesterase, 166
 skeletal muscles, 266
 skin, 264
 splanchnic vascular bed, 265
 sympathetic activity, 260
BOL-148, 274
Bone, 191
Botulism, 400, 406
 acetylcholine, 408–410
 anticholinesterases, 410
 antishock treatment, 410
 atropine, 410
 Cl. botulinum, 400
 Cl. tetani, 400
 food poisoning, 400
 geographical distribution, 406
 lesions, 409, 410
 muscle end plate, 409
 paralysis, 408
 Shigella shiga toxin, 400
 toxin, 401–418
Botulinus toxin, *see* Toxin, botulinus
Bradykinin, 37
Brain
 adenyl cyclase system, 191
 amphetamine, 191
 cyclic AMP, 191
 epinephrine, 191
 ISO, 191

Taenia coli, 190
theophyllene, 312
uterus, 316
vasodilation, 311
ventricular arrhythmias, 320
ventricular fibrillation, 320
ventricular tachycardias, 320
Decamethonium (C-10; syncurine), 10
Denervation, supersensitivity, 162–168
2-Deoxyglucose, 187
Desacetylgermitetrine, 349, 350
Dexamphetamine, 67, 171
DFP, *see* Diisopropylfluorophosphate
DHE (dihydroergotamine), 185–187, 189, 213
Diabetes insipidus, 264
Dibenamine (*N,N*-dibenzyl-β-chloroethylamine), 133
administration, 249
analeptic, 275
antihistaminic action, 248
arrhythmias, epinephrine-cyclopropane, 320
arterenol, 51
atrial pressures, 270
α-blocking agent, 210, 245, 307
blocking dose, 249
blood pressure, 270
blood vessels, 189, 261
cardiac output, 270
central nervous system, 270
cholinergic vasodilation, 248
congestive heart failure, 290
coronary vessels, 268
EEG, 275
emesis, 272
epinephrine, 189
ethylamine, 133
free fatty acids, 199, 318
heart, 258–260
hyperglycemia, 184, 185
intestinal muscle, 281
lateral olfactory tract, 274
lipolysis, 199
metabolic responses, 278, 279
nictitating membrane, 162, 170, 279
norepinephrine, 201
ovulation, 276
peristaltic reflex, 139
phenylephrine, 77
potassium, 212
pulmonary blood vessels, 269
pulmonary congestion, 290
pulmonary edema, 290
salivary glands, 206, 282
schizophrenics, 272
splanchnic blood vessels, 265
stomach muscle, 190
sweating, 282
uterus, 139, 156, 212, 280
veratrum alkaloids, 349
Dibenyline, 246
2-Dibenzylaminoethanol, 259, 276
Dibenzyline (SKF688A), 131
α-blocker, 246
calorigenic effects, 202
metanephrine, 171
nictitating membrane, 162, 170
peristaltic reflex, 139
uterus, 139, 156
Dibenzylone, *see* Phenoxybenzamine
Dibozane [1,4-(bis-1,4-benzodioxan-2-yl methyl], 256
blood lactate, 187
catecholamine blockade, 189
epinephrine, 199
hyperglycemia, 184
intestine, 134
lipolysis, 199
Dibucaine, 381
Dichloroisoproterenol [DCI; 1-(3,4-dichlorophenyl)-2-isopropylamino-ethanol], 21, 39, 41, 79, 157, 183, 185, 309
β-blocking agent, 307, 309
central nervous system, 275
lateral olfactory tract, 274
metabolic response, 277, 278
2,4-Dichlorophenoxyacetate, 379
Digitalis
heart, 260, 320, 321
potassium, 359
toxicity, 359
Dihalophenylethylamine, 199
Dihydroergocornine, 277, 308
Dihydroergotamine (DHE), 133, 153
α-blockers, 250
central nervous system, 275
epinephrine, 185
intestinal muscle, 281

heart, 259, 260
lipolysis, 198
metabolic responses, 277, 278
norepinephrine, 201
phosphorylase, 185
β-receptor blocking, 308
smooth muscle stimulant, 251
sweating, 282
veins, 271
Dihydroergotamine methanesulfonate, 157
Dihydro-oubain, 355
Dihydroxyacetone phosphate, 189
Dihydroxyephedrine, 141, 164
Dihydroxynorephedrine, *see* Corbasil
Diisopropylfluorophosphate (DFP), 10
Dihydroxyphenylalanine, 138
Dihydroxyphenylalkylamines, 139, 152
Dihydroxyphenylserine, 138
Dimenhydrinate (Dramamine), 365
Dinitrophenol, 379
Diodrast, 263
Diphenhydrazine, 79
Dopa, 204
Dopamine, 10, 17, 29, 67, 78
adipose tissue, 198
arterenol, 78, 79
biosynthesis, 132
blood pressure, 79
breakdown, 78
cardiac output, 17, 78
choline xylyl ether, 173
dichloroisoproterenol, 79
diphenhydrazine, 79
epinephrine, 17, 78
formation, 78
hyperglycemia, 185
intestines, 131, 212
norepinephrine, 17, 132
oxygen consumption, 203
peripheral resistance, 80
phenoxybenzamine, 79
piloerection, 81
reserpine, 63, 79
skeletal muscle circulation, 80
skin circulation, 80
source, 78
species, 132
structure, 78
Dramamine, *see* Dimenhydrinate
Ductus deferens, 190
Duodenum, 140, 142, 143
Dyspnea, paroxymal nocturnal, 260
Dystrophia myotonica, 380

E

Ecolid, *see* Chlorisondamine
EDTA (ethylenediaminetetraacetic acid), 153
EEG, 275
Emboli, 288
Emesis, 272, 273, 363–365
ENE, 308, 316, *see also* Ethylnorepinephrine
Ephedrine (phenylisopropanolmethylamine), 4, 24, 29, 62, 67, 70, 122, 138, 172
action, 20
adipose tissue, 198
arterenol, 63
atropine, 71
blood pressure, 71
blood vessels, 66
breakdown, 70
cardiac output, 71
circulation, 71
cerebral, 73
intestinal, 72
kidney, 73
liver, 72
skeletal muscle, 72
skin, 72
spleen, 73
epinephrine, 20, 170
formation, 70
glycogenolysis, 187, 189
heart, 20
hyperglycemic action, 12, 125, 184
lactic acid, 141
nictitating membrane, 164, 170
peripheral resistance, 72
phosphorylase, 187
β-receptors, 20
reserpine, 20, 63
source, 20
structure, 70
sympathetic activity, 11
tyramine, 170
vasoconstriction, 64
veratramine, 361

Epinephrine, 1, 3, 29, 60–63
adenyl cyclase system, 182, 190
adipose tissue, 197
adrenal gland, 32
adrenergic blocking agents, 209
amylase, 206
analogs, 309, 310
antagonists, 186
antihistaminics, 189, 317
arrhythmias, 14, 319, 320, 322
arterenol, 60
ascorbic acid, 194
ATP, 159
auricles, 211
blood flow, 61, 186
glucose, 181, 203
lactic acid, 181, 186–188
pressure, 33–36, 61, 79, 317
vessels, 165, 166, 189
bone, 191
brain, 191
bretylium, 172
bronchial smooth muscle, 314
calcium, 15, 212, 213
calorigenic action, 12, 200, 204, 207
carbacol, 156
carbohydrate metabolism, 142, 180, 181, 186
cardiac arrest, 16
cardiac contractions, 16, 57
cardiac output, 16, 33, 34
castrate, 190
chemical mediation, 30
chemical structure, 32
chlorpromazine, 39, 210
cholesterol, 194
circulation, 33, 186
cerebral, 45
intestinal, 43
kidney, 44
liver, 43
pulmonary, 112, 121, 315
citrate, 181
cocaine, 17, 19, 150, 167, 168, 189, 203
corbasil, 170
coronary flow, 16, 313, 314
creatine phosphate, 159
cyclic AMP, 185, 188
cyclopropane, 320
DCI, 188, 203, 205, 212, 313, 317, 321
depolarization, diastolic, 319
depressor action, 35
destruction, 16
DHE, 189, 204
Dibenamine, 189
Dibenzyline, 202
dibozane, 199
dichloroisoproterenol, 39, 41
diglycerides, 193
dihydroergotamine, 133, 189
dihydroxyacetone phosphate, 189
dilator action, 39, 40, 44
dexamphetamine, 171
dopamine, 78
ductus deferens, 190
duodenum, 140
electrolytes, 13–15
endocrine glands, 13
ENE, 308
ephedrine, 17, 20, 141
epinine, 170
ergonovine, 317
ergot alkaloids, 317
ergotamine, 185, 204, 212, 317
erythrocytes, 191, 210
ethionine, 186
extrasystole, ventricular, 319
fat metabolism, 73, 191, 318
fetal intestine, 141
formation, 32, 33
free fatty acids, 193, 198, 202, 318
fructose-1,6-diphosphate, 189
fructose-6-P, 188, 189
fructose-6-P_2, 188
glucose, 204, 205, 207, 212
glucose-6-P, 188, 189
glycerol, 194
glycogenolysis, 189, 316, 317
guanethidine, 172
heart, 33, 60, 188, 205, 206, 312, 319
hen rectal cecum, 147
hepatic glycogenolysis, 12, 185–187, 193, 316
hexosemonophosphate, 188
histamine, 40
hyperglycemia, 182, 184, 185, 209, 317
ileum, 140, 213

IMA, 186
imipramine, 171
inactivation, liver, 17
intestine, 131, 135, 142, 212, 316
ISO, 194
isoproterenol, 41
inotropic effect, 15
jejunum, 190
kidney
glycogen, 191
lactate, 191
lactate, 188, 203, 204, 207, 317
lipolysis, 199, 206
liver
glycogen, 181
oxygen consumption, 205
potassium, 208, 209
membrane polarization, 135, 159, 160
membrane potential, 14, 210, 319
metabolic actions, 12, 316
metabolism, 33, 179
metanephrine, 170
MJ-1999, 186
monoglycerides, 193
mucopolysaccharide, 190
muscle, glycogenolysis, 12, 181, 187, 316
nictitating membrane, 161, 162, 164, 166–168, 170
norepinephrine, 156, 170
obesity, 193
oxidation, 16
oxygen consumption, 13, 186, 200, 205–207
pacemaker, 20, 319, 359
palmitate, 205
papillary muscle preparation, 206, 321
parathyroid gland, 213
paredrine, 170
peripheral resistance, 36
pH, 202
phenoxybenzamine, 39, 190, 203–205, 321
pheniprazine, 171
phentolamine, 202, 213
phosphate, 13, 188
phosphofructokinase, 182, 188
phospholipids, 194
phosphorylase, 181–183, 185, 188–191, 312
piprandol, 171
potassium, 188, 208, 209, 212
precursor, dopamine, 17
pronethalol, 39, 186, 202, 313, 317, 322
propranolol, 204
prostaglandin, 193
protein catabolism, 13
protoveratrine A, 353
pulmonary
arterial flow, 120
arterial pressure, 120
potential effects, 113
isolated lungs, 113–117
open chest, 113, 118, 119
natural conditions, 116
pyruvate, 121, 188
salivary glands, 206, 213
serum phosphate, 187
skeletal muscle, glucose uptake, 181
sodium, 211, 212
spleen, 45
stomach, 206
^{35}S-sulfate, 190
Taenia coli, 212, 213
theophylline, 188, 189
tracheal muscle, 190
tyramine, 170
uterus, 206, 212, 213
yohimbine, 169
l-Epinephrine, 152
Epinine, 122, 138, 161, 164, 170
Ergocornine, 250
Ergocrestine, 250
Ergokryptine, 185, 250
Ergonovine, 277, 317
Ergot (ergotamine, dihydroergot compounds), 133
epinephrine, 141
heart, 258, 259
hyperglycemia, 185
lactic acid, 141
salivary glands, 282
spleen, 266
sympathetic activity, 11
tyramine, 18
uterus, 150, 280
Ergot alkaloids, 249
angina pectoris, 251
arterial pressure, 270

atrial pressure, 270
blood lactate, 317
blood vessels, 251
cardiac output, 270
central nervous system, 251, 272
circulation, 250–253
skin, 265
coronary vessels, 268
dihydroergotamine, 250, 251
emesis, 272
epinephrine, 316
ergotamine, 250
ergotoxin, 250
glucogenolysis, 316
hydergine, 250, 251
hyperglycemia, 184, 317
intestinal muscle, 281
isoproterenol, 250
metabolic responses, 277, 278
migraine, 251
pulmonary blood vessels, 269
renal circulation, 262
respiration, 253
side effects, 250
smooth muscle stimulant, 251
temperature regulation, 253
uterus, 280
Ergotamine, 212, *see also* Ergot
adenyl cyclase system, 185
α-adrenergic blocker, 250
AMP, 185
blood lactate, 187
epinephrine, 185, 317
erythrocytes, 191
fat, epididymal, 193
free fatty acids, 318
glucagon, 185
heart, 259, 260
hepatotoxicity, 266
hyperglycemia, 317
intestinal muscle, 281
lipolysis, 198
metabolic responses, 277, 278
phosphorylase, 185
tachycardia, 252
Ergotoxin, 102, 169, 250
Erythrocytes, 191, 210
Erythrophleine, 379
Eserine (physostigmine), 10, 144, 150, 161, 163
Estradiol, 154, 159
Estrogen, 158
Etamon, *see* Tetraethylammonium
Ethionine, 186
Ethoxybutamoxane, 273
Ethylenediaminetetraacetic acid (EDTA), 153
α-Ethylnoradrenaline, 138
N-Ethylnoradrenaline, 138
Ethylnorepinephrine (ENE, butanephrine), 183, 187, 308
Ethyl yohimbine, 257
Evipal, 183
Eye
α-adrenergic agents, 279
belladonna, 279
Dibenamine, 279
ergot, 279
ergot alkaloids, 279
glaucoma, 279
intraocular pressure, 279
parasympathetic innervation, 279
phenoxybenzamine, 279
piperoxan, 279
pupil, 279
sympathetic stimulation, 279
tolazoline, 279
yohimbine, 279

F

Fasting, 193
Fat
brown, 207, 208
epididymal, 193
Fat metabolism
adipose tissue, 192
catecholamines, 192
epinephrine, 191
free fatty acids, 192
glucose, 192
glycerophosphate, 192
hyperlipemia, 316
lactate, 192
liver triglycerides, 192
norepinephrine, 192
pyruvate, 192
sympathetic nerves, 192
Fat transport, 192
FFA, *see* Free fatty acids
Fibrillation, ventricular, 17, 260, 320

Finkelman preparation, 143
Flaxedil, 204
Food poisoning, 400
Free fatty acids (FFA), 192
  acetylcholine, 192
  adipose tissue, 195
  adrenocorticotropic hormone, 318
  aging, 193
  antidiuretic hormone, 318
  ascorbic acid, 194
  benzoic acid, 193
  N-t-butylmethoxamine, 199
  caffeine, 193
  carbacol, 198
  carbohydrate metabolism, 194
  catecholamines, 193, 199, 207, 318
  cocaine, 193
  DCI, 199, 318
  Dibenamine, 199, 318
  epinephrine, 193, 198, 206, 318
  ergotamine, 318
  fasting, 193
  guanethidine, 198
  heart, 188, 206
  IMA, 199
  insulin, 193
  N-isopropyl methoxamine, 318
  liver, 194
  methoxamine, 318
  α-methyldopa, 318
  α-methylnorepinephrine, 198
  α-methyltyrosine, 198
  MJ-1999, 199
  nicotine, 193, 194
  norepinephrine, 193, 198, 318
  phenoxybenzamine, 318
  phentolamine, 318
  pronethalol, 199, 318
  β-receptors, 200
  reserpine, 193
  salicylic acid, 193
  scorbutic animals, 194
  thyrotropic hormone, 318
  tyramine, 198
Frenquel, *see* Azacyclonol
Frostbite, 288
Fructose-6-P, 188, 189
Fructose-6-P_2, 188

G

Germerine, 334, 342, 347, 348
Germidine, 334, 356, 370
Germine, 334, 347, 369
  bronchoconstriction, 363
  calcium, 379
  chemical structure, 337
  ester alkaloids
    heart, 355
    pulmonary stretch receptors, 362
    skeletal muscles, 370
  jumping fits, 365
  muscle twitch, tension, 375
  reflex excitability, 365
  respiration, 363
  semisynthetic esters, 366
Germitetrine, 334, 356
Germitrine, 334, 368
Glucagon, 209, 210, 212
  blood lactate, 186
  DCI, 185
  DHE, 186
  ergotamine, 185
  glycogenolytic agent, 186
  metabolic responses, 278
  phosphorylase, 185
  β-receptor blocking compounds, 323
Glucose, 207, *see also* Blood glucose
  calcium, 213
  catecholamines, 191
  DCI, 212
  epinephrine, 212
  ergotamine, 212
  fat metabolism, 192
  glucagon, 210
  heart, 188
  ISO, 192
  oxidation, 188, 191, 205, 213
  sympatol, 204
Glucose-6-phosphatase, 181, 187–189
Glutamate, 188
Glycerides, 193
Glycerol, 192, 194
Glycerophosphate, 192
Glycogen, 154, 155
  castrate, 190
  catecholamines, 190
  epinephrine, 181, 191
  heart, 188
  kidney, 191

lactate, 182
muscle, 187
uterus, 190
Glycogenolysis
blood vessels, 189
bone, 191
catecholamines, 187
DCI, 187
DHE, 187
epinephrine, 189, 190
heart, 188
catecholamines, 189
ephedrine, 189
jejunum, 190
nephenterimine, 189
metanephrine, 189
methoxamine, 189
naphazoline, 189
phenylephrine, 189
reserpine, 189
p-sympatol, 189
tetrahydropapaveroline, 189
theophylline, 189
tyramine, 189
IMA, 187
Glycogen synthetase (uridine diphosphate glucose α-glucan transferase), 182
catecholamines, 187
cyclic AMP, 182
ductus deferens, 190
heart, 189
Gonadotropic hormones, 154
Guanethidine, 8, 65, 67, 144
epinephrine, 9, 172
free fatty acids, 198
hypertension, 285, 286
nictitating membrane, 172
norepinephrine, 172
sympathetic activity, 11, 143
tyramine, 172

H

Haloalkylamines, 245
blood vessels, 261
catecholamines, 248
central nervous system, 248, 272, 273
heart, 259
metabolic responses, 279
myocardium, 248
ovulation, 276
pressor response, 248
shock, 289
spleen, 266
β-Haloalkyl moiety, 246
Harderian gland, 163, 164
Heart
acetylcholine, 323
acetylcholinesterase, 323
adrenaline, 258–260
α-adrenergic blockade, 258–260
adrenergic drugs, 1
amphetamine, 21
anginal attack, 324
antiaccelerator action, 359
antihistaminics, 189
antiveratrine substances, 372
arrhythmias, 258–260, 319
DCI, 319
isoproterenol, 17
digitalis glycosides, 320
ventricular, 319
artrial pressures
auricles 11, 361
A-V conduction, 17
A-V node, 5, 6
benzodioxans, 259, 260
bigeminal rhythm, 356
block, 6
arrhythmias
cyclopropane, 290
haloalkylamine, 290
catecholamines, 319
ephedrine, 20
hydroxyamphetamine, 21
isoproterenol, 17
vanilloylzygadenine, 356
veratridine, 356
veratroylzygadenine, 356
calcium, 212
catecholamines, 258, 312, 319
cevine, 354
conduction
adrenergic drugs, 6
cyclic AMP, 188
glucose phosphorylation, 188
hexosemonophosphates, 188
isoproterenol, 17, 188
lactate, 188
phosphorylase kinase, 188

Purkinje fibers, 321
transmembrane potential, 321
congestive failure, 290, 324
contraction, 6
coronary occlusion, 259, 260
coronary vessels, 313, 314
cortisone, 323
cyclopropane, 259
DCI, 205
decelerator action, 360
depolarization, diastolic, 319
dibenamine, 258–260
2-dibenzylaminoethanol, 259
digitalis, 260, 320
dihydroergotamine, 259, 260
dyspnea, paroxysmal nocturnal, 260
ectopic beats, 320
electrical
alternans, 356
stimulation, 259, 260
ephedrine, 20
epinephrine, 33, 34, 188, 205, 206, 212
ergot, 258, 259
ergotamine, 259, 260
extrasystole, ventricular, 319
failure, 260
fibrillation, ventricular, 260
free fatty acids, 188, 206
germerine, 347
glucagon, 323
glucose oxidation, 188
glutamate, 188
glycerol, 206
glycogen, 188
glycogenolysis, 188
haloalkylamines, 259
hexosemonophosphates, 188
histamine, 323
hydrocarbon, sensitized, 319
5-hydroxytryptamine, 323
ISO, 205
lactate oxidation, 188
lipolysis, 206
mephentermine, 21, 205
methamphetamine, 21
methyl xanthines, 20
myocardial conduction, 356
nicotine, 323
nodal discharges, 356
noradrenaline, 259
norepinephrine, 205
oubain, 321, 356
oxygen consumption, 205, 206
pacemakers, 319
phenoxybenzamine, 205
phenylephrine, 20
phosphorylase, 13, 188, 189
plasma membrane, 4
action potentials, 5
depolarization, 5
excitation, 5
permeability, 5
potassium, 5
refractory periods, 5
resting potential, 5
sodium, 5
potassium, 5, 211, 260, 355, 356, 372
pronethalol, 322–324
Purkinje conduction, 356
pyruvate, 188
quinidine, 257
β-receptor blockade, 312
receptors, 320
refractory periods, 356
reserpine, 360
tetraethylammonium, 323
tolazoline, 260
tyramine, 18
ventricular
fibrillation, 320, 358
tachycardias, 320
veratridine, 354, 356
veratrine response, 372
veratrum alkaloids, 324
883F, 260
933F, 260
Hemicholinium, 11, 144, 163
Hemorrhage, 262–265, 267, 271
Hepatic glycogenosis, 193
Hepatotoxicity, 266
Hexamethonium (Bistrium; C-6), 10, 162, 193, 281
Hexosemonophosphates, 188
Hexosephosphates, 182
Histamine, 40, 67, 144, 253
β-adrenergic blocking agents, 189
gastric secretion, 253
haloalkylamines, 248
heart, 189

nictitating membrane, 165
phosphorylase, 189
pronethalol, 189
protoveratrine, 347
β-receptor blocking compounds, 323
5-HT (5-hydroxytryptamine), 204
Hydergine, 184, 250, 251
arterial pressure, 270
atrial pressure, 270
cardiac output, 270
lipolysis, 198
skin circulation, 265
veins, 271
Hydralazine (Apresoline), 263
Hydroxyamphetamine (Paredrine), 21, 67, 122
6-Hydroxydopamine, 9
p-Hydroxyephedrine, 164
p-Hydroxy-*N*-methylamphetamine, 164
p-Hydroxy-β-phenylethanolamine, 154
p-Hydroxyphenylethyltrimethylammonium iodide, 151
Hydroxytryamine, 138, 156, 164
5-Hydroxytryptamine (5-HT; serotonin), 37, 67, 144, 172, 253, 274
assay, 145
carcinoid syndrome, 291
cocaine, 167, 168
dexamphetamine, 171
haloalkylamines, 247
lateral olfactory tract, 274
pheniprazine, 171, 172
β-receptor blocking compounds, 323
stomach, 134, 145
uterus, 190
Hyoscine, 134
Hyperalkemia, 210
Hyperglycemia, 185, 193, 210, 316, 317
Hyperlipemia, 316
Hypertension
benzothiadiazine diuretics, 384
essential
guanethidine, 285, 286
noradrenaline, 287
phenoxybenzamine, 285, 286, 288
phentolamine, 287
protoveratrine A, 384
pulmonary
adrenergic blockade, 269
ganglionic blockade, 269
hypoxia, 269
pCO_2, 269
rauwolfia alkaloids, 384
renal circulation, 262
tolazoline, 254
veratrum alkaloids, 331, 383, 384
Hypotension, 272, 347
Hypothalamus, 32
Hypoxia, 269

I

Ileum
amines, 139
atropine, 141, 143
calcium, 213
cholinergic fibers, 144
epinephrine, 140, 142, 143, 213
eserine, 144
guanethedine, 143, 144
hemicholinium, 144
hexamethonium, 143, 144
nerve stimulation, 144
norepinephrine, 143
parasympathetic innervation, 143
reserpine, 143
sympathetic innervation, 143, 144
Ilidar, *see* Azapetine
IMA (*N*-isopropyl methoxamine), 184, 186, 187, 189, 199
Imidazolines, 252, 253, 262, 280
Imipramine, 171
Insects, 430
bee stings, 430
acetylcholine, 430
histamine, 430
melittin, 431
scorpions, 433
spiders, 432
ticks, 432
wasps, 431
Insulin, 193
Intermittent claudication, 287, 288
Intestine
adrenaline, 280, 281
asphyxia, 135
ATP, 159
catecholamines, 131–133
circulation, 43
creatine phosphate, 159
Dibenamine, 281

dibozane, 134
dihydroergotamine, 281
dopamine, 131, 132
epinephrine, 131, 134, 135, 141, 159, 190, 212
fetal, 141
glucose, 212
glycogenolysis, 190
hexamethonium, 281
isoproterenol, 134
lactate, 190
metabolic rate, 135
muscles, 56
atropine, 281
benzodioxans, 281
DCI, 316
ergot alkaloids, 281
ergotamine, 281
hexamethonium, 281
neostigmine, 282
noradrenaline, 281
papaserine, 281
phenoxyethylamines, 281
receptors, 316
nerve stimulation, 142
nicotine, 281
norepinephrine, 131, 132, 134, 212
phenylephrine, 134, 281
receptors, 133, 134, 280
sodium, 212
sympathomimetic amines, 137, 138, 141
Taenia coli, 159
temperature, 135
Inversine, *see* Mecamylamine
Iodoacetic acid, 135, 379
Iproniazid, 16, 131, 166, 167, 171
Iris, 165
ISO (isoproterenol)
adenyl cyclase, 191
adipose tissue, 197
brain, 191
calcium, 213
calorigenic effects, 204
cyclic AMP, 191
DCI, 190, 203, 205
epinephrine, 194
fat transport, 192
FFA, 192, 202
glucose, 192, 202, 204, 207
glycerol, 194
heart, 205
lactate, 192, 202, 204, 207
norepinephrine, 194
oxygen consumption, 192, 202, 204, 205, 207
pH, 202
phenoxybenzamine, 190, 205
potassium, 209, 212
pronethalol, 190
propranolol, 204
reserpine, 204
RQ, 202
salivary glands, 213
stomach, 212
uterus, 212
Isoprenaline, 138
Isoprophenamine HCl, 309
Isopropylarterenol, *see* Isoproterenol
N-Isopropyl methoxamine (IMA), 184, 318
N-Isopropylphenylethanolamines, 309
Isoproterenol (ISO, isopropylarterenol; isuprel), 4, 29, 56, 61, 122
adrenal gland, 17
β-adrenergic agent, 17, 317
AMP, 185
analogs, 309
antifibrillatory agent, 17
A-V conduction, 17
β-blocking agent, 308, 309
blood lactate, 186
blood pressure, 57, 310
bronchial smooth muscle, 314
cardiac arrhythmias, 17
cardiac output, 57
circulation
cerebral, 60
coronary, 16, 313
kidney, 265
liver, 59
skeletal muscle, 58
skin, 58, 264
spleen, 60
chemical structure, 58
DCI, 312, 321
dichloroisoproterenol, 41
epinephrine, 41
ergot alkaloids, 250
formation, 56

glycogenolysis, 12, 185, 187
heart block, 17
hyperglycemia, 183, 185, 317
intestine, 59, 134, 316
lactic acid, 141, 184, 317
oxygen consumption, 13
pacemaker, 17, 20
papillary muscle preparation, 321
peripheral resistance, 58
phenoxybenzamine, 321
phosphorylase, 185
pronethalol, 312
pulmonary blood vessels, 315
salivary glands, 282
serum phosphate, 187
Stokes-Adams attacks, 17
sweating, 282
tachycardia, 310
uterus, 152, 154, 316
venodilation, 313
ventricular fibrillation, 17
ventricular pacemaker, 319
Isoxsuprine, 323
Isuprel, *see* Isoproterenol

J

Jejunum, 190
Jerveratrum alkaloids, 355
Jervine, 334, 335, 360, 365
Jumping fits, 365

K

Kidney
circulation, 262
Addison's disease, 264
adrenaline, 264
α-adrenergic blockade, 262, 263
azapentine, 262
catecholamines, 263, 315
denervation, 263, 264
diabetes insipidus, 264
Diodrast, 263
epinephrine, 44, 191, 315
ergot alkaloids, 262
glucose-6-phosphatase, 181
hemorrhage, 262, 263
hydralazine, 263
hypertension, 262
imidazolines, 262
isoproterenol, 262, 315
noradrenaline, 262, 264
phenoxybenzamine, 262–264
pituitary, 264
potassium, 264
α-receptors, 262
β-receptors, 262, 263
shock, 263
sodium, 264
steroids, 264
sympathetic nerves, 262
tolazoline, 262
typhoid vaccine, 263
glycogen, 191
lactate, 191
β-receptor blockade, 315
DCI, 315
epinephrine, 315
isoproterenol, 315
pronethalol, 315
Kö, 189, 199
Krebs-Myerhof pathway, 188

L

Lactate
blood, 186, 187
blood vessels, 189
DHE, 189
Dibenamine, 189
epinephrine, 188–191, 317
ergot alkaloids, 317
fat metabolism, 192
glucagon, 186
heart, 188
ISO, 192
jejunum, 190
kidney, 191
liver glycogen, 182
oxidation, 188
phosphofructokinase, 182
potassium, 189
stomach muscle, 190
sympatol, 204
Lactic acid, 207
blood sugar, 181
corbasil, 141
3,4-dihydroxyephedrine, 141
ephedrine, 141
epinephrine, 141, 181
ergotamine, 141
isoproterenol, 141

muscle, 181
norepinephrine, 141
m-Sympatol, 141
uterus, 155
Lactyladrenaline, 138
Lactylnoradrenaline, 138
Lateral olfactory tract (LOT), 274
Levarterenol, 99, 101, *see also* Norepinephrine
blood, resting levels, 100
bronchiolar circulation, 104–109
ergotoxin, 102
hypertension, 100
hypoxia, 112
pheochromocytoma, 100
potential effects, 102
pulmonary arterial pressure, 104
pulmonary circulation
intact animal, 108, 109, 111
isolated perfused lungs, 104, 105
open chest, 106–110
systemic blood pressure, 100
vasoconstriction, 100, 102, 103
wedge pressure, 105, 108, 111, 112
Levophed, *see* Norepinephrine
Linoleic acid, 193
Lipid, adipose tissue, 192
Lipolysis, 198, 199, 202, 206
Liver
circulation, 43
epinephrine, 208
free fatty acids, 194
glucose-6-phosphatase, 181
glycogenolysis, 187
oxygen consumption, 205
potassium, 208, 209
toxicity
carbon tetrachloride, 266
catecholamines, 266
ergotamine, 266
phenoxybenzamine, 266
phentolamine, 266
Lizards, 441
Lobeline, 345
LOT, *see* Lateral olfactory tract
LSD-25, 274
Lungs
isolated perfused, 102, 104, 105
vascular bed, 268
adrenaline, 268, 269
Dibenamine, 269
ergot alkaloids, 269
noradrenaline, 268, 269
piperoxan, 269
tolazoline, 269
vasomotor fibers, 101
Lysergic acid diethylamide, 157

M

Magnesium, 382
MAO inhibitors, 11
McN-822 (*cis*-2-Amino-4-methyl-5-phenyl-2-oxazoline), 21
Mast cells, 65, 66
Mecamylamine (Inversine), 10
Medmain, 157
Membranes
calcium, 381, 382
dibucaine, 381
labilizers, 380
magnesium, 382
model systems, 380
polarization, 160
acetylcholine, 136
cadmium, 158
calcium, 136, 158
epinephrine, 136, 158, 159
pacemaker, 158
potassium, 136
smooth muscle, 157, 158
sodium, 136
stretch, 136
strontium, 158
uterus, 158
potential
epinephrine, 210
estrogen, 159
progesterone, 159
procaine, 381
protoveratrine A, B, 382
stabilizers, 380
veracevine, 381
veratramine, 381
veratridine, 381
veratrine, 381, 382
veratrum alkaloids, 380, 382
Mephentermine (Wyamine), 4, 11, 21, 63, 67, 122, 189, 205
Mepyramine, 156
Meratran, *see* Pipradol
Mescaline, 146

Metabolic responses
adenyl cyclase, 278
adrenaline, 277, 278
α-adrenergic agents, 277
α-adrenergic blockade, 277
catecholamines, 277, 278
cyclic 3′,5′-AMP, 278
DCI, 278
Dibenamine, 278, 279
dichlorisoproterenol, 277, 278
dihydroergocornine, 277
dihydroergotamine, 277, 278
ephedrine, 278
ergonovine, 277
ergot alkaloids, 277
ergotamine, 277, 278
glucagon, 278
haloalkylamines, 279
phenoxybenzamine, 277, 278
phentolamine, 278
promethalol, 278
thyroxine, 277
Metanephrine, 132, 133, 170, 203
Metaproterenol, 204
Metaraminol (Aramine), 4, 8, 10–12, 21, 63, 64, 122
Metacholine, 282
Meta-tyramine, 20, 164
Methamphetamine (Methedrine), 122
atropine, 74
blood pressure, 74
cardiac output, 74
central nervous system, 275
circulation
kidney, 75
skeletal muscle, 75
skin, 74
heart, 21
oxygen consumption, 204
sympathetic activity, 11
Methanesulfonanilide, 309
Methantheline (Banthine), 10
Methedrine, *see* Methamphetamine
Methoxamine (Vasoxyl), 4, 63, 64, 122
blood glucose, 184
EEG, 275
free fatty acids, 318
glycogenolysis, 187, 189
heart, 21, 205
phosphorylase, 186, 187
Methoxyphenamine (Orthoxine), 11, 308
Methylamphetamine, 64, 66, 146, 164
Methylatropine, 164
α-Methyl dopa, 11, 198
N-Methylepinephrine, 185
α-Methylnorepinephrine, 185, 198
o-Methyl transferase, 170
α-Methyltyrosine, 198
Methylxanthines, 20
Migraine, 251
Mistletoe, 18
MJ-1999, 184, 186, 187, 199
Mollusca, 434
Monoamine oxidase, 8, 18, 132, 133
Monohydroxyphenylamines, 153
Morphine, 134
Mucopolysaccharide, 190
Muscle
after contraction, 376, 377, 379
anoxia, 379
cyanide, 379
dinitrophenol, 379
iodoacetic acid, 379
β-adrenotropic receptor, 187
blood vessels, 266
adrenaline, 266, 267
asphyxia, 267
azapetine, 266, 267
cevadine, 376
hemorrhage, 267
metabolic effects, 267
noradrenaline, 266
phenoxybenzamine, 266
phenotolamine, 266, 267
β-receptors, 266
shock, 267
sympathetic innervation, 266
tolazoline, 266, 267
botulism, 409
catecholamines, 187
contracture, 374
Dibenamine, 248
electrolytes, 379
end plate, 409
glucose-6-phosphatase, 181
glycogenolysis, 186, 187
potassium, 375
veratrine, 367
Myasthenia, 376
Myotonias, 380

N

Naphazoline (Privine), 11, 189
NE, *see* Norepinephrine
Neogermidine, 370
Neogermitrine, 334, 342, 356
Neostigmine (Prostigmine), 10, 282, 376
Neosynephrine, *see* Phenylephrine
Nethalide, *see* Pronethalol
Neurotoxins, 399
  amphibia, 437
  animal, 427
  annelida, 430
  arthropoda, 430
    insects, 430
    scorpions, 433
    spiders, 432
    ticks, 432
  botulism, 400
  coelenterata, 429
  echinodermata, 435
  mammalia, 441
  mollusca, 434
  pices, 435
  protozoa, 428
  reptilia, 438
    lizards, 441
    snakes, 438
  tetanus, 418
Nialamide, 171
Nicotinamide, 194
Nicotine, 9–11, 161, 162, 281, 323
Nicotinic acid, 207
Nictitating membrane
  acetylcholine, 162–165, 170
  acetylcholinesterase, 163
  adrenaline, 162
  adrenalone, 161, 170
  amine oxidase, 165
  amphetamine, 164, 170
  atropine, 161–163
  bretylium, 172
  calcium chloride, 165
  catecholamine content, 166
  cholinesterase, 163
  choline xylyl ether, 172
  chromaffin cells, 162
  cocaine, 161, 165
  corbasil, 164
  denervation, 162–168
  Dibenamine, 162, 170, 279
  Dibenzyline, 162, 170
  dihydroxyephedrine, 164
  ephedrine, 164
  epinephrine, 161, 162, 164–168, 170
  epinine, 161, 164
  eserine, 161, 163
  guanethidine, 172
  Harderian gland, 163, 164
  hemicholinium, 163
  hexamethonium, 162
  histamine, 165
  p-hydroxyephedrine, 164
  p-hydroxy-*N*-methylamphetamine, 164
  p-hydroxy-β-phenylethanolamine, 164
  hydroxytyramine, 164
  impramine, 171
  innervation, 160
  iproniazid, 166
  metanephrine, 170, 171
  meta-tyramine, 164
  N-methylamphetamine, 164
  methylatropine, 164
  neosynephrine, 165
  nerve stimulation, 161
  nialamide, 171
  nicotine, 161, 162
  noradrenaline, 162
  norepinephrine, 161–168, 170
  paredrine, 170
  pheniprazine, 171
  β-phenylethanolamine, 164
  pilocarpine, 165
  pipradol, 171
  potassium chloride, 165, 170
  reserpine, 162, 163, 166, 167, 169
  sympatol, 170
  tyramine, 164, 168, 170
  yohimbine, 165
  933F, 165
Nitrogen mustards, 246
Nitroglycerine, 206
Nodose ganglion, 344, 363, 364
Noradrenaline, B.P., 138, *see also* Arterenol
  blood flow, 270
  blood vessels, 271
  central nervous system, 272
  chlorpromazine, 257
  coronary vessels, 268
  EEG, 275

heart, 259
hypertension, 287
intestinal muscle, 281
lateral olfactory tract, 274
muscle, blood vessels, 266
nictitating membrane, 162
ovulation, 276
phenoxybenzamine, 248
phentolamine, 271
pheochromocytomas, 285
pulmonary blood vessels, 268, 269
renal circulation, 262, 264
splanchnic blood vessels, 265
sweating, 282
Norephedrine
antihistaminics, 189
cold acclimatization, 201
hyperglycemia, 185
oxygen consumption, 200, 201
phenoxybenzamine, 201
phosphorylase, 312
protoveratrine, 347
reserpine, 189
theophylline, 189
Norepinephrine (Levarterenol, Levophed), 1, 3
adenosine triphosphate, 9
adenylic cyclase, 191
adipose tissue, 197
adrenergic drugs, 8
aging, 193
AMP, 185
analogs, 309, 310
arrhythmias, 14, 319, 320
auricles, 211
benzoic acid, 193
blood lactate, 186, 187, 203, 204, 207
blood vessels, 165, 166
brain, 191
bretylium, 172
calorigenic effect, 207, 208
catechol-*o*-methyl transferase, 19
cholesterol, 194
cocaine, 172, 184, 189, 201
cold acclimatization, 204
coronary circulation, 16, 313, 314
cyclic AMP, 191
DCI, 201, 205, 312, 313, 317, 319, 320
depletion, 8
dexamphetamine, 171
Dibenamine, 201
Dibenzyline, 202
dopamine, 132
electrolytes, 13, 14
epinephrine, 156, 170
free fatty acids, 193, 198, 199, 202, 207, 318
glucose, 203, 204, 207, 212
glycerol, 194, 207
glycogenolysis, 185, 187
guanethidine, 172
heart, 205, 206, 211
hyperglycemia, 183–185, 193
intestines, 131, 132, 316
ISO, 194
lactic acid, 141
linoleic acid, 193
lipase, 199
metanephrine, 170
MJ-1999, 194
nicotinic acid, 193, 194, 207
nitroglycerine, 206
oleic acid, 193
oxygen consumption, 13, 204, 205, 207
pacemaker, 359
palmitic acid, 193
papillary muscle, 206
pH, 202
pheniprazine, 171
phenoxybenzamine, 190, 205
phentolamine, 211
phosphate, 13
phosphorylase, 185, 188
potassium, 210–212
precursor, 17
pronethalol, 205, 312, 313
propanolol, 204
prostaglandin, 193, 194
pulmonary blood vessels, 315
^{86}Rb, 211
refractory period, 14
release from storage
acetylcholine, 9
bretylium, 9
guanethidine, 9
nicotine, 9
reserpine, 169
RQ, 202

salicylic acid, 193
salivary glands, 206
serum phosphate, 187
sodium, 211, 212
stearic acid, 193
stomach, 134, 145, 212
storage, 9, 10
sympathetic activity, 11, 143
synthesis, 173
Taenia coli, 211
tyramine, 18, 172
uterus, 147, 150, 151, 154, 156, 212
ventricular arrhythmias, 320
dl-Norepinephrine, 152
Normetanephrine, 170, 171, 203
m-Norsynephrine, 138
p-Norsynephrine, 138
Novadral (*m*-hydroxyphenylethanolamine), 203

O

Obesity, 193
Octamethylpyrophosphoramide (OMPA), 10
Oenethyl, 21
Oleic acid, 193
OMPA, *see* Octamethylpyrophosphoramide
Orthoxine, *see* Methoxyphenamine
Oubain, 321, 355, 356, 372, 379
Ovulation
adrenaline, 276
α-adrenergic blockade, 276
dibenamine, 276
2-dibenzylaminoethanol, 276
haloalkylamines, 276
noradrenaline, 276
phenoxybenzamine, 276
phentolamine, 176
Oxygen, 269, 270

P

Pacemaker action, 5, 6, 17, 20
Palmitate, 205
Palmitic acid, 193
Papaverine, 281
Papillary muscle, 206, 321, 323
Parathion, 10
Parathyroid gland, 213
Paredrine (hydroxyamphetamine), 138, 170
Paredrino, *see* Pholedrine
Pendiomid, *see* Azamethonium
Pentamethonium (C-5), 10
Pentolinium (Ansolysen), 10
Pentylenetetrazol, 275
Pheniprazine, 171, 172
Phenmetrazine (Preludin), 146
Phenothiazine derivatives, 365
Phenothiazines, 257, 273
Phenoxybenzamine (dibenzylone)
administration, 249
analeptic, 275
antihistaminic action, 248
α-blocker, 42, 246, 247
blocking dose, 249
blood
flow, 270
glucose, 183–185
lactate, 187, 188
vessels, 271
capillary pressures, 271
carcinoid syndrome, 291
catecholamine blockade, 189, 248
catecholamines, 187
central nervous system, 272–275
cholesterol, 199
dopamine, 79
EEG, 275
epididymal fat, 193
epinephrine, 39, 190, 205, 321
erythrocytes, 191
free fatty acids, 199, 318
hemidilution, 271
hemorrhage, 271
hepatotoxicity, 266
5-hydroxytryptamine, 190
hypertension, 287
ISO, 190, 205
isoproterenol, 321
lipolysis, 199
metabolic responses, 277, 278
muscle, blood vessels, 266
noradrenaline, 201, 248
norepinephrine, 190, 205
ovulation, 276
pheochromocytomas, 248, 285
phosphorylase, 185, 190
plasma volume, 271
renal circulation, 262–264
salivary glands, 213

skin, circulation, 265
shock, 289, 290
splanchnic blood vessels, 265, 266
spleen, 266
sweating, 282
sympathetic activity, 11
uterus, 150, 190
vagal blockade, 248
veins, 271
Phenoxyethylamine, 281
N-Phenoxyisopropyl-*N*-benzyl-β-chloroethylamine, 246
Phentolamine (Regitine; Rogitine; 2-[*N'*,*p*-tolyl-*N'*-(*m*-hydroxyphenyl)-aminomethyl]-imidazoline)
adipose tissue, 198
blood vessels, 271
carcinoid syndrome, 291
central nervous system, 275
epinephrine, 202
free fatty acids, 199, 200, 318
glycogenolysis, 187
hepatotoxicity, 266
hyperglycemia, 184
imidazolines, 253
intestine, 253
lateral olfactory tract, 274
metabolic degradation, 253
metabolic responses, 278
muscle, blood vessels, 266, 267
norepinephrine, 211
ovulation, 276
parasympathomimetic properties, 254
pheochromocytomas, 283–285
phosphorylase, 185, 186
side effects, 254
sweating, 282
sympathetic activity, 11
vasodilation, 253
Phenylalkylamines, 153
Phenylephrine (Neosynephrine)
adipose tissue, 198
blood pressure, 76
breakdown, 76
cardiac output, 76
circulation, 76
cerebral, 77
kidney, 77
skin, 77
Dibenamine, 77
ENE, 308
formation, 76
glycogenolysis, 189
hyperglycemia, 185
intestine, 134, 281, 316
nictitating membrane, 165
pacemaker, 20
peripheral resistance, 76
pulmonary vasoconstriction, 122
reserpine, 63, 169
structure, 76
sympathetic activity, 11
uterus, 316
vasoconstriction, 64, 308
β-Phenylethanolamine, 164, 169
Phenylethylamine, 2
amine oxidase, 16
arterenol, 63
nictitating membrane, 164
reserpine, 63, 169
stomach, 134, 145, 146
uterus, 151
Phenylisopropanolmethylamine, *see* Ephedrine
Phenylpropanolamine (Propadrine), 20, 122, 138, 151
Pheochromocytomas, 31, 49, 266, 284, 285
catecholamines, 283, 285
levarterenol, 100
noradrenaline, 285
phenoxybenzamine, 284, 285
phentolamine, 283–285
piperoxan, 256, 284
pronethalol, 324
Phlebitis, 288
Phlebothrombosis, 288
Pholedrine (Paredrins), 122
Phosphate, 188
Phosphofructokinase, 182, 188
Phosphorylase
activation, 181, 182, 185
adrenergic blocking agents, 190
amphetamine, 191
blood vessels, 189
calcium chloride, 312
castrate, 190
catecholamines, 187, 190
cyclic AMP, 185, 209
DCI, 185–187, 312

DHE, 185, 186
digitalis glycosides, 312
dihydroergotamine, 185, 186
ductus deferens, 190
epinephrine, 183, 188–190, 196, 312
ergotamine, 185
ethionine, 186
glucagon, 185
heart, 186, 189
histamine, 189
IMA, 187
kinase
catecholamines, 187
cyclic AMP, 182
epinephrine, 188
liver, 181, 183
methoxamine, 186
methyl xanthines, 20
norepinephrine, 188, 312
phenoxybenzamine, 185
phentolamine, 185, 186
pronethalol, 185, 187, 189
Taenia coli, 160, 490
theophylline, 188, 312
tracheal muscle, 190
uterus, 155, 190
Photofluorimetric method, 145, 157
Physostigmine, *see* Eserine
Pilocarpine, 165, 254
Piperoxan [Benodaine; 933F; 2-(1-piperidylmethyl)-1,4-benzodioxan], 11, 255, 256, 269, 284, 285
Pipradol (Meratran), 146, 171
Pices, 435
Pituitary, 264
Plasma volume, 271
Polyephedrine, 261
Potassium, 41
α-adrenergic receptors, 209
blood vessels, 189
catecholamines, 210
Dibenamine, 212
epinephrine, 188, 208, 211, 212
erythrocytes, 210
glucagon, 209, 210
heart, 205, 206, 211, 260, 372
ISO, 209, 212
lactate, 189
liver, 208, 209
nictitating membrane, 165, 170
norepinephrine, 210–212
oubain, 355, 356
renal circulation, 264
Taenia coli, 211, 212
uterus, 212
veratinic response, 380
veratridine, 355, 374
veratrum alkaloids, 359, 374
Preludin, *see* Phenmetrazine
Priscoline, *see* Tolazoline
Probanthine, *see* Propantheline
Procaine, 381
Procaine amide, 380
Progesterone, 149, 158
Progestin, 149
Pronethalol [Nethalide; Alderlin; 2-isopropyl-amino-1-(2-naphthyl) ethanol], 39
adipose tissue, 199
arrhythmias, 319–324
arterial pressure, 311
atria, 322
β-blocker, 42, 184, 186
bronchial smooth muscle, 314
calcium chloride, 312
cardiac output, 311
catecholamines, 189, 203, 312, 319, 323
clinical use, 323
congestive heart failure, 324
coronary disease, 324
depressant action, 322
digitalis, 312, 324
dosage, 310, 311
epinephrine, 202, 205, 211, 313, 317, 322
free fatty acids, 199, 318
glycogenolysis, 187
heart, 310, 311, 319
hyperglycemia, 185, 317
ISO, 190
isoproterenol, 312
isoxsuprine, 313
intestinal muscle, 316
lactic acid, 317
metabolic responses, 278, 317
myocardial depressant, 324
norepinephrine, 312, 313
pacemaker, 322
pheochromocytomas, 324

phosphorylase, 185, 187
β-receptor blocking, 309
reserpine, 322
serum phosphate, 187
theophylline, 312
toxicity, 310
tumors, 310
vasodilation, 311
vasopressin, 323
ventricles, 322
uterus, 316
Propadrine, *see* Phenylpropanolamine
Propamidine, 131
Propantheline, 10, *see also* Probanthine
Propiophenone, 320
Propranolol, 189, 199, 204
Propylhepedrine (Benzedrex), 11
Prostaglandin, 193
Prostigmine, *see* Neostigmine
Prosympal [883F; 2-(diethylamino-methyl)-1,4-benzodioxan], 255
Protalba, *see* Protoveratrine A
Protoveratridine, 334, 370
Protoveratrine, 334
arrhythmias, 356
bigeminal rhythm, 357
bronchoconstriction, 363
cardiac acceleration, 352
cardiac refractory periods, 356, 357
chemical structure, 337
chlorpromazine, 365
ester alkaloids
calcium, 379
heart, 355
hypotensive-emetic relations, 365
skeletal muscles, 370
respiration, 363
histamine, 347
hypertension, 377
metabolic effects, 382, 383
myocardial conduction, 356, 357
nodal discharges, 356, 357
nodose ganglion, 364
norepinephrine, 347
pressor response, 352
Purkinje conduction, 356
respiratory depression, 362
retching, 364
ventricular tachycardia, 357
veratrine response, 370
Protoveratrine A (Protalba, Puroverine), 385
analeptic, 363
barbiturates, 363
bigeminal rhythm, 356
calcium, 374, 379
cardiac acceleration, 352
coronary arteries, 342
epinephrine, 353
hypertension, 384
hypotension, 345, 365
LD_{50}, 366
membrane ion leaks, 374, 379
model systems, 382
nodose ganglionectomy, 344
pressor response, 352
procaine, 363
protoveratrine B, 384
receptors, 344, 345
reflex hypertension, 352
respiratory depression, 363
Protoveratrine B (Veralba), 334, 385
bigeminal rhythm, 356
calcium, 374
hypotension, 365
LD_{50}, 366
membrane, ion leaks, 374
model systems, 382
protoveratrine A, 384
Protoveratrine, A and B maleates, *see* Provell maleate
Protozoa
Gonyaulex catenella, 428
saxitoxin, 428
toxic effects, 428, 429
Provell maleate (Protoveratrine, A and B maleates), 385
Pseudocholinesterase, 166
Pseudojervine, 334, 360, 382
Pulmonary
blood vessels
DCI, 315
Dibenamine, 269
epinephrine, 315
ergot alkaloids, 269
isoproterenol, 315
norepinephrine, 315
piperoxan, 269
β-receptors, 315
sympathetic nerve stimulation, 315

circulation
adrenergic drugs, 97
amines, synthetic sympathomimetic, 121, 122
capillary blood flow, 111
vascular activity, 98
vascular pressure gradient, 111
edema, 290
lesions, 269
Puroverine, *see* Protoveratrine A
Pyrogallol, 171
Pyruvate, 182, 188, 192

Q

Quinidine, 256, 259, 322, 360, 372, 380, 386
Quinine, 360, 376, 380

R

Rauwiloid, 365
Rauwolfia alkaloids, 384
^{86}Rb, 211, 270
Receptor(s), 3, 7, 42, 55, 166, 307
α, 11, 42, 59, 61, 133, 212, 243, 244, 262, 264
β, 7, 8, 42, 59, 61, 133, 244, 262, 263, 266, 268, 280, 314, 320, 322
γ, 319
δ, 134
atrial, A and B, 346
antihistamines, 362
baroreceptors, 343
deformation, 342
hepatic adrenergic, 186
intestine, 133, 280, 316
pulmonary, 362
stretch, 379
veratidine, 362
β-Receptor blockade
catecholamines
cardiovascular system, 312, 313
intestine, 315
kidney, 315
lungs, 314, 315
metabolic effects, 316
uterus, 316
competitive inhibition, 312, 312
specificity, 311
Reflex, excitability, peristaltic
Dibenamine, 139
SKF-688A, 139
SY-28, 139
tolazoline, 139
933F, 139
Regitine, *see* Phentolamine
Renal circulation, 262, 263, 264
Reserpine
acetylstrophanthidin, 321
adrenomedullated preparation, 193
amphetamine, 63, 169
arrhythmias, 321
arterenol, 62, 63, 79
central nervous system, 273
cocaine, 168
dopamine, 63, 169
ephedrine, 20, 63, 169
epinephrine, 63, 169
fasting, 193
free fatty acids, 193, 198
glycogenolysis, 189
heart, 189, 360
ISO, 204
metaproterenol, 204
nictitating membrane, 162, 163, 166, 169
norepinephrine, 169
phenylephrine, 63, 169
phenylethanolamine, 169
phenylethylamine, 63, 169
stomach, 145
sympathetic activity, 11, 143
tyramine, 19, 63, 168, 169
Rogitine, *see* Phentolamine
Ryanodine, 15

S

Sabadine, 370, 379
Salicylamide, 194
Salivary glands
adrenaline, 282
calcium, 213
DHE, 213
Dibenamine, 206, 282
epinephrine, 206, 213
ergot, 282
isoproterenol, 213, 282
noradrenaline, 282
norepinephrine, 206
phenoxybenzamine, 213
synephrine, 282

tartrate, 206
tolazoline, 282, 283
Schizophrenia, 272
Scorpion venom, 376
Sensitization, effectors, 65, 162–173
Serotonin (5-hydroxytryptamine), 274
Serum phosphate, 187
Shock
adrenaline, 289
endotoxin, 289
haloalkylamines, 289
hemorrhage, 289
muscle, blood vessels, 267
noradrenaline, 289
phenoxybenzamine, 289, 290
renal circulation, 263
skin circulation, 264, 265
splanchnic blood vessels, 265
sympathetic nervous system, 289
trauma, 289
Sino-auricular node, 5, 6, 14, 17
SKF-501, 156
SKF-688A, *see* Dibenzyline
Shigella shiga toxin, 400
Shrew, 441
Skin, circulation
adrenaline, 264
asphyxia, 264
azapetine, 265
ergot alkaloids, 265
hemorrhage, 264
hydergine, 265
isoproterenol, 264
phenoxybenzamine, 265
α-receptors, 264
shock, 264, 265
sympathetic nervous system, 264
temperature, 264
tolazoline, 265
Snakes, 438
Sodium, 210–212, 264, 379
Sodium fluoride, 155
Sparteine, 360
Splanchnic vascular bed
adrenaline, 265
asphyxia, 265
atropine, 265
azapetine, 265, 266
Dibenamine 265
g.i. muscle tone, 265
hemorrhage, 265
nerve stimulation, 265
noradrenaline, 265
phenoxybenzamine, 265, 266
shock, 265
Spleen, 45, 172, 266
Stearic acid, 193
Steroids, 16, 264
Stokes–Adams attacks, 17
Stomach
acetylcholine, 145
amphetamine, 134, 145, 146
dibenamine, 190
epinephrine, 134, 145, 190, 206
hexamethonium, 144
5-hydroxytryptamine, 134, 145
hyoscine, 134
ISO, 212
lactate, 190
mescaline, 146
methyl amphetamine, 146
morphine, 134
norepinephrine, 134, 145, 212
phenmetrazine, 146
β-phenylethylamine, 134, 145, 146
pipradol, 146
potassium, 212
reserpine, 145
sympathin, 145
tryptamine, 146
tyramine, 145
vagal stimulation, 144
Strophanthine-K, 15
Strychnine, 425, 427
Submaxillary gland, 191
Succinylcholine (Anectine), 10
^{35}S-Sulfate, 190
Sweating
acetylcholine, 282, 283
acetylcholinesterase, 282, 283
adrenaline, 282
atropine, 283
catecholamines, 282
cholinergic stimuli, 282
Dibenamine, 282
dihydroergotamine, 282
isoproterenol, 282
methacholine, 282
noradrenaline, 282

phenoxybenzamine, 282
phentolamine, 282
SY-28, 139
Sympathetic ganglia, 10
Sympathetic nervous system, 11
acetylstrophanthidin, 321
arrhythmias, 321
blood flow, 270
blood vessels, 271
bronchial smooth muscle, 314
calcium metabolism, 213
circulation
cerebral, 267
renal, 262
skin, 264
colon, 143, 144
fat metabolism, 192
heart, 324
hemicholium, 11
mephentermine, 11
nicotine, 11
parathyroid gland, 213
pulmonary blood vessels, 315
ventricular arrhythmias, 321
Sympathetic postganglionic fibers, 11
Sympathin, 30, 145
Sympatholytic drugs, 139, 140, 153
Sympathomimetic compounds, 3
Sympatol, 138, *see also* Synephrin
glucose, 204
glycogenolysis, 189
hyperglycemia, 184
lactate, 204
nictitating membrane, 170
oxygen consumption, 204
m-Sympatol, 138, 141
Syncurine, *see* Decamethonium
Synephrine (Sympatol), 122
hyperglycemia, 185
lipolytic activity, 198
salivary glands, 282
Syrosingopine, 11

T

Tachycardia, paroxysmal, 17, 356
Taenia coli
α-adrenergic blocking agents, 190
β-adrenergic blocking agents, 190
ATP, 159
calcium, 213
creatine phosphate, 159
cyclic AMP, 190
DCI, 190
epinephrine, 159, 190, 212, 213
norepinephrine, 211
phosphorylase, 160, 190
Tartrate, 206
TEA, *see* Tetraethylammonium
Temperature, skin circulation, 264
TEPP, *see* Tetraethylpyrophosphate
Tetanus, 418–427
Tetraethylammonium (Etamon, TEA, 10, 323, 384
Tetraethylpyrophosphate (TEPP), 10
β-Tetrahydronaphthylamine carbonate, 157
Tetrahydropapaveroline, 189
Tetrodotoxin, 436
Theophylline, 20
catecholamine blockade, 189
DCI, 312
epinephrine, 188
glycogenolysis, 189
heart, 189
phosphorylase, 188, 312
pronethalol, 312
Thorazine, *see* Chlorpromazine
Thromboangitis obliterans, 288
Thyroid
catecholamines, 191
epinephrine, 13, 193
free fatty acids, 193
glucose oxidation, 191
Thyrotropic hormone (TSH), 318
Thyroxine, 277
TM 10 (xylocholine, choline, xylyl ether), 11
α-Tocopherol phosphate, 380
Tolazoline (Priscoline, 2-benzyl-2-imidazoline)
adrenaline, 254
atropine, 254
bronchial smooth muscle, 314
circulation
renal, 262
skin, 265
excretion, 253
gastric secretion, 253
gastrointestinal muscle, 254
heart, 254, 260

histamine, 253
hyperglycemia, 184, 185
hypertension, 254
imidazolines, 253
intestine, 253
muscle, blood vessels, 266, 267
nictitating membrane, 254
oxygen consumption, 202
parasympathomimetic properties, 254
peristaltic reflex, 139
pulmonary blood vessels, 269
salivary glands, 282, 283
side effects, 254
sympathetic activity, 11, 254
uterus, 139, 253
vasodilation, 253
Tolbutamide, 277
Toxemia, pregnancy, 193
Toxin
botulism
absorption, 413, 414
activation phenomena, 416
antitoxin, 401, 406, 421
m-bromophenylether choline, 412
central effects, 413
cholinergic denervation, 412
cholinergic endings, 411
danger, investigators, 411
darmstoff, 412
detoxification, 414
dimethylphenylpiperazinium, 412
electric organ, fish, 410
eye, 411
lymph, 414
metabolism, 414, 415
5-methylfuryltrimethylammonium, 412
molecular weight, 405
muscarine, 2268F, 412
nicotine, 412
oral potency, 414
sedimentation, 402, 403
specific toxicities, 402
type D
adrenergic nerves, 413
catechol amines, 412
ephedrine, 412
hexamethonium, 412
nicotine reversal, 412
pilomotor response, 412
reserpine, 412
smooth muscle, 412
tetanus
acetylcholine, 421
antitoxin, 412–423
cholinergic lesion, 421
gangliosides, 426, 427
inhibitory mechanisms, 425
nerve section, 423
paralytic symptoms, 421
poisoning, 424
port of entry, 422
potency, 419
site of action, 420, 421
tetanus toxoid, 421
Tracheal muscles, 190
Tranquilizer, 273
Transmitter substances, 30–32
Trauma, 288
Trichlorethylene, 362
Triglyceride, 192
Trimethaphan (Arfonad), 10
Tryptamine, 146
TSH, *see* Thyrotropic hormone
Tuamine, *see* Tuaminoheptane
Tuaminoheptane (Tuamine), 11
d-Tubocurarine, 10, 369
Tumor, carcinoid, 37, 310
Typhoid vaccine, 263
Tryptamine, 63
Tyramine, 4, 8, 10, 29, 62, 68, 138
action, 19
adipose tissue, 198
amine oxidase, 16
arterenol, 63
blood pressure, 69
breakdown, 68
bretylium, 172
cardiac output, 68
circulation
intestinal, 70
kidney, 70
skin, 69
cocaine, 167, 168, 171, 172
dexamphetamine, 171
epinephrine, 172
formation, 68
free fatty acids, 198
glycogenolysis, 189
guanethidine, 172

heart, 18
hyperglycemia, 185
lipolytic activity, 198
nialamide, 171, 172
nictitating membrane, 164, 170
norepinephrine, 18, 172
pheniprazine, 171, 172
pulmonary vasoconstriction, 122
reserpine, 18, 19, 63, 168
source, natural, 18
stomach, 145
structure, 68
sympathetic activity, 11
tyrosine, 18
uterus, 18, 151
Tyrosine, 18

U

U-0882, 320
Unitensin acetates, 385, *see also* Cryptenamine acetates
Unitensin tannates, 385, *see also* Cryptenamine tannates
Uridine diphosphate glucose α-glucan transferase, *see* Glycogen synthetase
Uterus
acetylcholine, 150, 154, 157
action potentials, 159
adrenaline, 280
α-adrenergic blockade, 280
β-adrenergic blockade, 280
atropine, 152
benzodioxans, 280
5-benzyloxygramine, 157
bretylium, 152, 155
calcium, 153, 155, 157, 213
carbacol, 156, 157
catechol, 151
catecholamines, 147, 157
choline xylyl ether, 155
cocaine, 150, 152
cupric chloride, 155
DCI, 19, 316
Dibenamine, 139, 156, 212, 280
Dibenzyline, 156
dichloroisoproterenol, 157
dihydroergotamine, 153
dihydroergotaminemethanesulfonate, 157
dihydroxyphenylalkylamines, 153
EDTA, 153
electrolytes, 154
ENE, 316
epinephrine, 147–154, 156, 157, 159, 190, 206, 212, 213, 316
ergot, 148, 280
ergot alkaloids, 251, 258
eserine, 150
estradiol, 154, 159
estrogen, 158
glycogen, 154, 155, 190
gonadotropic hormones, 154
hydroxytryptamine, 190
hydroxytyramine, 156
hypertrophy, 148
hypogastric nerves, 148, 152
p-hydroxyphenylethyltrimethylammonium iodide, 151
5-hydroxytryptamine, 190
imidazolines, 280
ISO, 154, 155, 190, 212
isoproterenol, 153, 157, 316
lactic acid, 155
lysergic acid diethyl amide, 157
medmain, 157
membrane potential, 158, 159
monohydroxyphenylamines, 153
norepinephrine, 147, 149–151, 154, 156, 190, 212
dl-norepinephrine, 152
l-norepinephrine, 152
ovariectomy, 148
oxygen consumption, 155
pacemaker, 158
phenoxybenzamine, 190
phenylalkylamines, 153
phenylephrine, 316
phenylethylamine, 151
phosphorylase, 155, 190
potassium, 212
pregnancy, 148, 152
progestin, 149
progestrone, 149, 158, 159
pronethalol, 190, 316
receptors, 316
SKF501, 156
SKF688A, 139, 158
sodium fluoride, 155
species, 148–157
SY28, 139

sympathetic innervation, 160
β-tetrahydronaphthylamine carbonate, 157
tolazoline, 139
veratramine, 157
933F, 139
U-0882, 320

V

Vagal body, 364
Vanilloylveracevine, 334
Vanilloylzygadenine
electrical alternans, 356
heart block, 356
veratrine response, 370
Vasopressin, 323
Vasoxyl (methoxamine), 4
Veins, 271
Veracevine, 334, 370
bronchoconstriction, 363
chemical structure, 336
ester, alkaloid, 355
jumping fits, 365
model systems, 381
reflex excitability, 365
respiration, 363
Veralba, 385
Veratramine
anti-accelerator action, 360
atropine, 359
auricular flutter, 361
cardio-decelerator action, 360
central nervous system, 365
chemical structure, 335
dioxolane derivatives, 366
ephedrine, 361
epinephrine, 359, 360
ether, 366
heart, 355, 359
mental derangements, 366
mephenesin, 366
metabolic effects, 382
model systems, 381
muscle, electrolytes, 379
periodic rhythm, 361
seizures, 365, 366
tremors, 366
Veratridine
abdominal receptors, 343
adrenal medulla, 353
after contraction, 376
anesthetics, 345
apnea, 362
Bezold–Jarisch effect, 374
blood flow, 348
bradycardia, 347, 351
bretylium, 346
cardiac output, 346
cardio-accelerator response, 352
central action, 351
cisterna magna, 363
coronary arteries, 342
electrical alternans, 342
epinephrine, 353
fourth ventricle, 363
heart, 354, 356
hypotension, 347
intracisternal injection, 352
intracranial receptors, 343
intravertebral arterial injection, 352
metabolic effect, 382
model systems, 381
muscle
human, 376
twitch-tension, 375
myasthemia patients, 376
myocardium, 346
nodose ganglion, 344
potassium, 355, 356, 359, 374
pressor response, 352
reflex hypotension, 346
refractory period, 359
respiration, 362, 363
toxicity, 359
tubocurarine, 369
twitches, spontaneous, 368
vagal action potentials, 342
vasodilation, 345
Veratrine
after-potential, negative, 376
anti-veratrinic substances, 371
arrhythmias, 356
baroreceptors, 344, 345
cardiac refractory periods, 356
carotid body, 363
carotid sinus, 344
contracture, 376
cortex, electrical changes, 366
ectopic pacemaker, 359
electrical alternans, 357
end plate potentials, 369

hypotension, 344, 345
model systems, 381, 382
myocardial conduction, 356
potassium, 359
Purkinje conduction, 356, 359
respiration, 363
responses, 366
calcium, 379
contracture, 367
denervation, 367
ionic effect, 379
muscle, skeletal, 367, 376
myasthemic patients, 376
neogermitrine, 370
sodium, 379
stimulation, effects, 367
toxicity, 359
vagal action potentials, 342
vagal chemoreceptors, 343
Veratrinic responses
andromedotoxin, 379
calcium, 380
2,4-dichlorophenoxyacetate, 379
diptropic myotonica, 380
myotonias, 380
potassium, 380
procaineamide, 380
quinidine, 380
quinine, 380
scorpion venom, 379
α-tocopherol phosphate, 380
Veratrosine, 334, 360, 365, 382
Veratroylzygadenine, 334, 356, 370
Veratrum alkaloids, 331
adrenal medulla, 353
after-potentials, negative, 373
alkamines, 354
Bezold–Jarisch effect, 340, 374
bradycardia, 383
calcium, 359
cardiac failure, 384
cardiac output, 349, 350, 383
cardiac receptors, 342
cardio-acceleration, 352
cardiovascular effects, 340, 383
cardiovascular reflexes, 342, 343
carotid sinus reflexes, 343
central action, 385
chemistry, 333
clinical use, 385
Dibenamine, 349
eclampsia, 384
emetic action, 363, 365, 384, 385
encephalopathy, 384
excretion, 339
heart, 354, 385, 386
hypertension, 352, 383
hypotension, 349
intestinal muscle, 370
model system, 380, 382
nausea, 384, 385
peripheral sites, action, 341, 342
pharmacological action, 339
potassium, 359, 374
pulmonary receptors, 362
quinidine, 386
respiration, 361
retinopathy, 384
semi-synthetic alkaloids, 338
source, 332, 334
stretch receptors, 379
sympathetic tone, 346, 350, 383
tachyphylaxis, 339
tetanic tension, 375
thiopyranoindole derivatives, 342
toxemias, pregnancy, 384
toxicity, 359, 385
vasoconstriction, 352
vasomotor tone, 349, 383
venous tone, 350
ventricular arrhythmias, 385, 386
ventricular fibrillation, 358
veratrine response, 366
veratrum emesis, 343, 349
Veriloid (Alkavervir), 385
carotid body, 352
coronary arteries, 342
emesis, 363, 365
heart, 354
hypertension, 352
hypotension, 344, 349, 351
vagal action potentials, 342
vagal body, 364
vagal chemoreceptors, 343
vasodepressor center, 351

W

Wyamine (mephentermine), 4

X

Xylocholine (TM 10), 11

Y

Yohimbine, 165
  α-adrenergic blocker, 257
  aphrodisiac properties, 257
  epinephrine, 169
  hyperglycemia, 184
  sympathetic activity, 11

Z

Zyacine, 334, 370
Zygadenine, 334, 336, 355, 369, 370

933F, 139, 165, 171, 260, *see also* Piperoxan
883F, 260, *see also* Prosympal